Precalculus

with Trigonometry

CONCEPTS AND APPLICATIONS

Instructor's Guide

DEBORAH DAVIES

PAUL A. FOERSTER

SECOND EDITION

Key Curriculum Press
Innovators in Mathematics Education

Editor: Kendra Lockman
Project Editor: Andres Marti
Production Editor: Kristin Ferraioli
Copyeditor: Elliot Simon
Editorial Production Supervisor: Christine Osborne
Production Coordinator: Jennifer Young
Production Director: McKinley Williams
Art Editor: Jason Luz
Technical Art: Lineworks, Inc., Interactive Composition Corporation
Compositor: Interactive Composition Corporation
Cover Designer: Jensen Barnes
Cover Photo Credit: ©Grafton Marshall Smith/Corbis
Prepress and Printer: Versa Press, Inc.

Textbook Product Manager: James Ryan
Executive Editor: Casey FitzSimons
Publisher: Steven Rasmussen

Key Curriculum Press
1150 65th Street
Emeryville, CA 94608
510-595-7000
editorial@keypress.com
www.keypress.com

Printed in the United States of America
10 9 8 7 6 5 4 3 2   12 11 10 09 08
ISBN 978-1-55953-790-2

Contents

Precalculus with Trigonometry: Instructor's Guide
© 2007 Key Curriculum Press

Quick Guide to Instructor's Resources

In this table, the number of checks in each column indicates the number of resources available for a particular lesson. For the final section of each chapter, checks in the Test column indicate Chapter Tests or Cumulative Tests. The checks under Technology Resource indicate Dynamic Precalculus Explorations, data sets, and calculator programs.

| Lesson | Instructor's Resource Book | | | Instructor's Resource CD and Web Resources | | Assessment Resources |
	Blackline Master	Exploration Master	Technology Activity	Presentation Sketch	Technology Resource	Test
1-1		✓				
1-2		✓✓				
1-3	✓	✓✓✓✓	✓✓✓	✓✓	✓✓	✓
1-4	✓	✓		✓		
1-5	✓	✓		✓		✓
1-6	✓	✓		✓✓		
1-7						
1-8	✓					✓
2-1		✓				
2-2		✓				
2-3	✓✓	✓✓✓				
2-4		✓✓	✓	✓	✓	✓
2-5		✓✓✓				✓
2-6						✓
3-1		✓✓				
3-2	✓✓	✓✓				
3-3		✓✓		✓	✓	✓
3-4	✓	✓✓		✓		
3-5		✓	✓	✓✓✓	✓✓✓	
3-6		✓✓				
3-7		✓✓	✓		✓	
3-8		✓				
3-9	✓					✓✓
4-1						
4-2		✓			✓	
4-3		✓✓✓				✓
4-4		✓✓			✓✓✓	✓
4-5		✓✓		✓		
4-6		✓✓✓				
4-7						✓
5-1						
5-2		✓✓✓			✓	
5-3						✓
5-4	✓✓✓	✓✓✓✓	✓✓	✓✓		✓
5-5	✓	✓	✓	✓✓✓	✓	
5-6		✓				
5-7	✓✓	✓				✓
6-1		✓				
6-2		✓✓	✓	✓	✓	
6-3		✓✓			✓	
6-4		✓✓	✓	✓	✓	✓
6-5		✓✓				
6-6		✓✓				
6-7		✓✓				
6-8						
6-9	✓					✓✓
7-1						
7-2		✓				
7-3		✓✓✓				✓
7-4		✓				
7-5						
7-6						

	Instructor's Resource Book			Instructor's Resource CD and Web Resources		Assessment Resources
Lesson	**Blackline Master**	**Exploration Master**	**Technology Activity**	**Presentation Sketch**	**Technology Resource**	**Test**
7-7		✓	✓	✓		✓
7-8	✓	✓				✓
8-1		✓				
8-2		✓✓✓	✓	✓	✓✓	
8-3	✓	✓			✓✓✓✓	
8-4	✓		✓✓	✓✓	✓✓✓✓✓✓	
8-5		✓✓			✓✓✓✓✓✓✓	
8-6	✓	✓	✓		✓✓	✓
9-1						
9-2						
9-3		✓				
9-4		✓				
9-5		✓				✓
9-6		✓				
9-7		✓	✓		✓	
9-8		✓				
9-9		✓				
9-10						✓✓
10-1	✓					
10-2	✓	✓	✓			
10-3		✓				
10-4		✓✓✓	✓	✓	✓	✓
10-5		✓				
10-6		✓✓		✓	✓✓	✓
10-7		✓				
10-8		✓✓✓				
10-9	✓	✓✓✓✓✓				✓
11-1						
11-2		✓✓✓				
11-3		✓✓	✓	✓✓	✓✓	
11-4	✓	✓✓✓✓			✓	✓
11-5	✓	✓✓		✓	✓	
11-6		✓✓✓				
11-7	✓	✓				✓
12-1						
12-2		✓✓	✓	✓✓✓✓✓	✓✓	
12-3		✓✓		✓		
12-4	✓	✓✓✓✓✓	✓	✓✓✓	✓	✓
12-5		✓	✓		✓	
12-6		✓				
12-7	✓	✓✓✓✓				✓
13-1						
13-2		✓✓	✓	✓✓	✓✓✓✓✓	
13-3		✓		✓		
13-4		✓✓✓		✓✓✓		✓
13-5	✓			✓✓	✓	
13-6	✓	✓✓✓✓✓✓				✓
13-7		✓				✓
14-1		✓				
14-2		✓✓	✓✓	✓		
14-3		✓✓✓✓✓	✓	✓✓	✓✓	
14-4		✓✓				✓
15-1		✓				
15-2		✓✓			✓	
15-3		✓		✓		✓
15-4		✓✓		✓		
15-5	✓	✓	✓	✓	✓	
15-6	✓	✓✓✓				
15-7	✓					✓✓

Overview of *Precalculus with Trigonometry: Concepts and Applications*

Precalculus with Trigonometry: Concepts and Applications is designed for a full-year course following algebra and geometry to familiarize students thoroughly with the functions they will encounter in the subsequent calculus course. Up to a semester may be spent on trigonometric and circular functions for students who need this background.

The text is based on the premise that in order to succeed in calculus, students must understand the idea that variables really *vary*, not simply stand for unknown constants. To achieve this knowledge, students use functions as mathematical models of real-world phenomena. For instance, they find the best-fitting logistic function from a set of data on restrained population growth and then use the function to predict the population at various times and the times to reach various populations. In triangle trigonometry, students investigate the distance between two planets as the angle at the Sun varies. Students use sequences and series to find, for instance, the amount of money in a savings account as a function of the number of compounding periods or the number of periods to reach a specified amount. Probability is presented as the analysis of functions of a random variable. Vectors measure the position of a moving object as a function of its distance from a fixed point in space. Students investigate matrix transformations of plane figures as the number of iterations increases, sometimes leading to fractal figures representing snowflakes or ferns. With the gut understanding that variables really vary, students will be well prepared, as they later study calculus, to master the *rate* at which variables vary.

The text allows for two sequences of presentation. After an introduction to transformations of functions and their use as mathematical models in Chapter 1, students can either continue with these techniques for periodic functions in Chapters 2 through 6 or branch directly to fitting functions to data in Chapters 7 and 8. Thereafter, the instructor is free to choose topics for the rest of the course, depending on the specifications for the course and students' needs. It is recommended that the last chapter, Chapter 15, form the culmination of the course because it ties together much of what they have learned throughout the year and introduces the concept of instantaneous rate of change, using limits that have been studied earlier in the course. A formal study of derivatives and integrals is deliberately withheld so that students are not lulled into a false sense of security when they encounter these topics in calculus.

Chapter Overviews

Introductory Material, Chapter 1

CHAPTER 1: FUNCTIONS AND MATHEMATICAL MODELS

Here students refresh their memories about functions they have studied in algebra. The unifying concept is that familiar functions are built up by transformations of a few basic parent functions. For instance, the point-slope form of the linear function, $y - y_1 = m(x - x_1)$, is a dilation of the parent function, $y = x$, by a factor of m in the y-direction and translations by x_1 and y_1 in the x- and y-directions, respectively. Reflections are studied as dilations by a factor of -1. Composition of functions allows the formal definition of inverses of functions. Piecewise functions and their inverses are brought alive using Boolean variables with the graphing calculator to restrict the domain. The Explorations, designed for students to work in cooperative groups, are introduced in this chapter. The "Reading Analysis" questions and the "Quick Review" problems begin in Section 1-3. The Reading Analysis questions are designed to help students learn how to read a mathematics textbook, and the Quick Review problems give students a time-efficient review of relevant concepts and techniques. One concept students should grasp is that mathematics can be learned four ways: graphically, algebraically, numerically, and verbally. After Chapter 1, the course can branch to Chapter 7 or continue with the study of periodic functions in Chapters 2 through 6.

Periodic Functions and Trigonometry, Chapters 2–6

CHAPTER 2: PERIODIC FUNCTIONS AND RIGHT TRIANGLE PROBLEMS

Periodic functions are introduced in Section 2-1 by having students analyze the motion of a Ferris wheel. They plot $y = \sin x$ on the grapher and then use the dilations and translations from Chapter 1 to make the resulting sinusoid fit the real-world situation. Thereafter, students see how to extend the familiar cosine and sine functions from previous courses to angles greater than 180° or less than 0° by considering an angle to be a variable that measures rotation. By finding values of all six functions on the calculator, students learn the reciprocal properties, thus paving the way for the formal study of properties and identities in Chapter 4. The chapter concludes with right triangle trigonometry, possibly a familiar topic, for the main purpose of introducing the inverse trigonometric functions in a meaningful context, as well as providing practice with the definitions of the six functions.

CHAPTER 3: APPLICATIONS OF TRIGONOMETRIC AND CIRCULAR FUNCTIONS

In this chapter students put together what they have learned about periodic functions in Chapter 2 and transformations in Chapter 1 to sketch a graph of any sinusoid from its equation. The terms *concavity* and *point of inflection* are introduced in Section 3-2, preparing students for their use later in this text and in calculus. By reversing the graph-sketching process, students learn to write an equation of a sinusoid with any given period, amplitude, phase displacement, or vertical position. Thus, they can use sinusoidal functions as mathematical models of periodic functions in the real world. The introduction of circular functions with arguments in radians (which have no inherent units) makes the functions more reasonable in applications where the independent variable is time or distance rather than an angle. Students learn that arccosine is multiple valued as they find values of x for a given value of y. A side trip in Section 3-3 shows students tangent and secant graphs, including application to a beam cast by a rotating lighthouse beacon. In Section 3-8, students apply their knowledge of angles and circular functions to find angular and linear velocities in rotary motion.

CHAPTER 4: TRIGONOMETRIC FUNCTION PROPERTIES, IDENTITIES,
AND PARAMETRIC FUNCTIONS

Here students broaden their repertoire, adding the Pythagorean and quotient properties to the reciprocal properties they learned in Chapter 2. Sometimes they are asked to transform an expression to another form, and sometimes they are asked to prove that a given equation is an identity. Both kinds of problem use the same technique. Students reinforce the proof style they learned in geometry, starting with "Proof:" to show where statement of the identity ends and proving begins, and ending with a statement of what they have proved, including the abbreviation "Q.E.D." The properties are also used to solve equations, adding arcsine and arctangent to the arccosine learned in Chapter 3. Parametric functions, introduced in Section 4-5, allow students to plot these inverse circular relation graphs by giving them an x= menu in addition to the familiar y= menu. The information overload (the "identity crisis") students usually experience with identities is avoided by postponing the properties involving more than one argument, such as the double argument properties, until the next chapter.

CHAPTER 5: PROPERTIES OF COMBINED SINUSOIDS

This chapter introduces the other properties of trigonometric functions. A grapher makes it possible to study these properties as combinations of sinusoids rather than as purely algebraic properties. Thus, students learn by graphing that a linear combination of cosine and sine with equal periods is another sinusoid with a phase displacement. The composite argument properties (sometimes called addition formulas) are then used to prove this fact by expressing $\cos(A - B)$ as $\cos A \cos B + \sin A \sin B$. By learning to say this property verbally, "Cosine of first minus second equals cosine of first, cosine of second plus sine of first, sine of second," students can more easily apply it to such expressions as $\cos\left(\frac{\pi}{2} - A\right)$. Sums or products of sinusoids with unequal periods lead to graphs with varying amplitude or varying sinusoidal axes. Students then learn the reverse process, harmonic analysis, to find the sinusoids that were added or multiplied to get a given graph. The sum and product properties allow students to see that a product of sinusoids with much different periods is equivalent to a sum of sinusoids with nearly equal periods, the basis of AM radio waves. The double and half argument properties become simple extensions of the composite argument properties that you can derive quickly rather than having to memorize. It is the combined verbal, graphical, and algebraic approach to the properties that avoids the difficulties students usually experience.

CHAPTER 6: TRIANGLE TRIGONOMETRY

This chapter begins with the law of cosines, first discovered by measurement on accurately drawn graphs and then proven by algebraic methods. Hero's formula allows students to calculate the area of a triangle from three side lengths. The other area formula, "half of side times side times side times sine of included angle," leads to the law of sines in Section 6-2. This area formula also lays the foundation for the cross product of vectors in Chapter 10. The ambiguous case is approached through a single calculation using the law of cosines. The resulting quadratic equation's solution leads to both possible side lengths and reveals whether there are two triangles, just one triangle, or no triangle. Section 6-6, on vector addition, can be used to introduce students to the unit vectors in the x- and y-directions, although some instructors prefer to postpone vectors until Chapter 10. The chapter concludes with triangle problems from the real world. The main purpose, other than showing students that trigonometry ("triangle measurement") has applications, is to force students to decide which triangle technique to use based on the merits of the problem, not on the section in which the problem appears. A cumulative review of Chapters 1 through 6 appears in Section 6-9.

Data Analysis, Chapters 7–9

CHAPTER 7: PROPERTIES OF ELEMENTARY FUNCTIONS

This chapter is the reentry point if you choose to postpone the study of periodic functions in Chapters 2 through 6. Students learn to tell which kind of function might fit a given set of data, by recognizing first the geometric pattern of the graph and then the numerical pattern followed by regularly spaced points. The numerical patterns include the add–multiply property for exponential functions and the multiply–multiply property for power functions. As they study logarithms in Sections 7-4 through 7-6, students learn that logarithmic functions have the multiply–add property, as would be expected for the inverse of an exponential function. Section 7-4 focuses on common logarithms, so that properties can be explored in the familiar context of powers of 10. In Example 1 of Section 7-5, students learn a verbal way to remember the definition of logarithm, namely that a logarithm is an exponent, that eliminates most mistakes they make here. Natural logarithms and common logarithms are presented so that students will know what ln x means on their calculator and thus will have heard the words before encountering natural logarithms in calculus. The chapter concludes with the modeling of restrained population growth with the logistic function, whose graph has horizontal asymptotes and points of inflection. Periodic functions are not mentioned in this chapter because it is not assumed that students will have studied Chapters 2 through 6. In the Concept Problems, students encounter semilog and log-log graph paper, which they will learn more about in Section 8-4.

CHAPTER 8: FITTING FUNCTIONS TO DATA

In this chapter, students learn the basics of linear regression. They distinguish between deviation and residual (actually, residual deviation). By calculating the sum of the squares of the residuals on their graphers, students learn that the regression line minimizes SS_{res}. The computations that lead to the slope and intercept of the regression line are left to a course in elementary statistics so that more time will be available in this course for topics leading to calculus. However, Section 8-2 presents the computation of coefficient of determination as the fraction of SS_{dev} that is removed by the regression, as well as the fact that the correlation coefficient is a square root of the coefficient of determination. Section 8-3 introduces power, exponential, quadratic, logarithmic, and logistic regression. Once students choose the kind of function based on graphical patterns and endpoint behavior, they do the regression on a grapher and verify the result by residual plots. In this way, students avoid the trap of choosing a function simply because it has the correlation coefficient closest to ±1. Section 8-4 introduces logarithmic graph paper and linearization of exponential, logarithmic, and power functions and data.

Several problems and examples relate to data sets that students may want to enter into a grapher. Data sets with ten or more data points are available on the *Instructor's Resource CD* and at *www.keymath.com/precalc*. The data sets can be downloaded onto a TI-83 or TI-84 calculator, into an Excel spreadsheet, or into a Fathom document. Along with the data sets that accompany problems and examples, there are additional data sets that you may find useful for creating extra examples or test questions.

CHAPTER 9: PROBABILITY, AND FUNCTIONS OF A RANDOM VARIABLE

This chapter provides a time-efficient way for students to learn the counting principles leading to analysis of permutations and combinations. They learn to calculate probabilities of complex events from the probabilities of the components of those events. The topic fits in with the rest of the course as students learn that probability is the dependent variable in functions of a random (independent) variable. They learn the binomial distribution and touch upon other functions. The chapter concludes with mathematical expectation, a topic that allows students to see more clearly why people would want to study probability theory. A cumulative review of Chapters 7 through 9 appears in Section 9-10.

Analysis of Geometric Figures, Chapters 10–13

CHAPTER 10: THREE-DIMENSIONAL VECTORS

This chapter starts a series of precalculus topics that continues to the end of the book. The topics are tied together as much as possible, to show students they are learning a unified body of material. The bonds that tie the topics together are mostly motivational rather than prerequisite. It is possible to select which chapters to include, as well as the sequence in which you present them, without risk of students being ill prepared.

Chapter 10 is a substantive study of three-dimensional vectors. After a brief presentation of two-dimensional vectors, students learn to extend the concept to vectors used to measure the position of points in space. Vector differences measure the change in position, and vector sums measure the effect of consecutive displacements. Dot products allow students to calculate the angle between two vectors and the projection of one vector onto another. The cross products allow students to find a vector perpendicular to two other vectors. The vector techniques enable students to find equations of lines and planes in space. Real-world applications include the forensic analysis of a bullet's path through the wall, ceiling, and roof of a house.

Throughout the chapter, the components format for vectors, $3\vec{i} + 4\vec{j} - 2\vec{k}$, is used rather than the ordered triple format, (3, 4, −2). Although the ordered triple format saves time, using the components format helps students understand the concepts and techniques and ensures that they do not confuse vector notation and point notation.

CHAPTER 11: MATRIX TRANSFORMATIONS AND FRACTAL FIGURES

Multiplication of matrices, the main topic of this chapter, is directed toward applications in which one matrix transforms a pre-image matrix into an image matrix. The dilation, rotation, and translation parts of the transformation matrix are presented in a novel way that is easy for students to remember. By performing a transformation repeatedly (iteratively) and having the grapher do the plotting, students find that the images are attracted to a fixed point. If several transformations are performed iteratively, the images are attracted to an infinite number of fixed points. These *strange attractors* can take the form of various real-world shapes, such as ferns, trees, or snowflakes. The figures are so complex that their dimensions are fractions, not integers. Thus students get an introduction to fractal geometry, one of the newest branches of mathematics, while learning the properties of matrices. The Explorations include an introduction to Markov chains, an application of iterative matrix transformations to problems from economics.

CHAPTER 12: ANALYTIC GEOMETRY OF CONIC SECTIONS AND QUADRIC SURFACES

This chapter concentrates on the similarities and differences in the algebraic and geometric properties of ellipses, circles, and hyperbolas, with a brief treatment of parabolas. Students learn that parametric forms of the equations lead to more satisfactory computer graphs of the conic sections and also refresh their memories on the properties of trigonometric functions. Terminology such as "x-radius" and "y-radius" makes an easy connection with dilations from earlier in the course and avoids the popular misconception that the major or transverse axis is always in the x-direction. Rotation of the conic section graphs about an axis generates quadric surfaces. Inscribing variable cones and cylinders inside these surfaces gives students a taste of three-dimensional sketching and maximum/minimum problems they will later encounter in calculus. For analytic properties of conic sections, the familiar focal radius terminology is extended to include major and minor radius and directrix radius for the ellipse and transverse and conjugate radius for the hyperbola. Ellipse construction on an index with string, included in the Explorations, gives each student a hands-on tool that he or she can file in a notebook for future reference and use.

CHAPTER 13: POLAR COORDINATES, COMPLEX NUMBERS, AND MOVING OBJECTS

Students first learn about polar coordinates by plotting given points by hand on polar coordinate paper. This seems to be the best way to convey the concept of negative radius. Thereafter, they use their grapher to plot given equations and find intersections of polar curves. Writing complex numbers in polar form gives geometric meaning to products of the numbers. A complex product has modulus equal to the product of the moduli of the factors and argument equal to the sum of the arguments of the factors. The composite argument properties from Chapter 5 are reviewed in the algebraic proof of this property. Extension to powers and roots allows students to discover that any complex number, including any real number, has exactly n distinct nth roots. The chapter concludes with application of polar coordinates, parametric equations, and vectors to analyze some of the classic curves from analytic geometry, such as the involute of a circle formed as a string unwinds from a circle. The Explorations provide students with accurate graphs upon which they can make actual measurements to verify the geometric definitions and properties of the curves.

Other Precalculus Topics: Chapters 14–15 and Appendices

CHAPTER 14: SEQUENCES AND SERIES

This chapter teaches students to distinguish between a sequence, such as 1, 3, 5, 7, . . . , and a series, such as $1 + 3 + 5 + 7 + \cdots$, which is the indicated sum of the terms of a sequence. Students learn that under favorable conditions, a geometric series may approach a limit as the number of terms becomes infinite, thus strengthening the exposure to limits from earlier in the course and preparing for limits at the beginning of calculus. On the graphing calculator, students experience convergence by watching more and more decimal places in the partial sum remain fixed as the number of terms increases. Binomial series and sequences representing area and length give students a review of probability from Chapter 9 and fractal figures from Chapter 11.

CHAPTER 15: POLYNOMIAL AND RATIONAL FUNCTIONS, LIMITS, AND DERIVATIVES

This concluding chapter ties together much of what students have learned and gives them a push toward calculus. Regression is reviewed by having students fit polynomial functions to data. The properties of polynomial functions, possibly previously studied by students, are combined with operations on algebraic fractions to get rational functions representing the average rate of change over a given interval. By taking the limit as the width of the interval approaches zero, students learn to compute the instantaneous rate of change, or the derivative. Division by zero creates a removable discontinuity in the graph, so called because it can be removed by factoring and canceling. A cumulative review of Chapters 10 through 15 appears in Section 15-7. Following recommendations of the College Board, calculus itself is not treated in this text. Although the words *limit* and *derivative* appear in this chapter, the concepts are not stressed with the rigor required in a calculus course.

APPENDIX A: TYPES OF NUMBERS, AXIOMS, AND OTHER PROPERTIES

This appendix provides reference material for students concerning the names of various sets of numbers, the field axioms for addition and multiplication, and other properties of numbers that can be proven from the axioms.

APPENDIX B: MATHEMATICAL INDUCTION

Induction is motivated first by showing students how to prove the extended distributive property for any finite number of terms by contradiction using the well-ordering axiom. Then they see how to shorten the proof to four steps, establishing an anchor, making an induction hypothesis, proving that if the property is true for $n = k$, then it is also true for $n = k + 1$, and concluding its truth for all finite n.

Calculators and Computers

It is assumed that each student will have a handheld programmable graphing calculator (a "grapher") available at all times, except when it is specifically withheld for testing purposes. The calculator should have at least the capacity to plot graphs in arbitrary windows, make tables of data, solve equations numerically, and download previously written programs. Calculator instructions and programs provided with the course materials are written for a TI-83 or TI-84. However, most graphers use a similar programming language to these calculators, so the instructions and programs could be modified slightly to work on other graphers.

There are several computer-based activities available for each chapter. These are listed as Technology Options and summarized in the Technology Notes in the Instructor's Commentary for each section. Some of these activities require the availability of Fathom Dynamic Data™ Software or Dynamic Geometry® software, such as The Geometer's Sketchpad®. However, the course can be taught without the use of more sophisticated computers and software. The Dynamic Precalculus Explorations associated with some problems are available at *www.keymath.com/precalc,* and they require nothing more than a standard Java-enabled Web browser.

Types of Student Activities

Many problems in the text are for drill and practice so that students will become familiar with the algebraic, numerical, graphical, and verbal techniques needed to prepare for calculus. Other problems are more conceptual, revealing insights beyond drill and practice. Still other problems are designed to show how students can apply the mathematics they are learning in the real world. Most problem sets begin with ten Quick Review problems whose purpose is not only for review but also to get students used to doing routine things *quickly,* as they must on standardized tests and in mathematics contests. Most problem sets also begin with a Reading Analysis (RA) question. These questions are designed to teach students how to read a mathematics book by asking them to summarize the main ideas of the chapter in words. It is recommended that you always assign these problems. Some problem sets have problems designed to introduce students to a topic in the next section. The first problem set in most chapters is of this discovery type.

Several sections contain problems that require the use of a Dynamic Precalculus Exploration. These are interactive sketches that allow students to explore trigonometric concepts. The Dynamic Precalculus Explorations are available on the *Instructor's Resource CD* and at *www.keymath.com/precalc,* and they can be used with any Java-enabled Web browser.

Most sections have one or more Explorations, found in the *Instructor's Resource Book.* These activities are designed to allow students to learn on their own or in cooperative groups, following a brief introduction by the instructor. Some Explorations are designed to give students practice in discovering by reading the text, and others are intended for discovery without the text. Still other Explorations consist of a review of topics from several sections. It is not expected that students will work all of the Explorations. Sometimes you must present material by lecture, both for efficient use of time and for preparing students for the learning style they may need to use in later, college-level mathematics courses. Some of the Explorations can be enhanced by the use of technology, and these are mentioned in the Technology Notes in the Instructor's Commentary for the section. However, all Explorations are designed to be completed without the use of sophisticated technology.

At the end of each chapter is a chapter review and a test consisting of three types of problems.

- The Review Problems are keyed to the sections of the text. Thus, if you plan a test on Sections 5-1 through 5-4, you could assign students Problems R1 through R4 at the end of Chapter 5 as a "rehearsal" for the test. Answers appear in the back of the text for all Review Problems.

- The Concept Problems involve extensions of the material in the text, either to topics the students will learn later or to things above and beyond the scope of the text. Many of the Concept Problems are suitable for projects taking more than one day. No answers are provided in the text for the Concept Problems.

- The Chapter Test presents topics of the chapter, but not necessarily in the same order. Because these tests are designed as a "dress rehearsal" for students, the answers do not appear in the text.

Cooperative Group Learning

Although the text is suitable for presentation by the traditional lecture method, the course is more effective if the instructors take advantage of learning in cooperative groups. The Explorations in the *Instructor's Resource Book* form the basis for this work. A more detailed description of cooperative group learning methods appears later in this *Instructor's Guide*.

Precalculus Journal

Students are expected to keep a precalculus journal. Entries are to be made in the journal only after students have seen the topic in class and in homework assignments. It is to be a thoughtful distillation of things written hastily in class notes. The journal is useful to students when reviewing for tests. At times you may allow students to use the journal on certain parts of a test. The journal makes writing an integral part of the course, adding to the algebraic, numeric, and graphical techniques.

Pedagogical Features

There are several features in the student text to enhance the material so that both student and instructor get the most benefit from the text.

- Review of concepts and techniques from other courses is done in the context of studying new material rather than strictly as a repeat. For example, the first chapter reviews the function concept by showing students how they can build up familiar functions from algebra by transformations of a few basic parent functions. From day 1, therefore, students are learning new material.

- Students learn most techniques as *procedures* rather than simply as formulas. For instance, in calculating the nth term of a geometric series, students think, "Geometric series progress by multiplying. How many common ratios do I have to multiply by to get the nth term?" The composite argument property for $\cos (A - B)$ expresses something students *do* to an expression, for example, "cosine of first times cosine of second, plus sine of first times sine of second."

- Many problems, particularly those applying to the real world, have titles. For the students, this feature gives the feeling that the problem is important enough to deserve a title. For the instructor, this feature helps with making assignments and locating a particular problem using the Index of Problem Titles.

- Routine problems occur in equivalent pairs, one odd and one even. Answers to selected problems, usually the odd-numbered ones, appear in the back of the book. Students are expected to use "odd-problem rules," that is, "You aren't finished until you can get the answer in the back of the book."

Instructor's Resource Book

The *Instructor's Resource Book* comes separately and contains sets of supplementary materials:

- Blackline masters, containing enlargements of graphs from the text, that you can reproduce when the problem calls for students to draw on the given graph

- Explorations, keyed to the various sections of the text, for cooperative learning activities, whole-class guided discovery activities, or for ideas you may use in your classroom presentation

- Activities for The Geometer's Sketchpad, Fathom, and CBL 2™, the Calculator-Based Laboratory
- Programs for graphing calculators

Assessment Resources

The *Assessment Resources* comes separately and contains the following resources for assessing students' understanding of the material.

- Two versions of each Section, Chapter, and Cumulative Test, with complete solutions
- Assessment suggestions, expanding on the need for assessment of student achievement and the need for making instructional decisions and evaluating your course

These assessment resources are provided in electronic format on the *Instructor's Resource CD* that accompanies this *Instructor's Guide*. The tests are provided as PDF files, as well as Microsoft Word documents, so you can modify them to fit your particular testing needs.

Standard Schedule Timelines

Each timeline is based on 40- to 45-minute class periods. These are suggested timelines for each chapter in different types of courses.

<table>
<tr><td colspan="2">Comprehensive Course (185 Days)</td><td colspan="2">Standard Course (158 Days)</td></tr>
<tr><td>Chapter 1</td><td>10 days</td><td>Chapter 1</td><td>10 days</td></tr>
<tr><td>Chapter 2</td><td>8 days</td><td>Chapter 2</td><td>8 days</td></tr>
<tr><td>Chapter 3</td><td>12 days</td><td>Chapter 3</td><td>11 days</td></tr>
<tr><td>Chapter 4</td><td>14 days</td><td>Chapter 4</td><td>13 days</td></tr>
<tr><td>Chapter 5</td><td>12 days</td><td>Chapter 5</td><td>9 days</td></tr>
<tr><td>Chapter 6</td><td>12 days</td><td>Chapter 6</td><td>11 days</td></tr>
<tr><td>Cumulative Review</td><td>2 days</td><td>Cumulative Review</td><td>2 days</td></tr>
<tr><td>Chapter 7</td><td>11 days</td><td>Chapter 7</td><td>10 days</td></tr>
<tr><td>Chapter 8</td><td>9 days</td><td>Chapter 8</td><td>9 days</td></tr>
<tr><td>Chapter 9</td><td>15 days</td><td>Chapter 9</td><td>13 days</td></tr>
<tr><td>Cumulative Review</td><td>2 days</td><td>Cumulative Review</td><td>2 days</td></tr>
<tr><td>Chapter 10</td><td>14 days</td><td>Chapter 10</td><td>12 days</td></tr>
<tr><td>Chapter 11</td><td>13 days</td><td>Chapter 11</td><td>11 days</td></tr>
<tr><td>Chapter 12</td><td>17 days</td><td>Chapter 12</td><td>13 days</td></tr>
<tr><td>Chapter 13</td><td>14 days</td><td>Chapter 13</td><td>11 days</td></tr>
<tr><td>Chapter 14</td><td>8 days</td><td>Chapter 14</td><td>5 days</td></tr>
<tr><td>Chapter 15</td><td>10 days</td><td>Chapter 15</td><td>6 days</td></tr>
<tr><td>Cumulative Review</td><td>2 days</td><td>Cumulative Review</td><td>2 days</td></tr>
</table>

<table>
<tr><td colspan="2">Comprehensive Course with No 3-D Vectors or Matrices (158 Days)</td><td colspan="2">Semester Course with No Trigonometry (84 Days)</td></tr>
<tr><td>Chapter 1</td><td>10 days</td><td>Chapter 1</td><td>10 days</td></tr>
<tr><td>Chapter 2</td><td>8 days</td><td>Chapter 7</td><td>11 days</td></tr>
<tr><td>Chapter 3</td><td>12 days</td><td>Chapter 8</td><td>9 days</td></tr>
<tr><td>Chapter 4</td><td>14 days</td><td>Chapter 9</td><td>15 days</td></tr>
<tr><td>Chapter 5</td><td>12 days</td><td>Cumulative Review</td><td>2 days</td></tr>
<tr><td>Chapter 6</td><td>12 days</td><td>Chapter 12</td><td>17 days</td></tr>
<tr><td>Cumulative Review</td><td>2 days</td><td>Chapter 14</td><td>8 days</td></tr>
<tr><td>Chapter 7</td><td>11 days</td><td>Chapter 15</td><td>10 days</td></tr>
<tr><td>Chapter 8</td><td>9 days</td><td>Cumulative Review</td><td>2 days</td></tr>
<tr><td>Chapter 9</td><td>15 days</td><td colspan="2">Semester Course in Trigonometry with Polar Coordinates (81 Days)</td></tr>
<tr><td>Cumulative Review</td><td>2 days</td><td>Chapter 1</td><td>10 days</td></tr>
<tr><td>Chapter 12</td><td>17 days</td><td>Chapter 2</td><td>8 days</td></tr>
<tr><td>Chapter 13</td><td>14 days</td><td>Chapter 3</td><td>12 days</td></tr>
<tr><td>Chapter 14</td><td>8 days</td><td>Chapter 4</td><td>14 days</td></tr>
<tr><td>Chapter 15</td><td>10 days</td><td>Chapter 5</td><td>12 days</td></tr>
<tr><td>Cumulative Review</td><td>2 days</td><td>Chapter 6</td><td>12 days</td></tr>
<tr><td></td><td></td><td>Cumulative Review</td><td>2 days</td></tr>
<tr><td></td><td></td><td>Chapter 13</td><td>11 days</td></tr>
</table>

Suggested Assignments

All days marked with an * should be skipped if you are following the standard timeline.

On the day of the Chapter Test, you could assign either a Concept Problem from the Chapter Review or the problem set from the next chapter you are covering. The problem set is always listed as a day 1 assignment. Instructors who assign it the night of the Chapter Test can skip to day 2; they will have an extra day in the schedule to use for quizzes, extra problems, or catching up.

Chapter 1: Functions and Mathematical Models (10 Days)

Day	Section	Topics	Problems
1	1-1	Functions: Algebraically, Numerically, Graphically, and Verbally	1–5
2	1-2	Kinds of Functions	Recommended: 1–39 odd, 40, 41; also suggested: 42
3	1-3	Dilation and Translation of Function Graphs	RA, Q1–Q10, 1–6
4	1-3	Dilation and Translation of Function Graphs	RA, 7–21
5	1-4	Composition of Functions	RA, Q1–Q10, 1, 2, 5, 7, 9, 10, 12–15
6	1-5	Inverse of Functions	RA, Q1–Q10, 1, 3–5, 7, 9, 10, 13, 17, 18, 21, 29, 30
7	1-6	Reflections, Absolute Values, and Other Transformations	RA, Q1–Q10, 1–4, 5, 7, 9–14
8	1-7	Precalculus Journal	1
9	1-8	Chapter Review	R1–R6, T1–T28
10	1-8	Chapter Test	Recommended: C1 and Problem Set 2-1; also suggested: C2

Chapter 2: Periodic Functions and Right Triangle Problems (8 Days)

Day	Section	Topics	Problems
1	2-1	Introduction to Periodic Functions	1–4
2	2-2	Measurement of Rotation	RA, Q1–Q10, 1, 5, 9, 19, 21, 25, 27, 29, 30
3	2-3	Sine and Cosine Functions	RA, Q1–Q10, 1–23 odd
4	2-4	Values of the Six Trigonometric Functions	Recommended: RA, Q1–Q10, 1, 6, 7, 9, 11–14; also suggested: 4
5	2-4	Values of the Six Trigonometric Functions	15–19, 21–31 odd, 35, 39, 40–46
6	2-5	Inverse Trigonometric Functions and Triangle Problems	Recommended: RA, Q1–Q10, 1–5, 7, 9–11, 13, 14, 24; also suggested: 8, 21
7	2-6	Chapter Review	R0–R5, T1–T22
8	2-6	Chapter Test	Either C1 and C3 or Problem Set 3-1

Chapter 3: Applications of Trigonometric and Circular Functions (11 Days)

Day	Section	Topics	Problems
1	3-1	Sinusoids: Amplitude, Period, and Cycles	1–9
2	3-2	General Sinusoidal Graphs	RA, Q1–Q10, 1–11 odd
3	3-2	General Sinusoidal Graphs	Recommended: 2, 4, 13–25 odd, 26, 28, Supplementary Problem 7 of Section 2-5; also suggested: 27
4	3-3	Graphs of Tangent, Cotangent, Secant, and Cosecant Functions	Recommended: RA, Q1–Q10, 1–3, 5, 6, 9, 11–14; also suggested: 15, 16
5	3-4	Radian Measure of Angles	RA, Q1–Q10, 1–3, 9, 11, 17, 21, 25, 29, 31, 37–53 odd
6	3-5	Circular Functions	Recommended: RA, Q1–Q10, 1–3, 6, 7, 10, 11, 14, 15, 19, 23, 25, 27, 31, 37, 44, 49; also suggested: 45, 46, 48
7	3-6	Inverse Circular Relations: Given y, Find x	RA, Q1–Q10, 1–13 odd
8	3-7	Sinusoidal Functions as Mathematical Models	RA, Q1–Q10, 1, 2
9	3-7	Sinusoidal Functions as Mathematical Models	Recommended: 4, 5, 8, 11; also suggested: 14, 15
10	3-8	Rotary Motion	RA, Q1–Q10, 1–9 odd, 10, 11, 13–17
11	3-9	Chapter Review	R0–R8, T1–T24
12	3-9	Chapter Test	Either C1 or C2 or Problem Set 4-1

Chapter 4: Trigonometric Function Properties, Identities, and Parametric Functions (13–14 Days)

Day	Section	Topics	Problems
1	4-1	Introduction to the Pythagorean Property	1–6
2	4-2	Pythagorean, Reciprocal, and Quotient Properties	RA, Q1–Q10, 1–15 odd
3	4-2	Pythagorean, Reciprocal, and Quotient Properties	2–14 even
4	4-3	Identities and Algebraic Transformation of Expressions	RA, Q1–Q10, 1–25 odd
5	4-3	Identities and Algebraic Transformation of Expressions	27–55 odd
6*	4-3	Identities and Algebraic Transformation of Expressions	Even-numbered or one or more Explorations
7	4-4	Arcsine, Arctangent, Arccosine, and Trigonometric Equations	RA, Q1–Q10, 1–27 odd
8	4-4	Arcsine, Arctangent, Arccosine, and Trigonometric Equations	29–43 odd
9	4-5	Parametric Functions	RA, Q1–Q10, 1–3, 5, 15, 17, 18
10	4-5	Parametric Functions	7–13 odd, 16, 19, 21, 22
11	4-6	Inverse Trigonometric Relation Graphs	RA, Q1–Q10, 1–4, 5, 7, 9
12	4-6	Inverse Trigonometric Relation Graphs	Recommended: 11–23 odd, 24, 26; also suggested: 25
13	4-7	Chapter Review	R0–R6, T1–T15
14	4-7	Chapter Test	C1 or Problem Set 5-1

Chapter 5: Properties of Combined Sinusoids (9–12 Days)

Day	Section	Topics	Problems
1	5-1	Introduction to Combinations of Sinusoids	1–9
2	5-2	Composite Argument and Linear Combination Properties	RA, Q1–Q10, 1–15 odd, 16, 17
3	5-2	Composite Argument and Linear Combination Properties	Recommended: 19–27 odd, 29, 30, 33; also suggested: 28, 31, 32
4	5-3	Other Composite Argument Properties	RA, Q1–Q10, 1–9 odd, 10, 11–15 odd
5	5-3	Other Composite Argument Properties	Recommended: 14, 17–31 odd, 33, 36; also suggested: 40
6*	5-4	Composition of Ordinates and Harmonic Analysis	RA, Q1–Q10, 1–3, 5
7*	5-4	Composition of Ordinates and Harmonic Analysis	Recommended: 7–15 odd; also suggested: 12
8*	5-5	The Sum and Product Properties	RA, Q1–Q10, 1–25 odd, 29, 35
9	5-6	Double and Half Argument Properties	RA, Q1–Q10, 1–3, 5, 11–17 odd
10	5-6	Double and Half Argument Properties	7, 9, 19–43 odd
11	5-7	Chapter Review	R0–R6, T1–T19
12	5-7	Chapter Test	Problem Set 6-1

Chapter 6: Triangle Trigonometry (11–12 Days + 2 Days CR)

Day	Section	Topics	Problems
1	6-1	Introduction to Oblique Triangles	1–6
2	6-2	Oblique Triangles: Law of Cosines	RA, Q1–Q10, 1, 3, 6, 7, 9, 11, 13, 14, 15, 17, 19
3	6-3	Area of a Triangle	RA, Q1–Q10, 1, 3, 7–9, 11, 13, 14
4	6-4	Oblique Triangles: Law of Sines	RA, Q1–Q10, 1–9 odd, 10, 11, 13, 14
5	6-5	The Ambiguous Case	RA, Q1–Q10, 1–13 odd, 14
6*	6-5	The Ambiguous Case	Quiz/test students on the material in Sections 1–5, assign a selection of problems not previously assigned, or use the day to recap the chapter concepts
7	6-6	Vector Addition	RA, Q1–Q10, 2, 4, 5, 6
8	6-6	Vector Addition	7–17 odd, 18
9	6-7	Real-World Triangle Problems	RA, Q1–Q10, 1–9 odd
10	6-7	Real-World Triangle Problems	11–17 odd, 18, and have students write their own problem
11	6-8	Chapter Review	R0–R7, T1–T21
12	6-8	Chapter Test	Cumulative Review 1–24
13	6-9	Cumulative Review, Chapters 1–6	Cumulative Review 25–51
14	6-9	Cumulative Review, Chapters 1–6	Problem Set 7-1

Chapter 7: Properties of Elementary Functions (10–11 Days)

Day	Section	Topics	Problems
1	7-1	Shapes of Function Graphs	RA, 1–4
2	7-2	Identifying Functions from Graphical Patterns	Q1–Q10, 1–25 odd
3*	7-2	Identifying Functions from Graphical Patterns	2–10 even, 14–24 even
4	7-3	Identifying Functions from Numerical Patterns	Q1–Q10, 1–23 odd
5	7-3	Identifying Functions from Numerical Patterns	25–27, 29–32, 35
6	7-4	Properties of Logarithms	RA, Q1–Q10, 1–47 odd
7	7-5	Logarithms: Equations and Other Bases	RA, Q1–Q10, 1, 2, 3–49 odd
8	7-6	Logarithmic Functions	Recommended: RA, Q1–Q10, 1–13 odd; also suggested: 14
9	7-7	Logistic Functions for Restrained Growth	Recommended: RA, Q1–Q10, 1, 3, 5, 7; also suggested: 4
10	7-8	Chapter Review	R0–R7, T1–T28
11	7-8	Chapter Test	Problem Set 8-1

Chapter 8: Fitting Functions to Data (9 Days)

Day	Section	Topics	Problems
1	8-1	Introduction to Regression for Linear Data	1–6
2	8-2	Deviations, Residuals, and the Correlation Coefficient	RA, Q1–Q10, 1–5
3	8-3	Regression for Nonlinear Data	RA, Q1–Q10, 1–6
4	8-4	Linearizing Data—Logarithmic Graph Paper	RA, Q1–Q10, 1–17 odd
5	8-4	Linearizing Data—Logarithmic Graph Paper	Recommended: 19–21, 23, 24; also suggested: 22
6	8-5	Residual Plots and Mathematical Models	RA, Q1–Q10, 1–11 odd
7	8-5	Residual Plots and Mathematical Models	2–10 even
8	8-6	Chapter Review	R0–R5, T1–T20
9	8-6	Chapter Test	Problem Set 9-1

Precalculus with Trigonometry: Instructor's Guide
© 2007 Key Curriculum Press

Chapter 9: Probability, and Functions of a Random Variable
(13–15 Days + 2 Days CR)

Day	Section	Topics	Problems
1	9-1	Introduction to Probability	1–13
2	9-2	Words Associated with Probability	Q1–Q10, 1, 2
3	9-3	Two Counting Principles	RA, Q1–Q10, 1–15 odd, 16, 17
4	9-4	Probabilities of Various Permutations	RA, Q1–Q10, 1–19 odd
5*	9-4	Probabilities of Various Permutations	Selected even-numbered problems or Exploration exercises
6	9-5	Probabilities of Various Combinations	RA, Q1–Q10, 1–31 odd
7	9-5	Probabilities of Various Combinations	Selected even-numbered problems
8	9-6	Properties of Probability	RA, Q1–Q10, 1–13 odd
9*	9-6	Properties of Probability	Selected even-numbered problems
10	9-7	Functions of a Random Variable	RA, Q1–Q10, 1, 3, 5
11	9-7	Functions of a Random Variable	7, 9, 11, 14, and some even-numbered problems
12	9-8	Mathematical Expectation	RA, Q1–Q10, 1, 3, 5, 7
13	9-8	Mathematical Expectation	2, 4, 6, 8
14	9-9	Chapter Review	R0–R8, T1–T28
15	9-9	Chapter Test	Cumulative Review 1–13
16	9-10	Cumulative Review, Chapters 7–9	Cumulative Review 14–24
17	9-10	Cumulative Review, Chapters 7–9	Problem Set 10-1

Chapter 10: Three-Dimensional Vectors (12–14 Days)

Day	Section	Topics	Problems
1	10-1	Review of Two-Dimensional Vectors	1–8
2	10-2	Two-Dimensional Vector Practice	RA, Q1–Q10, 1–15 odd, 16
3	10-3	Vectors in Space	Recommended: RA, Q1–Q10, 1–17 odd, 18; also suggested: 19
4	10-4	Scalar Products and Projections of Vectors	RA, Q1–Q10, 1–17 odd
5	10-4	Scalar Products and Projections of Vectors	20, 21, 23–25, 27, 29–31
6	10-5	Planes in Space	RA, Q1–Q10, 1–15 odd
7*	10-5	Planes in Space	12, Supplementary Problems 7–13
8	10-6	Vector Product of Two Vectors	RA, Q1–Q10, 1–11 odd
9	10-6	Vector Product of Two Vectors	13–19, 21–23
10	10-7	Direction Angles and Direction Cosines	RA, Q1–Q10, 1–23 odd, 24
11	10-8	Vector Equations of Lines in Space	RA, Q1–Q10, 1–15 odd
12	10-9	Chapter Review	R0–R8, T1–T27
13*	10-9	Chapter Review	Selected problems from the text, supplementary problem set, or Explorations
14	10-9	Chapter Test	Problem Set 11-1

Chapter 11: Matrix Transformations and Fractal Figures (11–13 Days)

Day	Section	Topics	Problems
1	11-1	Introduction to Iterated Transformations	1–5
2	11-2	Matrix Operations and Solution of Linear Systems	RA, Q1–Q10, 1–23 odd
3*	11-2	Matrix Operations and Solution of Linear Systems	4, 8, 12, 16, 20
4	11-3	Rotation and Dilation Matrices	RA, Q1–Q10, 1–21 odd, 22
5	11-4	Translation with Rotation and Dilation Matrices	RA, Q1–Q10, 1, 3
6	11-4	Translation with Rotation and Dilation Matrices	2, 4
7	11-5	Strange Attractors for Several Iterated Transformations	RA, Q1–Q10, 1, 5, 9
8*	11-5	Strange Attractors for Several Iterated Transformations	2, 6–8
9	11-5	Strange Attractors for Several Iterated Transformations	10, 11
10	11-6	Fractal Dimensions	RA, Q1–Q10, 1, 2, 5
11	11-6	Fractal Dimensions	3, 4, 6
12	11-7	Chapter Review	R0–R6, T0–T19
13	11-7	Chapter Test	Exploratory problem set of the next chapter you plan to do

Chapter 12: Analytic Geometry of Conic Sections and Quadric Surfaces (13–17 Days)

Day	Section	Topics	Problems
1	12-1	Introduction to Conic Sections	1–8
2	12-2	Parametric and Cartesian Equations of the Conic Sections	RA, Q1–Q10, 1–4, 5–11 odd, 21–27 odd
3	12-2	Parametric and Cartesian Equations of the Conic Sections	13, 15, 17, 19, 28–33
4*	12-2	Parametric and Cartesian Equations of the Conic Sections	Even-numbered problems and supplementary problems as needed
5*	12-2	Parametric and Cartesian Equations of the Conic Sections	Even-numbered problems and supplementary problems as needed
6	12-3	Quadric Surfaces and Inscribed Figures	RA, Q1–Q10, 1–10
7	12-3	Quadric Surfaces and Inscribed Figures	11–17 odd
8	12-4	Analytic Geometry of the Conic Sections	RA, Q1–Q10, 1–4
9	12-4	Analytic Geometry of the Conic Sections	11–31 every other odd
10*	12-4	Analytic Geometry of the Conic Sections	Exploration Day
11*	12-4	Analytic Geometry of the Conic Sections	Selected even-numbered problems and/or the remaining odds as needed
12	12-5	Parametric and Cartesian Equations for Rotated Conics	RA, Q1–Q10, 1–11 odd
13	12-5	Parametric and Cartesian Equations for Rotated Conics	Recommended: 13–19 odd, 23; also suggested: 21, 22
14	12-6	Applications of Conic Sections	Q1–Q10, 1–4
15	12-6	Applications of Conic Sections	5–8
16	12-7	Chapter Review	R0–R6, T1–T18
17	12-7	Chapter Test	Exploratory problem set of the next chapter you plan to do

Chapter 13: Polar Coordinates, Complex Numbers, and Moving Objects (11–14 Days)

Day	Section	Topics	Problems
1	13-1	Introduction to Polar Coordinates	1–6
2	13-2	Polar Equations of Conics and Other Curves	RA, Q1–Q10, 1–9 odd
3	13-2	Polar Equations of Conics and Other Curves	11–23 odd
4	13-2	Polar Equations of Conics and Other Curves	Even-numbered problems as needed
5	13-3	Intersections of Polar Curves	RA, Q1–Q10, 1–9 odd
6	13-4	Complex Numbers in Polar Form	RA, Q1–Q10, 1–33 every other odd, 35, 39
7	13-4	Complex Numbers in Polar Form	The remaining odds and some evens as needed
8	13-5	Parametric Equations for Moving Objects	RA, Q1–Q10, 1–4
9	13-5	Parametric Equations for Moving Objects	7, 9
10*	13-5	Parametric Equations for Moving Objects	5, 11
11*	13-5	Parametric Equations for Moving Objects	The remaining problems and Explorations as desired
12*	13-5	Parametric Equations for Moving Objects	The remaining problems and Explorations as desired
13	13-6	Chapter Review	R0–R5, T1–T17
14	13-6	Chapter Test	Exploratory problem set of the next chapter you plan to do

Chapter 14: Sequences and Series (5–8 Days)

Day	Section	Topics	Problems
1*	14-1	Introduction to Sequences and Series	1–10
2*	14-2	Arithmetic, Geometric, and Other Sequences	RA, Q1–Q10, 1–6, 16, 17, 23, 24
3*	14-2	Arithmetic, Geometric, and Other Sequences	7–12, 13, 15, 18, 19
4	14-3	Series and Partial Sums	RA, Q1–Q10, 1, 2, 5, 11–27 odd
5	14-3	Series and Partial Sums	3, 4, 9, 12, 29–51 odd, 53–55
6	14-3	Series and Partial Sums	Even-numbered problems and Explorations as needed
7	14-4	Chapter Review	R0–R3, T1–T24
8	14-4	Chapter Test	Exploratory problem set of the next chapter you plan to do

Chapter 15: Polynomial and Rational Functions, Limits, and Derivatives (6–10 Days + 2 Days CR)

Day	Section	Topics	Problems
1	15-1	Review of Polynomial Functions	1–11
2	15-2	Graphs and Zeros of Polynomial Functions	RA, Q1–Q10, 1–17 odd, 27, 29–32
3*	15-2	Graphs and Zeros of Polynomial Functions	19–25 odd, 34, 37
4	15-3	Fitting Polynomial Functions to Data	Recommended: RA, Q1–Q10, 1, 3, 4, 6–8, 11, 14; also suggested: 12
5	15-4	Rational Functions: Discontinuities, Limits, and Partial Fractions	RA, Q1–Q10, 1, 2, 3–11 odd, 24
6*	15-4	Rational Functions: Discontinuities, Limits, and Partial Fractions	Recommended: 13–25 odd; also suggested: 26
7	15-5	Instantaneous Rates of Change of a Function: The Derivative	Q1–Q10, 1, 2, 4, 5
8*	15-5	Instantaneous Rates of Change of a Function: The Derivative	Recommended: 6, 7, 8, 9–25 odd; also suggested: 26
9	15-6	Chapter Review and Test	R0–R5, T1–T21
10	15-6	Chapter Review and Test	Cumulative Review 1–17
11	15-7	Cumulative Review, Chapters 10–15	Cumulative Review 18–32
12	15-7	Cumulative Review, Chapters 10–15	Cumulative Review 33–47

Precalculus with Trigonometry: Instructor's Guide
© 2007 Key Curriculum Press

Block Schedule Timelines

These are suggested timelines for each chapter in different types of courses. Each timeline is based on 85- to 90-minute class periods.

Standard Course (98 Days):

Chapter 1	6 days
Chapter 2	5 days
Chapter 3	7 days
Chapter 4	7 days
Chapter 5	5 days
Chapter 6	7 days
Cumulative Review	1 day
Chapter 7	7 days
Chapter 8	7 days
Chapter 9	8 days
Cumulative Review	1 day
Chapter 10	7 days
Chapter 11	6 days
Chapter 12	7 days
Chapter 13	6 days
Chapter 14	5 days
Chapter 15	5 days
Cumulative Review	1 day

Semester Course in Trigonometry (38 Days):

Chapter 1	6 days
Chapter 2	5 days
Chapter 3	7 days
Chapter 4	7 days
Chapter 5	5 days
Chapter 6	7 days
Cumulative Review	1 day

Standard Course with *No* 3-D Vectors or Matrices (85 Days):

Chapter 1	6 days
Chapter 2	5 days
Chapter 3	7 days
Chapter 4	7 days
Chapter 5	5 days
Chapter 6	7 days
Cumulative Review	1 day
Chapter 7	7 days
Chapter 8	7 days
Chapter 9	8 days
Cumulative Review	1 day
Chapter 12	7 days
Chapter 13	6 days
Chapter 14	5 days
Chapter 15	5 days
Cumulative Review	1 day

Semester Course with *No* Trigonometry (47 Days):

Chapter 1	6 days
Chapter 7	7 days
Chapter 8	7 days
Chapter 9	8 days
Chapter 12	7 days
Chapter 14	5 days
Chapter 15	5 days
Cumulative Review	1 day

Suggested Assignments

Chapter 1: Functions and Mathematical Models (6 Days)

Day	Section	Topics	Problems
1	1-1	Functions: Algebraically, Numerically, Graphically, and Verbally	1–5
	1-2	Kinds of Functions	1–39 odd, 40, 41
2	1-3	Dilation and Translation of Function Graphs	RA, Q1–Q10, 1–21 odd
3	1-4	Composition of Functions	RA, Q1–Q10, 1–9 odd, 10
	1-5	Inverse of Functions	RA, Q1–Q10, 1, 3, 5, 9, 11
4	1-5	Inverse of Functions	17, 19, 21, 29
	1-6	Reflections, Absolute Values, and Other Transformations	RA, Q1–Q10, 1–9 odd, 10, 12
5	1-7	Precalculus Journal	1
	1-8	Chapter Review	R1–R6, T1–T28
6	1-8	Chapter Test	
	2-1	Introduction to Periodic Functions	1–4

Chapter 2: Periodic Functions and Right Triangle Problems (5 Days)

Day	Section	Topics	Problems
1	2-2	Measurement of Rotation	RA, Q1–Q10, 1, 5, 9, 19, 27, 29
	2-3	Sine and Cosine Functions	RA, Q1–Q10, 1–13 odd
2	2-3	Sine and Cosine Functions	15–23 odd
	2-4	Values of the Six Trigonometric Functions	RA, Q1–Q10, 1, 6, 7, 9, 11–14
3	2-4	Values of the Six Trigonometric Functions	15–39 every other odd, 46
	2-5	Inverse Trigonometric Functions and Triangle Functions	RA, Q1–Q10, 1–13 odd, 24
4	2-6	Chapter Review	R0–R5, T1–T20
5	2-6	Chapter Test	
	3-1	Sinusoids: Amplitude, Period, and Cycles	1–10

Chapter 3: Applications of Trigonometric and Circular Functions (7–8 Days)

Day	Section	Topics	Problems
1	3-2	General Sinusoidal Graphs	RA, Q1–Q10, 1–25 odd, 26, 28
2	3-3	Graphs of Tangent, Cotangent, Secant, and Cosecant Functions	RA, Q1–Q10, 1–3, 5, 6, 9, 11–14
	3-4	Radian Measure of Angles	RA, Q1–Q10, 1, 2, 3, 9, 11, 17, 21
3	3-4	Radian Measure of Angles	25, 29, 31, 37, 39, 41–53 odd
	3-5	Circular Functions	RA, Q1–Q10, 1–3, 6, 7, 10, 11, 14, 15, 19, 23
4	3-5	Circular Functions	25, 27, 31, 37, 44, 49
	3-6	Inverse Circular Relations: Given y, Find x	RA, Q1–Q10, 1–13 odd
5	3-7	Sinusoidal Functions as Mathematical Models	RA, Q1–Q10, 1, 2, 10, 14, 15
6	3-8	Rotary Motion	RA, Q1–Q10, 1–9 odd, 10, 11, 13–17
7	3-9	Chapter Review	R0–R8, T1–T24
8	3-9	Chapter Test	
	4-1	Introduction to the Pythagorean Property	1–9

Chapter 4: Trigonometric Function Properties, Identities, and Parametric Functions (7 Days)

Day	Section	Topics	Problems
1	4-2	Pythagorean, Reciprocal, and Quotient Properties	RA, Q1–Q10, 1–15
2	4-3	Identities and Algebraic Transformation of Expressions	RA, Q1–Q10, 1–54 multiples of three, 55
3	4-4	Arcsine, Arctangent, Arccosine, and Trigonometric Equations	RA, Q1–Q10, 1–21 odd, 25, 29, 33, 35, 43
4	4-5	Parametric Functions	Q1–Q10, 1–3, 5, 7, 13, 15, 17–19
5	4-6	Inverse Trigonometric Relation Graphs	RA, Q1–Q10, 1–4 , 5–15 odd, 26
6	4-7	Chapter Review	R0–R6, T1–T15
7	4-7	Chapter Test	
	5-1	Introduction to Combinations of Sinusoids	1–9

Chapter 5: Properties of Combined Sinusoids (5–7 Days)

Day	Section	Topics	Problems
1	5-2	Composite Argument and Linear Combination Properties	RA, Q1–Q10, 1–33 every other odd
2	5-3	Other Composite Argument Properties	RA, Q1–Q10, 1–33 odd
3	5-4	Composition of Ordinates and Harmonic Analysis	RA, Q1–Q10, 1, 2, 3–15 odd
4	5-5	The Sum and Product Properties	RA, Q1–Q10, 1–25 odd, 29, 35
5	5-6	Double and Half Argument Properties	RA, Q1–Q10, 1–41 every other odd
6	5-7	Chapter Review	R0–R6, T1–T19
7	5-7	Chapter Test	
	6-1	Introduction to Oblique Triangles	1–6

Chapter 6: Triangle Trigonometry (7 Days + 1 Day CR)

Day	Section	Topics	Problems
1	6-2	Oblique Triangles: Law of Cosines	RA, Q1–Q10, 1, 3, 6, 7, 9, 11, 13, 15, 17
	6-3	Area of a Triangle	RA, Q1–Q10, 1, 3, 7, 8
2	6-3	Area of a Triangle	9, 11, 14
	6-4	Oblique Triangles: Law of Sines	RA, Q1–Q10, 1–9 odd, 10, 14
3	6-5	The Ambiguous Case	RA, Q1–Q10, 1–13 odd, 14
4	6-6	Vector Addition	RA, Q1–Q10, 2, 4, 5, 6, 7–17 odd
5	6-7	Real-World Triangle Problems	RA, Q1–Q10, 1, 3, 6, 7, 9, 13, 15, 18
6	6-8	Chapter Review	R0–R7, T1–T21
7	6-8	Chapter Test	
	6-9	Cumulative Review, Chapters 1–6	Cumulative Review 1–26
8	6-9	Cumulative Review, Chapters 1–6	Cumulative Review 27–51
	7-1	Shapes of Function Graphs	1–4

Chapter 7: Properties of Elementary Functions (7 Days)

Day	Section	Topics	Problems
1	7-2	Identifying Functions from Graphical Patterns	RA, Q1–Q10, 1–15
2	7-3	Identifying Functions from Numerical Patterns	RA, Q1–Q10, 1–24 multiples of three, 25, 30, 33
3	7-4	Properties of Logarithms	RA, Q1–Q10, 1–47 odd
4	7-5	Logarithms: Equations and Other Bases	RA, Q1–Q10, 1–7 odd, 15–37 odd, 41
5	7-6	Logarithmic Functions	RA, Q1–Q10, 1–9 odd,
	7-7	Logistic Functions for Restrained Growth	RA, 1, 3
6	7-7	Logistic Functions for Restrained Growth	Q1–Q10, 5, 7
	7-8	Chapter Review	R0–R7, T1–T28
7	7-7	Chapter Test	
	8-1	Introduction to Regression for Linear Data	1–6

Chapter 8: Fitting Functions to Data (7 Days)

Day	Section	Topics	Problems
1	8-2	Deviations, Residuals, and the Correlation Coefficient	RA, Q1–Q10, 1–6
2	8-3	Regression for Nonlinear Data	RA, Q1–Q10, 1–6
3	8-4	Linearizing Data—Logarithmic Graph Paper	RA, Q1–Q10, 1–17 odd
4	8-4	Linearizing Data—Logarithmic Graph Paper	19, 20
	8-5	Residual Plots and Mathematical Models	RA, Q1–Q10, 1–11 odd
5	8-5	Residual Plots and Mathematical Models	2–10 even
6	8-5	Chapter Review	R0–R5, T1–T20
7	8-5	Chapter Test	
	9-1	Introduction to Probability	1–13

Chapter 9: Probability, and Functions of a Random Variable
(8 Days + 1 Day CR)

Day	Section	Topics	Problems
1	9-2	Words Associated with Probability	Q1–Q10, 1, 2
	9-3	Two Counting Principles	RA, Q1–Q10, 1–7 odd
2	9-3	Two Counting Principles	9–15 odd, 16, 17
	9-4	Probabilities of Various Permutations	RA, Q1–Q10, 1–9 odd
3	9-4	Probabilities of Various Permutations	11–19 odd
	9-5	Probabilities of Various Combinations	RA, Q1–Q10, 1–31 odd
4	9-6	Properties of Probability	RA, Q1–Q10, 1–13 odd
5	9-7	Functions of a Random Variable	RA, Q1–Q10, 1–11 odd, 14
6	9-8	Mathematical Expectation	RA, Q1–Q10, 1–5, 7
7	9-9	Chapter Review	R0–R8, T1–T28
8	9-9	Chapter Test	Cumulative Review 1–24
9	9-10	Cumulative Review, Chapters 7–9	
	10-1	Review of Two-Dimensional Vectors	1–8

Chapter 10: Three-Dimensional Vectors (7 Days)

Day	Section	Topics	Problems
1	10-2	Two-Dimensional Vector Practice	RA, Q1–Q10, 1–15 odd, 16
	10-3	Vectors in Space	RA, Q1–Q10, 1–9 odd
2	10-3	Vectors in Space	11–17 odd, 18
	10-4	Scalar Products and Projections of Vectors	RA, Q1–Q10, 1–17 odd
3	10-4	Scalar Products and Projections of Vectors	20, 21, 23–25, 27, 29–31
	10-5	Planes in Space	RA, Q1–Q10, 1–15 odd
4	10-6	Vector Product of Two Vectors	RA, Q1–Q10, 1–11 odd, 13–19, 21–23
5	10-7	Direction Angles and Direction Cosines	RA, Q1–Q10, 1–23 odd, 24
	10-8	Vector Equations of Lines in Space	RA, Q1–Q10, 1–7 odd
6	10-8	Vector Equations of Lines in Space	9–15 odd
	10-9	Chapter Review	R0–R8, T1–T27
7	10-9	Chapter Test	
	11-1	Introduction to Iterated Transformations	1–5

Chapter 11: Matrix Transformations and Fractal Figures (6 Days)

Day	Section	Topics	Problems
1	11-2	Matrix Operations and Solution of Linear Systems	RA, Q1–Q10, 1–23 odd
2	11-3	Rotation and Dilation Matrices	RA, Q1–Q10, 1–21 odd, 22
	11-4	Translation with Rotation and Dilation Matrices	RA, Q1–Q10, 1, 3
3	11-4	Translation with Rotation and Dilation Matrices	2, 4
	11-5	Strange Attractors for Several Iterated Transformations	RA, Q1–Q10, 1, 5, 9
4	11-5	Strange Attractors for Several Iterated Transformations	10, 11
	11-6	Fractal Dimensions	RA, Q1–Q10, 1, 2, 5
5	11-6	Fractal Dimensions	3, 4, 6
	11-7	Chapter Review	R0–R6, T1–T19
6	11-7	Chapter Test	
	12-1	Introduction to Conic Sections	1–8

Chapter 12: Analytic Geometry of Conic Sections and Quadric Surfaces (7 Days)

Day	Section	Topics	Problems
1	12-2	Parametric and Cartesian Equations of the Conic Sections	RA, Q1–Q10, 1–4, 5–27 odd, 31
2	12-3	Quadric Surfaces and Inscribed Figures	RA, Q1–Q10, 1–10, 11–17 odd
3	12-4	Analytic Geometry of the Conic Sections	RA, Q1–Q10, 1–4, 11–31 every other odd
4	12-5	Parametric and Cartesian Equations for Rotated Conics	RA, Q1–Q10, 1–23 odd
5	12-6	Applications of Conic Sections	RA, Q1–Q10, 1, 5, 7, 8
6	12-7	Chapter Review	R0–R6, T1–T18
7	12-7	Chapter Test	
	13-1	Introduction to Polar Coordinates	1–6

Chapter 13: Polar Coordinates, Complex Numbers, and Moving Objects (6 Days)

Day	Section	Topics	Problems
1	13-2	Polar Equations of Conics and Other Curves	RA, Q1–Q10, 1–15 odd
2	13-2	Polar Equations of Conics and Other Curves	17–23 odd
	13-3	Intersections of Polar Curves	RA, Q1–Q10, 1–9 odd
3	13-4	Complex Numbers in Polar Form	RA, Q1–Q10, 1–33 every other odd, 35, 39
4	13-5	Parametric Equations for Moving Objects	RA, Q1–Q10, 1–4, 5, 11
5	13-6	Chapter Review	R0–R5, T1–T17
6	13-6	Chapter Test	
	14-1	Introduction to Sequences and Series	1–10

Chapter 14: Sequences and Series (5 Days)

Day	Section	Topics	Problems
1	14-2	Arithmetic, Geometric, and Other Sequences	RA, Q1–Q10, 1–6, 16, 17, 23, 24
2	14-3	Series and Partial Sums	RA, Q1–Q10, 1, 2, 5, 11–27 odd
3	14-3	Series and Partial Sums	3, 4, 9, 12, 29–51 odd, 53–55
4	14-4	Chapter Review	R0–R3, T1–T24
5	14-4	Chapter Test	
	15-1	Review of Polynomial Functions	1–11

Chapter 15: Polynomial and Rational Functions, Limits, and Derivatives (6 Days + 1 Day CR)

Day	Section	Topics	Problems
1	15-2	Graphs and Zeros of Polynomial Functions	RA, Q1–Q10, 1–27 odd, 29–32, 37
2	15-3	Fitting Polynomial Functions to Data	RA, Q1–Q10, 1, 3, 4, 6–8, 11, 14
3	15-4	Rational Functions: Discontinuities, Limits, and Partial Fractions	RA, Q1–Q10, 1, 2, 3–11 odd, 24
4	15-5	Instantaneous Rate of Change of a Function: The Derivative	RA, Q1–Q10, 1–5, 9–25 odd
5	15-6	Chapter Review	R0–R5, T1–T21
6	15-6	Chapter Test	
	15-7	Cumulative Review, Chapters 10–15	Cumulative Review 1–32
7	15-7	Cumulative Review, Chapters 10–15	Cumulative Review 33–47

Precalculus with Trigonometry: Instructor's Guide
© 2007 Key Curriculum Press

Cooperative Learning Suggestions

Paul A. Foerster

Overview

The traditional way to teach mathematics has been the lecture method. The instructor delivers a well-thought-out presentation of a particular topic. Students copy down notes, being careful to balance their time between frantic writing and listening so that they will remember something about what they have written. The result is a semitextbook containing mathematics "the way it is," flowing smoothly from definitions and axioms through rigorously proven theorems to possible applications. The method is a time-efficient way to cover the material in the course.

Therein lies the flaw. As instructors, we should be *uncovering* the material. The logical sequence of topics is representative neither of the historical development of mathematics nor of the way students learn. Students wind up with the false impression that mathematics is just a collection of formulas for working certain specific problems. They make a statement such as "I can't work this problem because I don't remember the formula" or "All I did wrong was use the incorrect formula." When mathematics is presented as a lecture-only subject, students don't have a personal stake in the mathematics and feel that they never could have come up with the techniques on their own.

In the past 10–20 years there has been a movement away from the lecture method as the sole means of delivery. The movement has been toward cooperative learning, with students working in groups to discover the mathematics and make connections with what they have learned before, both in this course and from previous courses. The cooperative learning method takes more time. Students have to make mistakes, back up and try different approaches, slow down to bring other members of their group up to speed, and so on. The classroom becomes noisy with students vying to be heard. But the payoff is that students have actually *understood* the concept by learning it when they need it, not when you present it. And they have done it in a way that models more accurately the way they will need to work when they get jobs in the "real world."

It is not necessary to use cooperative learning every day, or even all period on any one day. A combination of cooperative learning and lectures will hold your students' interest. This is especially true in a block-schedule environment, where classes may last up to two hours. Don't rely completely on what students discover in cooperative group learning. Just because they have understood a concept in class does not guarantee they will remember it later. Short introductory lectures may be needed to get students thinking about the mathematics you want them to learn instead of about what they experienced on their way to class. "Closure" activities are needed to make sure they have discovered the right thing. You must still assign homework, some of which will be of a "drill and practice" nature.

This section includes ideas I use in my own classes and other ideas I have picked up from colleagues. You are invited to try these ideas with your students!

Classroom Arrangement

I arrange my classroom in the "double horseshoe" pattern. This U-shaped arrangement is described by David R. Johnson in his booklet *Every Minute Counts* (see the Bibliography of Precalculus Resources section of this book). The accompanying figure shows the essentials of the arrangement. As you can see, no student can hide from the instructor behind several rows of other students, as is possible in the traditional rectangular arrangement of desks.

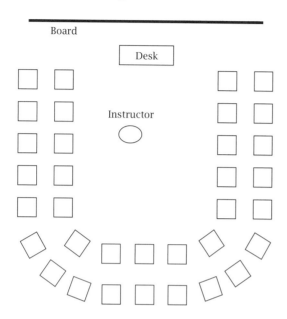

At the beginning of the year, students are seated alphabetically, starting, for example, at the left front desk in the outside U, going around the U, looping back into the inside U at the right front desk, and ending at the left front desk in the inside U. The seating chart for each class is a map of blank squares such as shown in the figure. Students' names are written on sticky notes from pads cut to 1″ by 1″ at the school's print shop. The sticky notes are stuck to the seating chart with the adhesive side *toward* you so that they curl upward for ease of viewing when the chart is flat on the desk. This plan allows for instant changes of seating when necessary. It also allows you to make up the seating chart before the first class without worrying about having to redo it several days later and gives you more time for mathematics the first day. Another advantage is that you can call students by name starting on the first day.

For preliminary information and whole-group closure activities, students face the center of the U, perhaps rotated toward the board. You are free to move inside the U. You can place an overhead projector on the desk and project it directly onto the board (rather than onto a screen) so that you or students can write on the graphs or images being projected. For homework checks, you can make *one* pass between the two rows and see each student's paper. On test days students move their desks apart into "test positions," which is defined as "enough space between the desks so that I can walk between you without stepping on anyone's toes."

For cooperative group activities, groups are formed by the simplest method possible. Students on the inside U turn their desks around to face students in the outside U. Then the instructor designates groups of four (sometimes three or five) as Group 1, Group 2, Group 3, and so on. Students move their desks together more or less as shown in the following figure.

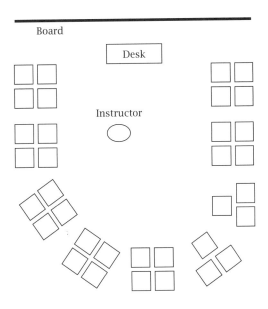

Other instructors use more elaborate arrangements with permanent positioning of desks or with round tables. Whatever arrangement you choose must, of course, suit your own classroom and teaching style.

Considerations in Assigning Groups

I use the alphabetical seating arrangement and geometric positioning of the desks, as just mentioned, in assigning students to groups. The plan has the advantage of simplicity. If necessary, individual students can be reassigned to different groups if there is not satisfactory cooperation. You can change the groups periodically by rotating the entire class in a circular permutation by an odd number of spaces, usually three. This plan puts each student in a different place and virtually ensures that no two students will be in the same group after the move.

More elaborate methods of assigning groups require more work on your part but may have advantages. For instance, after several weeks, some instructors will assign groups according to ability. When you have enough grades to ascertain how well the students are doing, you can divide the class into quarters and choose groups of four consisting of one from the highest quarter, one from the lowest quarter, and two from the middle half.

Kinds of Cooperative Activities

There are two kinds of cooperative group activities I use regularly. One kind is the Explorations that appear in the *Instructor's Resource Book*. These activities are designed to lead students to discover something new by working a carefully sequenced set of problems. When you use these Explorations, remember to introduce them with enough words so that students will know what they are expected to do. Provide time for closure, preferably at the end of the period or, at the latest, the beginning of the next period.

The other kind of cooperative activity is the Concept Problems at the end of each chapter. These problems are usually difficult enough that students working on their own would have difficulty completing or, possibly, starting them. By working in groups, students develop an esprit de corps that gives them both confidence in their work and a way to get feedback on the correctness of their answers.

I also use "guided discovery," a combination of lecture and cooperative activities, by having students work an Exploration one problem at a time. I say, "You have two minutes to do Problem 1." They work with their group members and come up with answers while I circulate, monitor progress, check answers, and nudge groups in the right direction. Then students stop work and Problem 1 is discussed at the board. Subsequent problems are handled the same way. This method is particularly effective in classes where the students tend to dawdle when given the entire Exploration to do at once.

There are numerous good ways to have students do these activities. One such way is called "Think, Pair, Share." Students are given a problem with which they are unfamiliar. They think about it on their own for two minutes. For the next few minutes, they pair up with one member of their group and discuss what they have been thinking. On cue, they stop working in pairs and share with the entire class what the pairs have discovered. Think, Pair, Share is particularly effective for those Explorations designed for students to learn by reading the text.

Classroom Management Considerations

When you first try cooperative group learning, you will find that your class is noisier than for straight lecture. If you listen carefully to the noise, however, you will find it is usually productive noise from students discussing with each other how to do the problems. Beware of quiet groups. The quietness can often signal a lack of cooperation or simple copying of one group member's work by the other members. If a group gets off-task, you can use words such as "Okay, Group 5. Are you on-task?" The statement is more easily accepted by students because it is aimed at the group, not at a specific individual.

Some instructors use catchphrases to focus students' attention on noise abatement. For instance, you can tell them, "When working in groups, use your *12-inch* voice." This way the background noise level can be low enough for students to hear each other in their own group without being distracted by other groups.

Students often have difficulty shifting between cooperative-group and whole-group activities. Not all groups finish at the same time, and some will want to go on working when you are ready to summarize for a closure activity. Some instructors play soft music (classical music?) when students are supposed to be working cooperatively. Some also dim the lights. Students can be trained to know that when the music stops or the lights come back up, it is time to turn around and pay attention.

Answering Questions

A significant advantage of cooperative groups is that you have fewer entities to deal with. If students are working on discovery activities and you have 32 students in a class, then you will have only eight groups to keep track of, not 32 individuals. Ideally, you will answer a question only if all members of the group have the same question. In practice, though, you may need some flexibility with this rule.

Occasionally, you may have explained something to one group while other groups have the same question. One solution is to stop the group work momentarily (turn off the music!) and give a brief explanation at the board. Another approach is to have other groups send an "ambassador" to the one group to find out the information and take it back to her or his group.

Checking Homework

As mentioned earlier, the double-horseshoe classroom arrangement allows the instructor to make one pass between the rows and see each student's homework. If individuals' homework is to be graded, I usually assign 10 points (as opposed to 100 points for a test). Five of the points are given for attempting the homework, and the other five are for correct work. As I pass between the rows, I say, "Write down 5. Write down 5. Write down 5. Write down nothing [if the student hasn't done it!]. . . ." For simple problems, only the answer is checked. For more involved problems, students write down check marks for significant points they have reached correctly in their work. The grade is computed from this formula:

$$\frac{\text{number of checks}}{\frac{1}{5} \text{ total possible checks}} + 5$$

Another form of homework check is useful if students didn't quite understand the problems. Have one student volunteer to go to the board. This student has the "power of the chalk" (or the power of the dry-erase marker). He or she calls upon a student to read the problem or to tell what should be done next. That student is responsible for answering. Other members of the class must pitch in and help that student if necessary. The safest place to be in this situation is at the board! It is completely nonthreatening, at least as far as the mathematics is concerned. After the student has presented the problem, you can follow up with general comments about the concepts and techniques involved.

Grading Considerations

It is not necessary to assign a grade on every group activity that students do. For instance, if they are working one of the Explorations, the objective may be to learn something new. The activity then becomes part of the student's class notes rather than a graded paper.

If you have an activity handed in, there are two ways to do it. You can have each group member hand in his or her own paper, or you can have each group hand in a single paper. I have each student hand in a paper, assigning 10 points, as for homework. There are more papers to grade, but you can see each person's work and give comments. This fact is particularly important for the last questions in the Explorations: "What did you learn as a result of doing this Exploration that you did not know before?"

Some instructors give incentives for students to cooperate by holding the entire group responsible for the performance of each member in the group. One way this can be done is to give each group member a few extra points on a test if all members make at least a certain predetermined score.

You must be on the lookout for students who simply copy the work of others in their group. If you see a persistent wrong answer within the group, you need to point out to the students that they must do their own work. They should check answers with each other to ensure correctness. Simple copying does them little good.

Students also may begin to blur the distinction between what they can do in cooperative groups and what they can do on individual tests. They lose their awareness that copying from another student on a test is cheating. So watch out for this, and be prepared to deal with it. For cheating on a test, I assign a score of zero and an unsatisfactory citizenship grade for the grading period, and I make a phone call to the parents. However, I always give the student the opportunity to explain to me how, for example, he or she got a correct answer following incorrect work. Sometimes what looked like cheating really wasn't. I will not accuse a student of cheating based solely on circumstantial evidence.

For students who score below passing on a test, I assign a grade of zero until the corrections are completed. The philosophy is "You don't get paid till the job is done *right*," a phenomenon they will encounter over and over again in the world of work. I mark the raw score inconspicuously on an edge of their paper so that only the student and I know how badly he or she did. When every error or omission has been corrected, which sometimes takes several tries, the student is assigned a score halfway between the raw score and the passing score. So a student cannot pass a test just by doing corrections. But he or she can turn a disaster into something that can be brought up by subsequent test grades. I do not offer this opportunity on cumulative tests such as six-week or semester exams because I believe that the student should have learned enough from correcting mistakes to make an acceptable score on a test of the same material.

The scoring technique just mentioned is particularly effective for students with learning disabilities. Instead of giving students extra time to complete the test, I have them hand in what they have done by the end of the test period. I record a score on what they have attempted, such as 65 out of 74. When the corrections and completions have been done, the score is assigned based on the quality of the work they completed in class, for example, (65/74)(100) = 88%. So the learning-disabled student is not stigmatized by having to stay after class, and nobody but the student and the instructor knows how the grade was determined.

At the end of each grading period, the average is found by adding the student's total number of points (10s or sometimes 20s for homework and classwork exercises and 100s for tests) and dividing by the total possible number of points. If the cumulative test is higher than this average, I count it twice, thus rewarding a student for finally learning what was difficult before.

References

There are a number of good books available on cooperative learning. In addition to David Johnson's *Every Minute Counts*, there is *Cooperative Learning in Mathematics*, edited by Neil Davidson. The Marilyn Burns Association has many publications on cooperative group activities, some of which apply at the advanced high school mathematics level. The Teacher's Edition of Michael Serra's *Discovering Geometry*, another publication of Key Curriculum Press, has extensive information about cooperative group learning. See the Bibliography of Precalculus Resources (next section) for more details about these references.

Bibliography of Precalculus Resources

Anscombe, Frank J. 1973. *Graphs in Statistical Analysis.* This American Statistician, Vol. 27. Alexandria, Virginia: American Statistical Society.

Banks, Robert B. 1998. *Towing Icebergs, Falling Dominoes, and Other Adventures in Applied Mathematics.* Princeton, New Jersey: Princeton University Press.

Barnsley, Michael F. 1988. *Fractals Everywhere.* Boston: Academic Press.

Beckman, Peter. 1976. *History of π.* New York: St. Martin's Press.

Blatner, David. 1997. *The Joy of π.* New York: Walker Publishing Company.

Davidson, Neil, ed. 1990. *Cooperative Learning in Mathematics: A Handbook for Teachers.* Menlo Park, California: Addison-Wesley Publishing Company.

Fadiman, Clifton, ed. 1958. *Fantasia Mathematica.* New York: Simon & Schuster.

Goodstein, David L., and Judith R. 1996. *Feynman's Lost Lecture.* New York: W. W. Norton & Company.

Guillen, Michael. 1995. *Five Equations That Changed the World: The Power and Poetry of Mathematics.* New York: Hyperion.

Hall, Nina, ed. 1994. *Exploring Chaos: A Guide to the New Science of Disorder.* New York: W. W. Norton & Company.

Johnson, David R. 1997. *Every Minute Counts: Making Your Math Class Work.* Parsippany, New Jersey: Pearson Learning.

Mandelbrot, Benoit B. 1977. *Fractals: Form, Chance, and Dimension.* San Francisco: W. H. Freeman & Company.

Mandelbrot, Benoit B. 1983. *The Fractal Geometry of Nature.* New York: W. H. Freeman & Company.

Maor, Eli. 1998. *e: The Story of a Number.* Princeton, New Jersey: Princeton University Press.

Maor, Eli. 1991. *To Infinity and Beyond: A Cultural History of the Infinite.* Princeton, New Jersey: Princeton University Press.

Maor, Eli. 1998. *Trigonometric Delights.* Princeton, New Jersey: Princeton University Press.

Nahin, Paul J. 1998. *An Imaginary Tale: The Story of $\sqrt{-1}$.* Princeton, New Jersey: Princeton University Press.

Peitgen, Heinz-Otto, Hartmut Fürgens, and Dietmar Saupe. 1992. *Fractals for the Classroom.* New York: Springer-Verlag.

Prusinkiewicz, Przemyslaw, and Aristid Lindenmayer. 1990. *The Algorithmic Beauty of Plants.* New York: Springer-Verlag.

Serra, Michael. 2003. *Discovering Geometry: An Inductive Approach, Teacher's Edition.* Emeryville, California: Key Curriculum Press.

Serra, Michael. 1997. *Discovering Geometry: An Inductive Approach, Teacher's Guide and Answer Key.* Emeryville, California: Key Curriculum Press.

Yates, Robert C. 1974. *Curves and Their Properties.* Classics in Mathematics Education, Vol. 4. Washington, D.C.: National Council of Teachers of Mathematics.

Web Resources

These four Web sites are the main Internet resources for the text.

http://www.keymath.com/precalc is the Precalculus Resource Center for *Precalculus with Trigonometry: Concepts and Applications,* Second Edition. It contains useful links and downloadable resources, including calculator programs and Sketchpad activities. Several problems in the text ask students to use this Web site to access a Dynamic Precalculus Exploration, which is an activity centered around an interactive sketch. You may wish to ask your students to familiarize themselves with the Web site at the beginning of the course.

http://www.keypress.com/sketchpad is The Geometer's Sketchpad Resource Center, and *http://www.keypress.com/fathom* is the Fathom Resource Center. Both Web sites provide product information and software updates.

http://education.ti.com/us/product/tech/datacollection/guide/cbl2guideus.html has links to three CBL 2™ guidebooks.

The following Web sites provide useful resources for lesson plans, further Web links, and databases.

http://illuminations.nctm.org/index.aspx contains lesson plans and PDF files of worksheets for several supplementary topics. For example, Trout Pond is an interesting activity to use in conjunction with Section 14-2 of the text. You can choose to display only lesson plans for grades 9–12 by using a pull-down menu.

http://lib.stat.cmu.edu/DASL/ is the Web site for the Data and Story Library. This is a useful resource for finding statistical problems and data tables.

http://www.mathforum.com/precalc/precalc.html contains resources and links for precalculus teachers.

http://www.pbs.org/teachersource/mathline/lessonplans/search_9-12.shtm is the Public Broadcasting Service (PBS) resource of mathematical lesson plans with videos.

Instructor's Commentary

The following pages present information useful to instructors for planning the presentation of the materials in the text. Commentary for each section includes

- The objective of the section, restated from the text
- Approximate amount of class time to spend on that section
- Suggested homework assignments
- A list of technology options that are relevant to the section
- Important terms and concepts
- Lesson notes, including teaching suggestions
- Exploration notes, summarizing Explorations for the section
- Technology notes, briefly describing the technology options
- Additional class examples
- Problem notes, giving highlights and background for most problems
- Supplementary problems and exercises

Key to Technology Option Icons

Most sections of the text have related technology options, which are listed and described in the Instructor's Commentary. All Dynamic Precalculus Explorations, Explorations, presentation sketches, calculator programs, and many activities are available with the standard course materials. The remaining activities are from other publications available from Key Curriculum Press. You may wish to look at the Instructor's Commentary for Sections 3-5 and 3-7 for examples of how the technology option icons are used. It is not expected that you use all available technology options for a section. For example, Section 3-5 has far more technology options than are reasonable to assign.

This icon depicts Dynamic Precalculus Explorations, available at *www.keymath.com/precalc*. These explorations are most often related to particular problems, in which case they will be listed in the Instructor's Commentary with the problem number and title. If the exploration is mentioned in the narrative of a section, it will be listed in the Instructor's Commentary with the number of the figure under which the exploration is mentioned.

This icon depicts presentation sketches and activities that require The Geometer's Sketchpad. Some Explorations are also noted with this icon, indicating that the Exploration can be enhanced by the use of Sketchpad, but does not require it.

This icon depicts activities that require Fathom Dynamic Data Software. Some Explorations are noted with this icon, indicating that the Exploration can be enhanced by the use of Fathom, but does not require it.

This icon depicts calculator programs, as well as activities that require the use of the Texas Instruments CBL 2™, the second-generation Calculator-Based Laboratory™.

Contents of the *Instructor's Resource CD*

The *Instructor's Resource CD* that accompanies this book contains electronic files for the Exploration masters and Solutions; Section, Chapter, and Cumulative Tests and Solutions; programs for graphing calculators; data sets that contain more than ten data points (for Chapter 8); Dynamic Precalculus Explorations; Sketchpad presentation sketches; and activities, and their related Sketchpad or Fathom documents. The files are provided in these formats:

- Exploration masters and Solutions: Portable Document Format (PDF)

- Section, Chapter, and Cumulative Tests and Solutions: PDF and Microsoft® Word

- Programs for graphing calculators: TI Program

- Data sets: Microsoft® Excel, Fathom Dynamic Data, TI List

- Dynamic Precalculus Explorations: Web page

- Activities: PDF

- Presentation sketches: Sketchpad

The following list shows what software you will need to access files of each extension type.

Extension	Software
.pdf	Adobe® Reader®
.doc	Microsoft Word 97 or later for the PC, or Word 5.1 or later for Macintosh
.xls	Microsoft Excel 97 or later for the PC, or Excel 98 or later for Macintosh
.8xp	TI Connect
.83l	TI Connect
.html	Any Web browser such as Safari, Firefox, Netscape®, or Microsoft Internet Explorer
.gsp	The Geometer's Sketchpad
.ftm	Fathom Dynamic Data

1 Functions and Mathematical Models

Here students refresh their memories about functions they have studied in algebra. The unifying concept is that familiar functions are built up by transformations of a few basic parent functions. For instance, the point-slope form of the linear function, $y - y_1 = m(x - x_1)$, is a dilation of the parent function, $y = x$, by a factor of m in the y-direction and translations by x_1 and y_1 in the x- and y-directions, respectively. Reflections are studied as dilations by a factor of -1. Composition of functions allows the formal definition of inverses of functions. Piecewise functions and their inverses are brought alive using Boolean variables with the graphing calculator to restrict the domain. The Explorations, designed for students to work in cooperative groups, are introduced in this chapter. The "Quick Review" problems begin in Section 1-3, giving students a time-efficient review of other concepts and techniques. One concept students should grasp is that mathematics can be learned four ways: graphically, algebraically, numerically, and verbally. After Chapter 1, the course can branch to Chapter 7 or continue with the study of periodic functions in Chapters 2 through 6.

1-1

Functions: Graphically, Algebraically, Numerically, and Verbally

Objective

Work with functions that are defined graphically, algebraically, numerically, or verbally.

Class Time

1 day

Homework Assignment

Problems 1–5

Technology Options

Refer to page 37 for a description of Technology Options and a key to the technology icons.

 Exploration 1-1a: Paper Cup Analysis

 Activity: Equations of Lines

 Activity: Reading the News

 Activity: A Function by Any Other Name

Important Terms and Concepts

Function

Expressing mathematical ideas graphically, algebraically, numerically, and verbally

Mathematical model

Dependent variable

Independent variable

Domain

Range

Asymptote

Extrapolation

Interpolation

Lesson Notes

This section reviews functions graphically, numerically, and algebraically. It begins by presenting a graph and equation for the relationship between coffee temperature and time. An exciting way to begin the year is to assign students to groups and have them use a Calculator-Based Laboratory

(CBL 2) to gather their own time and temperature data. Students can then fit a graph to their data and compare it to the graph in the text. If you vary the initial temperature of the coffee for different groups, each group will create a slightly different graph. Allow 40 minutes for the CBL 2 experiment.

Discuss *domain, range,* and *asymptote,* and point them out on the graph, as shown in Figure 1-1b of the student book. Emphasize domain and range throughout the year so that students become familiar with how to determine both. Real-world problems always have restrictions, and many of the calculus problems students solve next year will require them to consider domain and range restrictions.

Exploration Notes

Exploration 1-1a may be used as a time-efficient way to refresh students' memories about functions and their use as mathematical models.

Technology Notes

 Exploration 1-1a: Paper Cup Analysis, in the *Instructor's Resource Book,* has students collect data on the heights of stacks of paper cups and then fit lines to their data. Students can do this exploration with Fathom. They enter the data into a case table, make a scatter plot, plot conjectured functions to test them, and use tracing to make a prediction.

 Activity: Equations of Lines, in *Exploring Geometry with The Geometer's Sketchpad,* allows students to review equations of lines while learning basic Sketchpad skills. This activity can be combined with or preceded by The Slope of a Line, as well as Slopes of Parallel and Perpendicular Lines. All of these activities are in Chapter 1 of *Exploring Geometry with The Geometer's Sketchpad,* and they all have demonstration sketches on the *Exploring Geometry* CD. Allow 15–30 minutes for Equations of Lines, 30 minutes for The Slope of a Line, and 25–40 minutes for Slopes of Parallel and Perpendicular Lines.

 Activity: Reading the News, in Chapter 1 of *Teaching Mathematics with Fathom,* has students collect data on how long it takes to read a newspaper, make a scatter plot, and fit a line to the data in order to make predictions. This activity also provides an introduction to Fathom. Students can review linear equations by experimenting with more activities in Chapter 1 of *Teaching Mathematics with Fathom.* Allow 25–40 minutes.

Activity: A Function by Any Other Name, in *A Watched Cup Never Cools,* is a writing assignment that helps students make sense of the notion of a function. It can be an assignment for a journal or a minor paper.

Problem Notes

- *Problem 1,* the Archery Problem, requires students to analyze and interpret a graph, including providing verbal descriptions and explanations of terminology.

- *Problem 2,* the Gas Temperature and Volume Problem, lists a table of values that students must hand-plot on graph paper. Although a best-fit line is not formally defined, students are asked to draw one in part a of this problem. Students frequently think a best-fit line needs to go through the first and last points. This is not necessarily true. This problem introduces the terms *extrapolation* and *interpolation.* Try to help students understand that extrapolation involves using the pattern in the data to estimate values *beyond* the given values, whereas interpolation involves estimating values *between* given data values. Caution students that extrapolated results may not be valid because the pattern may not exist beyond the given data.

- *Problem 3,* the Mortgage Payment Problem, provides an equation from which students create a table and graph on a grapher. In this problem, the number of months is the independent variable and the balance is the dependent variable. You might ask students to explain why it would be inappropriate to say that the number of months depends on the number of dollars.

- *Problem 4,* the Stopping Distance Problem, gives a description of a situation from which students draw a reasonable graph and then practice using vocabulary.

- *Problem 5,* the Stove Heating Element Problem, requires students to draw a reasonable graph to match a given description.

1-2
Types of Functions

Objective

Make connections among the algebraic equation for a function, its name, and its graph.

Class Time

1 day

Homework Assignment

Recommended: Problems 1–39 odd, Problems 40–41

Also suggested: Problem 42

Technology Options

 Exploration 1-2a: Names of Functions

 Exploration 1-2b: Restricted Domains and Boolean Variables

 Activity: Asymptotic Behavior of Functions

Important Terms and Concepts

Ordered pair

Relation

Function

y-intercept

x-intercept

$f(x)$ terminology

Argument of a function

Polynomial function

Quadratic function

Linear function

Direct variation function

Power function

Exponential function

Inverse variation function

Rational algebraic function

Boolean variable (using to plot a function in a *restricted domain*)

Restricted domain

Vertical line test

Lesson Notes

Begin the lesson by reviewing the definition of *function.* Make sure students understand that for a relation to be a function, it must be true that for each value in the domain there is *only one* corresponding value in the range. In other words, the correspondence from the domain to the range must be *unique.* It *is* possible for the same range value to correspond to more than one domain value. To illustrate this, you might discuss the function $y = x^2$. For this function, every nonzero value in the range corresponds to two values in the domain. For example, the range value 9 corresponds to the domain values −3 and 3.

Students should be familiar with function notation from Algebra II. You may want to discuss briefly this notation, emphasizing that the parentheses in $f(x)$ mean *substitution,* not *multiplication.*

The Names of Functions section presents the graphs and equations of eight types of functions. To help students review these functions, you might assign Exploration 1-2a. Some students have difficulty distinguishing between power functions and exponential functions. The location of the variable is the key to the difference. Power functions have a variable *base,* while exponential functions have a variable *exponent.* The confusion arises because some students do not distinguish between "exponent" and "power." Actually, in the expression 5^3, for instance, the exponent is only the 3. The power is the entire expression, 5^3. Thus, 3^x has a variable as its *exponent,* while x^3 is a *power of x.*

A direct variation function is a special case of a linear function, power function, and polynomial function. Specifically, it is a linear function with *y*-intercept 0, a power function with a power of 1, and a polynomial function with only a linear term. The graph of a direct variation function is a straight line through the origin. An inverse variation function is a power function with a negative exponent. The graph of an inverse variation function has asymptotes at both axes. Students may be familiar with direct and inverse variation functions from their science classes. To help students transfer learning and increase their understanding of both precalculus and science, you might ask them for examples of equations used in science that are direct or inverse variations. For example, Newton's second law of motion, $F = ma,$ is a direct variation if the mass *m* or the acceleration *a* is constant. If the force is constant, the equation is an inverse variation.

Example 1 illustrates how to plot a function with a restricted domain using a grapher. This kind of problem prepares students for the *piecewise functions* (functions composed of two or more functions) they will encounter in future courses. Students may need help understanding the idea of a Boolean variable. A Boolean variable is represented by a *condition,* not a letter like the variables students are familiar with. A Boolean variable has only two possible values: It is equal to 1 if the condition is true, and it is equal to 0 if the condition is false.

In the given examples, only part of the function is divided by the Boolean variable because it is easier to enter into a grapher. That is, the functions are written in the form $y_1 = 3x + 26/(x \geq 3$ and $x \leq 10)$ rather than $y_1 = (3x + 26)/(x \geq 3$ and $x \leq 10)$. You might want to ask students why the two forms yield the same graph. They are both undefined when the Boolean variable is zero.

Example 1 also asks students to give the range of the function. Students sometimes mistakenly try to determine the range of a function by substituting the endpoints of the domain. Point out that, in this example, the endpoints of the range do *not* correspond to the endpoints of the domain.

Exploration Notes

Exploration 1-2a provides a short summary review of seven of the eight functions covered in the text (the direct variation function is not included). Students working in groups with the aid of graphers can easily complete the seven questions in 15–20 minutes. It's probably best to summarize the Exploration and answer questions on it before presenting the examples from the textbook.

Exploration 1-2b lets students see a restricted domain in a real-world context. The gravitational attraction for an object above Earth's surface is inversely proportional to the square of the object's distance from the center of Earth. Below the surface, the attraction is directly proportional to the distance. This follow-up Exploration takes about 15 minutes.

Technology Notes

 Exploration 1-2a: Names of Functions, in the *Instructor's Resource Book,* can be done with Sketchpad.

 Exploration 1-2b: Restricted Domains and Boolean Variables, in the *Instructor's Resource Book,* can be accomplished using Fathom, but only if they employ nested if-then statements rather than Boolean variables.

 Activity: Asymptotic Behavior of Functions, in *Connecting Mathematics with Science,* asks students to collect data to find the pH of various dilutions of ammonia. Students analyze the domain and range of this nonlinear function and observe its asymptotic behavior. Allow 45 minutes.

Problem Notes

- *Problems 1–18* are similar to Example 1.

- *Problems 19–28* require students to name types of functions from their graphs.

- *Problems 29–32* are similar to Example 2.

- *Problems 33–38* require students to identify which relations are functions.

- *Problem 39* presents the *vertical line test,* which all students should know and use. Be sure to discuss this problem when you review the homework. To reinforce the concept, question students periodically in future assignments about whether graphs "pass the vertical line test."

- *Problems 40 and 41* require students to demonstrate understanding of some of the terminology associated with functions.

- *Problem 42* is a research problem that requires students to write.

Supplementary Problem

1. *Restricted Domain Problem:* Figure 1-2a shows the graph of $y = x^2 - 8x + 11$ in the domain $2 \le x \le 7$. Reproduce this graph on your grapher. Describe how you did it.

Figure 1-2a

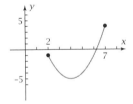

1-3
Dilation and Translation of Function Graphs

Objective

Transform a given pre-image function so that the result is a graph of the image function that has been dilated by given factors and translated by given amounts.

Class Time

1–2 days

Homework Assignment

Day 1: Reading Analysis (always assign these), Q1–Q10 (always assign these), Problems 1–6

Day 2: Problems 7–21

Technology Options

 *Problem 21:* Dynamic Transformations Problem

Presentation Sketch: Translation Work.gsp

Presentation Sketch: Dilation Present.gsp

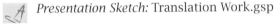 *Activity:* Translation of Functions

Activity: Dilation of Functions

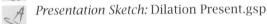 *Activity:* Exploring Translations and Dilations

Activity: Translations in the Coordinate Plane

Activity: Function Transformations

Activity: Foundations Work

Important Terms and Concepts

Dilation

Translation

Transformation

Inside transformation

Outside transformation

Image

Pre-image

Friendly grapher window

Lesson Notes

It is recommended that you spend two days on this lesson. Begin the first day of instruction by assigning Exploration 1-3a as a small-group activity.

Then cover the material through Example 2. On the second day, start by assigning Exploration 1-3c. Then cover the remaining material in the chapter.

Discuss the idea of using a "friendly" grapher window with your students. A friendly window is one that gives "nice" coordinate values when a function is traced. When you trace a function, the cursor moves one pixel at a time. Setting the window so that Xmax − Xmin is a multiple of the number of pixels in the horizontal direction ensures that the x-coordinates displayed when the function is traced will be nice numbers. For example, the TI-83 and TI-84 calculators have 94 pixels in the horizontal direction. If Xmin = 0 and Xmax = 94 or if Xmin = −47 and Xmax = 47, the x-coordinate will change by 1 with each trace step. If Xmin = −9.4 and Xmax = 9.4, the x-coordinate will change by 0.2 with each trace step.

If the coefficients in a function are rational, you can also set Ymin and Ymax so that nice y-coordinates are displayed. The TI-83 has 62 pixels in the vertical direction. So, for example, using the settings Ymin = 0 and Ymax = 62 or Ymin = −6.2 and Ymax = 6.2 will give nice y-coordinates when the function is traced. (*Note:* The y-coordinate is calculated by evaluating the function for the x-coordinate. So, if the coefficients in a function are irrational, the y-coordinates will not be nice, even in a friendly window.) The documentation for each grapher will explain more about friendly windows.

It is important for students to be familiar with both forms of the dilation rule, $\frac{1}{a}g(x) = f\left(\frac{1}{b}x\right)$ and $g(x) = af\left(\frac{1}{b}x\right)$. The form $g(x) = af\left(\frac{1}{b}x\right)$ is the more common, and it is the form used when a function is entered into a grapher. However, the form $\frac{1}{a}g(x) = f\left(\frac{1}{b}x\right)$ allows students to see that "the same thing happens to x as to y." That is, both x and y are *divided by* their respective scale factors. (To make this clearer, you may want to write the rule as $\frac{1}{a}y = f\left(\frac{1}{b}x\right)$ rather than $\frac{1}{a}g(x) = f\left(\frac{1}{b}x\right)$.) Similarly, the translation rule can be written as $h(x) − c = f(x − d)$ or $h(x) = c + f(x − d)$. The form $h(x) − c = f(x − d)$ illustrates that the vertical translation is subtracted from y just as the horizontal translation is subtracted from x. You want to avoid students coming to the false conclusion that the two variables are treated in different ways.

Point out that if a function is *only* dilated, the x-dilation is the number you can substitute for x to make the argument equal to 1. If the function is *only*

translated, the x-translation is the number you can substitute for x to make the argument equal to 0. Stress that multiplying or dividing variable x can lead to dilations and that adding to or subtracting from variable x leads to translations.

Should you venture into doing more complicated transformations that involve combinations of reflections, dilations, and translations, then caution students to be mindful of the order of operations: They must apply the reflections and dilations first and then the translations. Students will have significant additional exposure to transformations of sinusoidal functions in Section 3-2.

Encouraging students to describe transformations in words (such as "Dilate the function in the x-direction by 2") helps them move from the graph to an equation and vice versa.

Exploration Notes

Exploration 1-3a introduces vertical and horizontal translations and dilations by having students numerically determine image graphs for a given pre-image function. This activity works well as a small-group discovery lesson at the beginning of the first day of instruction. Allow students 15–20 minutes to complete the activity.

Exploration 1-3b and Exploration 1-3d can be used either as reviews or as a quiz after students complete Section 1-3. Exploration 1-3b takes about 20 minutes and Exploration 1-3d takes about 15 minutes.

Exploration 1-3c presents six graphs that illustrate various transformations and combinations of transformations. Problem 5 is an absolute value transformation, $g(x) = |f(x)|$, and Problem 6 is a horizontal dilation by a factor of −1. These two problems preview Section 1-6. You might want to use this Exploration to begin the second day of instruction. Allow small groups of students about 15–20 minutes to complete the activity.

Technology Notes

 Problem 21: The Dynamic Transformations Problem asks students to explore two Dynamic Precalculus Explorations at *www.keymath.com/precalc.* The Translation Exploration allows students to manipulate sliders to observe how a function plot is translated both algebraically and geometrically; the Dilation Exploration allows them to observe how it is dilated.

 Presentation Sketch: Translation Work.gsp, on the *Instructor's Resource CD,* uses sliders to translate a function plot both geometrically and algebraically. This sketch is related to the activity Translation of Functions.

 Presentation Sketch: Dilation Present.gsp, on the *Instructor's Resource CD,* uses sliders to translate a function plot both geometrically and algebraically. This sketch is related to the activity Dilation of Functions.

Activity: Translation of Functions, in the *Instructor's Resource Book,* gives students an opportunity to translate points and translate function plots both geometrically and algebraically. It takes 25–45 minutes, depending on students' familiarity with Sketchpad.

Activity: Dilation of Functions, in the *Instructor's Resource Book,* asks students to explore stretching and compressing functions both horizontally and vertically, both algebraically and geometrically. Allow 30–40 minutes.

Activity: Exploring Translations and Dilations, in the *Instructor's Resource Book,* provides hands-on experience with these kinds of transformations of the parent quadratic function. Allow 20–30 minutes.

 Activity: Translations in the Coordinate Plane, in *Exploring Geometry with The Geometer's Sketchpad,* provides a geometric, nonfunctional approach to translations that students might enjoy. Allow 35–45 minutes.

Activity: Function Transformations, in *Teaching Mathematics with Fathom,* leads students who are fairly new to Fathom through a study of translations, dilations, and reflections of the parent quadratic. It will take 50–100 minutes, depending on student experience. Optionally, you can use a prepared document.

Activity: Foundation Work, in *A Watched Cup Never Cools,* provides an extensive graphing calculator–based investigation of a variety of functions. The four parts of the laboratory lead up to translations and dilations of quadratics expressed in general form. It may take 1–3 hours, depending on how well students handle open-ended explorations.

Problem Notes

- The Reading Analysis questions begin in Section 1-3. These questions are designed to help students learn to read a mathematics textbook. Students need to develop the skill to read dense material slowly and carefully. Encourage them to read with a pencil in hand and a calculator nearby.

- *Problems Q1–Q10* are short problems that do not require detailed work. Students like the opportunity to solve problems mentally instead of showing all the steps on paper. You may find that students are more willing to show detailed work on other problems if you allow them to show minimal work on the daily Quick Review problems.

- *Problems 1–6* allow students to see the effects of six different transformations on the same function.

- *Problems 7–12* require students to identify transformations based on graphs of the pre-image and image functions. Because students are not given explicit formulas for the pre-image f, they must write the equation for the image g in terms of f.

- *Problems 15–20* do not give students an explicit formula for the pre-image function and so require students to perform transformations without plotting points by calculating their coordinates. When an explicit formula for the pre-image function is given, students are more likely to approach the problem by using the formula to plot points and miss the fundamental idea of transforming functions. A blackline master for these problems is available in the *Instructor's Resource Book.*

- *Problem 21* requires students to use Dynamic Precalculus Explorations at *www.keymath.com/ precalc* to investigate dilations and translations. These are Java-based sketches that do not require additional software.

1-4
Composition of Functions

Objective

Given two functions, graph and evaluate the composition of one function with the other.

Class Time

1–2 days

Homework Assignment

RA, Q1–Q10, Problems 1–2, 5, 7, 9–10, 12–15

Technology Options

 Presentation Sketch: Composition Present.gsp

 Activity: Composition of Functions

Important Terms and Concepts

Composite function

Input

Output

Inside function

Outside function

Notation for a composite function: $f(g(x))$, $f \circ g(x)$, $(f \circ g)(x)$

Domain and range of a composite function

Lesson Notes

This section explores compositions of functions through application problems and the use of a grapher. It is important that students understand the underlying concept of composition. The first two examples do not give explicit functions, so students cannot depend on their algebraic skills to solve the problems. Make sure it is clear that the inside function is applied first and then the outside function is applied to the result.

Example 3 shows how to evaluate a composite function at various values and then find an explicit formula for $f(g(x))$.

Example 5 shows how to find the domain and range of a composite function. Make sure students understand that for a value x to be in the domain of a composite function $f \circ g$, x must be in the domain of the inside function g, and $g(x)$ must be in the domain of the outside function f.

In Example 5d, the range of $f \circ g$ is found by substituting the endpoints of the domain, $4 \le x \le 7$, into the equation of the composite function. Emphasize that this technique works because $f \circ g$ is linear (a linear function does not "change directions," so the least and greatest y-values occur at the endpoints of the domain). Using the endpoints gives the correct range for any function that is monotone increasing or decreasing on the entire domain. For other types of functions, students should examine the graph to determine the range.

Exploration Notes

Exploration 1-4a can be used to introduce the idea of composition of functions. Allow 15 minutes.

Technology Notes

 Presentation Sketch: Composition Present.gsp, on the *Instructor's Resource CD,* uses dyna-graphs to show composition of functions. This sketch also includes a page that illustrates domains and ranges for function composition. This sketch is related to the activity Composition of Functions.

 Activity: Composition of Functions, in Chapter 1 of *Exploring Precalculus with The Geometer's Sketchpad,* uses a prepared file of dynagraphs to allow exploration of the domain and range of a composition and possible commutativity. Allow 30–40 minutes.

Problem Notes

- *Problem 1,* the Flashlight Problem, is similar to the example of dropping a pebble into a pond. Students should assume that the radius of the spot of light increases at a *constant* rate of 7 cm/s. In calculus, students will encounter related-rate problems in which rate changes but not at a constant rate.

- *Problem 2,* the Bacterial Culture Problem, asks students to determine whether the area and radius of a bacteria culture are growing at an increasing rate or at a decreasing rate. This problem is a good preview of the related-rate problems students will solve in calculus. Students taking AP Biology may do experiments similar to the one described in Problem 2. You may want to ask the AP Biology teacher to suggest problems similar to Problem 2 that the students will actually perform in AP Biology.

- *Problem 3* involves a step function.

- *Problems 5 and 6* ask students to answer questions about a composite function from graphs without using explicit formulas for the functions. A blackline master for these problems is available in the *Instructor's Resource Book*.

- *Problems 7 and 8* use numeric information to find values of composite functions.

- *Problems 9 and 10,* the Composite Function Algebraically Problems 1 and 2, are similar to Example 5.

- *Problem 11* requires students to work with square root functions. Because the square root of a negative number doesn't exist among real numbers, the square root functions in these problems have restricted domains.

- *Problem 12,* the Horizontal Translation and Dilation Problem, connects Sections 1-3 and 1-4.

- *Problems 13–15* prepare students for later sections, so it is important to assign them.

- *Problem 15,* the Linear Function and Its Inverse Problem, asks students to compose a function and its inverse and to observe that the two functions "undo" one another.

Supplementary Problems

Supplementary Problems 1 and 2 are excellent problems to prepare students for related-rate questions in calculus, whether they study AP Calculus in high school or calculus in college. You can assign one of the problems for practice and the other as a quiz or test question. Problems 3 and 4 are similar to textbook Problems 9 and 10 and can be used as practice, quiz, or test questions.

1. *Conical Tank Problem:* A conical tank (Figure 1-4a) in a chemical plant is being emptied of liquid benzene at a constant rate of 5 ft^3/min. At time $t = 0$ min, 100 ft^3 of benzene is in the tank.

Figure 1-4a

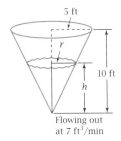

a. Explain why you can express the volume of benzene in the tank by the equation $V(t) = 100 - 5t$.

b. Recall that the volume of a cone is given by

$$V = \frac{1}{3}\pi r^2 h$$

where r is the radius and h is the altitude. Because the radius of the tank is 5 ft and the altitude is 10 ft, the radius, r, of the liquid will always equal $\frac{1}{2}$ the altitude, h, of the liquid. Explain why the volume of the liquid in this particular tank is

$$V = \frac{\pi}{12}h^3$$

c. Write an equation expressing h as a function of V. Use the result and the information in part a to write an equation for the composite function $h(V(t))$.

d. At what time t will the tank be completely empty? At what negative value of t was the tank completely full? What, then, is the domain of the function $h \circ V$?

2. *Balloon Problem:* A spherical balloon is being filled with air. Its volume, V, measured in cubic centimeters, is a function of the radius, r, measured in centimeters, as follows:

$$V = \frac{4}{3}\pi r^3$$

a. Transform the equation to express r as a function of V.

b. Suppose that $V = 100$ cm^3 at time $t = 0$ s and that the balloon is being filled at 20 cm^3/s. Write an equation expressing V as a function of t.

c. Because r depends on V and V depends on t, r is a composite function of t. Write an equation expressing r as a function of t.

d. Plot the graph of r as a function of t. Would it be meaningful in the real world for t to be negative? What is a lower bound on the domain of t?

e. The balloon will pop if the radius reaches 7 cm. Find an upper bound for the domain of t.

3. *Two Linear Functions:* Let g and f be defined by

$$g(x) = 10 - 2x \qquad 1 \le x \le 4$$
$$f(x) = x + 2 \qquad 3 \le x \le 7$$

a. Plot the graphs of g, f, and $f \circ g$ on the same screen. Sketch the result.

b. Find $f(g(3))$. Show on your sketch from part a the two steps by which you can find this value directly from the graphs of f and g.

c. Find the domain and range of $f \circ g$ algebraically. Show that both agree with the graph.

d. Show that $g(f(2))$ and $g(f(5))$ are both undefined but for different reasons.

e. Try to plot $y = g(f(x))$. What do you notice?

f. Find the domain of $g \circ f$ algebraically, thus confirming what you observed in part e.

g. Find $f(f(4))$. Show that $g(g(2))$ is undefined.

4. *Quadratic and Linear Function:* Let f and g be defined by

$$f(x) = x^2 - 6x + 10 \qquad 0 \le x \le 5$$

$$g(x) = 2x - 10 \qquad 2 \le x \le 6$$

a. Plot the graphs of f, g, and $f \circ g$ on the same screen. Sketch the results.

b. Find $f(g(1))$ and $g(f(1))$. Explain why $g(f(0))$ is undefined even though $f(0)$ *is* defined.

c. Find the domain of $f \circ g$ algebraically. Show that it agrees with your graph in part a.

d. Find an equation for $f(g(x))$ explicitly in terms of x. Simplify as much as possible. Plot the graph of this equation on the same screen as your graph in part a, observing the domain in part c. Does the graph coincide with the one you plotted in part a?

1-5
Inverse of a Function

Objective

Given a function, find its inverse relation, and tell whether or not the inverse relation is a function.

Class Time

1 day

Homework Assignment

RA, Q1–Q10, Problems 1, 3, 5, 7, 9–10, 13, 17–18, 21, 29, 30

Technology Options

 Presentation Sketch: Inverse Present.gsp

Activity: Inverses of Functions

Important Terms and Concepts

Inverse

Inverse function

Inverse function notation: $f^{-1}(x)$

f and f^{-1} reflect across the line $y = x$

Invertible function

One-to-one function

Strictly increasing function

Strictly decreasing function

Parametric equations

Therefore symbol, $\therefore$

Q.E.D.

Lesson Notes

This section discusses the inverse of functions, identifying the conditions necessary for a function to have an inverse function.

You can teach this section in one day. You should emphasize that when the variables are interchanged, you get the inverse relation, which may or may not be a function. Discussing Examples 1 and 2 helps prepare the definition of an invertible function. Example 2 shows how to graph a function and its inverse using parametric equations. Students often think parametric graphing is truly bizarre, but reinforce that since $x = t$ then x can be replaced by t in the first set of parametric equations. In the second set of parametric equations, simply interchange the equations for *x* and *y* in the first set. Example 3 provides an example for an invertible function and shows an important feature of these functions: $f^{-1}(f(x)) = x$.

Discussing the concept of a one-to-one function is very important in relation to inverse functions. It will help students' understanding to give additional examples for invertible functions: $f(x) = x^3$, or other power functions with odd exponents, and $f(x) = e^x$ and its transformed forms. Also give additional examples for noninvertible functions, such as $f(x) = x^4$, or other power functions with even exponents, and $f(x) = |x|$.

You might want to start your lesson with an explanation of why the concept of inverse is useful by referring to Problem 29, the Braking Distance Problem. You can use the example of police investigators to show that they would need to find the inverse of a function to find the speed from the skid mark evidence.

Because many students use the word *inverse* to refer to the reciprocal, or multiplicative inverse, of a number, they may mistakenly think that the inverse of a function $y = f(x)$ is $y = \dfrac{1}{f(x)}$. Explain that $f^{-1}(x)$ is a *functional inverse*, whereas $\dfrac{1}{f(x)}$ is a *multiplicative inverse*. Also emphasize that $f^{-1}(x)$ is read "*f* inverse of *x*." Later in the course, students often mistakenly believe trigonometric inverses are equal to reciprocal trigonometric functions (for example, $\sin^{-1} x = \csc x$). If you reserve the term *inverse* to mean *functional inverse* and refer to the multiplicative inverse as the *reciprocal,* you can avoid errors later.

A memorable way to illustrate that the graph of the inverse of a function is the mirror image of the graph of the function is to have students hold a small mirror so that one edge is on the line $y = x$. The graph of the inverse will appear in the mirror.

Exploration 1-5a can be used to introduce students to inverses of functions.

Exploration Notes

Exploration 1-5a introduces students to inversion of functions by having them find the inverse of a linear, a quadratic, and an exponential. Students do this by a combination of numerical, graphical, and algebraic techniques. Along the way, they demonstrate that whether or not the inverse relation is a function, it is a mirror image of the parent function in the line $y = x$. Allow about 20 minutes.

Technology Notes

 Presentation Sketch: Inverse Present.gsp, on the *Instructor's Resource CD,* demonstrates properties of inverses on a dynagraph. It also includes a page that demonstrates the relationship between the graph of a function and that of its inverse. The final page allows exploration of linear functions that are their own inverses. This sketch is related to the activity Inverses of Functions.

 Activity: Inverses of Functions, in *Exploring Precalculus with The Geometer's Sketchpad,* allows students to explore inverse relations, determining when the inverse of a function is a function. Allow 30–35 minutes.

Problem Notes

• *Problems 1 and 2* are applications of inverses to real-world situations. They emphasize inverse function notation and the reflection of a function and its inverse across the line $y = x$.

• *Problems 3, 5–8* provide practice in sketching the inverse relation for a given graph. A blackline master for these problems is available in the *Instructor's Resource Book.*

• *Problem 4,* the Discrete Function Problem, requires students to apply the idea of invertibility to a new situation. The function presented in this problem is made up of a *discrete* set of points (a set of points with "gaps" between them). Although the function is not strictly increasing or strictly decreasing, it is one-to-one and is therefore invertible.

• *Problems 9–20* require students to write equations for and then graph inverses of given functions.

• *Problems 21–24* require students to write equations for and then graph the inverses of given functions and decide whether the inverses are functions.

• *Problems 25 and 26* present two functions that are their own inverses.

• *Problems 27–29* are application problems with multiple questions and require students to use several skills. Problems structured like this appear in the free-response section of the AP Calculus test. If most of your students will take AP Calculus next year, try creating similar problems on your chapter tests in addition to assigning these kinds of problems for homework.

• *Problem 30,* the Horizontal Line Test Problem, introduces the *horizontal line test* to determine invertibility. It is important to familiarize students with this visual clue to determine the invertibility of functions.

1-6
Reflections, Absolute Values, and Other Transformations

Objective

Given a function, transform it by reflection and by applying *absolute value* to the function or its argument.

Class Time

1 day

Homework Assignment

RA, Q1–Q10, Problems 1–4, 5, 7, 9–14

Technology Options

 Problem 14: Dynamic Reflection Problem

 Presentation Sketch: Reflection Present.gsp

 Presentation Sketch: Absolute Value Present.gsp

 Activity: Exploring Translations and Dilations

 Activity: Reflection of Functions

 Activity: Absolute Value of Functions

 Activity: Reflections in the Coordinate Plane

 Activity: Symmetry and Even Functions

Important Terms and Concepts

Reflection

Reflection across the y-axis

Reflection across the x-axis

Displacement

Piecewise function

Absolute value transformations

Even function

Odd function

Step discontinuity

Greatest integer function, $f(x) = [x]$

Lesson Notes

This section discusses reflections across the x- and y-axes, absolute value transformations, and even and odd functions.

You can teach this section in one day. Start by discussing Example 1, and you could challenge students to sketch the graphs of functions with which they are familiar and then to graph $y = f(-x)$ and $y = -f(x)$. Because $y = f(-x)$ is a *horizontal* dilation by a factor of -1, students may mistakenly think it is a reflection across the *horizontal* axis. Make sure students understand that $y = f(-x)$ represents a translation across the vertical axis, or y-axis. Similarly, make sure they understand that although $y = -f(x)$ is a *vertical* dilation, it is a reflection across the *horizontal* axis, or x-axis.

Before discussing absolute value transformations, you may need to review the definition of absolute value. The fact that $|x| = -x$ for $x < 0$ is troubling to many students because they mistakenly think that $-x$ always represents a negative number. Using the words "the opposite of" instead of "negative" can help clarify the definition for students. Try saying, "If the number inside the absolute value sign is negative, then its absolute value is *the opposite of* the negative number." You might illustrate with an example:

> If $x = -3$, then $|x| = |(-3)| = -(-3)$. The value of $-(-3)$ is *the opposite of* -3, which is 3.

Spend some time in class explaining the difference between the $y = |f(x)|$ and $y = f(|x|)$ transformations. Use the graphs of familiar functions to demonstrate how the $y = |f(x)|$ transformation affects the range and the $y = f(|x|)$ transformation affects the domain of f.

Finally, you can introduce the discussion of even and odd functions by raising this question: For which functions will the $y = f(-x)$ transformation result in the original function, and for which does it give the opposite of the original function? In other words, for which functions is $f(-x) = f(x)$, and for which is it $f(-x) = -f(x)$? Ask students to give examples (such as $y = kx$, $y = x^2$, $y = -x^2$, $y = x^3$, $y = |x|$), and perhaps have them discuss the question in small groups. Once students have recognized the properties of functions that satisfy these equations (functions symmetrical to the y-axis or to the origin), you can introduce the terms *even* and *odd*. If you run out of time, you could assign this question as homework.

Trigonometric functions are either odd or even functions. For example, $\sin(-x) = -\sin x$ and $\cos(-x) = \cos x$. Studying odd and even polynomial functions now will prepare students for studying trigonometric functions and their properties.

Exploration 1-6a may be used as a follow-up assignment or quiz to see if students have learned about the transformations of this section.

Exploration Notes

Exploration 1-6a presents students with eight transformations of the same function. (The function is cubic with a restricted domain, but this fact is not mentioned in the exploration.) In each case, students are presented with an equation for *y* in terms of function *f*, and they are asked to name the transformation and sketch the transformed graph. Allow about 20 minutes.

Technology Notes

 Problem 14: The Dynamic Reflection Problem asks students to use a Dynamic Precalculus Exploration at *www.keymath.com/precalc.* The Dilation Exploration allows students to explore reflections across the *x*- and *y*-axes by changing one or both of the dilation sliders to −1.

 Presentation Sketch: Reflection Present.gsp, on the *Instructor's Resource CD,* demonstrates the effects of reflecting the graph of a square root function across coordinate axes. The presentation demonstrates the effects on the coordinates as well as on the algebraic description of the function. This sketch is related to the activity Reflection of Functions.

 Presentation Sketch: Absolute Value Present.gsp, on the *Instructor's Resource CD,* demonstrates the graphical effect of composing a quadratic function with absolute value. This sketch is related to the activity Absolute Value of Functions.

 Activity: Exploring Translations and Dilations, in the *Instructor's Resource Book,* focuses on translations and dilations, but you could extend it to include investigations of reflections.

 Activity: Reflection of Functions, in *Exploring Precalculus with The Geometer's Sketchpad,* asks students to explore reflections of a traced point as well as a square root function. The activity is for intermediate Sketchpad users. Allow 20–30 minutes.

 Activity: Absolute Value of Functions, in *Exploring Precalculus with The Geometer's Sketchpad,* makes use of reflections to understand absolute values. Students with intermediate Sketchpad experience will complete the activity in about 20–25 minutes.

 Activity: Reflections in the Coordinate Plane, in Chapter 2 of *Exploring Geometry with The Geometer's Sketchpad,* allows students to explore changes of coordinates under reflections across the *x*- and *y*-axes and the line *y* = *x*. It is for beginning or intermediate Sketchpad users and will take 30–40 minutes.

 Activity: Symmetry and Even Functions, in *Connecting Mathematics with Science,* has students explore an even function (based on absolute value) that arises from plotting the connectivity of acid-based solutions. Allow 45 minutes.

Problem Notes

• *Problems 1–4* provide practice in applying the transformations introduced in this section to the graphs of functions.

• *Problems 5 and 6* ask students to use their graphers to plot the functions in Problems 3 and 4 and to verify their results for part d.

• *Problems 7–10* provide practice for and promote understanding of the concepts of absolute value transformations and even and odd functions. If you have time after discussing the concepts with them, have students work in small groups to solve these problems in class. A blackline master for Problem 7d is available in the *Instructor's Resource Book.*

• *Problems 11–13* are important to assign and discuss with students because of the significance of the concepts of discontinuity, piecewise function, the greatest integer function, and some interesting applications.

• *Problem 14* refers students to the Precalculus Resource Center Web site and gives them opportunity to work with reflections dynamically.

1-7
Precalculus Journal

Objective

Start writing a journal in which you can record things you have learned about precalculus mathematics and questions you have concerning concepts about which you are not quite clear.

Class Time

$\frac{1}{2}$ day

Homework Assignment

Problem 1

Important Terms and Concepts

Journal

Lesson Notes

This section introduces writing in a journal. One of the four ways students learn mathematics is verbally. In recent years, college and high school mathematics curricula and standardized tests have placed increased emphasis on having students verbalize mathematical concepts and ideas. Students will improve their writing skills over the year if you require them to write periodically. In addition to assigning journal entry problems for homework, you may want to include writing questions on chapter tests. At first you may encounter some resistance, but eventually students will write willingly.

Establish a set of guidelines for how journal entries will be graded. Limit your guidelines to five or fewer instructions. Here is a sample.

- Answer the writing prompt. Write at least four complete sentences.

- Be specific. Use at least three new vocabulary words. Explain their meaning, and give examples where applicable.

- Give real-world examples for the applications of the new concepts and procedures.

- Exemplary journal entries receive extra credit. Vague, rambling statements receive no credit.

Have students read this section, including the sample journal entry. Discuss with students whether the sample meets all of your guidelines.

Assign Problem 1. Allow about 15–20 minutes of class time for students to write. Then you could call on volunteers to read their entries. Point out something in each volunteer's entry that meets the guidelines, is unusually well written, or sheds new insight. It's good to avoid negative comments at this time. Circulate about the room so that you can see whether students are actually reading something they wrote and not just creating *oral* statements on the spot.

You may want to assign the Section 1-8 Chapter Review Problems the same day you explain Section 1-7 so that students who finish their journal entries early can start working on those problems. Alternatively, you may want to assign the journal as homework following your test on Chapter 1.

A good material to use for the journal is a tablet of spiral-bound index cards, 4×6 or 5×8 inches. On the ruled part of the card, students write conclusions, equations, properties, and items on which they are not clear. On the blank part of the previous card (facing the ruled side when the journal is open), they draw graphs.

Be sure your students realize that the journal is *not* the place to write their class notes. Rather, it is the place to record briefly some things they can distill from their notes, especially when they have finally mastered difficult topics.

You may occasionally allow students to use journals on their tests. For instance, the test on trigonometric identities from the beginning of Chapter 4 could have a no-calculator and no-journal part where students write down the Pythagorean properties and so forth—and a second part where they can use the properties and techniques for proving identities that they have recorded in their journals.

Point out to students that the journal they keep this year will be useful in courses they take next year.

Throughout the year, ask students periodically to read from their journals. The last five minutes of class are a good time for this activity. It's good to keep track of which students have participated so that all students have a turn.

1-8
Chapter Review and Test

Objective

Review and practice the major concepts of this chapter.

Class Time

2 days (including 1 day for testing)

Homework Assignment

Day 1: R1–R6, T1–T28

Day 2 (after Chapter 1 Test): Problem C1 and all of Problem Set 2-1, Recommended Problem C2

Important Terms and Concepts

Sine function

Periodic function

Period of a periodic function

Lesson Notes

The last section of each chapter includes a set of Review Problems, numbered according to the sections in the chapter, and a sample Chapter Test, which can also be used for review. Most chapters also have a set of Concept Problems that extend the concepts in the chapter or introduce concepts for the next chapter. Concept Problems make excellent group activities or projects. Answers for the Review Problems are provided in the back of the book so that students can monitor their own progress. Answers are not provided for the Chapter Test or Concept Problems.

You may want to assign the Section 1-8 Chapter Review Problems the same day you explain Section 1-7 so that students who finish their journal entries early can start working on those problems. This would also be a good time to assign any problems you will have due the day after a Chapter Test.

Problem Notes

- *Problems R3 and R5* both require students to answer questions about functions based on their graphs. A blackline master for these problems is available in the *Instructor's Resource Book.*

- *Problem C2* introduces the sine function, which students will study in Chapter 2. In the problem, students look at the periodic behavior of the function, determine whether it is odd or even, and explore transformations of the function. A blackline master for this problem is available in the *Instructor's Resource Book.*

2 Periodic Functions and Right Triangle Problems

Periodic functions are introduced in Section 2-1 by having students analyze the motion of a Ferris wheel. They plot $y = \sin x$ on their graphers and then use the dilations and translation from Chapter 1 to make the resulting sinusoid fit the real-world situation. Thereafter, students see how to extend the familiar cosine and sine functions from previous courses to angles greater than 180° or less than 0° by considering an angle to be a variable that measures rotation. By finding values of all six trigonometric functions on the calculator, students learn the reciprocal properties, thus paving the way for the formal study of properties and identities in Chapter 4. The chapter concludes with right triangle trigonometry, possibly a familiar topic, for the main purpose of introducing the inverse trigonometric functions in a meaningful context, as well as providing practice with the definitions of the six functions.

2-1

Introduction to Periodic Functions

Objective

Find the function that corresponds to the graph in Figure 2-1b of the student book, and graph it on your grapher.

Class Time

$\frac{1}{2}$ day

Homework Assignment

Problems 1–4

Technology Options

 Activity: A Sine Wave Tracer

Important Terms and Concepts

Periodic functions

Theta (θ)

Sine function

Degree mode (calculator setting)

Sinusoids

Parent sine function

Lesson Notes

This section introduces the sine function and the concept of angle as a measure of rotation. It lays the foundation for using trigonometric functions as mathematical models. You can assign Section 2-1 as homework on the night of the Chapter 1 test or as a group activity to be completed in class. Alternatively, you can use Exploration 2-1a. No classroom discussion is needed before students begin the activity.

Technology Notes

 Activity: A Sine Wave Tracer, in the *Instructor's Resource Book,* allows students to construct a sine wave by tracing a point as two points are animated. The tracer is constructed based on radian angle measure, but it can be adapted as a basic introduction to the sine function and its graph. This activity is for intermediate Sketchpad users and will take 30–40 minutes.

Problem Notes

• *Problem 1* introduces the sine function.

• *Problem 2* requires students to recall the work they did with transformations in Chapter 1.

• *Problem 4* asks students to think about angles with negative measure and with measures greater than 180°.

2-2
Measurement of Rotation

Objective

Given an angle of any measure, draw a picture of that angle.

Class Time

1 day

Homework Assignment

RA, Q1–Q10, Problems 1, 5, 9, 19, 21, 25, 27, 29, 30

Important Terms and Concepts

Initial position

Terminal position

Standard position

Counterclockwise

Clockwise

Coterminal angles ($\phi = \theta + 360n°$)

Reference angle

Degrees, minutes, seconds

Lesson Notes

If you did not assign Section 2-1 as homework on the night of the Chapter 1 test, you can cover Sections 2-1 and 2-2 on the same day. Section 2-1 is a good group activity.

The main point to get across in this section is that angles can have measures outside the range of 0° to 180°. To illustrate, you might present the familiar example of the number of degrees rotated by the hands of a clock.

It is worth spending a few minutes making sure students are comfortable pronouncing and writing the Greek letters often associated with angles.

Example 1 illustrates how to sketch angles with measures between 0° and 360° in standard position and then calculate the measure of the reference angle.

Example 2 shows how to find the reference angle for an angle greater than 360° by first finding a

coterminal angle with measure between 0° and 360°. Help students see that they can find the number of whole revolutions by dividing the angle measure by 360°. Then to find the coterminal angle, they can either multiply the decimal part of the quotient by 360° or subtract 360° times the number of whole revolutions from the original angle measure.

Make sure students understand that the reference angle is always a positive, acute angle that is "nestled against" the horizontal axis. Because a reference angle must be acute, angles of 0°, 90°, 180°, and 270° and angles coterminal with these four angles do not have reference angles. Emphasize that a reference angle is *never* measured between the vertical axis and the terminal side of the angle. Also stress that reference angles always go in a *counterclockwise* direction. Thus, some reference angles go from the horizontal axis to the terminal side, whereas others go from the terminal side to the horizontal axis. Even the best students sometimes draw and calculate reference angles incorrectly.

Exploration Notes

Exploration 2-2a can be completed in 10–15 minutes. For Problem 8 of this Exploration, students must recall the relationships among the sides of a 30°-60°-90° triangle. This Exploration is useful as a quick quiz or can be omitted.

Problem Notes

- *Problems 1–20* require students to sketch angles in standard position and find the measures of the reference angles.

- *Problems 21–26* involve arithmetic with angle measures given in *degrees, minutes,* and *seconds.* Students may need to review how to convert among these units. Some calculators have a feature that converts angle measures from degrees, minutes, and seconds to degrees with decimals. However, these conversions are fairly simple, and students should be able to do them without this feature.

- *Problems 27 and 28* ask students to sketch reasonable graphs for situations that exhibit periodic behavior.

- *Problems 29 and 30* review the transformations studied in Chapter 1 and prepare students for the next section.

2-3
Sine and Cosine Functions

Objective

Extend the definitions of sine and cosine for any angle.

Class Time

1 day

Homework Assignment

RA, Q1–Q10, Problems 1–23 odd

Technology Options

 Figure 2-3g: Sine Wave Tracer

 Exploration 2-3b: uv-Graphs and θy-Graphs of Sinusoids

Important Terms and Concepts

Periodic function

Cycle

Period

Trigonometric functions

Displacement

Right triangle definitions of sine and cosine

Sine function of any size angle

Cosine function of any size angle

Sinusoid

Parent sine function

Critical points

Lesson Notes

In previous courses, students learned how to find the sine and cosine of the acute angles in a right triangle. In this section, the definitions of sine and cosine are extended to angles of any measure, making it possible to discuss $y = \sin\theta$ and $y = \cos\theta$ as periodic functions called *sinusoids*. It is important to take time to make sure students understand that the definitions are extending to angles of any measure. Otherwise, they will be forever wedded to the triangle definitions and will have trouble working with non-acute angles.

The goals of this section are to have students understand and learn the definitions of the sine and cosine functions and to understand and learn parent graphs of the sine and cosine functions.

For this section, and throughout the remainder of the chapter, graphers should be in degree mode. Some calculators use radian mode as the default setting. Show students how to change their calculators to degree mode, and remind them to check the mode each time they turn on the calculator or clear the memory.

To introduce the topic of periodic functions, have students graph the function $y = \sin x$ on their graphers. Then have them trace the function and observe that the y-values repeat every 360°. Use the graph to explain the concepts of *cycle* and *period*.

When $y = \sin x$ and $y = \cos x$ become periodic functions, right triangle definitions of sine and cosine are extended. Review the right triangle definitions of sine and cosine with students. Then discuss the material in the text that explains how the definitions can be extended to angles of any measure. Note that the reference angle determines a reference *triangle* to which the right triangle definitions apply. Make sure students understand that (u, v) is *any* point on the terminal side of the angle and r is the distance from (u, v) to the origin. Emphasize that r is *always* positive because it is a distance, but u and v can be either positive or negative. Therefore, the sine or cosine of an angle can be positive or negative.

Point out to students that coterminal angles have the same sine values and the same cosine values because they have the same terminal position. This explains why the sine and cosine functions are periodic, with cycles that repeat every 360°.

Example 1 illustrates the relationship between the cosine of an angle and the cosine of the corresponding reference angle. Be sure to discuss the note after Example 1, which emphasizes the importance of including the degree sign when denoting the sine or cosine of an angle in degrees. If the degree sign is not included, the angle is assumed to be in radians. So, for example, to denote the cosine of an angle with measure 147°, students should write cos 147°, not cos 147.

Example 2 demonstrates how to apply the definitions of sine and cosine to find the sine and cosine of an angle based on a point on the terminal side of the angle.

Example 3 shows how to graph a transformation of the sine function by plotting critical points. A blackline master of Figure 2-3i is available in the *Instructor's Resource Book.*

Consider giving students a copy of the Trigonometric Ratios Table from the Blackline Masters section in the *Instructor's Resource Book.* Have students keep the table in a folder for their reference. They can continue to fill in values as they learn about more trigonometric ratios in Section 2-4 and when they learn about radian measure in Section 3-4.

Exploration Notes

There are three Explorations for Section 2-3. If you have time for only one Exploration, it is recommended that you use Exploration 2-3a.

Exploration 2-3a connects the right triangle definitions of sine and cosine to the extended definitions and can be used in place of Example 1. It requires students to use a ruler and a protractor to make accurate measurements. Allow 15–20 minutes for students to complete the Exploration.

Exploration 2-3b demonstrates the relationship between a unit circle and the graphs of $y = \sin x$ and $y = \cos x$. The Exploration takes about 20 minutes. You can use this Exploration with Section 3-4 instead of with Section 2-3 if you prefer.

Exploration 2-3c explores the graph and transformations of the parent function $y = \sin x$. If you work through the problems with the class as a whole, this Exploration can replace Example 3.

Technology Notes

 The discussion below Figure 2-3g suggests the use of the Dynamic Precalculus Exploration Sine Wave Tracer, which can be found at *www.keymath.com/precalc.* The exploration allows students to investigate properties of the sinusoidal wave using an interactive tracer. It is also used in Section 2-4, Problem 45.

 *Exploration 2-3b: uv-*Graphs and θy-Graphs of Sinusoids, in the *Instructor's Resource Book,* can be done with the help of Sketchpad. The resolution of the graphics in Sketchpad is higher than that of calculators, which makes information easier to read for this activity.

Problem Notes

• *Problems 1–6* explore the relationship between the sine and cosine of an angle and the sine and cosine of the corresponding reference angle. Problem 23 follows directly from the work on these problems. If you gave students the Trigonometric Ratios Table from the *Instructor's Resource Book,* you might ask them to refer to the table while completing these problems.

• *Problems 7–14* are similar to Example 2 and help students learn the definitions of sine and cosine.

• *Problems 15–20* give students a chance to apply their transformation skills from Chapter 1 to the parent sine and cosine graphs. A blackline master for these problems is available in the *Instructor's Resource Book.*

• *Problems 21 and 22* ask students to make generalizations about when $\sin \theta$ and $\cos \theta$ are positive and when they are negative.

• *Problem 23,* the Functions of Reference Angles Problem, presents the property that relates the sine and cosine of an angle to the sine and cosine of the reference angle.

• *Problem 24,* the Construction Problem, requires students to construct a right triangle with particular measures. Then they can observe that the sine and cosine of an angle do not change if the triangle is dilated. If students do not use a computer graphing program, they will need a protractor for this problem. Centimeter graph paper from the Blackline Masters section in the *Instructor's Resource Book* may be used.

2-4

Values of the Six Trigonometric Functions

Objective

Be able to find values of the six trigonometric functions approximately, by calculator, for any angle and exactly for certain special angles.

Class time

2 days

Homework Assignment

Day 1

Recommended: Q1–Q10, Problems 1, 6, 7, 9, 11–14

Also suggested: Problem 4

Day 2

Problems 15–19, 21–31 odd, 35, 39, 40–46

Technology Options

 Problem 45: Sine Wave Tracer Project

 Activity: Trigonometry Tracers

 Activity: Trigonometric Ratios

 Activity: Adaptable options

Important Terms and Concepts

Tangent

Cotangent

Secant

Cosecant

Reciprocal properties

Unit circle

Ellipsis format

Complementary angles

Lesson Notes

Section 2-4 defines the four remaining trigonometric functions—tangent, cotangent, secant, and cosecant—and introduces the reciprocal properties.

If you gave students a Trigonometric Ratios Table in Section 2-3, have them fill in more of the values as you introduce the other four ratios. You might ask

them to apply relationships between functions, such as $\csc \theta = \dfrac{1}{\sin \theta}$, $\tan \theta = \dfrac{\sin \theta}{\cos \theta}$, and $\sin \theta = \cos(90° - \theta)$, to fill out the table.

This section will take about two days to complete. On the first day, cover the material through Example 2. You might begin the day by assigning Exploration 2-4a, suggesting that students read their books to find the information needed to answer the questions. When students have finished, discuss their results. If students seem to understand the material, you may be able to skip some of the examples in the text.

Explain to students that an ellipsis is used to indicate that the digits of a number continue after the last digit displayed. A rounded answer should be preceded with an approximately equal to sign ($\approx$) to indicate that the answer is an approximation. When a problem does not specify how to round a number, students should round appropriately, depending on the real-world context of the problem. If students plan to use the result of a calculation in subsequent calculations, they should use the unrounded value. One way to do this is to store the result in their calculator's memory and then use the stored value rather than the rounded value in the calculation. You may need to explain how to store values.

Watch for students who think that a function and its cofunction—for example, secant and cosecant—are reciprocals. Emphasize the correct reciprocal relationships, and be sure to discuss Problem 43 in class to reinforce that cofunctions are not reciprocal functions.

When drawing reference triangles to find the values of trigonometric functions, students often make the mistake of labeling all sides with positive values. Emphasize the importance of thinking about the sign used for each label. Because the labels for the horizontal and vertical sides correspond to the u and v values, they may be positive or negative values, depending on the quadrant the terminal side of the angle is in. Because the value of r is the radius of a circle, the hypotenuse label should always be positive.

When a radical occurs in the denominator, such as in Example 2, the text discourages students from *rationalizing* the expression. It was once customary to transform fractions containing radicals so that the denominators were *rational* numbers. The technique had advantages for finding decimal approximations because it is much easier to divide by a rational number when using long division.

Now that calculators are widely available, denominators usually are not rationalized.

Here are some good class discussion questions.

Question: Tell which trigonometric functions are positive and which are negative in Quadrants I, II, III, and IV.

Answer: Quad I: all are +; Quad II: sin and csc are +; Quad III: tan and cot are +; Quad IV cos and sec are +.

Question: For angles that terminate on a quadrant boundary, the values of the trigonometric functions are 0, ±1, or undefined. Find the exact values of the six trigonometric functions of 270°.

Answer: sin 270°= −1; cos 270° = 0; tan 270° is undefined; cot 270° = 0; sec 270° is undefined; csc 270° = −1.

Question: In what quadrant does −250° terminate?

Answer: Quadrant II

Question: Describe how sin θ, cos θ, and tan θ vary as θ increases from 0° to 90°.

Answer: sin θ increases; cos θ decreases; tan θ increases.

Exploration Notes

Exploration 2-4a requires students to use the definitions of all six trigonometric functions. You might begin the instruction for this section by having students work on this Exploration in small groups for 15–20 minutes.

Exploration 2-4b reinforces students' understanding of the definitions of sine, cosine, and tangent. This Exploration should take about 10 minutes and could be used as a quiz or included as part of a homework assignment.

Technology Notes

 Problem 45: Sine Wave Tracer Project asks students to explore properties of the sine wave and write down what they learned. This can be done with the help of the Dynamic Precalculus Exploration of the same name, at the Web site *www.keymath.com/precalc.*

 Activity: Trigonometry Tracers, in the *Instructor's Resource Book,* has students compute the sine, cosine, and tangent of several angles based on the coordinates of a point on the unit circle. The activity is based on radian measure of angles, but it can be adapted to use degrees. You may wish to save this activity for Section 3-5. Allow 30–40 minutes.

 Activity: Trigonometric Ratios, in *Exploring Geometry with The Geometer's Sketchpad,* has students construct a right triangle, measure the ratios for sine, cosine, and tangent of an acute angle, and explore properties of the ratios. Parts of the last question are related to inverse trigonometric functions, but it is still appropriate for exploration at the introductory level. The activity is for an intermediate Sketchpad user. Allow 20–30 minutes.

 Activity: Adaptable options. See Section 3-5 for radian-based activities that could be adapted for use here.

Additional Class Examples

1. Find the six trigonometric functions of θ if θ terminates in Quadrant III and $\sin \theta = -\frac{2}{3}$.

   Solution

   Sketch an angle terminating in Quadrant III, as shown in Figure 2-4a. Pick a convenient point on the terminal side. Because

   $$\text{sine} = \frac{\text{vertical coordinate}}{\text{radius}}$$

   the most convenient point is 3 units from the origin with a vertical coordinate of −2. The horizontal coordinate can be found by applying the Pythagorean theorem.

   $$-\sqrt{3^2 - (-2)^2} = -\sqrt{5}$$

   Choose the negative square root because the horizontal coordinate is negative for a point in Quadrant III.

   Figure 2-4a

   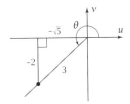

   Once the figure is sketched, the problem becomes an "old" problem, as in Example 2 in the student book.

   $$\sin \theta = \frac{-2}{3} = -\frac{2}{3} \qquad \text{(given)}$$

   $$\cos \theta = \frac{-\sqrt{5}}{3} = -\frac{\sqrt{5}}{3}$$

   $$\tan \theta = \frac{-2}{-\sqrt{5}} = \frac{2}{\sqrt{5}} \qquad \text{Note that } \tan \theta \text{ is positive if } \theta \text{ terminates in Quadrant III.}$$

$$\cot \theta = \frac{1}{\tan \theta} = \frac{\sqrt{5}}{2}$$

$$\sec \theta = \frac{1}{\cos \theta} = -\frac{3}{\sqrt{5}}$$

$$\csc \theta = \frac{1}{\sin \theta} = -\frac{3}{2}$$

2. Find *exact* values (no decimals) of the six trigonometric functions of 45°.

Solution

Figure 2-4b shows a 45° angle in standard position. Any perpendicular from the terminal side to the horizontal axis forms a 45°-45°-90° right triangle. Thus, its legs have equal length. A convenient point to pick is $(u, v) = (1, 1)$. From the Pythagorean theorem, the hypotenuse length is

$$r = \sqrt{1^2 + 1^2} = \sqrt{2}$$

Figure 2-4b

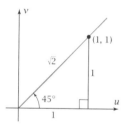

Take the positive root because r is always positive. The values of the six functions can now be written by inspection, as before.

$$\sin \theta = \frac{1}{\sqrt{2}} \qquad \cos \theta = \frac{1}{\sqrt{2}}$$

$$\tan \theta = \frac{1}{1} = 1 \qquad \cot \theta = \frac{1}{\tan \theta} = 1$$

$$\sec \theta = \frac{1}{\cos \theta} = \sqrt{2} \qquad \csc \theta = \frac{1}{\sin \theta} = \sqrt{2}$$

Problem Notes

- *Problems 1-6* are similar to Example 1.

- *Problems 7-10* are similar to Example 2.

- *Problems 11-14* ask students to use the value of one trigonometric function and the terminating quadrant for the angle to determine the value of the other trigonometric functions. These problems are similar to Additional Class Example 1.

- *Problems 15-32* are similar to Example 3. They require students to use relationships in 30°-60°-90° and 45°-45°-90° triangles to find the

function values for angles whose reference angles are multiples of 30° or 45°.

- *Problems 33 and 34* ask students to find all the angles for which the function values are 0 or 1.

- *Problems 35-42* introduce students to the notation $\sin^2 \theta$. Initially, write $\sin^2 \theta$ as $(\sin \theta)^2$ to help them understand this notation.

- *Problem 43* helps students make sense of the prefix *co-* in the cofunction trigonometric functions. In the class discussion of this problem, ask students to complete equations such as these:

  $\sin 16° = \cos \underline{\quad}°$; *Answer:* 74°

  $\tan 43° = \cot \underline{\quad}°$; *Answer:* 47°

  $\sec 36° = \underline{\quad} 54°$; *Answer:* csc

- *Problem 44*, the Pattern in Sine Values Problem, asks students to look for patterns in the exact values of sin 0°, sin 30°, sin 45°, sin 60°, and sin 90°. Some students find this pattern interesting and remember it for use in future problems.

- *Problem 45*, the Sine Wave Tracer Project, is a good exercise to build understanding of the sine function. As the point *P* rotates around the circle, students can see how the sine function relates to the unit circle.

Supplementary Problems

1. *Sketchpad Project—Ranges of Sine, Cosine, and Tangent:* On The Geometer's Sketchpad, create the figure shown in Figure 2-4c. The circle is centered at *A* and has radius *AB*. Angle *BAC* is constructed through point *C* on the circle. Point *E* is the intersection of a line through *A* and *C* and a perpendicular to segment *AB* drawn through *B*. Segment *CD* is perpendicular to segment *AB*. Display the measurements and calculations shown.

Figure 2-4c

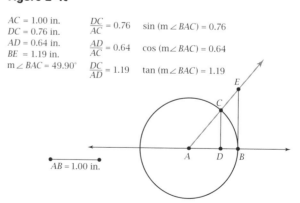

a. Move point *C* around the circle. Describe what happens to the lengths *AC*, *AD*, and *DC*. How is the behavior of segment *BE* different from that of the parallel segment *DC*?

    b. As you drag *C* around the circle, the three ratios show change and the values of sine, cosine, and tangent change. Explain the relationships you notice between the ratios and the function values.

    c. Why is tan 90° undefined?

2. Find the exact values of the six trigonometric functions if

    a. (4, −3) is on the terminal side.

    b. (−5, 7) is on the terminal side.

    c. $\sec \theta = 4$ and θ terminates in Quadrant IV.

    d. $\theta = 60°$

    e. $\theta = 135°$

    f. $\theta = 360°$

2-5
Inverse Trigonometric Functions and Triangle Problems

Objective

Given two sides of a right triangle or a side and an acute angle, find measures of the other sides and angles.

Class Time

1 day

Homework Assignment

Recommended: RA, Q1–Q10, Problems 1–5, 7, 9–11, 13, 14, 24

Also suggested: Problems 8, 21

Suggestion: Assign these problems on the day the section is covered in class. Then proceed to Chapter 3 and assign one other problem from Section 2-5 each day for a week or more.

Technology Options

 Activity: Right Triangle Trigonometry

Important Terms and Concepts

Inverse trigonometric functions

Principal branch

Mathematical-world answer

Real-world answer

Lesson Notes

Section 2-5 opens with the definition of the inverse cosine function as "an angle whose cosine is *x*." Students quickly pick up the idea of an inverse function "undoing" the original function. It is extremely important to emphasize that the notation $\cos^{-1} x$ is *not* the same as $(\cos x)^{-1}$, the reciprocal of cos *x*. This is particularly confusing because in the previous lesson the exponent 2 in $\sin^2 \theta$ was "moved" to get the equivalent expression $(\sin \theta)^2$. Explain to students that the −1 in $\cos^{-1} x$ is *not* an exponent; rather, it is a shorthand notation used to indicate an inverse function. Remind them that they saw this notation in Chapter 1, when $f^{-1}(x)$ was used to represent the inverse of $f(x)$.

At this point, the text avoids the incorrect calculator answer for $\cot^{-1}$ (*negative argument*) by not asking questions of this type. This topic is covered in Section 4-6, where properties of inverse circular functions are discussed. Because there is no cot key on the calculator, to calculate $\cot^{-1} x$ the TAN key is used. This is why for negative arguments, $\cot^{-1} x$ will incorrectly give an answer in Quadrant IV instead of in Quadrant II. The range of $\tan^{-1} x$ function is $[-90°, 90°]$, whereas the range of $\cot^{-1} x$ is $[0°, 180°]$.

The primary focus of the section is to solve for angles and/or sides of right triangles in real-world contexts. Note the difference in the text between mathematical-world answers, which are unrounded, and real-world answers, which are rounded. You may want to reread the Lesson Notes in Section 2-4 for comments on rounding issues and using answers in subsequent parts of the same problem. Note also that the solutions to the examples end with a summary statement (e.g., "The tower is about 62.8 m high."). Writing a summary statement after the mathematical equations provides students an opportunity to demonstrate that they understand what their mathematical work represents. In recent years, students have been asked to write similar statements on the AP Calculus exam.

Example 1 involves an *angle of elevation.* Several homework problems involve *angles of depression.* You may need to refresh your students' memories about what these terms mean. An angle of elevation lies above the horizontal, whereas an angle of depression lies below the horizontal. This illustration shows that an angle of elevation corresponds to a congruent angle of depression.

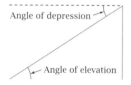

In Example 2, the phrase "at its closest point of approach" ensures that a right triangle is formed. Students should recall from geometry that the closest distance from a point to a line is the perpendicular distance. Part b can also be solved using the Pythagorean theorem. Encourage students to use a trigonometric method to solve the problem and then to check their answers with the Pythagorean theorem.

Exploration Notes

Exploration 2-5a introduces the "inverse tangent" function key on the calculator. Students need a centimeter ruler and protractor for this activity. The Exploration can be completed in 15–20 minutes.

Exploration 2-5b emphasizes that "calculate" means to find the answer with equations, using algebra and

trigonometric definitions. This Exploration can be used as a 10-minute quiz.

Exploration 2-5c works well as small-group Exploration, an example to work with the whole class, or a 15-minute quiz.

Technology Notes

 Activity: Right Triangle Trigonometry, in the *Instructor's Resource Book,* gives students practice at applying the definitions of sine, cosine, and tangent, as well as the Pythagorean theorem, to calculate forces. Some use of vectors is also involved, so you might want to delay this activity until Section 10-2. Allow 45 minutes.

Additional Class Example

This example illustrates how to find inverse trigonometric function values for a function that does not appear on the calculator.

1. Find $\csc^{-1} 3.2$.

Solution

$\theta = \csc^{-1} 3.2$ — Choose a letter to stand for the angle.

$\csc \theta = 3.2$ — Use the definition of inverse cosecant.

$\dfrac{1}{\sin \theta} = 3.2$ — Get a function that is on the calculator. Cosecant is the reciprocal of sine.

$\sin \theta = \dfrac{1}{3.2}$

Take the reciprocal of both sides of the equation.

$\theta = \sin^{-1} \dfrac{1}{3.2} = 18.2099...° \approx 18.2°$

Take the inverse sine of both sides.

Problem Notes

• *Problem 8,* the Construction Problem, gives you and your students an opportunity to use The Geometer's Sketchpad.

• *Problems 10–14* involve angles of elevation and depression.

• *Problem 24,* the Pyramid Problem, provides an opportunity for students to work in three dimensions. You may wish to have students actually build the model described in the problem.

Supplementary Problems

1. *Principal Branch of Cosine Problem:* Figure 2-5a shows the principal branch of $y = \cos \theta$ (solid) superimposed on the entire cosine graph.

Figure 2-5a

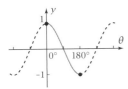

a. The principal branch of the cosine function has domain $0° \leq \theta \leq 180°$. Explain why this domain has to be different from the domain of the principal branch of the sine function shown in Figure 2-5f of the student book for the principal branch to be invertible.

b. Find $\theta = \cos^{-1}(-0.9)$. Explain why it is *not* a negative number.

2. *Construction Problem:* Draw accurately a right triangle with legs of lengths 7.4 cm and 5.8 cm. Draw on paper with a ruler and protractor or on the computer with a program such as The Geometer's Sketchpad.

a. Measure the larger acute angle correct to the nearest degree, and measure the hypotenuse correct to the nearest 0.1 cm.

b. Calculate the measure of the larger acute angle and the length of the hypotenuse using the appropriate trigonometric functions. Show that the measured and calculated angles agree within 1° and that the measured and calculated hypotenuse lengths agree within 0.1 cm.

3. *Moon Crater Problem:* Scientists estimate the heights of features on the moon by measuring the lengths of the shadows they cast on the moon's surface. From a photograph, you find that the shadow cast on the inside of a crater by its rim is 325 m long (Figure 2-5b). At the time the photograph was taken, the Sun's angle of elevation was 23.6°. How high does the rim rise above the inside of the crater? (See NASA's Web site on the Internet for pictures of the moon! Go to *www.nasa.gov.*)

Figure 2-5b

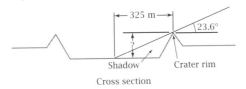

4. *Lighthouse Problem:* An observer in a lighthouse 80 ft above the surface of the water measures an angle of depression of 0.7° to a distant ship (Figure 2-5c). How many miles is the ship from the base of the lighthouse? (A mile is 5280 ft.)

Figure 2-5c

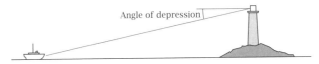

5. *Guy Wire Problem:* A television transmission tower 2000 ft high is supported by guy wires running from the ground to the top. The wires make an angle of 63° with the ground (Figure 2-5d).

Figure 2-5d

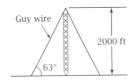

a. How long is each wire?

b. How far from the base of the tower are the wires anchored to the ground?

6. *Volcano Problem:* Haleakela (pronounced "hallay-ah-keh-la") is a 10,000-ft-high dormant volcano on Maui, Hawaii (Figure 2-5e). The horizontal distance from the peak of the volcano to the ocean is about 30,000 ft.

Figure 2-5e

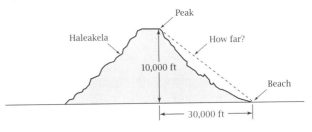

a. At what angle would you have to look up to see the peak if you were standing on the beach?

b. What is the straight-line distance from the beach to the peak?

7. *Cable Car Problem:* As Wendy Upmore waited for a cable car in the 600 block of Powell Street in San Francisco, she decided to figure out what angle the steep street makes with the horizontal. On a nearby wall, she measured horizontal and vertical distances of 33 cm and 5 cm, respectively (Figure 2-5f).

Figure 2-5f

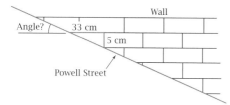

a. What angle does Powell Street make with the horizontal?

b. While she waited, Wendy walked to the top of the block, counting 101 paces. Being tall, she figured that each pace is 1 m long. How many meters did she go vertically?

c. If Powell Street were level instead of slanted, how many paces would Wendy have to go to walk the 600 block of Powell Street? Does the answer surprise you?

8. *Rocket Problem:* An observer 5.2 km from the launch pad observes a rocket ascending (Figure 2-5g).

Figure 2-5g

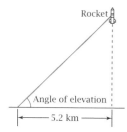

a. At a particular time, the angle of elevation is 31.45°. How high is the rocket? How far is it from the observer?

b. Assuming that the rocket continues to travel straight up, what will be the angle of elevation when the missile reaches an altitude of 30 km?

2-6
Chapter Review and Test

Objective

Review and practice major concepts of this chapter.

Class Time

2 days (including 1 day for testing)

Homework Assignment

Day 1: R0–R5, T18–T20

Day 2 (after Chapter 2 Test): Problems C1 and C3 *or* Problem Set 3-1

Important Terms and Concepts

Cycle of a sinusoidal function

Slope

Lesson Notes

Section 2-6 contains a set of Review Problems, a set of Concept Problems, and a Chapter Test. The Review Problems include one problem for each section in the chapter. You may wish to use the Chapter Test either as an additional set of review problems or as homework for the test.

Encourage students to practice the no-calculator problems without a calculator so that they are prepared for the test problems for which they cannot use a calculator.

Problem Notes

• *Problem C1,* the Tide Problem, prepares students for Chapter 3. This works well as a group problem.

• *Problem C3* prepares students for Chapter 4. All students should be able to complete this problem individually.

• *Problem C4* prepares students for calculus and will probably be a challenge even for your best students.

Supplementary Problems

Discuss Additional Class Example 1 in Section 2-5 for these supplementary questions.

For Problems 1–3, use your calculator to find

1. $\sec^{-1} 2.5$ 2. $\cot^{-1} 0.2$ 3. $\csc^{-1} 10$

3 Applications of Trigonometric and Circular Functions

In this chapter students put together what they have learned about periodic functions in Chapter 2 and transformations in Chapter 1 to sketch a graph of any sinusoid from its equation. The terms *concavity* and *point of inflection* are introduced in Section 3-2, preparing students for their use later in the text and in calculus. By reversing the graph-sketch process, students learn to write an equation of a sinusoid with any given period, amplitude, phase displacement, or vertical position. Thus, they can use sinusoidal functions as mathematical models of periodic functions in the real world. The introduction of circular functions with arguments in radians (which have no inherent units) makes the functions more reasonable in applications where the independent variable is time or distance rather than angle. Students learn that arccosine has multiple values as they find values of x for a given value of y. A side trip in Section 3-3 shows students tangent and secant graphs, including application to a beam cast by a rotating lighthouse beacon. In Section 3-8, students apply their knowledge of angles and circular functions to find angular and linear velocities in rotary motion.

3-1
Sinusoids: Amplitude, Period, and Cycles

Objective

Learn the meanings of *amplitude, period, phase displacement,* and *cycle of a sinusoidal graph.*

Class Time

$\frac{1}{2}$ day

Homework Assignment

Recommended: Problems 1–9

Suggested: See *Instructor's Guide,* Section 3-2, on photographs or computer images of sinusoidal curves.

Technology Options

 Exploration 3-1a: Periodic Daily Temperatures

Important Terms and Concepts

Cycle

Amplitude

Period

Argument

Phase displacement

Sinusoidal axis

Lesson Notes

Section 3-1 is an exploratory activity in which students investigate how the amplitude, period, phase displacement, vertical translation, and cycle of a sinusoidal graph are related to transformations of the parent sinusoid. You can assign Section 3-1 for homework the night of the Chapter 2 test or as a group activity to be completed in class. No classroom discussion is needed before students begin the activity. Students should be able to complete the problems "by hand" and then verify the answers with their graphers. After they have completed Section 3-1, have students work in groups on Exploration 3-1a.

Exploration Notes

Exploration 3-1a previews both the sinusoidal graph transformations in Section 3-2 and the real-world problems in Section 3-7. It is one of the most important explorations in Chapter 3, for these reasons:

- Plotting points using pencil and paper helps students internalize the pattern of sinusoidal graphs.

- The use of real-world data demonstrates that sinusoidal graphs are relevant and useful, providing motivation for students to learn about them.

Have students work through the exploration in groups after completing Section 3-1. Allow about 30–35 minutes for all seven questions. Problem 1 asks students what they should plot for month 0. Be sure to discuss this question in class. Some students will not realize that month 0 is December of the preceding year because they do not yet truly understand the term *periodic.* You may need to help groups with Problems 5 and 6. Problem 7 asks students to make scatter plots on their graphers. If your students do not know how to do this, either do Problem 7 with the whole class or omit it.

Exploration 3-1b requires students to plot the sine and cosine graphs on graph paper. Problem 4 of the exploration requires students to find values of inverse trigonometric functions. You may wish to use this exploration as a quiz after Section 3-2 instead of using it with Section 3-1.

Technology Notes

 Exploration 3-1a: Periodic Daily Temperatures, in the *Instructor's Resource Book,* asks students to transform a cosine graph to fit data on the average daily temperature for a city. This can be done easily with sliders in Fathom.

3-2
General Sinusoidal Graphs

Objective

Given any one of these sets of information about a sinusoid, find the other two.

- The equation
- The graph
- The amplitude, period or frequency, phase displacement, and sinusoidal axis

Class Time

2 days

Homework Assignment

Day 1

RA, Q1–Q10, Problems 1–11 odd. As mentioned earlier, you might want to assign some application problems throughout Chapter 3. You'll find some among the Supplementary Problems in Section 2-5. Use Supplementary Problem 4 of Section 2-5.

Day 2

Recommended: Problems 1–5, 13–25 odd, 26, 28, Supplementary Problem 7 of Section 2-5

Also suggested: Problem 27

Technology Options

 Activity: Jupiter's Moons

 Activity: Adaptable options

Important Terms and Concepts

Period

Frequency

General sinusoidal equation

Concave

Convex

Point of inflection

Upper bound

Lower bound

Critical points

Lesson Notes

Section 3-2 investigates equations of sinusoids, using the concepts of horizontal and vertical

dilations and translations studied in the previous chapters. Students learn to write an equation for a sinusoidal function given an entire cycle of the graph, part of a cycle of the graph, or a verbal description of the graph. They also learn to write more than one equation for the same graph by using different phase displacements, negative dilations, and sine as well as cosine.

It is recommended that you spend two days on this section. On the first day, discuss the material up through Example 2 and assign Exploration 3-2a. Cover the remainder of the section on the second day, possibly using Exploration 3-2b. Example 4 involves writing different equations for the same sinusoid. If your class is not very strong, you may omit this example, along with Problems 23 and 24. However, encourage your best students to work through these items.

When you assign homework for this section, be sure to include problems that require students to write equations for sinusoids. Such problems prepare students for the real-world problems in Section 3-7. If a problem does not indicate which parent function to use, encourage students to write the equation using the cosine function. Because cosine starts a cycle at a high point, it is easier to get the correct phase displacement. It is also easier to find the general solution of an inverse cosine equation than of an inverse sine equation, so students will find the real-world problems in future lessons easier to solve if they use the cosine function.

Use the new vocabulary introduced in Section 3-2 frequently and correctly. *Concavity, point of inflection, upper bound,* and *lower bound* are all terms students will use in calculus.

This section introduces the idea of *frequency,* which is used to describe many real-world phenomena. The book *Mathematics: An Introduction to Its Spirit and Use,* published by *Scientific American* in 1979, shows the frequencies of the sounds of several musical instruments, the human voice, and the jangle of keys.

It is most important that students understand the effects of the constants *A, B, C,* and *D* on the graphs of $y = C + A \cos B(\theta - D)$ and $y = C + A \sin B(\theta - D)$. Students usually have the most difficulty understanding the effect of the constant *B.* It is helpful to point out that $|B| = \frac{360°}{period}$.

Emphasize that the distance between a critical point and the next point of inflection is a quarter of a cycle, or $\frac{period}{4}$. This fact is useful for Example 3 and Problems 15–18.

From their earlier work with the parent cosine and sine functions, students should know that the cosine function starts a cycle at a high point, whereas the sine function starts a cycle on the sinusoidal axis going up. Stress that a sine function starts on its sinusoidal axis, not on the horizontal axis of the coordinate plane. Students often misunderstand this distinction because the sinusoidal axis of the parent sine graph coincides with the horizontal axis of the coordinate plane. Another error students make is marking a critical point or point of inflection on the y-axis for *every* sinusoidal graph. Emphasize that students must think about both the phase displacement and the period when marking critical points and inflection points.

To prepare students for Problems 5–8, you might ask them to evaluate the function in Example 2 for $\theta = 595°$. Show students how to find y numerically by using the table feature on their graphers and algebraically by using function notation.

$$f(\theta) = 9 + 47 \cos 18 (\theta - 3°)$$

$$f(595°) = 9 + 47 \cos 18 (595° - 3°)$$

$$f(595°) = -19.936089...$$

In Example 4, students use graphers to confirm that all four equations give the same graph. If their graphers allow it, have students use different line styles for each graph. Some graphing calculators can be set to display a circle that follows the path created by the graph. Using this feature allows students to see that each subsequent graph retraces the preceding graphs.

Ask students to identify the domain and range of the functions in Examples 1–4. Emphasize that the domain is "all real numbers *of degrees*." Specifying *degrees* is important because real numbers without degrees are assumed to be radians.

	Domain	Range
Example 1	θ = all real numbers of degrees	$-12 \le y \le 2$
Example 2	θ = all real numbers of degrees	$-38 \le y \le 56$
Examples 3 and 4	θ = all real numbers of degrees	$3 \le y \le 13$

As an interesting assignment, you might ask each student to find a photograph or a computer image of a sinusoidal curve and write a reasonable equation for the curve. Encourage students to find out what might be reasonable units for their photos. If you show a few examples in class, students will see that such curves are common and will be able to find examples on their own. Create a bulletin board of the photos and equations students find. You may want to give this assignment the day you begin

Chapter 3, but schedule its due date for *after* you finish Section 3-7. As students study each new section, they will get better ideas for possible pictures of sinusoids. This will also bring up the need for a nondegree angle measure.

Examples of naturally occurring sinusoids abound. Aerial photos of rivers and the crests of desert sand dunes form sinusoidal curves. Each monthly issue of the magazine *Astronomy* contains a colorful page spread of the sinusoidal path of the moon. In addition, each month the sinusoidal paths of four of Jupiter's moons—Io, Callisto, Europa, and Ganymede—are shown. The book *Mathematics: An Introduction to Its Spirit and Use* has photographs of musical notes recorded by an oscilloscope. The fundamental harmonic has one cycle; the second harmonic has two cycles; the third harmonic has three cycles; and the fourth harmonic has four cycles. The December 1996 issue of *National Geographic* shows places on Earth photographed during 30 years of space flights and also shows the path of a typical spacecraft. Distinctive sinusoidal paths are visible in these photographs.

Exploration Notes

Exploration 3-2a gives students practice in graphing particular cosine and sine equations; identifying period, amplitude, and other characteristics; writing an equation from a given graph; checking their work using a grapher; and finding a y-value given an angle value. Assign this Exploration as a group activity *after* you have presented and discussed Examples 1 and 2. This gives students supervised practice with the ideas presented in the examples before they leave class. Students may need help with Problem 5, which asks them to find y when $\theta = 35°$. Allow 20–30 minutes for the Exploration.

Exploration 3-2b can be assigned as a quiz or as extra homework practice. It can also be assigned later in the year as a review of sinusoids. Problem 1 of the Exploration asks students to sketch two cycles of a given sinusoid. Problems 2 and 3 ask them to write two equations—one using sine and one using cosine—for the same sinusoid and then to check their equations using their graphers. Problems 5 and 6 give students practice writing equations based on a half-cycle or quarter-cycle of a sinusoid. Allow 20 minutes for the entire Exploration or 8–10 minutes for just Problems 5 and 6.

Technology Notes

 Activity: Jupiter's Moons, in *Teaching Mathematics with Fathom,* provides the translation of a sinusoid, though without using the term *sinusoid.* Referring to a data file, students who have prior experience with Fathom can vary the period, phase, and amplitude of a periodic function to model data of the orbits of Jupiter's four largest moons. It takes about 30–45 minutes. Alternately, this activity might be used in Section 3-7.

 Activity: Adaptable options. See Section 3-5 for radian-based activities that could be adapted for use here.

Problem Notes

- *Problems 1–4* should all be assigned so students get sufficient practice in graphing transformed sinusoids.

- *Problems 5–8* are important not only because students must create equations for given graphs but also because they must find *y*-values for given angle values. This is an excellent preview of Section 3-7, in which students use sinusoidal equations to predict results in real-world problems. Be sure to discuss finding the *y*-values during the class discussion of the homework. A blackline master for these problems is available in the *Instructor's Resource Book.*

- *Problems 9–18* provide practice in writing equations from graphs that show complete cycles or parts of cycles. This is another critical skill required to solve the real-world problems in Section 3-7. A blackline master for these problems is available in the *Instructor's Resource Book.*

- *Problems 13 and 14* use different variables to name the horizontal and vertical axes. When you discuss homework, make sure students have used the correct variables and not just the usual variables *y* and *θ*.

- *Problems 19 and 20* require students to find *y*-values corresponding to given angle values.

- *Problems 21 and 22* require students to write equations for sinusoids based on verbal descriptions.

- *Problems 23 and 24* ask students to write four possible equations for each graph by using both positive and negative dilations of both sine and cosine equations. These problems will challenge your best students. A blackline master for these problems is available in the *Instructor's Resource Book.*

- *Problem 25,* the Frequency Problem, gives students practice determining frequency.

- *Problem 26,* the Inflection Point Problem, reinforces the ideas of *inflection point, concave up,* and *concave down.* These ideas are very important in the study of calculus. Be sure to assign this problem.

- *Problem 27,* the Horizontal vs. Vertical Transformations Problem, provides practice in transforming a given equation to another form by using algebra. The final form of the equation helps students see that horizontal and vertical transformations follow the same rules.

- *Problem 28* is a journal entry that gives students practice with the vocabulary in Section 3-2. You might tell the class that you will randomly choose five students to read their journal entries to the class.

3-3

Graphs of Tangent, Cotangent, Secant, and Cosecant Functions

Objective

Plot the graphs of the tangent, cotangent, secant, and cosecant functions, showing their behavior when the function value is undefined.

Class Time

1 day

Homework Assignment

Recommended: RA, Q10, Problems 1–3, 5–6, 9, 11–14

Also suggested: Problems 15, 16

Technology Options

 Problem 16: Dynamic Variation of Tangent and Secant

 Presentation Sketch: Trig Tracers Present.gsp

 Exploration 3-3a: Tangent and Secant Graphs

Important Terms and Concepts

Unit circle

Vertical asymptote

Discontinuous

Quotient properties for tangent and cotangent

Lesson Notes

Section 3-3 introduces the graphs of the tangent, cotangent, secant, and cosecant functions. If you prefer, you can wait until after Section 3-7 to cover this section because the topics in Section 3-4 through Section 3-7 do not depend on the graphs of these four functions. If you do reorder the sections, do not assign any Review or Quick Review problems that involve the graphs of the tangent, cotangent, secant, or cosecant functions. Another important outcome of this section is introducing the quotient properties to students before they see them in Chapter 4.

The graphs of the tangent, cotangent, secant, and cosecant functions are shown near the beginning of the section. When working with functions that have vertical asymptotes, it can be helpful to use a friendly window where the horizontal range is a decimal multiple of 94. Also, the θ-min should be a multiple of 90°. For example, the graphs of $y = \tan \theta$

and $y = \sec \theta$ could have a θ window $-270° \le \theta \le 670°$. Note that $\theta_{\max} - \theta_{\min} = 670 - (-270) = 10 \cdot 94$, so each pixel move represents a change of 10° in θ. This can be helpful in tracing the graph of the function. The Lesson Notes for Section 1-3 contain more information on friendly graphing windows.

The graphs in Figures 3-3a and 3-3b can be replicated on a grapher with viewing ranges $-360° \le \theta \le 630°$, $-6 \le y \le 6$ for $y = \tan \theta$ and $y = \sec \theta$, and $-180° \le \theta \le 720°$, $-6 \le y \le 6$ for $y = \cot \theta$ and $y = \csc \theta$. All four graphs have θ-scale 90 and y-scale 1. Before giving students the window dimensions, encourage them to explore the domain and range of functions in order to find appropriate viewing windows. Make sure their graphers are set in degree mode for this section. Notice that these are not friendly windows, as mentioned earlier. As a result, students with older graphers (such as TI-82 and TI-83) will see that the top of one section of a graph is connected to the bottom of the next section, where there should be an asymptote. This can be partially remedied by pressing the MODE button and selecting DOT rather than CONNECTED, or it can be fully remedied by using a friendly graphing window, as earlier.

In the examples, Explorations, and problems, students learn how to sketch these graphs by relating them to the sine and cosine graphs. For example, because $\sec \theta = \frac{1}{\cos \theta}$, the graph of $y = \sec \theta$ is undefined where $\cos \theta = 0$, has value 1 where $\cos \theta = 1$, and has value -1 where $\cos \theta = -1$. When you present the secant graph, sketch a graph of the cosine function and show that the secant graph "bounces off" the high and low points of the cosine graph because secant is the reciprocal of cosine. Similarly, because cosecant is the reciprocal of sine, the cosecant graph "bounces off" the high and low points of the sine graph.

You might begin the instruction for this section by working through Problems 1–7 of Exploration 3-3a as a whole class. Then have students complete the Exploration in small groups. After students have finished, discuss Problem 7 from the textbook so students understand why the period of the tangent and cotangent functions is 180° rather than 360°. Students may need to be reminded of this fact throughout the year.

Next, discuss Problem 9, which asks students to find the domain of $y = \sec \theta$. Have students list several angle values at which there are asymptotes. Eventually someone should point out that the asymptotes appear 180° apart and will attempt to state the domain. Once the domain is given, have students examine the graphs of the tangent, cotangent, and cosecant functions. Point out the general pattern where θ is undefined in the domain: θ = (location of 1st asymptote) + (distance between asymptotes) · *n*, where *n* is an integer.

Summarize the lesson with the chart below.

Exploration Notes

Exploration 3-3a is a good whole-class activity. You can begin the instruction for Section 3-3 by guiding students through Problems 1–7 of the Exploration. Then have students work in groups of two or three on the remaining problems. Allow 30 minutes for the exploration.

Exploration 3-3b requires students to graph tangent and cosecant equations and to write tangent and secant equations for graphs. You may want to assign this Exploration as additional homework practice if you do not have time to use it in class.

Technology Notes

 Problem 16: The Variation of Tangent and Secant Problem asks students to explore the behaviors of the six trigonometric functions as the angle of measurement varies. They may create their own sketch using Sketchpad, or they may use the Dynamic Precalculus Exploration at *www.keymath.com/precalc.*

 Presentation Sketch: Trig Tracers Present.gsp is a presentation sketch that traces out the graphs of the six trigonometric functions as a point is animated on a unit circle.

 Exploration 3-3a: Tangent and Secant Graphs has students discover what the graphs of tangent and secant look like and how they relate to the graphs of sine and cosine. The better resolution available in Fathom may be useful for the parts where they are asked to use a grapher. Sketchpad could also be employed here.

Problem Notes

- *Problems 1–4* reinforce the work done in Exploration 3-3a.

- *Problems 5–10* provide the practice necessary for students to *learn* the graphs.

- *Problems 11–14* require students to consider transformations of the parent tangent, cotangent, secant, and cosecant graphs. The instructions ask students to make the graphs on their graphers, but the equations in Problems 13 and 14 can also be sketched by hand using the technique demonstrated in Example 1. For example, to sketch the equation in Problem 13, replace the sec in the equation with cos and sketch the graph of the resulting equation. Then draw asymptotes where the sinusoid crosses its sinusoidal axis, draw the upward branch of the secant function where the sinusoid reaches its maximum value, and draw the downward branch of the secant function where the sinusoid reaches its minimum value.

- *Problem 15,* the Rotating Lighthouse Beacon Problem, may cause some students difficulty. You may want to solve this as a whole-class activity rather than assigning it as homework. Because future problems do not rely on this problem, it can be omitted. Supplementary Problem 2 extends this problem to include a secant graph. Point out to students that you are distinguishing between the two light beams and keeping track of which one is pointing in the positive direction and which one is pointing in the negative direction as it rotates. The terminal side of θ is the positive direction. Thus, as the beacon rotates past $90°$, L becomes negative because it is the negatively oriented beam of light that hits the shore.

Supplementary Problems

1. *Division by Zero Problem:* The tangent function has vertical asymptotes at regular intervals.

Function	Period	Domain	Range
$y = \tan \theta$	180°	θ = all real numbers of degrees except $\theta = 90° + 180°n$, where *n* is an integer	y = all real numbers
$y = \cot \theta$	180°	θ = all real numbers of degrees except $\theta = 180°n$, where *n* is an integer	y = all real numbers
$y = \sec \theta$	360°	θ = all real numbers of degrees except $\theta = 90° + 180°n$, where *n* is an integer	$y \geq 1$ or $y \leq -1$
$y = \csc \theta$	360°	θ = all real numbers of degrees except $\theta = 180°n$, where *n* is an integer	$y \geq 1$ or $y \leq -1$

These asymptotes mark places where the graph is **discontinuous** because the tangent is undefined. Figure 3-3a shows why tan 90° is undefined.

Figure 3-3a

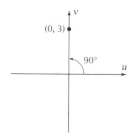

If $(u, v) = (0, 3)$ is a point on the terminal side of a 90° angle, then

$$\tan 90° = \frac{\text{horizontal coordinate}}{\text{vertical coordinate}} = \frac{3}{0}$$

Undefined because of division by zero.

In this problem you will investigate two different things that can happen to a fraction as its denominator gets closer and closer to zero.

a. Consider the algebraic fraction $\frac{3}{x}$. Evaluate this fraction for $x = 0.1$, $x = 0.01$, and $x = 0.001$. Evaluate it again for $x = -0.1$, $x = -0.01$, and $x = -0.001$. Why is the fraction undefined if $x = 0$? Why can it be said that a fraction becomes **infinite** if its denominator goes to zero but its numerator is not zero? Why is it *not* correct to say that this fraction *equals* infinity if the denominator equals zero?

b. Consider the algebraic fraction $\frac{5x}{x}$. Evaluate this fraction for $x = 0.1$, $x = 0.01$, and $x = 0.001$. Evaluate it again for $x = -0.1$, $x = -0.01$, and $x = -0.001$. Why is the fraction undefined if $x = 0$? Why is it *not* correct to say that this fraction becomes infinite if its denominator goes to zero and the numerator also goes to zero?

c. Figure 3-3b shows the function $f(x) = \frac{5x}{x}$. The graph has a **removable discontinuity** at $x = 0$. Although $f(0)$ involves division by zero, the discontinuity can be "removed" by "canceling" the x's first. Explain why the discontinuities in the tangent function graph are vertical asymptotes rather than removable discontinuities.

Figure 3-3b

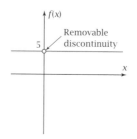

2. *Rotating Lighthouse Beacon Problem Extension:* Refer to Problem 15 and the accompanying diagram in the text. Let L be the directed distance of the light beam shown at angle θ from the lighthouse to the spot on the shore. (The other light beam is represented by negative values of L.)

f. Write an equation involving L and θ, and graph it with the same graphing range as in part a.

g. Explain why L is negative for $90° < \theta < 270°$.

h. Explain the physical significance of the asymptotes in the graph.

3-4
Radian Measure of Angles

Objectives

- Given an angle measure in degrees, convert it to radians, and vice versa.

- Given an angle measure in radians, find trigonometric function values.

Class Time

1 day

Homework Assignment

RA, Q1–Q10, Problems 1–3, 9, 11, 17, 21, 25, 29, 31, 37, 39, 41, 43, 45, 47, 49, 51, 53

Technology Options

 Presentation Sketch: Radians Present.gsp

Activity: Introduction to Radians

Important Terms and Concepts

Radian

Unit circle

Subtends

Unitless number

Dimensional analysis

Wrapping function

Arc length

Lesson Notes

Section 3-4 introduces radian measures for angles. Measuring angles in radians makes it possible to apply trigonometric functions to real-life units of measure, such as time, that can be represented on the number line. Try to do at least one of the explorations for Section 3-4 so that students will *understand* that a radian is really the *arc length* of a circle (with a radius of one unit).

The Explorations also help students understand the relationship between radians and degrees. If they do not complete one of these activities, students may simply memorize how to convert from degrees to radians without understanding how the units are related.

Explain that degrees and radians are two units for measuring angles, just as feet and meters are two units for measuring length. An angle measuring

30 radians is *not* the same size as an angle measuring 30 degrees (just as a length of 30 meters is not equal to a length of 30 feet) because the units are different.

The relationship between radians and degrees can be used to convert measurements from one unit to the other. Because π radians is equivalent to 180 degrees, the conversion factor is $\frac{\pi \text{ radians}}{180 \text{ degrees}}$, a form of 1. Students should see that multiplying a number of degrees by this factor causes the degrees to cancel out, leaving a number of radians.

$$\frac{30 \text{ degrees}}{1} \cdot \frac{\pi \text{ radians}}{180 \text{ degrees}} = \frac{1}{6}\pi \text{ radians}$$

Similarly, multiplying a number of radians by $\frac{180 \text{ degrees}}{\pi \text{ radians}}$, another form of 1, lets the radians cancel, leaving a number of degrees. If the units don't cancel, the student has the conversion factor upside down.

Another way to make sure students can visualize a radian is to have each student hold up her or his hands, heel-to-heel, to form a 1-radian angle. A radian is about 57 degrees. If the angle is much too big or too small, you can correct them quickly.

To help students develop a good understanding of radians, draw a large circle and mark several exact radian measures, including both integers and multiples of π. On the same circle, show the decimal approximations for some of the radian measures, especially $\frac{\pi}{2}$, π, $\frac{3\pi}{2}$, and 2π. Knowing decimal approximations for multiples of $\frac{\pi}{2}$ allows students to determine which quadrant an angle given in radians falls in. This helps students understand why expressions like cos 3.487 and sin 5.9 represent negative quantities. If you gave students a Trigonometric Ratios Table in Chapter 2, have them complete it by filling in the Radians column.

Exploration Notes

Exploration 3-4a is an excellent activity for groups of two or three students. It gives each student an opportunity to measure radians on a circle. If you have time for only one Exploration, do Exploration 3-4a. Show students how to hold the index card on its edge and bend it to follow the curve of the circle. Allow about 10–15 minutes for this activity.

Exploration 3-4b can be completed as a whole-class activity. Problem 5 requires a protractor. It is important because it gives students an estimate of the number of degrees in 1 radian. Allow about 20–25 minutes for this Exploration.

Technology Notes

 Presentation Sketch: Radians Present.gsp, on the *Instructor's Resource CD,* allows you to animate a point along the radius of a circle to demonstrate the size of a one-radian angle measure. The sketch on the second page allows the point to animate all the way around the circle and visually demonstrates the approximate number of radians in 360° as well as the approximation $\pi \approx \frac{22}{7}$.

 Activity: Introduction to Radians, in *Exploring Precalculus with The Geometer's Sketchpad,* helps students learn about radian measurement. Allow 20–30 minutes.

Problem Notes

- *Problem 1,* the Wrapping Function Problem, introduces the next section and reinforces the ideas in Exploration 3-4a. Be sure to assign this problem.

- *Problem 2,* the Arc Length and Angle Problem, develops the general formula for finding the length of an arc given the angle measure and the radius of the circle. Be sure to assign this problem and review it in the homework discussion.

- *Problems 3–10* provide skill practice in converting from degrees to *exact* radians.

- *Problems 11–14* provide skill practice in converting from degrees to *approximate* decimal forms of radians.

- *Problems 15–24* provide skill practice in converting from radians to *exact* degree measures.

- *Problems 25–30* provide skill practice in converting from radians to *approximate* decimal forms of degrees.

- *Problems 31–34* provide skill practice in finding *approximate* function values of angles in radians. Remind students to use the radian mode on their calculators.

- *Problems 35–38* require students to find an angle in radians given a *y*-value. Remind students to use radian mode on their calculators and that $\sin^{-1} 0.3$ doesn't mean $\frac{1}{\sin 0.3}$. Discuss how students can find $\cot^{-1}$ and $\csc^{-1}$ on the calculator using the $\tan^{-1}$ and $\sin^{-1}$ keys.

- *Problems 39–48* provide skill practice in finding the *exact* function values for special angles in radians. Problems 46–48 are examples of trigonometric properties students will study in Chapter 4.

- *Problems 49–54* review concepts from previous chapters. A blackline master for Problems 49 and 50 is available in the *Instructor's Resource Book.*

3-5
Circular Functions

Objective

Learn about the circular functions and their relationship to trigonometric functions.

Class Time

1 day

Homework Assignment

Recommended: RA, Q1–Q10, Problems 1–3, 6, 7, 10, 11, 14, 15, 19, 23, 25, 27, 31, 37, 39, 44, 49

Also suggested: Problems 45, 46, 48

Technology Options

 Problem 45: Sinusoid Translation Problem

 Problem 46: Sinusoid Dilation Problem

 Problem 48: The Inequality $\sin x < x < \tan x$ Problem

 Presentation Sketch: Circular Functions Present.gsp

 Presentation Sketch: Circular Transforms Present.gsp

 Presentation Sketch: Sine Challenge Present.gsp

 Exploration 3-5a: Circular Function Parent Graphs

 Activity: Trigonometry Tracers

 Activity: Transformations of Circular Functions

Activity: Six Circular Functions

Important Terms and Concepts

Circular functions

Standard position

Lesson Notes

Section 3-5 introduces *circular functions.* Circular functions are identical to trigonometric functions except that their arguments are real numbers without units rather than degrees. The radian, introduced in the previous section, provides the link between trigonometric functions and circular functions.

For Example 2 and the homework problems, you may need to remind students that the period for the parent tangent graph and the parent cotangent graph is π, not 2π.

Summarize the lesson with this chart to help students learn the clues (words and symbols) that determine whether degree or radian mode should be used.

	Degrees	Radians
Phrase	Trigonometric	Circular
Variable	θ	x
Symbol	$^\circ$	None (π)

Note: Although there is no symbol for radians—π is a number without any units—students can use it as a clue for radians.

Exploration Notes

Exploration 3-5a requires students to investigate graphs of parent trigonometric and circular functions. Problems 1–3 ask students to sketch the parent sine, cosine, and tangent graphs from 0° through 720°. Problems 4–6 have students graph the same three functions in radian mode. Problem 7 asks students to relate the periods of the graphs to degrees and radians. Problem 8 asks students to write an equation for a given sinusoid (same as in Example 2 in the student book). You can use this Exploration to introduce the section or as a quiz after the section is completed. If you use it as an introduction, allow 25 minutes. If you use it as a quiz, allow less time and consider asking students to do their work without their graphers.

Technology Notes

 Problem 45: The Sinusoid Translation Problem asks students to explore translations of sine and cosine graphs with the help of the Dynamic Precalculus Exploration at *www.keymath.com/precalc.*

 Problem 46: The Sinusoid Dilation Problem asks students to explore, with the help of the Dynamic Precalculus Exploration at *www.keymath.com/precalc,* dilations of the sine graph and the effects the dilations have on the period of the graph.

 Problem 48: The Inequality $\sin x < x < \tan x$ Problem asks students to explore the inequality $\sin x < x < \tan x$ with the help of an interactive sketch in the Dynamic Precalculus Exploration at *www.keymath.com/precalc.*

 Presentation Sketch: Circular Functions Present.gsp, on the *Instructor's Resource CD,*

demonstrates all six trigonometric functions as lengths of certain legs of a triangle constructed around the unit circle. This sketch could serve as an introduction to the later activity Six Circular Functions, in which students are asked to construct these triangles themselves.

 Presentation Sketch: Circular Transforms Present.gsp, on the *Instructor's Resource CD,* animates a point on the unit circle to show the graphs of sine, cosine, and tangent as well as a horizontal dilation of these three graphs. This could serve as an introduction to the activity Transformations of Circular Functions.

 Presentation Sketch: Sine Challenge Present.gsp, on the *Instructor's Resource CD,* plots a point and asks for a dilation of the sine function that passes through the point. You may wish to have students experiment with the sketch on their own.

 Exploration 3-5a: Circular Function Parent Graphs, in the *Instructor's Resource Book,* can be enhanced by using Sketchpad. Students can graph in either radians or degrees by changing the Preferences in the Edit menu.

 Activity: Trigonometry Tracers, in the *Instructor's Resource Book,* guides students through a Sketchpad construction of the graphs of sine, cosine, and tangent based on the coordinates of a point on a unit circle. Allow 30 minutes.

 Activity: Transformations of Circular Functions, in the *Instructor's Resource Book,* has students start with a base sketch and build it up to be similar to the presentation sketch Circular Transforms Present.gsp, mentioned earlier. It is an extended activity emphasizing the effect on period and amplitude of dilations of the sine and cosine graphs. Allow 45 minutes.

 Activity: Six Circular Functions, in *Exploring Precalculus with The Geometer's Sketchpad,* has students construct a diagram, based on the unit circle, that contains segments of lengths equal to the six trigonometric functions. Allow 35–50 minutes.

Problem Notes

- *Problems 1–24* review ideas from Section 3-4. Problems 9–12 check that students understand that on a unit circle the length of an arc is equal to the radian measure of the corresponding angle.

Students are often puzzled by these problems because they seem too simple. Do not provide an example for Problems 9–12. Allow students to think the problems through.

- *Problems 25–32* provide practice in graphing a circular function given its equation. Watch for students who use 2π instead of π as the period of the parent tangent and cotangent graphs.

- *Problems 33–42* require students to write the equation of a circular function given its graph. Problems 41 and 42 provide only a portion of one cycle.

- *Problems 43 and 44* prepare students for the next section. Definitely assign one of these problems.

- *Problem 46* has students investigate horizontal stretches of sinusoids using a Dynamic Precalculus Exploration at *www.keymath.com/ precalc*. Students should already feel comfortable with these transformations, but this problem gives them an opportunity to examine them from a different perspective.

- *Problem 47,* The Circular Function Comprehension Problem, is a good journal problem.

- *Problem 48,* The Inequality sin $x < x <$ tan x Problem, makes an excellent group activity. Sin x is the length of the vertical segment v, and tan x is the length of the vertical segment if the radius is extended to a point $(1, \tan x)$.

Supplementary Problem

1. *Sinusoid Reflection Problem:* Figure 3-5a shows the graph of $y = \sin x$. In this problem you will reflect it and translate it in various ways.

Figure 3-5a

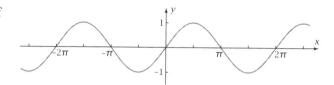

a. Recall from Chapter 1 that the graph of $f(-x)$ is a reflection of the graph of f across the y-axis. Use this fact to sketch the graph of $y = \sin(-x)$.

b. Also recall that the graph of $-f$ is a reflection of the graph of f across the x-axis. Use this fact to sketch the graph of $y = -\sin x$. How does the result compare to part a?

c. Show numerically that sin $(-1) = -\sin 1$. How does this result confirm what you observed graphically in part b?

d. Graph $y = \sin(\pi - x)$ or $y = \sin(-x + \pi)$. What transformations were applied to the sine function? What image function results from these two transformations? Confirm your answer numerically by letting $x = 1$.

e. Sketch an angle of 1 radian and an angle of $\pi - 1$ radian in a uv-diagram. Use the sketch to explain why sin $x = \sin(\pi - x)$.

3-6

Inverse Circular Relations: Given y, Find x

Objective

Given the equation of a circular function or trigonometric function and a particular value of y, find specified values of x or θ:

- Graphically
- Numerically
- Algebraically

Class Time

1 day

Homework Assignment

RA, Q1–Q10, Problems 1–13 odd

Technology Options

 Exploration 3-6a: Sinusoids, Given y, Find x Numerically

Important Terms and Concepts

Inverse cosine function

Inverse cosine relation

Arccosine

Arccos

General solution

Principal value

Inverse circular function

Lesson Notes

Section 3-6 introduces students to the inverse cosine relation, or arccosine, and discusses the general solution for the arccosine of a number. This section is critical for understanding how to solve equations involving circular functions and must not be omitted. The real-world problems in Section 3-7 require the skills learned in this section.

To introduce this section numerically, have students find the following cosine values (radian mode).

1. $\cos \dfrac{\pi}{3} = $ —?—   Answer: 0.5

2. $\cos \dfrac{2\pi}{3} = $ —?—   Answer: 0.5

3. $\cos \dfrac{7\pi}{3} = $ —?—   Answer: 0.5

4. $\cos \dfrac{8\pi}{3} = $ —?—   Answer: 0.5

Then have them press the inverse cosine *function*, $\cos^{-1} 0.5$. The answer is the single value 1.0471..., which equals only $\frac{\pi}{3}$. The inverse cosine *relation,* arccos 0.5, has an *infinite* number of values, including all four of the values shown in 1–4. Ask students to find the difference between the angles in 1 and 3, and between the angles in 2 and 4. (The difference is 2π, an angle of one complete revolution.) Then ask them why the difference between the angles in 1 and 2 is not also 2π. (There are two angles in each revolution that have equal cosines.) It is important that students understand that the definition of arccosine given in the text requires that n stand for any integer and that the arccosine of a number is a *collection* of angle measurements.

Follow up graphically by having students work Exploration 3-6a. Algebraic solutions for x as presented in Exploration 3-6b can be done the same day in longer block-scheduling periods.

The examples in Section 3-6 use graphical, numerical, and algebraic methods to find the x-values of a sinusoid that correspond to a particular y-value. Be sure to discuss the numerical method in detail so students understand that they must find *both* of the adjacent x-values and then find additional answers by adding multiples of the period to each of these values. Have students store each of the adjacent x-values in the memory of their calculators.

In Example 2, point out the difference between the = sign and the $\approx$ sign.

Example 3 shows how to find a general solution of the equation $9 + 7 \cos \frac{2\pi}{13}(x - 4) = 5$. When discussing this example, emphasize that after the general solution is substituted for arccosine, the coefficient $\frac{13}{2\pi}$ must be distributed over *both* terms. In solving equations like this, students often forget to distribute the coefficient over the $2\pi n$. Point out that the coefficient of n in the general solution should match the period of the graph.

Once a general solution is found, particular solutions can be obtained by substituting integer values for n. A grapher table is an efficient way to find particular solutions. To use this method, enter the two general solutions for x in the $y=$ menu of a grapher, using y in place of x and x in place of n. Then make a table of values.

$$y_1 = 4 + 13/(2\pi)\cos^{-1}(-4/7) + 13x$$
$$y_2 = 4 - 13/(2\pi)\cos^{-1}(-4/7) + 13x$$

x (or n)	y_1	y_2
−1	−4.4915...	−13.5084...
0	8.5084...	−0.5084...
1	21.5084...	12.4915...
2	34.5084...	25.4915...

Before allowing students to use grapher tables to find solutions, make sure they have had sufficient practice finding solutions using the paper-and-pencil method and that they demonstrate an understanding of the idea behind selecting values of n.

Exploration Notes

Exploration 3-6a asks questions based on a given sinusoidal graph. You can use this Exploration instead of doing the examples with your class. The examples in the student book can reinforce what students learned through the Exploration. Students find values graphically, numerically, and algebraically. This Exploration can be used as a small-group introduction to the lesson, as a daily quiz after the lesson is completed, or as a review sheet to be assigned later in the chapter. If you use the Exploration to introduce the lesson, make sure students have written a correct equation for Problem 2 before they work on the other problems. Allow 20 minutes for the Exploration.

Exploration 3-6b has students find the same x-values for the same function as in Exploration 3-6a, but using algebraic methods rather than graphical ones. Allow 15–20 minutes for this Exploration.

Technology Notes

 Exploration 3-6a: Sinusoids, Given y, Find x Numerically in the *Instructor's Resource Book* can be done with the aid of Sketchpad or Fathom.

Supplementary Examples and Lesson Notes

If you have time or very strong students, you may wish to introduce inverse sine relations and inverse tangent relations in this section instead of waiting until Section 4-4. At this point, students do not need to understand the principal values of the inverse sine and inverse tangent functions.

The names *arcsine* and *arctangent* are used for the inverse sine and inverse tangent relations, respectively. The ± sign used in the general solution of arccosine does not work for the general solutions

of arcsine and arctangent. Figures 3-6a and 3-6b show how the general solutions are related to the inverse functions.

Figure 3-6a

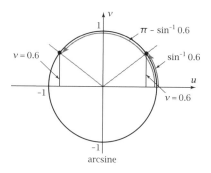

arcsine

Figure 3-6b

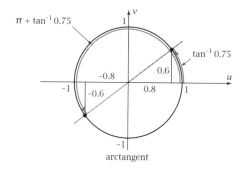

arctangent

For arcsine, the v-values for the solution angles are the same. For arctangent, the u-values are opposites and the v-values are opposites as well. Thus, their ratio is the same in both cases. Compare these with arccosine, for which the two u-values are the same (Figure 3-6a) in the student book.

Example 1

Find arcsin 0.6.

Solution

$$\text{arcsin } 0.6 = \sin^{-1} 0.6 + 2\pi n \quad \text{or}$$
$$\pi - \sin^{-1} 0.6 + 2\pi n \quad \text{See Figure 3-6a.}$$
$$= 0.6435... + 2\pi n \quad \text{or}$$
$$2.4980... + 2\pi n \quad \text{By calculator.}$$

Example 2

Find arctan 0.75.

Solution

$$\text{arctan } 0.75 = \tan^{-1} 0.75 + 2\pi n \quad \text{or}$$
$$\pi + \tan^{-1} 0.75 + 2\pi n$$
$$\text{See Figure 3-6b.}$$
$$= 0.6435... + 2\pi n \quad \text{or}$$
$$3.7850... + 2\pi n \quad \text{By calculator.}$$

Note: There is a simpler way to write arctangent. Because the two points are half a revolution apart, you can add integer multiples of π to the inverse tangent function value.

$$\arctan 0.75 = \tan^{-1} 0.75 + \pi n$$

DEFINITIONS: Inverse Circular Relations

$\arcsin x = \sin^{-1} y + 2\pi n$ or
$\pi - \sin^{-1} y + 2\pi n$

Verbally: Inverse sines come in supplementary pairs with all their coterminals.

$\arctan x = \tan^{-1} y + 2\pi n$ or
$\pi + \tan^{-1} y + 2\pi n = \tan^{-1} y + \pi n$

Verbally: Inverse tangents come in pairs a half-revolution apart with all coterminals.

Problem Notes

- *Problems 1–4* provide students with practice solving inverse circular relation equations. Because no method is specified, students may find the solutions numerically, graphically, or algebraically.

- *Problems 5–10* require students to write equations for sinusoids and use graphical, numerical, and algebraic methods to find x-values corresponding to a particular y-value. These problems are similar to the examples and to Exploration 3-6a. In part a of Problems 5–10, students should estimate the graphical solutions from the graph and not use the intersect feature on their calculators.

- *Problems 11 and 12* involve inverse trigonometric functions rather than inverse circular functions. In the homework discussion, point out the similarities and differences between Problems 11 and 12 and Problems 5–10.

- *Problem 13* asks students to use algebra to find solutions to $\cos x = -0.9$. Be sure to assign this problem because it requires students to find a very large x-value not shown on the graph.

Supplementary Problems

If you introduce arcsine and arctangent, you may wish to assign these problems.

For Problems 1 and 2, find the first five positive values of the inverse circular function.

1. arcsin 0.7
2. arctan 4

3. Figure 3-6c shows the parent circular sine function $y = \sin x$.

Figure 3-6c

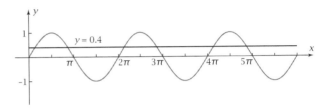

a. Find algebraically the six values of x shown for which $\sin x = 0.4$.

b. Find algebraically the first value of x greater than 100 for which $\sin x = 0.4$.

4. Figure 3-6d shows the parent circular tangent function $y = \tan x$.

Figure 3-6d

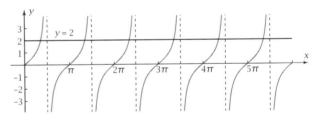

a. Find algebraically the six values of x shown for which $\tan x = 2$.

b. Find algebraically the first value of x greater than 50 for which $\tan x = 2$.

3-7
Sinusoidal Functions as Mathematical Models

Objective

Given a verbal description of a periodic phenomenon, write an equation using sine or cosine functions and use the equation as a mathematical model to make predictions and interpretations about the real world.

Class Time

2 days

Homework Assignment

Day 1: RA, Q1–Q10, Problems 1, 2

Day 2

Recommended: Problems 4, 5, 8, 11

Also suggested: Problems 14, 15

Technology Options

 Example 1: Waterwheel Problem

 Exploration 3-7a: Chemotherapy Problem

 Exploration 3-7b: Oil Well Problem

 Activity: Transformations of Trigonometric Functions

 Activity: The Concept of Periodic Functions

Activity: Properties of Sine and Cosine

Important Terms and Concepts

Mathematical model

Lesson Notes

Section 3-7 contains a wide variety of real-world problems that illustrate how common sinusoids are in real life. It is recommended that you spend two days on this section. On the first day, do Exploration 3-7a as a whole-class activity. Then have students work in small groups on Problem 11 in the textbook. This problem is very similar to the Chemotherapy Problem. On the second day, discuss the homework and have students work on other problems.

To answer part d of Example 1 correctly, students must analyze the graph. If students try to find the

solution without looking at the graph, they are likely to give the first positive *t*-value that gives a *d*-value of 0. However, this solution is the time when the point first *enters* the water, *not* the time when it *emerges* from the water.

Some of the problems in the problem set make excellent projects. For example, you might divide the class into groups of three to five students and have each group make a video demonstrating the situation described in one of the problems. Ask students to use real stopwatches, tape measures, and other measuring devices to accurately measure times and distances. From their collected measurements, students can write a particular equation and use it to find *x*-values given *y*-values and to find *y*-values given *x*-values. Students have great fun making videos of themselves riding Ferris wheels or roller coasters!

Another suggestion is to have groups of three or four students each present the solution to one of the homework questions on the board. Members of the group should take turns explaining different parts of their assigned problem.

A key point to emphasize in this section is that *almost all* real-world sinusoid problems involve working with real numbers (i.e., radians) and that students need to have their calculators in radian mode. Students must learn to decide whether to use radians or degrees based on the context of a problem, not just on whether the problem includes x or θ or π.

Exploration Notes

Exploration 3-7a may be used as a whole-class activity to begin the second day of instruction. Be careful, because the topic might be sensitive for students who have had a close relative suffering from cancer. Check student progress after each question, and make sure everyone gets the correct answer before moving on to the next question. Problem 4 may generate a discussion about whether the year in question is a leap year. Note that Problem 6 asks for *dates,* not *days.* Therefore, students must convert their answers to a month and a day of the month. You may want to have students write the answer to Problem 6 as an inequality. Allow about 30 minutes for the Exploration.

Exploration 3-7b can be used as a classroom group activity. It is significant because it requires students to find an *x*-value far from the given piece of the graph. It also shows how a small change in initial conditions can make a large change in an extrapolated answer.

Precalculus with Trigonometry: Instructor's Guide
© 2007 Key Curriculum Press

Technology Notes

 Example 1: Waterwheel Problem asks several questions about a point traveling along a waterwheel that is partially submerged in water. The example is demonstrated in the Dynamic Precalculus Exploration at *www.keymath.com/precalc.*

 Exploration 3-7a: Chemotherapy Problem, in the *Instructor's Resource Book,* can be done with sliders in Sketchpad or Fathom.

 Exploration 3-7b: Oil Well Problem, in the *Instructor's Resource Book,* can be done with sliders in Sketchpad or Fathom.

 Activity: Transformations of Trigonometric Functions, in the *Instructor's Resource Book,* has students study the periodic motion of a mass on an elastic spring as a function of time. This activity provides a decent review of the chapter. Allow 45 minutes.

 Activity: The Concept of Periodic Functions, in *Connecting Mathematics with Science,* helps students understand the period of a function in an electrocardiogram in terms of the heart rate (pulse). Allow 15 minutes.

 Activity: Properties of Sine and Cosine, in *Connecting Mathematics with Science,* helps students see how the periodic motion of a pendulum can be modeled by sinusoids. Allow 45 minutes.

Problem Notes

- *Problem 1,* the Steamboat Problem, is similar to Example 1.

- *Problem 2,* the Fox Population Problem, requires students to write an inequality to answer part d.

- *Problem 3,* the Bouncing Spring Problem, describes only half of a cycle. Students may miss the period of the sinusoid if they draw or interpret the graph incorrectly.

- *Problem 4,* the Rope Swing Problem, involves a *y*-variable that is a horizontal distance. Students may find it easier to draw the graph if they turn their books so that the river in the illustration is "up" and the riverbank is "down."

- *Problem 5,* the Roller Coaster Problem, asks students to calculate the lengths of the horizontal and vertical support beams needed for a roller coaster. Some students double the horizontal beam lengths because the diagram shows only half of a cycle.

- *Problem 6,* the Buried Treasure Problem, shows only half of a cycle.

- *Problem 7,* the Sunspot Problem, asks students to consult a reference in order to check the accuracy of their model. One possible reference is the September 1975 issue of *Scientific American.*

- *Problem 8,* the Tide Problem, requires students to convert date and time information to the number of hours since midnight on August 2.

- *Problem 9,* the Shock Felt Round the World Problem, is fairly straightforward and usually does not present trouble for students. However, some students do not realize that at time 0 the vertical displacement of Earth is also zero. Such students start the graph at a minimum value instead of at zero.

- *Problem 10,* the Island Problem, provides both a sketch and an equation of the sinusoid. Part f requires students to write an inequality.

- *Problem 11,* the Pebble in the Tire Problem, is similar to Example 1. The period is 2π times the radius, so the equation does not contain π.

- *Problem 12,* the Oil Well Problem, is not difficult if students realize that half of a cycle occurs between the *x*-values of -30 and -100.

- *Problem 13,* the Sound Wave Problem, provides practice with frequency and is quite easy. It does not require students to write a sinusoidal equation. You may wish to add this part d to the question.

    d. Research in the library or on the Internet the physics of organ pipes. You might try looking up "The Physics of Organ Pipes," by Neville Fletcher and Suzanne Thwaites, in the January 1983 issue of *Scientific American.* Describe the results of your research in your journal.

- *Problem 14,* the Sunrise Project, introduces the concept of a variable phase displacement in part e.

- *Problem 15,* the Variable Amplitude Pendulum Project, is time consuming but worthwhile. Students measure the period and amplitude of the pendulum and calculate the equation of its motion. This is a good project to connect theory and practice and to talk about modeling.

Supplementary Problems

1. *Ferris Wheel Problem:* As you ride a Ferris wheel, your distance from the ground varies sinusoidally with time. When the last seat is filled and the Ferris wheel starts, your seat is in the

position shown in Figure 3-7a. Let t be the number of seconds after the Ferris wheel starts. When $t = 3$ s, you first reach the top, 43 ft above the ground. The wheel makes a revolution every 24 s. The diameter of the wheel is 40 ft.

Figure 3-7a

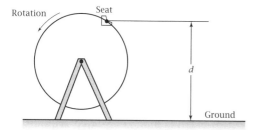

a. Sketch the graph of the sinusoid.

b. What is the lowest you go as the Ferris wheel turns? Why is it reasonable for this number to be greater than zero?

c. Write a particular equation for distance as a function of time.

d. Predict your height above the ground when $t = 20$.

e. Find the first three times you are 18 ft above the ground.

2. *Extraterrestrial Being Problem:* Researchers find a creature from an alien planet. Its body temperature varies sinusoidally with time. Thirty-five minutes after they start timing, the body temperature reaches a high of 120°F. Twenty minutes after that, it reaches its next low, 104°F.

a. Sketch the graph of this sinusoid.

b. Write a particular equation for body temperature as a function of minutes since the researchers started timing.

c. What was the creature's body temperature when they first started timing?

d. Find the first three times after they started timing at which the temperature was 114°F.

3. *Tidal Wave Problem:* A tsunami is a high-speed deep ocean wave caused by an earthquake. It is popularly called a tidal wave because its effect is a rapid change in tide as the wave approaches land. The water first goes down from its normal level and then rises the same amount above its normal level. The period of a tsunami is about 15 min. Suppose that a tsunami of amplitude 10 m is approaching a place on Waikiki beach in Honolulu where the water is 9 m deep.

a. Assume that the depth of the water varies sinusoidally with time as the tsunami passes.

Make a table showing the depth every 2 min as the tsunami passes.

b. According to your mathematical model, what will be the minimum depth of the water? How do you explain the answer in terms of what will happen in the real world?

c. Between what two times will there be *no* water at this particular point on the beach?

d. The **wavelength** of a wave is the distance between two consecutive crests of the wave. If a tsunami is traveling 1200 km/h, what is its wavelength?

e. If you were on a ship at sea, explain why you would not notice a tsunami passing by, even though the wave moves so fast.

4. *Spaceship Problem:* When a spaceship is fired into orbit from a site not on the equator, such as Cape Canaveral, it goes into an orbit that takes it alternately north and south of the equator. The path it traces on the surface of Earth is a sinusoidal function of time (Figure 3-7b). Suppose that a spaceship reaches its maximum distance, 4000 km north of the equator, 10 min after it leaves Cape Canaveral. Half a cycle later it is at its maximum distance south of the equator, also 4000 km. The spaceship completes an orbit every 90 min.

Figure 3-7b

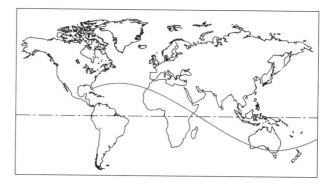

a. Let y be the number of kilometers the spaceship is *north* of the equator (consider distances south of the equator to be negative). Let t be the number of minutes elapsed since liftoff. Write a particular equation for y as a function of t.

b. Use your equation to predict y when $t = 25$, 41, and 163 min.

c. What is the smallest positive value of t for which the spaceship is 1600 km south of the equator?

d. Based on your mathematical model, how far is Cape Canaveral from the equator?

e. Check a map or some other reference to see how far Cape Canaveral *really* is from the equator. Give the source of your information.

5. *Rock Formation Problem:* An old rock formation is warped into the shape of a sinusoid. Over the centuries the top has eroded away, leaving the ground with a flat surface from which various rock formations are cropping out (Figure 3-7c). Because you have studied sinusoids, the geologists call on you to predict the depth of a particular stratum (boundary surface) at various points. You construct an x-axis along the ground and a y-axis at the edge of an outcropping, as shown. A hole drilled at $x = 100$ m shows that the top of the stratum is 90 m deep at that point.

Figure 3-7c

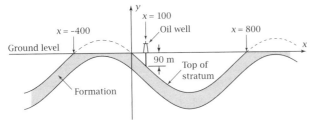

a. Write a particular equation expressing y as a function of x.

b. If a hole were drilled to the stratum at $x = 510$ m, how deep would it be?

c. What is the maximum depth of the stratum, and what is the smallest positive value of x at which it reaches that maximum depth?

d. How high above the present ground level did the stratum go before it eroded away?

e. For what values of x between 0 and 800 m is the stratum within 120 m of the surface?

f. The geologists decide to drill holes to the stratum every 50 m from $x = 50$ to $x = 750$ m, searching for valuable minerals. On your grapher, make a table of values of y for each of these x-values. Include a column in the table for the cost of drilling each hole if drilling costs $75/m. What is the total cost of drilling the holes?

6. *Biorhythm Problem:* According to biorhythm theory, your body is governed by three independent sinusoidal functions, each with a different period:

- Physical function: period = 23 days
- Emotional function: period = 28 days
- Intellectual function: period = 33 days

a. Phoebe is at a high point on all three cycles today! This means that she is at her very

highest ability in all three functions. Assume that the amplitude of each sinusoid is 100 units and that the sinusoidal axis runs along the horizontal coordinate axis. Write a particular equation for each of the three functions.

b. Plot the graphs of all three functions on the same screen. Use a friendly window with an x-range of about [0, 100].

c. Phoebe will be at her next intellectual high 33 days from now. What will be the values of her emotional and physical functions on that day? Use the most time-efficient way to find these values, and indicate how you got the answers.

d. Biorhythm theory says that the most dangerous time for a particular function is when it crosses the sinusoidal axis. For each function, find the first positive time at which that function is most dangerous.

e. Just for fun, see if you can figure out how long it will be before all three of Phoebe's functions are again simultaneously at a high point.

f. Research biorhythms on the Internet or via some other reference source. In what cultures are biorhythms used extensively? When did biorhythm theory originate?

7. *Electrical Current and Voltage Problem:* The electricity supplied to your house is called alternating current (AC) because the current varies sinusoidally with time. The voltage that causes the current to flow also varies sinusoidally with time. Both the current and the voltage have a frequency of 60 cycles per second in the United States but have different phase displacements (Figure 3-7d).

Figure 3-7d

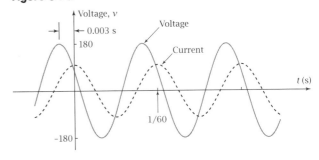

a. Suppose that the current is at its maximum, $i = 5$ A (A is for amperes) when $t = 0$ s. Find a particular equation for this sinusoid.

b. As shown in Figure 3-7d, the voltage leads the current by 0.003 s, meaning that it reaches a maximum 0.003 s *before* the current does. ("Leading" corresponds to a negative phase displacement, and "lagging" corresponds to a positive phase displacement.) If the peak voltage is $v = 180$ V (V is for volts), find a particular equation for voltage as a function of time. (Note that the 115 V supplied to your house is an *average* value, whereas the 180 V is an *instantaneous* peak voltage.)

c. What is the voltage at the time the current is a maximum?

d. What is the current at the time the voltage is a maximum?

e. What is the first positive value of t at which v reaches 170?

8. *Sun Elevation Problem:* The angle of elevation of an object above you is the angle between a horizontal line and the line of sight to the object (Figure 3-7e). As the Sun rises, its angle of elevation increases rapidly at first, then more slowly, reaching a maximum near noontime. Then the angle decreases until sunset. The next day the phenomenon repeats itself. Assume that when the Sun is up, its angle of elevation varies sinusoidally with the time of day.

Figure 3-7e

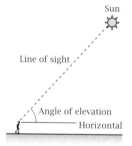

a. Suppose that at this time of year the sinusoidal axis is at $E = -5°$ and the maximum angle of elevation, $E = 55°$, occurs at 12:45 p.m. The period is 24 hours. Find a particular equation for E as a function of t, the number of hours elapsed since midnight.

b. Plot at least two cycles of the sinusoid on your grapher. Sketch the result.

c. What is the real-world significance of the t-intercepts? What is the real-world significance of the fact that part of the sinusoid is below the t-axis?

d. What is the angle of elevation at 9:27 a.m. and at 2:30 p.m.?

e. What does E equal at sunrise? What is the time of sunrise?

f. The maximum angle of elevation of the Sun increases and decreases with the changes in season. Also, the times of sunrise and sunset vary with the seasons. What *one* change could you make in your mathematical model that would allow you to predict the angle of elevation at any time on any day of the year?

Rotary Motion

Objective

Given information about a rotating object or connected rotating objects, find linear and angular velocities of points on the objects.

Class Time

2 days

Homework Assignment

Day 1: RA, Q1–Q10, Problems 1–9 odd, 10, 11

Day 2: Problems 13–17

Important Terms and Concepts

Angular velocity

Linear velocity

Dimensional analysis

rpm (revolutions per minute)

Gear train

Reduction ratio

Lesson Notes

You may want to consider beginning the lesson by using *Exploration: Rotary Motion* or the ideas in it. Point out to students that all points on a rotating object, including the center, have the same angular velocity but that the linear velocity of points on the rotating object will differ. The speed of a moving vehicle equals the linear velocity of the rims of its wheels.

You may want to inform students that in the real world, "revolutions per minute" often appears as the acronym "rpm" rather than "rev/min" as used in this book.

In Example 1, the difference between angular velocity and linear velocity is demonstrated by

investigating the motion of an old LP record. Remind students that they used dimensional analysis when they converted degrees to radians, and vice versa.

Example 2 demonstrates how angular velocity and linear velocity are related on connected rotating objects. This example uses a bicycle as the model. See if you can get any of your students to explain how the gears and their ratios work. If not, you might want to assign an Internet search of this topic.

The statements in the box Conclusions: Connected Rotating Objects are key concepts for this section and will be used in the exercises and explorations.

Exploration Notes

Introduction to Angular and Linear Velocity has a nice low-tech way of introducing angular and linear velocity. When summarizing the Exploration, use a chart similar to the one at the bottom of the page.

Students find that using a chart makes this material easier. Allow about 15 minutes to complete this Exploration.

Adam Ant Problem gives students practice in working with the linear and angular velocities of a rotating object. Make sure students understand that the units of the radius are cm/rad. Allow about 15 minutes for this Exploration.

Motorcycle Problem uses the concepts about connected rotating objects discussed in Example 2. This Exploration is a good follow-up of a class discussion on Example 2. Allow about 15 minutes to complete this Exploration.

Problem Notes

If students are having problems, encourage the use of a chart like the one drawn in the Exploration Notes.

- Problems 1–8 are similar to Example 1. They involve angular and linear velocities of a rotating object.

- Problems 9–17 compare the angular and linear velocities of connected objects.

Exploration Notes: Rotary Motion

	Angle (radians)	Arc Length (cm)	Time (s)	Linear Velocity (cm/s)	Angular Velocity (rad/s)
Outer	2	60	5	60/5 = 12	2/5
Inner	2	24	5	24/5 = 4.8	2/5

Chapter Review and Test

Objective

Review and practice the major concepts presented in this chapter.

Class Time

2 days (including 1 day for testing)

Homework Assignment

Day 1: R0–R7, T1–T17

Day 2 (after Chapter 3 Test): Problem Set 4-1

Important Terms and Concepts

Parametric

Lesson Notes

Section 3-9 contains a set of Review Problems, a set of Concept Problems, and a Chapter Test. The Review Problems include one problem for each section in the chapter. You may wish to use the Chapter Test as an additional set of review problems. Note that all the sinusoids on the test are circular functions, with real-number arguments, rather than trigonometric functions.

Encourage students to practice the no-calculator problems without a calculator so that they are prepared for the test problems for which they cannot use a calculator.

Exploration 3-9a can also be used as a "rehearsal" for the chapter test.

Exploration Notes

Exploration 3-9a requires a calculator for Problems 4, 10, and 11–16. Problems 1–6 involve radians and conversions between radians and degrees. Problems 7–10 require students to write an equation based on a verbal description and a partially drawn graph of a sinusoid and then use the equation to make predictions. Problems 11–16 present a graph and its equation. Students must analyze the graph to answer some questions and use the equation to answer others. Students should complete the exploration individually. Allow 55–60 minutes.

Problem Notes

- *Concept Problem C1,* the Pump Jack Problem, presents a challenge even to the best students because they must connect and apply several concepts from the chapter.

- *Concept Problem C2,* the Inverse Circular Relation Graphs Problem, involves ideas from Chapter 4 and can be assigned to small groups of students. This is also a good review question after you complete Chapter 4.

- Problems T1 and T2 ask students to visually approximate 2.3 radians on a unit circle. A blackline master for these problems is available in the *Instructor's Resource Book.*

4 Trigonometric Function Properties, Identities, and Parametric Functions

Here students broaden their repertoire, adding the Pythagorean and quotient properties they learned in Chapter 2. Sometimes they are asked to transform an expression to another form, and sometimes they are asked to prove that a given equation is an identity. Both kinds of problem use the same technique. Students reinforce the proof style they learned in geometry, starting with "Proof:" to show where statement of the identity ends and proving begins, and ending with a statement of what they have proved, including the abbreviation "Q.E.D." The properties are also used to solve equations, adding arcsine and arctangent to the arccosine learned in Chapter 3. Parametric functions, introduced in Section 4-5, allow students to plot these inverse circular relation graphs by giving them an x= menu in addition to the familiar y= menu. The information overload (the "identity crisis") students usually experience with identities is avoided by postponing the properties involving more than one argument, such as the double argument properties, until the next chapter.

Introduction to the Pythagorean Property

Objective

Investigate the sum of the squares of the cosine and sine of the same argument.

Class Time

$\frac{1}{2}$ day

Homework Assignment

Problems 1–6

Important Terms and Concepts

Pythagorean property

Lesson Notes

Section 4-1 is an exploratory activity in which students discover the Pythagorean property $\cos^2 x + \sin^2 x = 1$. You can assign Section 4-1 for homework the night of the Chapter 3 test or as a group activity to be completed in class. No classroom discussion is needed before students begin the activity.

The problems are to be completed using a grapher. Remind students to check that their graphers are in the appropriate mode (degrees or radians) for each problem. You may also need to remind students to adjust the window settings after they switch from radian mode to degree mode.

Hopefully, students will note that the graphs of $y = \cos^2 x$ and $y = \sin^2 x$ look suspiciously like sinusoids. Students will learn the double argument identities, $\cos^2 x = \frac{1}{2} + \frac{1}{2}\cos 2x$ and $\sin^2 x = \frac{1}{2} - \frac{1}{2}\cos 2x$, in Chapter 5. However, some students may be able to make correct conjectures about alternate equations for $y = \cos^2 x$ and $y = \sin^2 x$ based on their knowledge of transformations of sinusoidal functions.

Problem Notes

- *Problem 3* asks students to graph $y = \cos^2 x$, $y = \sin^2 x$, and $y = \cos^2 x + \sin^2 x$ in the same window. If their graphers allow it, have students use a different line style for each graph.

- *Problems 2–4* lead students to discover the Pythagorean property and to observe that it holds whether x is measured in degrees or radians.

- *Problems 5 and 6* show students how the Pythagorean property gets its name.

4-2
Pythagorean, Reciprocal, and Quotient Properties

Objective

Derive algebraically three kinds of properties expressing relationships among trigonometric functions.

Class Time

2 days

Homework Assignment

Day 1: Q1–Q10, Problems 1–15 odd

Day 2: Problems 2–14 even

Technology Options

 Problem 15: Dynamic Unit Circle Properties Problem

Important Terms and Concepts

Reciprocal properties

Quotient properties

Pythagorean properties

Cofunction

Dual

Lesson Notes

In Chapter 3, students learned the reciprocal and quotient properties of trigonometric functions. In Section 4-1, they explored a Pythagorean property. In this section, students will derive these properties algebraically. It is recommended that you spend two days covering this section. The material is extremely important, and students should master it before they move on. If you need additional problems, see the Supplementary Problems on the next page.

The properties discussed in this section are stated in terms of *x*. Make sure students understand that the argument *x* is used for *both* degrees *and* radians. So, for example, $\cos^2 x + \sin^2 x = 1$, regardless of whether *x* is in degrees or radians.

Students need to memorize the three reciprocal properties and understand how to graph the functions $y = \sec x$, $y = \csc x$, and $y = \cot x$ based on graphs of $y = \cos x$, $y = \sin x$, and $y = \tan x$, respectively. Students learned to sketch such graphs in Section 3-3, but you may want to review the process here. Emphasize that students should focus

on points on the sine, cosine, or tangent graph with *y*-values −1, 1, and 0. Because the reciprocal of 1 is 1 and the reciprocal of −1 is −1, points with *y*-values −1 and 1 are in the same locations in the graph of the reciprocal function. Because the reciprocal of 0 is undefined, points with *y*-value 0 correspond to vertical asymptotes on the graph of the reciprocal function. Mention that the reciprocal of a small negative number is a "large" negative number. A similar statement is done for small positive numbers. Because the reciprocal of a very large value is close to 0, points with very large *y*-values correspond to *y*-values close to 0 in the graph of the reciprocal function. Mention signs here, too.

Students need to memorize the quotient properties $\tan x = \frac{\sin x}{\cos x}$ and $\cot x = \frac{\cos x}{\sin x}$ and be able to show that $\tan x = \frac{\sec x}{\csc x}$ and $\cot x = \frac{\csc x}{\sec x}$.

Students discovered one of the Pythagorean properties, $\cos^2 x + \sin^2 x = 1$, in Section 4-1. You might want to demonstrate graphically why this property makes sense. Figure 4-2a shows graphs of $y = \cos^2 x$, $y = \sin^2 x$, and $y = \cos^2 x + \sin^2 x$.

Figure 4-2a

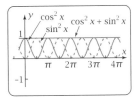

As students discovered in Section 4-1, the graph of $y = \cos^2 x + \sin^2 x$ is the horizontal line $y = 1$. The graphs of $y = \cos^2 x$ (shown with a solid line) and $y = \sin^2 x$ (shown with a dashed line) are sinusoids with axes at $y = 0.5$. As you can see, these sinusoids are exactly a half-cycle out of phase with each other. The student text explains how the property $\cos^2 x + \sin^2 = 1$ is derived by considering the terminal point (u, v) of an arc of length *x* on a unit circle. Review this derivation with students. Then demonstrate how this property can be used to derive the two other Pythagorean properties.

The first Pythagorean property, $\cos^2 x + \sin^2 x = 1$, is extremely important. Students must memorize it and be able to derive quickly from it the other two Pythagorean properties. Some students will prefer to memorize properties, but they should also be able to derive them.

The first Pythagorean property is deliberately written with cosine first. In this form, it is easier for students to see the connection to the double argument property, $\cos 2x = \cos^2 x - \sin^2 x$, introduced in Chapter 5, and the Pythagorean property for hyperbolic functions, $\cosh^2 x - \sinh^2 x = 1$, which comes up in calculus.

Consider giving regular quizzes and tests for sections involving trigonometric properties. It will help students recognize which identities are the most useful and which ones to use when.

Exploration Notes

Exploration 4-2a is a good activity with which to begin the second day of instruction. Students can use the think-pair-share strategy to review and reinforce the concepts introduced on the first day. Allow about 15 minutes for the Exploration.

Technology Notes

 Problem 15: The Dynamic Unit Circle Properties Problem asks students to explore a Dynamic Precalculus Exploration at *www.keymath.com/precalc.* The Unit Circle Exploration allows students to investigate relationships between trigonometric functions as a point moves around a unit circle.

Problem Notes

• *Problems 1–4* emphasize and help develop an understanding of the quotient and reciprocal properties.

• *Problem 6* requires students to derive the Pythagorean property involving $\cot^2 x$ and $\csc^2 x$.

• *Problems 9 and 10* are important. Students use algebraic means to manipulate the Pythagorean properties into other forms they will encounter and use frequently.

• *Problem 13,* the Duality Property of Trigonometric Functions Problem, is worth spending some time on. It can help students see patterns in the properties they will learn throughout Chapter 4.

• *Problem 14* asks students how $\cos \theta$ relates to the coordinate u when θ terminates in a quadrant other than Quadrant I.

Supplementary Problems

1. Write the reciprocal property for $\csc x$.

2. Explain why $(\cos x)(\sec x) = 1$.

3. Write $\cot x$ in terms of $\sin x$ and $\cos x$.

4. Show how the reciprocal property $\tan x = \frac{\sin x}{\cos x}$ can be transformed to express $\tan x$ in terms of $\sec x$ and $\csc x$.

5. Show that the Pythagorean property $\cos^2 \theta + \sin^2 \theta = 1$ is true for trigonometric functions by drawing a right triangle with acute angle θ and using the definitions of the trigonometric functions.

6. By appropriate operations on the Pythagorean property $\cos^2 x + \sin^2 x = 1$, derive the Pythagorean property $1 + \tan^2 x = \sec^2 x$.

7. Sketch the graph of the trigonometric function $y = \cos \theta$. On the same axes, sketch the graph of $y = \sec \theta$ by using the fact that a y-value for $\sec \theta$ is the reciprocal of the corresponding y-value for $\cos \theta$. Where do the asymptotes occur in the secant graph?

8. On your grapher, make a table with columns showing the values of the circular functions $\cos x$ and $\sin x$ and of the expression $\cos^2 x + \sin^2 x$ for $x = 0, 1, 2, 3, \ldots$. What do you notice about the values of the expression? How do you explain the result?

9. Show algebraically that $\cos^2 x = 1 - \sin^2 x$.

10. Show algebraically that $\tan^2 x = \sec^2 x - 1$.

11. Write equations expressing each of the six trigonometric functions in terms of $\sin x$.

12. Write equations expressing each of the six trigonometric functions in terms of $\cos x$.

4-3
Identities and Algebraic Transformation of Expressions

Objective

Given a trigonometric expression, transform it into an equivalent form that is perhaps simpler or more useful.

Class Time

2–3 days

Homework Assignment

Day 1: RA, Q1–Q10, Problems 1–25 odd

Day 2: Problems 27–55 odd

Day 3: Even-numbered problems similar to problems students need more practice on *or* one or more of the Explorations

Technology Options

 Exploration 4-3b: Trigonometric Transformations

Important Terms and Concepts

Identity

Conjugate binomials

Lesson Notes

In Section 4-3, students use the trigonometric properties they learned in the previous section to transform trigonometric expressions and prove trigonometric identities. Many newer textbooks do not cover these topics. However, there are several compelling reasons to include them. For example, transforming trigonometric expressions and proving identities

- Help students learn elementary trigonometric properties

- Give students an opportunity to sharpen their algebraic skills

- Show students how to write algebraic proofs

It is recommended that you spend two to three days on this section. Strong students will need only two days. The first day, cover transformations using Examples 1 and 2. You might want to end the day by assigning Exploration 4-3a or Exploration 4-3b. On the second day, introduce identities covering

Examples 3–5 and, if time permits, assign Exploration 4-3c, which is also a good way to introduce this topic.

On the third day, review the types of problems students are struggling with and complete any remaining Explorations. Make sure students realize that the technique for proving an identity is the same as for transforming an expression. The main difference is that they can choose either side to start with. Make sure students do not start by writing the identity, then transforming both sides until they get a true statement such as $\cos x = \cos x$. They cannot write the given identity as a step in the proof without being guilty of circular reasoning.

The first two examples illustrate techniques for transforming one trigonometric expression into another. It is strongly recommended that your students use the vertical format shown in the text:

$$\sin x \cot x$$
$$= \sin x \cdot \frac{\cos x}{\sin x}$$
$$= \cos x$$

rather than a horizontal format such as

$$\sin x \cot x = \sin x \cdot \frac{\cos x}{\sin x} = \cos x$$

The vertical form shows more clearly that students are starting with an expression (not an equation), which they then transform.

Encourage students to put in the transitive step at the end of their solutions. This will prepare them for proving identities. (Besides, students love using the symbol ∴ and writing Q.E.D.!)

Explain to students that there is often more than one way to transform one expression into another. To illustrate this point, you can present Additional Class Example 1, which presents three ways to solve the same problem.

Examples 3–5 involve proving identities. The groundwork for proving identities has already been laid with the work on transforming expressions. The one important difference is that when proving an identity, students may begin with either side of the equation.

Be sure to call students' attention to the second note, which points out that it is not correct to work on *both* sides of the equation. Working both sides *assumes* the equation is true, which is exactly what students are trying to *prove*. However, working with both sides can give insights into the steps that are needed to prove the identity.

The third note is extremely important. Students need to understand that although a graph or numerical chart may be used to *confirm* an identity, it does *not* constitute a proof. In confirming an identity graphically, a reasonable interval is at least two periods in length.

Proving identities can seem mysterious to students at first. One effective technique for making them feel more comfortable is to emphasize the reason for taking a particular step rather than the property that justifies the step. The three examples in the text illustrate the thought process, with the explanations written to the right of each step. Encourage students to look ahead. They know what the last line should be.

The box on page 166 summarizes some useful techniques for transforming expressions and proving identities. You might also suggest that, when all else fails, students rewrite the expression in terms of $\sin x$ and $\cos x$. This may not make the problem easier, but it may make it more familiar! Emphasize to students that there is no *one* right way to prove an identity. Be sure to show students multiple ways to prove some of the identities, and encourage them to write and present their own alternate proofs.

It is not unusual, if time permits, to spend more than the 2–3 days recommended on this section, including a test. The payoff is that students develop a genuine confidence with proving identities. The confidence they gain carries over to proofs later in the course, and speeds up work there. Note that the properties involving more than one argument, such as $\cos(A - B)$, are deliberately withheld until the next chapter. By spending enough time with the three properties of this section and delaying the more exotic properties, students will avoid the so-called "identity crisis."

Exploration Notes

Three Explorations accompany this section. You may want to use parts of them for a quiz or as an additional homework assignment.

Exploration 4-3a is a quick and easy Exploration used to review trigonometric properties and transform expressions. This Exploration should take about 10 minutes.

Exploration 4-3b gives students practice transforming trigonometric expressions. This Exploration is similar to Exploration 4-3a. Allow about 15 minutes to complete this Exploration.

Exploration 4-3c introduces the process of proving trigonometric identities. Students can work in groups to assist each other in applying the

strategies to prove an identity. Allow about 20 minutes to complete this Exploration.

Technology Notes

Exploration 4-3b: Trigonometric Transformations, in the *Instructor's Resource Book,* is primarily concerned with symbolic manipulation, but the grapher called for in Problem 5 could well be either Fathom or Sketchpad.

Additional Class Examples

1. Transform the expression $\sin x \sec x \cot x$ into 1.

   Solution

   Your thought process should be

   - Because the answer is 1, there must be some canceling that can be done.
   - Canceling requires fractions, which can be obtained from either the reciprocal properties or the quotient properties.

   Experiment with reciprocal and quotient properties until you find some that work.

$\sin x \sec x \cot x$	Start by writing the given expression.
$= \sin x \cdot \dfrac{1}{\cos x} \cdot \dfrac{\cos x}{\sin x}$	Use the reciprocal and quotient properties to make fractions.
$= 1$	Cancel the sines and cancel the cosines.

   $\therefore \sin x \sec x \cot x = 1$, Q.E.D.

   Use the transitive property.

   There is often more than one way to do a particular transformation. Example 1 could also be done this way:

$\sin x \sec x \cot x$	Start by writing the given expression.
$= \sin x \cdot \dfrac{1}{\cos x} \cdot \cot x$	Use a reciprocal property.
$= \dfrac{\sin x}{\cos x} \cdot \cot x$	
$= \tan x \cot x$	Use a quotient property.
$= 1$	Tan x and cot x are reciprocals of each other.

   $\therefore \sin x \sec x \cot x = 1$, Q.E.D.

   Use the transitive property.

   A third way to work Example 1 is to transform $\sin x$ to $\frac{1}{\csc x}$ and cot x to $\frac{\csc x}{\sec x}$ and then to reduce the fraction.

2. Prove algebraically that
$\csc \theta \cos^2 \theta + \sin \theta = \csc \theta$ is an identity.

Proof

$\csc \theta \cos^2 \theta + \sin \theta$ Start with the more complicated side of the equation.

$= \csc \theta \left(\cos^2 \theta + \dfrac{\sin \theta}{\csc \theta} \right)$ Factor out $\csc \theta$ because you want it in the answer.

$= \csc \theta (\cos^2 \theta + \sin \theta \cdot \sin \theta)$

         Eliminate the fraction by using the familiar reciprocal property.

$= \csc \theta (\cos^2 \theta + \sin^2 \theta)$ Square $\sin \theta$.

$= \csc \theta$ Use a Pythagorean property.

$\therefore \csc \theta \cos^2 \theta + \sin \theta = \csc \theta$, Q.E.D.

Notes:

1. Factoring out $\csc \theta$ in the second line of the proof is sometimes called "factoring out a rabbit." Like a magician, you reached in and pulled out a "common" factor that was not there. Multiplying the $\sin \theta$ in the first step by 1 in the form of $\frac{\csc \theta}{\csc \theta}$ puts the rabbit in the hat for the magician to pull out.

2. In the second example, encourage students to find an alternate solution.

3. In these examples, the reasons written by the steps are those you would *think* of when doing that particular step rather than simply the reason why the step is true.

Problem Notes

- *Problems 1–26* are similar to Examples 1 and 2 in the text.

- *Problems 27–36* are similar to Examples 3–5 in the text.

- *Problems 37–40* emphasize that graphs and tables can be used to confirm identities but not to prove them.

- *Problems 41 and 42* ask students to prove that a statement is not an identity. Make sure students understand that finding just *one* counterexample is enough to prove that a statement is not true.

Supplementary Problems

In Problems 1–8, prove the identity.

1. $\cot^2 A \csc^2 A - \cot^2 A = \cot^4 A$

2. $\sec^4 t - \tan^4 t = 1 + 2 \tan^2 t$

3. $\dfrac{\sec x}{\sin x} - \dfrac{\sin x}{\cos x} = \cot x$

4. $\dfrac{1}{\sec^2 x} + \dfrac{1}{\csc^2 x} = 1$

5. $\dfrac{1}{1 - \sin r} = \sec^2 r + \sec r \tan r$

6. $\dfrac{\sin x}{1 - \cos x} + \dfrac{1 - \cos x}{\sin x} = 2 \csc x$

7. $\dfrac{\sec x}{\sec x - \tan x} = \sec^2 x + \sec x \tan x$

8. $\sin^3 z \cos^2 z = \cos^2 z \sin z - \cos^4 z \sin z$

Problem 9 prepares the students for the next section.

9. *Multiple Values of Inverse Cosine, Sine, and Tangent Problem:* In Chapter 3 you learned how to find multiple values of the inverse cosine relation, or arccosine. In this problem you will do the same for inverse sine and inverse tangent.

Figure 4-3a   **Figure 4-3b**

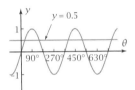 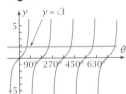

a. Figure 4-3a shows the graph of $y = \sin \theta$ and a horizontal line at $y = 0.5$. The values of θ where the line crosses the graph are values of arcsin 0.5. From memory or from your calculator, you know that the **principal value** of arcsin 0.5, or $\sin^{-1} 0.5$, is 30°. Find the four other values of arcsin 0.5 shown in the figure. Then try to find a compact way to write the general solution for arcsin 0.5. (Recall, for instance, that arccos $0.5 = \pm 60° + 360n°$.)

b. Figure 4-3b shows the graph of $y = \tan \theta$ and a horizontal line at $y = \sqrt{3}$. The values of θ where the line crosses the graph are values of arctan $\sqrt{3}$. From memory or from your calculator, you know that the **principal value** of arctan $\sqrt{3}$, or $\tan^{-1} \sqrt{3}$, is 60°. Find the four other values of arctan $\sqrt{3}$ shown in the figure. Then try to find a compact way to write the general solution for arctan $\sqrt{3}$.

4-4

Arcsine, Arctangent, Arccosine, and Trigonometric Equations

Objective

Find algebraically or numerically the solutions for equations involving circular or trigonometric sines, cosines, and tangents of one argument.

Class Time

2 days

Homework Assignment

Day 1: RA, Q1–Q10, Problems 1–27 odd

Day 2: Problems 29–43 odd

Technology Options

 Exploration 4-4a: Arccosine, Arcsine, and Arctangent

Important Terms and Concepts

Principal value

General solution

Particular solution

Solution set

Open interval

Closed interval

Interval notation

Quadratic forms

Trigonometric inequality

Lesson Notes

In this section, students find solutions for equations involving sines, cosines, and tangents. It is recommended that you spend two days on this section. Cover Examples 1 and 2 on the first day and Examples 3 and 4 on the second.

Students often have difficulty with the material in this section. It is important to make certain they understand the differences between the principal value, the general solution, and a particular solution. Students were introduced to these ideas in Section 3-6. You may find it helpful to review that section with students. Another problem students

have with this material is that they may have forgotten the ranges of the inverse sine, inverse cosine, and inverse tangent functions. Refer back to Section 2-5 to remind them.

As you work through each problem with students, be sure to make a sketch of the angle or arc so that the answer the calculator gives makes sense. Then use geometry to find other solutions.

Tell students that whenever possible they should solve an equation *algebraically* and then confirm the solutions using graphical techniques.

Note that the equations in Examples 1 and 4 are given in terms of radians, whereas the equations in Examples 2 and 3 are given in terms of degrees. Students should be able to solve trigonometric equations in either mode with equal ease.

The text after Example 1 introduces students to the notation for closed and open intervals. Be sure to alternate between interval and inequality notations when you present problems in class so that students become comfortable with both.

Students can use the table feature on their calculators to display the solutions to the problems in this section. The table should have a start value of 0 and a step value of 1. For most graphers, students will need to use y to represent x (or θ) and x to represent n. For instance, to display the solutions for Example 1, students need to enter

$$y_1 = 0.2 + \sin^{-1}(-0.3) + 2\pi x$$

$$y_2 = 0.2 + (\pi - \sin^{-1}(-0.3)) + 2\pi x$$

The grapher's table will show these entries. The numbers in bold are the solutions in the given domain.

x (really n)	y_1 (really x)	y_2 (really x)
0	−0.1046…	**3.6462…**
	First value is out of the domain.	
1	**6.1784…**	**9.9294…**
2	**12.4616…**	16.2126…
	Last value is out of the domain ($4\pi = 12.5663…$).	

For Example 2, students need to enter

$$y_1 = \frac{1}{2}\tan^{-1}(-1.25) + 90x$$

The grapher's table should show these entries. The numbers in bold are the solutions in the given domain.

x (really n)	y_1 (really θ)	
0	$-25.6700\ldots$	Not positive.
1	**64.3299…**	
2	**154.3299…**	
3	**244.3299…**	Stop at the third positive value.

The box after Example 2 summarizes the general solutions for arcsine, arccosine, and arctangent and should help students organize the concepts in this section. The summary includes symbolic representation as well as verbal and visual descriptions. Remind students that n is an integer.

Example 3 shows how to solve a trigonometric equation involving squares of trigonometric functions both by using the quadratic formula and by factoring. To use the quadratic formula, $x = \dfrac{-b \pm \sqrt{b^2 - 4ac}}{2a}$, an equation must be written in the form $ax^2 + bx + c = 0$. Make sure students understand that the "x" in this case is $\sin \theta$. So in the equation $\sin^2 \theta - \sin \theta - 2 = 0$, $a = 1$, $b = -1$, and $c = -2$. The quadratic formula gives $\sin \theta = \dfrac{-(-1) \pm \sqrt{(-1)^2 - 4(1)(-2)}}{2(1)}$. Students should get to the solution by factoring.

Example 4 shows how to solve a trigonometric equation numerically when algebraic methods fail. Emphasize that these numerical solutions are only approximations. Students are often surprised to learn that there are equations that cannot be solved algebraically.

The end of this section is a good place to stop, review the material in the first four sections, and possibly give a quiz or test. There are a lot of important ideas in these sections for students to assimilate.

Exploration Notes

Exploration 4-4a reviews and reinforces the ideas of principal value and general solution. This Exploration is a good lead-in to Examples 1 and 2. Allow about 15 minutes to complete this Exploration.

Exploration 4-4b reinforces solving trigonometric equations algebraically and graphically. You might also suggest that students verify their solutions numerically using a grapher table. Allow about 20 minutes to complete this Exploration.

Technology Notes

 Exploration 4-4a: Arccosine, Arcsine, and Arctangent, in the *Instructor's Resource Book,* is an Exploration meant to have students find certain arccosine, arcsine, and arctangent values by calculator. This Exploration may be done with the help of Sketchpad.

Problem Notes

• *Problems 29–36* require solving quadratic equations in order to solve trigonometric equations. Example 3 demonstrates this skill. Make sure students understand the connection between the solutions of the equations and the θ-intercepts of the graphs.

• *Problems 38–40* require students to solve equations numerically. These transcendental equations must be solved using graphical or numerical techniques because they cannot be solved algebraically. Emphasize that the solution(s) to these types of equation are approximations.

• *Problems 41 and 42* introduce trigonometric inequalities. Students should investigate different graphing styles until they discover the best.

• *Problem 43* is a "surprise" problem. When students attempt to solve the given equation, they find that it is an identity. Make sure students understand that this means that all x-values are solutions to the equation for which the expressions on both sides of the equation are defined.

Supplementary Problem

1. *Surprise Problem:* Solve this equation graphically. What does the result tell you about this equation? What do you conclude about the graph of the right side?

$$\sin 2x = 2 \sin x \cos x$$

4-5

Parametric Functions

Objective

Given equations of a parametric function, plot the graph and make conclusions about the geometrical figure that results.

Class Time

2 days

Homework Assignment

Day 1: RA, Q1–Q10, Problems 1, 2, 3, 5, 15, 17, 18

Day 2: Problems 7–13 odd, 16, 19, 21, 22

Technology Options

 Presentation Sketch: Parametric Present.gsp

 Exploration 4-5b: Parametric Equations for Ellipses

 Activity: Parametric Functions

 Activity: Parametrically Defined Functions

Important Terms and Concepts

Parametric function

Parametric equations

Parameter

Cartesian equation

Ellipse

Unit circle

Lesson Notes

Section 4-5 introduces parametric functions. It is recommended that you spend two days on this section. On the first day, cover Examples 1–3 and perhaps assign Exploration 4-5a. On the second day, cover Example 4 and then do problems from Problem Set 4-5, the Supplementary Problems, or Exploration 4-5b.

One reason for including a section on parametric functions at this point is so that they can be used to create graphs of inverse trigonometric relations (see Problem 22 and Section 4-6) and other relations that are not functions. A second reason is to ensure that students encounter parametric equations *through-*

out their precalculus course, not just at the end. Parametric functions are introduced using degrees because most students are more comfortable with degrees than radians.

Students should understand that in a parametric function the values of both *x* and *y* are *dependent* on the *independent* variable *t*. Explain that parametric functions make it possible to graph figures for which *y* is not a function of *x* (such as an ellipse). The ellipse in Example 1 is, in fact, a function. Students find this confusing because the ellipse does not pass the vertical line test. The way to explain this is to remind them that for every value of *t* there is exactly one ordered pair (x, y).

In Example 1, graphers need to be in degree and parametric modes. Students should first plot the graph using a window setting such as $0° \leq t \leq 360°$, *t*-step $= 5°$, $-7 \leq x \leq 7$, *x*-scale $= 1$, and $-9 \leq y \leq 9$. Then they should reset the window, or use ZOOM ZSquare if they are using graphers, to show equal scales on both axes. (This will make the ellipse have the proportions we expect.) Point out that the 5 in $x = 5 \cos t$ is the *x*-radius of the ellipse, which is the distance from the center to either *x*-intercept. Similarly, the 7 in $y = 7 \sin t$ is the *y*-radius, the distance from the center to either *y*-intercept. Students might originally select the window $0° \leq t \leq 360°$, $-10 \leq x \leq 10$, and $-10 \leq y \leq 10$. This will produce a very circular graph, and they may not realize it is an ellipse. They need to set the *x* and *y* ranges using a 3:2 ratio to roughly correspond to the number of pixels in the *x*- and *y*-directions on the calculator. In this case, $-15 \leq x \leq 15$ and $-10 \leq y \leq 10$ is a reasonable window.

To convince students that the parameter *t* is not an angle in standard position, have them trace the graph to find the point where $t = 45°$. (Note that tracing to the "right" increases the *t*-value.) At this point, $x = 3.53...$ and $y = 4.94....$ Because $y \neq x$, the point is not on the line $y = x$, and so the angle is not equal to 45°.

Encourage students to explore what happens when they make the *t*-step value smaller—say, 1°—or larger—say, 20°, 30°, or even 60°. The *t*-step value determines how many points the grapher calculates and plots. For example, if *t*-step $= 5°$ and $0° \leq t \leq 360°$, the grapher plots points for *t*-values of 0°, 5°, 10°, 15°, and so on. Consecutive points are connected to create a continuous graph. Using smaller steps slows the graphing process because more points are calculated, but it creates a smoother graph. Using larger steps speeds the process, but it creates a more jagged graph.

After students have done Example 1 in degrees, have them redo it in radians. They should set $0 \leq t \leq 2\pi$ and t-step = 0.1. If students calculate the x- and y-values for $t = \frac{\pi}{4}$, they will find that $x = 3.53\ldots$ and $y = 4.94\ldots$, which agree with the solution they got when tracing the graph.

In Example 2, the parameter of the parametric function from Example 1 is eliminated, giving a Cartesian equation relating x and y. (Note that for many pairs of parametric equations, the parameter *cannot* be easily eliminated.) From the Cartesian equation, $\left(\frac{x}{5}\right)^2 + \left(\frac{y}{7}\right)^2 = 1$, students can see that the ellipse is a dilation of the unit circle, which has equation $x^2 + y^2 = 1$. For more information about equations for ellipses and the unit circle, refer to the Supplementary Lesson Notes for this sections. Additional information about ellipses and other conic sections can be found in Chapter 12.

Example 3 demonstrates the effects of the constants h and k on the graph of $x = h + a \cos t$, $y = k + b \sin t$. The property box following Example 3 summarizes what students have learned about parametric equations for ellipses.

Students enjoy drawing three-dimensional shapes like the cylinder in Example 4. After the ellipses are drawn, have the students quit the graphing screen. On the TI-83 and TI-84 calculators, they can then press 2nd PRGM (DRAW), Line (and enter 2,9,11,9). Pressing ENTER will return students to the graphing window with the tops of the ellipses connected. Repeat the process to get the lower line.

The hidden part of the left ellipse can be eliminated by dividing one of the parametric equations by a Boolean variable.

$$x_2 = 2 + 1.3 \cos (t)/(90 \leq t \text{ and } t \leq 270)$$

$$y_2 = 5 + 4 \sin (t)$$

The hidden part can be drawn dashed by entering a third pair of parametric equations using dashed style. For this purpose, it is best to set the window with a t-range of $-90 \leq t \leq 270$. The equations would be

$$x_3 = 2 + 1.3 \cos (t)/(-90 \leq t \text{ and } t \leq 90)$$

$$y_3 = 5 + 4 \sin (t)$$

Figure 4-5a shows the final result.

Figure 4-5a

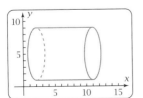

Exploration Notes

Exploration 4-5a is a good group activity. Students investigate pendulum motion, an application involving parametric equations. You may want to set up a few pendulums around the room so each group of students can "play" with the problem. At the very least, you need to have one pendulum set up for demonstration. You might use this activity on the first day of instruction, after you have introduced the idea of a parametric function. Allow about 25–30 minutes to complete the Exploration.

Exploration 4-5b provides students with extra practice on graphing three-dimensional figures. You can use this Exploration to supplement the problems in this section or as a review at the end of the chapter. Some of the problems can be done in class and the rest finished as a homework assignment. Allow 20 minutes for this Exploration.

Technology Notes

 Presentation Sketch: Parametric Present.gsp, on the *Instructor's Resource CD,* allows you to set a parameter and parametric equations and watch as a particle traces out a parametrically defined graph.

 Exploration 4-5b: Parametric Equations for Ellipses, in the *Instructor's Resource Book,* asks students to write parametric equations for ellipses that appear in certain figures, similar to those in Problems 7–14. Sketchpad could provide useful insight. This exploration could be reserved for or revisited in the study of conic sections in Section 12-2.

 Activity: Parametric Functions, in *Exploring Precalculus with The Geometer's Sketchpad,* allows students to explore parametric equations of several graphs in rectangular and polar coordinates. The activity extends parametric equations outside of conics. Allow 40–50 minutes.

 Activity: Parametrically Defined Functions, in *Connecting Mathematics with Science,* asks students to analyze the relationship between the incline of a treadmill and heart rate, both expressed as functions of time. This is a fairly easy experiment and should take students about 30 minutes.

Supplementary Lesson Notes

Background: Equations of Circles and Ellipses

In Example 2, students are asked to conclude that the Cartesian equation $\left(\frac{x}{5}\right)^2 + \left(\frac{y}{7}\right)^2 = 1$ is that of an ellipse. You may need to review ellipses and their equations with students. The equation of a unit circle centered at the origin is

$$x^2 + y^2 = 1$$

Figure 4-5b shows that this equation is a direct result of the Pythagorean theorem. For any point (x, y) on the unit circle, a right triangle can be drawn with legs of lengths $|x|$ and $|y|$ and with a hypotenuse of length 1.

Figure 4-5b

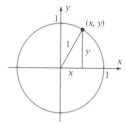

This unit circle serves as the parent graph for any other circle or any ellipse. For example, the ellipse in Figure 4-5c is a dilation of the unit circle by a factor of 5 in the horizontal direction and by a factor of 7 in the vertical direction. Recalling that the coefficients of x and y are the reciprocals of these dilation factors, the equation of the ellipse is

$$\left(\frac{1}{5}x\right)^2 + \left(\frac{1}{7}y\right)^2 = 1$$

This is equivalent to the equation in Example 2. Because the horizontal and vertical dilations are different, the ellipse has unequal radii in the x- and y-directions. The terms x-radius and y-radius can be used to distinguish between the two (Figure 4-5c).

Figure 4-5c

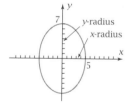

The dilated unit circle can also be translated in the x- and y-directions. For instance, the equation

$$\left(\frac{x - 6}{5}\right)^2 + \left(\frac{y + 3}{7}\right)^2 = 1$$

is a translation of the ellipse 6 units in the x-direction and -3 units in the y-direction (Figure 4-5c in the student book). Encourage students to leave the equation in this form. If it is

expanded, the translations and dilations are no longer apparent.

Problem Notes

- *Problems 1 and 2* have the students sketch parametric equations by hand and verify the results using their graphers. Emphasize the role of t as the independent variable and x and y as dependent variables. Students should choose at least five t-values for their tables, including negative t-values. Be sure to assign one of these.

- *Problems 3–6* require students to eliminate the parameter to turn the parametric equations into Cartesian equations.

- *Problems 7–14* are similar to Example 4.

- *Problem 15,* the Projectile Problem, shows how parametric equations can be used to describe and solve projectile motion problems.

- *Problem 16,* the Parametric Function Domain Problem, is important. It demonstrates that the restricted t-values in parametric form affect the domain and range in Cartesian form.

- *Problems 17–20* tell students to use radian mode. For all these problems, except Problem 18, students will get the same result if they use degree mode. Ask students why they will get a different graph if they use degree mode for Problem 18. (In the other problems, the parameter t is found only as an argument of trigonometric functions. As students know, circular and trigonometric functions are interchangeable. However, in Problem 18 the parameter also occurs as an algebraic expression in the equation, so it *does* make a difference whether the grapher is in degree or radian mode.)

- *Problem 21,* the Sine Curve Tracer Problem, provides an opportunity to develop a stronger understanding of parametric equations. It is highly recommended.

- *Problem 22,* the Graphs of Inverse Trigonometric Relations by Parametrics Problem, is a good lead-in to the next section. It should help students understand that the graph of $y = \arcsin x$ *is not* a function and that the graph of $y = \sin^{-1} x$ is a portion of the graph of $y = \arcsin x$ that *is* a function.

Supplementary Problems

1. *Hyperbola Problem:* Figure 4-5d shows graphs of two unit **hyperbolas** and the parametric equations for each one. In this problem you will graph transformed hyperbolas.

Figure 4-5d

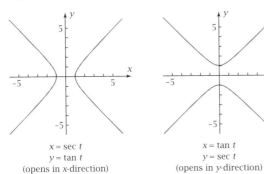

$x = \sec t$
$y = \tan t$
(opens in x-direction)

$x = \tan t$
$y = \sec t$
(opens in y-direction)

a. Plot the left graph on your grapher. Use degree mode, a t-range of 0° to 360°, and a t-step that makes grid points at 90° and 270° (where tangent and secant are undefined). Use the same scales on both axes. Does your graph agree with the one in Figure 4-5d?

b. The Cartesian equation of the unit hyperbola on the left is $x^2 - y^2 = 1$. Show how this equation can be derived from the parametric equations by eliminating the parameter t. The Pythagorean property relating secant and tangent should help.

c. Write the parametric equations of a hyperbola opening in the y-direction that has horizontal and vertical dilations of 5 and 3, respectively, and horizontal and vertical translations of −2 and 1, respectively.

d. Plot the parametric equations in part c. Use the same scales on both axes. Sketch the graph.

2. *Parametric Parabola Problem:* Consider the parametric function

$x_1 = \cos t$

$y_1 = \sin^2 t$

a. Set your grapher to radian mode. Plot the graph using a t-range of $[-2\pi, 2\pi]$ and a window that includes positive and negative values of x and y. Sketch the result.

b. The graph in part a should look like a parabola that opens downward. Confirm that it is a parabola by eliminating the parameter and showing that the Cartesian equation can be written as $y = f(x)$, where $f(x)$ has the form $ax^2 + bx + c$.

c. Plot the Cartesian equation in part b using parametric mode.

$x_2 = t$

$y_2 = f(t)$ $f(t)$ is the answer to y in part b, with t in place of x.

Explain why the Cartesian equation has a larger x-domain and y-range than the parametric equations.

Problems 3–7 involve parametric functions that have interesting graphs. Plot each graph on your grapher and sketch the result. Use radian mode.

3. $x = \sin 2t$ (a Lissajous or Bowditch curve)
$y = \cos^2 t$

4. $x = 5 \cos t - \cos 5t$ (an epicycloid of 4 cusps)
$y = 5 \sin t - \sin 5t$

5. $x = 2t + \sin t$ (a curtate cycloid)
$y = 2 - \cos t$

6. $x = t + 2 \sin t$ (a prolate cycloid)
$y = 1 - 2 \cos t$

7. $x = 2 \cot t$ (a witch of Maria Agnesi)
$y = 2 \sin^2 t$

8. $x = 2 \cos t + \cos 2t$ (a deltoid, or hypocycloid
$y = 2 \sin t - \sin 2t$ of 3 cusps)

9. *Historical Problem:* The inverse tangent function is relatively straightforward to calculate by computer. In later courses you'll learn that this is because it has a fairly simple **Taylor series** expansion,

$$\tan^{-1} x = x - \frac{1}{3}x^3 + \frac{1}{5}x^5 - \frac{1}{7}x^7 + \cdots$$

For this reason, some earlier computer software had only the inverse tangent function available. People were expected to calculate other inverse trigonometric functions from the value given for inverse tangent. In this problem you will see how that was done.

a. Using $x = 0.3$, find the sum of the first five terms, called the fifth partial sum, in the Taylor series above. Keep all the decimal places your calculator gives you. How does the answer compare with the value of $\tan^{-1} 0.3$ found directly from your calculator?

b. Use the techniques of this section to show that the function $\cos^{-1} x$ is given by

$$\cos^{-1} x = \tan^{-1} \frac{\sqrt{1-x^2}}{x} \text{ if } x \in (0, 1] \text{ or}$$

$$\pi + \tan^{-1} \frac{\sqrt{1-x^2}}{x} \text{ if } x \in [-1, 0)$$

c. Set each side of the equation in part b equal to y and plot them on the same screen. Use the domain $[-1, 1]$. Why does the original equation hold for all $x \in (0, 1]$ but not for $x \in [-1, 0)$?

d. Use the techniques of this section to show that the function $\sin^{-1} x$ is given by

$$\sin^{-1} x = \tan^{-1} \frac{x}{\sqrt{1-x^2}}$$

for all values of $x \in (-1, 1)$

e. Plot on the same screen the graphs of the two sides of the equation in part d. Sketch the results. How do the graphs confirm that the equation is true?

4-6
Inverse Trigonometric Relation Graphs

Objectives

- Plot graphs of inverse trigonometric functions and relations.

- Find exact values of functions of inverse trigonometric functions.

Class Time

2 days

Homework Assignment

Day 1: RA, Q1–Q10, Problems 1–4, 5–9 odd

Day 2: Problems 11–23 odd, 24, 26

Also recommended: Problem 25

Important Terms and Concepts

Reflection

Principal branch

General solution

Inverse trigonometric relation (inverse circular relation)

Inverse trigonometric function (inverse circular function)

Composite of a function and its inverse

Lesson Notes

In Section 4-6, students look at graphs of inverse trigonometric *relations* and learn how an inverse trigonometric *function* can be defined by restricting the range of the corresponding relation. They also find exact values of expressions involving inverse trigonometric functions. It is recommended that you spend two days on this section.

A Note on Terminology

Some texts use Arctan or Tan^{-1} (with the first letter capitalized) to indicate the inverse tangent function. In this text, tan^{-1} (all lowercase) is used to represent the inverse tangent function, and arctan (also lowercase) is used for the general, multiple-valued relation. Make sure students understand this distinction.

Begin the first day of instruction by discussing the material about the inverse tangent function in the text or by assigning Exploration 4-6a. The topics covered in the Exploration are similar to those in the text, but the inverse sine is used instead of the inverse tangent. Then have groups of students complete Exploration 4-6b. This activity helps students understand the concept of principal branches and how they are selected. If students struggle with this activity, have them read the criteria for selecting principal branches in their books, complete Problem 13 of the Exploration, and then work on the remaining problems. Be sure to follow the Exploration with a class discussion about what students discovered. Review the information in the definition box on page 186 and the text that follows the box.

Cover the remainder of Section 4-6 on the second day. Example 1 provides a straightforward geometric method for evaluating expressions involving the composition of a trigonometric function with an inverse trigonometric function. Example 2 applies the same method to a more abstract problem. Students are often confused when the graph of a semicircle does not appear to "touch" the x-axis when they graph it on a grapher. This is due to limitations in the grapher itself. You may wish to use this example to remind students that they should always be critical of what they see on their graphers.

Example 3 evaluates the composition of the cosine function and its inverse. When you discuss this example, be sure to focus on the domain and range of the composite function. Make sure students understand why the domain of the composite function $y = \cos(\cos^{-1} x)$ is limited to $[-1, 1]$. You might also want to discuss the composite function $y = \cos^{-1}(\cos x)$. Have students graph this composite function on their graphers, showing values from -4π to 4π on the x-axis and values from -2π to 2π on the y-axis (see Figure 4-6a).

Figure 4-6a

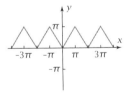

Discuss the shape of the graph and ask students why $y = \cos^{-1}(\cos x)$ has domain $[-\infty, \infty]$ and range $[0, \pi]$. Then point out that $y = \cos^{-1}(\cos x) = x$ only on the interval $[0, \pi]$.

Example 3 leads to the general property about the composition of a function and its inverse. It is important for students to understand that the property holds only if x is in *both* the range of the outside function *and* the domain of the inside function. Illustrate this point by referring to the composite functions $y = \cos(\cos^{-1} x)$ and $y = \cos^{-1}(\cos x)$. In Example 3, students saw that $\cos(\cos^{-1} x) = x$ for $x \in [-1, 1]$. These are the values that are in *both* the range of the cosine function *and* the domain of the inverse cosine function. Similarly, $\cos^{-1}(\cos x) = x$ only for $x \in [0, \pi]$. These are the values that are in *both* the range of $\cos^{-1} x$ *and* the domain of $\cos x$. Discuss the examples after the property box, which illustrate the restrictions. Problems 23 and 24 will give students additional practice working with the composite of a function and its inverse.

Exploration Notes

Exploration 4-6a is an investigation of the inverse sine relation and the inverse sine function. Students learn to graph the relation $y = \arcsin x$ on their graphers. Then they graph the function $y = \sin^{-1} x$ and use the graph to identify the principal branch of the arcsine curve. Students also observe that the sine and inverse sine graphs are reflections of one another through the line $y = x$. This Exploration is a good group activity to begin the first day of instruction. Allow 20 minutes for this Exploration.

Exploration 4-6b leads students to graph inverse trigonometric functions. They use their calculators to find the principal branches for the inverse sine, cosine, and tangent relations and then to reason about the best choices for principal branches for the inverse trigonometric functions. You might ask students why their calculator gives the wrong answer for $\cot^{-1}(-3)$. The answer is that they are using the reciprocal of $\tan^{-1}(-3)$ and the ranges of $y = \tan^{-1} x$ and $y = \cot^{-1} x$ are different from each other. See Supplementary Problem 1 on the next page. This Exploration is a good group activity for the first day of instruction. Allow 20 minutes for this Exploration.

Exploration 4-6c requires students to find multiple values for arcsin 0.8, arccos (−0.3), and arctan 4 and then to identify the value on the principal branch of each inverse relation. You might assign this Exploration as homework after the first day of instruction. This Exploration should take about 20 minutes.

Additional Class Example

Find the exact value of $\cos\left(\tan^{-1} \frac{3}{4}\right)$ geometrically. Check your answer by direct calculation.

Solution

Draw an angle in standard position whose tangent is $\frac{3}{4}$ (Figure 4-6b). The angle terminates in Quadrant I because the range of the inverse tangent function is Quadrants I and IV. Draw a reference triangle, and find the length of the hypotenuse. Then use the definition of cosine.

Figure 4-6b

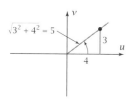

$$\cos\left(\tan^{-1}\frac{3}{4}\right) = \frac{4}{5} = 0.8$$

By calculator, $\cos\left(\tan^{-1}\left(\frac{3}{4}\right)\right) = 0.8$, which agrees with the geometric answer.

Problem Notes

- *Problems 1–4* emphasize the graphs of inverse trigonometric relations and functions. Be sure to assign these problems so that students become more comfortable using the parametric mode and switching back and forth between parametric and function modes. When graphing inverse trigonometric relations, it is important to set up the window so that Tmin and Tmax are equal to Ymin and Ymax. This will make the graphs fill the screen.

- *Problems 10, 12, and 14* involve the inverse cotangent, cosecant, and secant functions. You may need to review how to find values of these functions on a grapher.

- *Problems 11 and 12* produce results that may surprise students. In each case, drawing the appropriate reference triangle and using the definitions of the trigonometric functions should explain the surprise.

- *Problems 13 and 14* illustrate that $f(f^{-1}(x))$ may not equal x if x does not satisfy the restrictions stated in the property box on page 188.

- *Problem 23,* the Composite of a Function and Its Inverse Problem, helps students to prove that $f(f^{-1}(x)) = x$ and $f^{-1}(f(x)) = x$.

- *Problem 24,* the Interpretation Problem— Composite of a Function and Its Inverse, asks students to explore composites of trigonometric functions and their inverses. Students need to explain why the composite is equivalent to $y = x$ for all x in some cases and for only certain x-values in other cases. This is a good problem to discuss in class.

- *Problem 25,* the Tunnel Problem, presents a situation that can be modeled with a sinusoid.

Supplementary Problems

1. With your grapher in function mode, plot the graphs of $y = \sec^{-1} x$, $y = \csc^{-1} x$, and $y = \cot^{-1} x$. To do this, recall, for example, that $y = \sec^{-1} x$ is equivalent to $y = \cos^{-1}\frac{1}{x}$. Use a friendly window that includes $x = 1$ and $x = -1$ as grid points. How do the graphs compare with those shown in Figure 4-6d of the student book? Explain why the principal branches for the inverse secant and inverse cosecant functions have the same range as your graph, whereas the principal branch for the inverse cotangent has a different range.

   Note: The calculator produces the wrong graph for $y = \cot^{-1} x$ because $y = \cot^{-1} x$ must be entered as $y = \tan^{-1}\left(\frac{1}{x}\right)$ and the domain of the inverse tangent function, $\left(\frac{-\pi}{2}, \frac{\pi}{2}\right)$, is *not* the correct domain for the inverse cotangent function. The calculator graph for $y = \cot^{-1} x$ needs to be translated up by π when $x < 0$ and defined to be $\frac{\pi}{2}$ when $x = 0$.

2. With your grapher in parametric mode, plot the graphs of $y = \text{arcsec } x$, $y = \text{arccsc } x$, and $y = \text{arccot } x$. To do this for inverse secant, for example, enter

   $$x = 1/\cos t$$

   $$y = t$$

   Use a friendly window that includes $x = 1$ and $x = -1$ as grid points. Use equal scales on both axes. To make the graph fill the screen, the t-range should be the same as the y-range. How do the graphs compare with those shown in Figure 4-6d of the student book?

For Problems 3–10, calculate the exact value of the inverse function geometrically. Assume the principal branch in all cases. Check your answers by direct calculation.

3. $\cot\left[\sin^{-1}\left(-\frac{1}{\sqrt{2}}\right)\right]$ 4. $\tan\left[\text{arcsec}\left(-\sqrt{2}\right)\right]$

5. $\csc\,(\text{arccot } 3)$ 6. $\csc\left(\tan^{-1}\frac{1}{2}\right)$

7. $\csc\,(\text{arccsc } 2)$ 8. $\sin\left(\sin^{-1}\frac{2}{3}\right)$

9. $y = \tan\,(\cos^{-1} x)$ 10. $y = \sin\,(\cos^{-1} x)$

11. *Inverse of a Linear Function Problem:* Let f be the function with the following equation.

The equation of f: $\quad y = 3x + 2$

You can find the equation of the inverse relation by interchanging the variables x and y.

The equation of the inverse relation:
$x = 3y + 2$

a. Find the slope and the x- and y-intercepts of f.

b. Transform the equation of the inverse relation so that y is expressed in terms of x. Does the equation define a function? Explain.

c. Use the result of part b to find the slope and the x- and y-intercepts of f^{-1}. How do the slope and intercepts of f^{-1} compare with those of f?

d. Figure 4-6c shows the graphs of f and f^{-1}. How are the graphs related to the line $y = x$?

Figure 4-6c

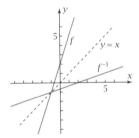

e. The equations of f and f^{-1} can be written as $f(x) = 3x + 2$ and $f^{-1}(x) = \frac{1}{3}x - \frac{2}{3}$. By appropriate substitution, show that $f(f^{-1}(x)) = x$ and $f^{-1}(f(x)) = x$.

12. *Inverse of a Quadratic Function:* Let g be the function with the following equation.

Equation of g: $\quad y = x^2$

You can find the equation of the inverse relation for g by interchanging the variables x and y.

The equation of the inverse relation:
$x = y^2$

a. Transform the g^{-1} equation so that y is in terms of x.

b. Plot the graphs of g and its inverse on the same screen. You will have to be clever to get both branches of the inverse relation graph.

c. Explain how you can demonstrate that the two graphs are reflections of each other across the line $y = x$. A sketch might help.

d. Is the inverse of g a function? Explain.

4-7
Chapter Review and Test

Objective

Review and practice the major concepts presented in this chapter.

Class Time

2 days (including 1 day for testing)

Homework Assignment

Day 1: R0–R6, T1–T15

Day 2 (after Chapter 4 Test): Problem C1 *or* Problem Set 5-1

Lesson Notes

Section 4-7 contains a set of Review Problems, a set of Concept Problems, and a Chapter Test. The Review Problems include one problem for each section in the chapter. You may wish to use the Chapter Test as an additional set of review problems.

Encourage students to practice the no-calculator problems without a calculator so that they are prepared for the test problems for which they cannot use a calculator.

5 Properties of Combined Sinusoids

This chapter introduces the other properties of trigonometric functions. A grapher makes it possible to study these properties as combinations of sinusoids rather than as purely algebraic properties. Thus, students learn by graphing that a linear combination of cosine and sine with equal periods is another sinusoid with a phase displacement. The composite argument properties (sometimes called addition formulas) are then used to prove this fact by expressing $\cos (A - B)$ as $\cos A \cos B + \sin A \sin B$. By learning to say this property verbally, "Cosine of first minus second equals cosine of first, sine of second plus sine of first, sine of second," students can more easily apply it to such expressions as $\cos\left(\frac{\pi}{2} - A\right)$. Sums or products of sinusoids with unequal periods lead to graphs with varying amplitude or varying sinusoidal axes. Students then learn the reverse process, harmonic analysis, to find the sinusoids that were added or multiplied to get a given graph. The sum and product properties allow students to see that a product of sinusoids with much different periods is equivalent to a sum of sinusoids with nearly equal periods, the basis of AM and FM radio waves. The double and half argument properties become simple extensions of the composite argument properties that you can derive quickly rather than having to memorize. It is the combined verbal, graphical, and algebraic approach to the properties that avoids the difficulties students usually experience.

5-1
Introduction to Combinations of Sinusoids

Objective

Investigate graphs formed by sums of sines and cosines.

Class Time

$\frac{1}{2}$ day

Homework Assignment

Problems 1–9

Lesson Notes

This exploratory problem set helps students see that when two sinusoids with *the same period* are added, the result is another sinusoid with the same period but with a different amplitude and phase displacement. You can assign Section 5-1 for homework the night of the Chapter 4 test or as a group activity to be completed in class. No classroom discussion is needed before students begin the activity.

Problem Notes

• *Problem 6* is not easy, and you might want to mention this to your students. The intention of this problem is partly this realization and for students to try to guess and see that simple combinations won't work. Some students might try to find the answer by reading ahead, which would also be fine.

• *Problems 7 and 8* make the point that cosine does *not* distribute over addition and subtraction. Discussing this problem in class will help students avoid this common pitfall. Similar problems will appear as homework in later sections.

5-2
Composite Argument and Linear Combination Properties

Objective

Derive a composite argument property expressing $\cos(A - B)$ in terms of cosines and sines of A and B, and use it to express a linear combination of cosine and sine as a single cosine with a phase displacement.

Class Time

2 days

Homework Assignment

Day 1

RA, Q1–Q10, Problems 1–15 odd, 16, 17

Day 2

Suggested: Problems 19–27 odd, 29, 30, 33

Also recommended: Problems 28, 31, 32

Technology Options

 Figure 5-2b: Linear Combination Property

 Exploration 5-2a: Linear Combination of Cosine and Sine

 Exploration 5-2a: Cosine of a Difference

Important Terms and Concepts

In phase

Linear combination

Composite argument property

Distance formula

Complement

Lesson Notes

In this section, students learn to express a linear combination of cosine and sine with the same period as a single cosine with a phase displacement. They also learn a composite argument property for expressing $\cos(A - B)$ in terms of cosines and sines of A and B. It is recommended that you spend two days on this lesson. Cover Example 1 on the first day and the remaining examples on the second day.

The section opens by revisiting the function $y = 3\cos\theta + 4\sin\theta$ from Section 5-1. In that section, students observed that the graph appears to be a sinusoid. The text explains that the function is indeed a sinusoid and demonstrates a technique for writing it in the form $y = A \cos(\theta - D)$.

Example 1 applies the technique to a different linear combination of sine and cosine. When you present this example, emphasize the importance of making a sketch to determine the quadrant for D.

The property box following Example 1 summarizes the technique used in the example. Emphasize to students that the property applies only to linear combinations in which the sine and cosine have *equal periods*. (Section 5-4 covers linear combinations of sinusoids with different periods.) Students will derive the property in Problem 32, after they have learned the composite argument property for $\cos(A - B)$.

In Section 5-1, students observed that $\cos(A - B)$ is *not* equal to $\cos A - \cos B$. The example in the book shows that although $\cos(58° - 20°) \neq \cos(58° - 20°)$, it *is* possible to express $\cos(58° - 20°)$ exactly in terms of cosines and signs of 58° and 20°. The text then shows a derivation of the composite argument property for $\cos(A - B)$. If you want students to work through the derivation on their own, you can assign Exploration 5-2c.

If your students studied multiplication and rotation of matrices in second-year algebra, you can show them how to derive formulas for $\cos(A + B)$ and $\sin(A + B)$ quickly and elegantly. On a unit circle, mark a point $(\cos A, \sin A)$, and write the point as a 2×1 matrix

$$R_A = \begin{bmatrix} \cos A \\ \sin A \end{bmatrix}$$

Left-multiplying by the matrix

$$\begin{bmatrix} \cos B & -\sin B \\ \sin B & \cos B \end{bmatrix}$$

rotates by an angle B. The product is

$$R_{A+B} = \begin{bmatrix} \cos A \cos B - \sin A \sin B \\ \sin A \cos B + \cos A \sin B \end{bmatrix}$$

From this matrix you can read the formulas for both $\cos(A + B)$ and $\sin(A + B)$:

$$\cos(A + B) = \cos A \cos B - \sin A \sin B$$

$$\sin(A + B) = \sin A \cos B + \cos A \sin B$$

To get the formula for $\cos(A - B)$, just rewrite it as $\cos(A + (-B))$ and apply the formula, remembering that sine is an odd function and cosine is an even function.

When you state the composite argument properties in this and future sections, it is helpful for students

if you state it in words. For instance, you might verbalize the composite argument property for $\cos(A - B)$ as "Cosine of first (angle) minus second (angle) equals cosine of first times cosine of second plus sine of first times sine of second." In addition to helping students remember the property as a *procedure,* this gives them flexibility to substitute expressions besides A and B for "first" and "second."

In Example 2, the composite argument property for $\cos(A - B)$ is used to express a cosine with a phase displacement as the sum of a cosine and a sine with equal periods. Example 3 shows how the linear combination property can be used to solve certain trigonometric equations algebraically. Again, emphasize the importance of making a sketch.

When you complete this section, consider giving a quiz.

Exploration Notes

Exploration 5-2a can be used as a guided discovery exercise to teach students the linear combination property on the second day of instruction or as a review sheet or a quiz. Allow students about 20 minutes to complete the Exploration.

Exploration 5-2b leads students to discover the composite argument property for $\cos(A - B)$. You could assign this activity before showing the derivation of the property, or you could use it as a review activity. Allow students 15–20 minutes to complete the activity.

Exploration 5-2c guides students through a derivation of the composite argument property for $\cos(A - B)$. You could assign this activity as an alternative to presenting the derivation to the class. When students have completed the activity, be sure to discuss the results with them. You could also assign this Exploration as a homework assignment to follow up Exploration 5-2b. Allow 10–15 minutes if you are doing the activity in class.

Technology Notes

 Figure 5-2b: Linear Combination Property is demonstrated in the Dynamic Precalculus Exploration at *www.keymath.com/precalc.* The sketch shows that $3 \cos x + 4 \sin x$ is a sinusoidal wave, and it asks students to estimate the amplitude and phase displacement.

 Exploration 5-2a: Linear Combination of Cosine and Sine, in the *Instructor's Resource Book,* asks students to write linear combinations $y = b \cos \theta + c \sin \theta$ as $y = A \cos(\theta - D)$. Using Sketchpad for graphing can greatly enhance this Exploration.

Exploration 5-2a: Cosine of a Difference, in the *Instructor's Resource Book,* asks students to write cos (A − B) in terms of cos A, cos B, sin A, and sin B. Using Sketchpad for graphing can greatly enhance this Exploration.

Problem Notes

- *Problems 1–16* give students practice applying the linear combination property.

- *Problems 19–22* give students practice applying the composite argument property for cos (A − B).

- *Problems 23–26* are similar to Example 3.

- *Problem 29,* the Cofunction Property for Cosines and Sines Problem, requires students to use the composite argument property to prove the cofunction property for cosines and sines. The cofunction properties will be used in Section 5-3 to derive composite argument properties.

- *Problem 30,* the Even Property of Cosine Problem, leads students to use the composite argument property to show algebraically that cos (−θ) = cos θ. This idea will be used in Section 5-3 to derive composite argument properties.

- *Problem 32,* the Linear Combination of Cosine and Sine Derivation Problem, leads students through a derivation of the linear combination property.

Supplementary Problems

1. Express the trigonometric function $y = \cos 5\theta + \sin 5\theta$ as a single sinusoid with a phase displacement. What effect does the "5" have on your work?

2. Figure 5-2a shows a cosine graph and a sine graph. Find equations for these two sinusoids. Then find an equation for the sum of the two sinusoids as a single sinusoid with a phase displacement. Verify your answers by plotting on your grapher.

Figure 5-2a

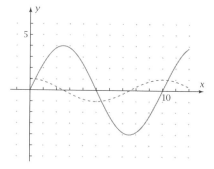

3. *Laser Beam Problem:* Two laser light beams are shining at a point on a wall. Both beams have a wavelength of 4000 angstroms, but they arrive at the point exactly a quarter-cycle out of phase. If x is time in seconds, the equations of the two laser beams are

$$y_1 = 50 \cos [(1.5\pi \cdot 10^{15})x] \quad \text{and}$$

$$y_2 = 70 \sin [(1.5\pi \cdot 10^{15})x]$$

The amplitudes, 50 and 70, measure the intensities of the beams.

a. The equation for the light arriving at the point on the wall is the sum of the equations for the two laser beams. Write an equation for this light as a single sinusoid with a phase displacement.

b. Is the intensity of the light spot on the wall the sum of the intensities of the two laser beams? Explain why or why not.

c. The wavelength of a sinusoidal beam of light is the distance the light travels in one period. An angstrom is 10^{-10} meters. Light moves at $3 \cdot 10^8$ meters per second. Show how the constant $1.5\pi \cdot 10^{15}$ in the two equations is derived from the information in this problem.

4. *Exact Value of cos 15° Problem:* You can write cos 15° as cos (45° − 30°). Use the composite argument property to show that

$$\cos 15° = \frac{\sqrt{6} + \sqrt{2}}{4}$$

Verify that this value is correct by evaluating the radicals and comparing the answer with the value of cos 15° found directly by calculator. (*Note:* This is Problem 34 in Section 5-3.)

5-3

Other Composite Argument Properties

Objective

For trigonometric functions f, derive and learn properties for:

- $f(-x)$ in terms of $f(x)$

- $f(90° - \theta)$ in terms of functions of θ or $f\left(\frac{\pi}{2} - x\right)$ in terms of functions of x

- $f(A + B)$ and $f(A - B)$ in terms of functions of A and functions of B

Class Time

2 days

Homework Assignment

Day 1

RA, Q1–Q10, Problems 1–9 odd, 10, 11–15 odd

Day 2

Recommended: Problems 14, 17–31 odd, 33, 36

Also suggested: Problem 40

Important Terms and Concepts

Odd-even properties

Parity

Complementary

Cofunction properties

Composite argument properties

Triple argument properties

Lesson Notes

This section introduces a host of new trigonometric properties. Thankfully, students do not need to memorize all of them because they can use the duality property of trigonometric functions (Section 4-2, Problem 13) to figure out the rest.

The odd-even properties are important in this course and in calculus. Students were introduced to even and odd functions in Section 1-6. Remind them that an even function is a function for which $f(-x) = f(x)$ for all x in the domain and that even functions are symmetric with respect to the y-axis. Present some examples, such as $y = x^2$, $y = 3x^4 + x^2$, and $y = |x|$. Then remind students that an odd

function is a function for which $f(-x) = -f(x)$. Odd functions have point symmetry with respect to the origin. Present examples of odd functions, such as $y = x$ and $y = x^3$. Then use the examples and graphs and Figure 5-3a in the student text to help explain why cosine is even, whereas sine and tangent are odd. Also explain that a reciprocal of a function has the same parity as the function.

Discuss the cofunction properties with students. Although twelve properties are presented, tell students they need to memorize only a quarter of these. Because trigonometric and circular functions exhibit the same properties, the number of properties is cut from twelve to six. Using the dual properties for trigonometric functions reduces these six properties to three. Students should learn the properties for $\cos \theta$, $\cot \theta$, and $\csc \theta$.

The odd-even and cofunction properties, along with the composite argument property for $\cos(A - B)$, can be used to derive the remaining five composite argument properties. Keeping the formulas straight is a formidable task. Advise students to try to understand the derivations rather than memorizing the formulas. Point out that if they memorize the formula for $\cos(A - B)$ and learn the odd-even and cofunction properties, they will be able to derive the other formulas when they need them. Some students may also want to memorize the formula for $\tan(A - B)$, as its derivation is rather tricky.

Example 1 uses the composite argument property for $\sin(A - B)$ to solve an equation algebraically. Reinforce that answers generated algebraically are exact. Students can use the trace and intersect features on their graphers to verify their solutions.

Consider giving a quiz when you complete this section.

Problem Notes

- *Problems 1–20* reinforce the odd-even properties, the cofunction properties, and the composite argument properties.

- *Problems 21–26* are similar to Example 1 and provide practice in solving equations using the composite argument properties.

- *Problems 27–32* call for exact answers in radical form. In spite of this instruction, some students will try to get by with decimal approximations. Again, emphasize the difference between an exact answer and an approximation. Remind students that there is a no-calculator part of the chapter test. It is important to be able to find the exact answers without the aid of a calculator.

- *Problems 39 and 40* introduce the cofunction properties for *inverse* circular functions.

- *Problems 41 and 42* require students to derive triple argument properties. You may want to help students get started by writing $\cos(A + B + C)$ as $\cos((A + B) + C)$ or $\cos(A + (B + C))$. You might have half the class use the first association while the other half uses the second. They can then compare their answers.

Supplementary Problems

Exact Function Value Problems: Figure 5-3a shows angles A and B in standard position in a *uv*-coordinate system. For Problems 1–6, use the information in the figure to find *exact* values (no decimals). Check your answers by calculating A and B, adding or subtracting them, and finding the function values directly.

Figure 5-3a

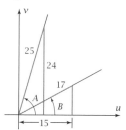

1. $\cos(A - B)$

2. $\sin(A - B)$

3. $\tan(A - B)$

4. $\cos(A + B)$

5. $\sin(A + B)$

6. $\tan(A + B)$

5-4
Composition of Ordinates and Harmonic Analysis

Objectives

- Given two sinusoids, form a new graph by adding or multiplying ordinates (*y*-coordinates).

- Given a graph formed by adding or multiplying two sinusoids, find the equations of the two sinusoids.

Class Time

2 days

Homework Assignment

Day 1: RA, Q1–Q10, Problems 1, 3, 5

Day 2: Problems 7–15 odd

Suggested: Problem 12

Technology Options

 Presentation Sketch: Sinusoidal Sum Present.gsp

 Presentation Sketch: Sinusoidal Product Present.gsp

 Exploration 5-4a: Sum or Product of Sinusoids with Unequal Periods

 Explorations 5-4b–5-4d: Harmonic Analysis

 Activity: Sums of Sinusoidal Functions

 Activity: Products of Sinusoidal Functions

Important Terms and Concepts

Composition of ordinates

Harmonic analysis

Variable sinusoidal axis

Variable amplitude

Envelope curve

Tangent

Lesson Notes

It is certainly possible to teach a very solid trigonometry course without covering the material in this section. However, there are several beautiful things about this section: The concepts presented give students an opportunity to integrate many different aspects of the trigonometry they have learned to date. It gives you an opportunity to explore an interesting area of trigonometry in some depth. In addition, the ideas have many interesting and useful real-world applications.

In this section, students use composition of ordinates to sketch graphs of sums and products of sinusoids. They use the reverse process, harmonic analysis, to "decompose" a complicated graph into a sum or product of sinusoids. Although harmonic analysis is not part of a traditional trigonometry course, graphing calculators have made this topic accessible to high school students.

Students have seen that the sum of two sinusoids with *equal* periods is another sinusoid with the same period. In this section, they learn that the sum of two sinusoids with *unequal* periods is periodic, though it is not necessarily sinusoidal. For instance, the graph in Figure 5-4c in the student text is not sinusoidal. Students sometimes think all wavy periodic functions are sinusoidal. Students can sketch the graph of the sum of two sinusoids by adding ordinates (*y*-coordinates) for the two graphs. This technique is illustrated in Example 1, which shows that the sinusoid with the greater period acts as a variable sinusoidal axis for the other sinusoid. A blackline master of Figure 5-4d is available in the *Instructor's Resource Book*. You may want to give a copy of it to your students and ask them to add the two functions by hand.

The product of two sinusoids with *equal* periods is a sinusoid. (This will be proved in Section 5-6. In this section, students merely observe this fact.) However, the product of two sinusoids with *unequal* periods is a periodic function with a variable amplitude. Students can sketch the graph of the product of two sinusoids by multiplying ordinates for the two graphs. Example 2 shows that the function with the greater amplitude acts as an envelope for the composed graph.

Note that the property box following Example 2 talks about sinusoids with "greatly different periods." Supplementary Problem 17 addresses this issue. This problem is a lead-in to the sum and product properties in the next section.

Harmonic analysis allows us to reverse the process of composition of ordinates to find the "parent" sinusoids that were added or multiplied to create the more complicated graph. The techniques outlined in the section, along with a willingness to experiment using their graphing calculators, will help students decompose the graphs.

Exploration Notes

Exploration 5-4a is a good activity to introduce composition of ordinates. Have groups work for about five minutes on Problem 1 while you circulate around. Then, on a transparency of the Exploration, show how to find points on the combined graph. Where the small graph has zeros, the product graph also has zeros. Where the small graph has high points ($y = 1$), the product graph touches the larger graph. Where the small graph has low points ($y = -1$), the product graph touches the *reflection* of the larger graph. Then show how the points should be connected. After students have seen the solution to Problem 2, have them check by grapher as specified in Problem 3. Present the sum graph in Problems 5, 6, and 7 the same way. This time the sum graph crosses the larger graph where the small graph has zeros, and goes between 1 unit below and 1 unit above the larger graph. Make sure students understand the conclusions in Problems 8 and 9. Allow 15–20 minutes.

Exploration 5-4b is a good activity to introduce harmonic analysis as a guided discovery activity the second day. Working out each part separately, back-to-back, will help students further distinguish between sums and products of sinusoids. Allow 20 minutes for this activity.

Explorations 5-4c and 5-4d can be used as group activities or quizzes on subsequent days. Note that the third and fourth problems on each of these Explorations involve circular functions in radians. An easy way to find the coefficient for *x* or for θ in the smaller-period sinusoid when the period of the larger is not 2π or 360° is to multiply the coefficient in the larger by the number of cycles the given graph makes in one period. For instance, in Exploration 5-4c, Problem 3, the sinusoidal axis is $y_1 = 2 \sin \frac{\pi}{4}x$. The given graph makes 20 cycles for one cycle of the y_1 graph. So the coefficient of *x* in the smaller graph is $(20)(\pi/4) = 5\pi$, making $y_2 = 3 \cos 5\pi x$. Allow 15 minutes for Exploration 5-4c. By the time students encounter Exploration 5-4d, they should be confident enough to do it in 10 minutes.

Technology Notes

 Presentation Sketch: Sinusoidal Sum Present.gsp, on the *Instructor's Resource CD,* demonstrates the occurrence of beats present when two sinusoidal waves with close periods are added together. The functions can easily be changed to demonstrate the sum of other sinusoidal functions.

Presentation Sketch: Sinusoidal Product Present.gsp, on the *Instructor's Resource CD,* demonstrates the occurrence of beats present when two sinusoidal waves with different periods are multiplied together. The functions can easily be changed to demonstrate the product of other sinusoidal functions.

 Exploration 5-4a: Sum or Product of Sinusoids with Unequal Periods, in the *Instructor's Resource Book,* can be done with the aid of Sketchpad or Fathom.

 Explorations 5-4b–5-4d: Harmonic Analysis, in the *Instructor's Resource Book,* are all activities in which students are asked to write equations for given graphs of sums or products of sinusoids. The high resolution and dynamic atmosphere available on Sketchpad or Fathom may provide a useful tool for students as they do these Explorations.

 Activity: Sums of Sinusoidal Functions, in the *Instructor's Resource Book,* is for intermediate-to-advanced users. Students analyze the sums of sinusoidal waves as they model superposition and wave packets. A presentation sketch is also available. Allow 50 minutes.

Activity: Products of Sinusoidal Functions, in the *Instructor's Resource Book,* can be considered a follow-up to the previous activity. The included example sketch can make the activity accessible to beginning Sketchpad users. A presentation sketch is available. Allow 40–50 minutes.

Problem Notes

• *Problems 1 and 2* ask students several questions about the graphs of two sinusoids in Figure 5-4n. A blackline master of Figure 5-4n is available in the *Instructor's Resource Book.*

• *Problems 3–12,* Harmonic Analysis Problems, ask students to find equations for given graphs. When students think they have found a correct equation, they should "zoom in" on a portion of its graph to see if it has the same features as the graph in the text. Remind students to pay close attention to the scale on the horizontal axis and to write their equations using the appropriate unit, degrees or radians. A blackline master for these problems is available in the *Instructor's Resource Book.*

• *Problem 13,* the Submarine Sonar Problem, works well as a group activity.

• *Problem 14,* the Sunrise Project, or Supplementary Problem 16, the Musical Harmony Project, can form the basis for a project.

Supplementary Problems

For Problems 1-15, find the particular equation of
the graph shown. Each is the sum or product of two
sinusoids of unequal periods. Note whether the
argument is in degrees or radians.

1.

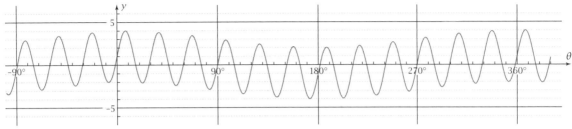

2.

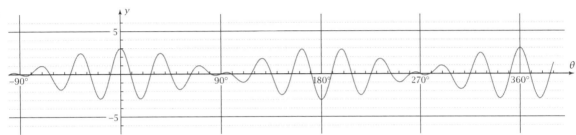

3.

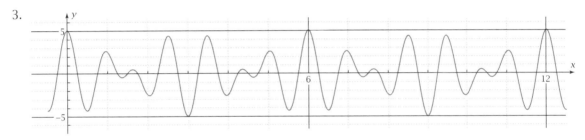

4.

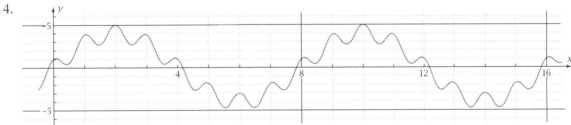

5.

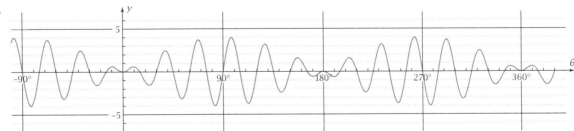

6.

7.

8.

9.

10.

11.

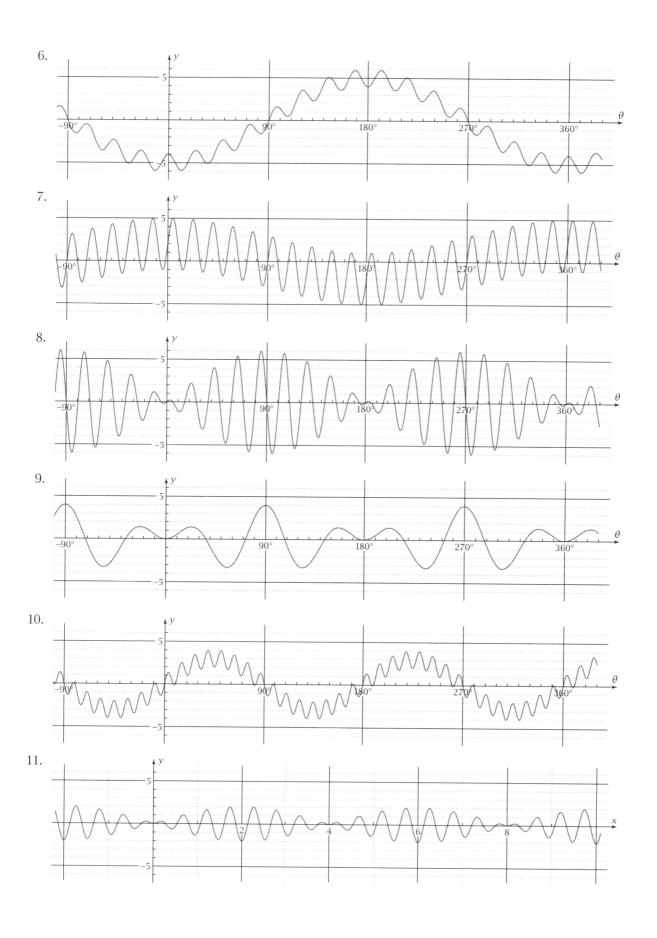

12.

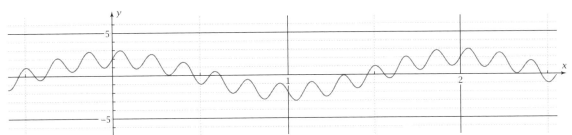

13.

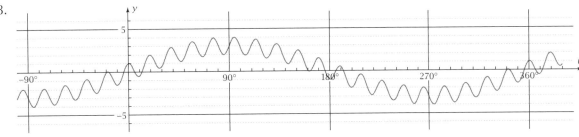

14.

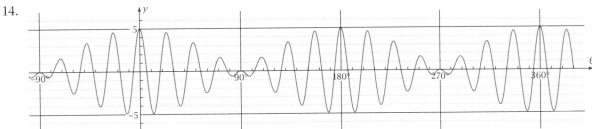

15.

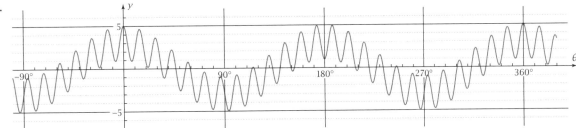

16. *Musical Harmony Project:* Musical notes are generated by vibrations of a voice or musical instrument. The vibrations cause the air pressure to increase and decrease slightly at the same frequency at which the instrument is vibrating. The pressure fluctuations move through the air at the speed of sound, about 750 mi/h, and cause the eardrum to vibrate at the same frequency. The brain interprets the vibration as sound. The *pitch* of the sound is measured by the frequency of the vibrations. The *loudness* of the sound is measured by the amplitude of the vibrations.

Each note has its own fundamental frequency, called the *tonic* by musicians. For instance, the tonic of the C below middle C is 264 cycles/s. A note is accompanied by *overtones*, which have frequencies that are multiples of the tonic.

a. Write an equation for the C below middle C. Let *y* be the pressure and *t* be time. Use the sine function and an amplitude of 1. (Because no angles are involved, you should use a *circular* function, not a trigonometric function.)

b. The first overtone will have a frequency two times that of the tonic, the second overtone will have a frequency three times that of the tonic, and so on. Write an equation for the second overtone of C. Use the sine function with an amplitude of 0.4.

c. The sound produced by C and its second overtone is the *sum* of the two sound waves. Plot the combined graphs of the equations from parts a and b. Use a friendly window with an *x*-range of about $0 \leq x \leq 0.01$ and a window with a suitable *y*-range. Sketch the result.

d. Two notes *harmonize* if they have many overtones in common. The table at right shows the frequencies of the notes C, F, and G, along with harmonics (multiples).

List the common multiples of:

i. C and G   ii. C and F   iii. G and F

e. Based on your answers to part d, which notes should harmonize well and which should not?

f. If the "harmonic" had an amplitude 0.4 times the tonic, as in part b, but a frequency 2.1 times the tonic, then the graph would look like the one in Figure 5-4a. Why do you suppose the note would no longer sound like "harmony"?

g. True or false: "'Harmonizes with'" is a *transitive* relationship."

h. Obtain a keyboard or tuning forks. Demonstrate that your answer to part e is correct.

Multiple	C	G $\left(\frac{3}{2}C\right)$	F $\left(\frac{4}{3}C\right)$
1	**264**	**396**	**352**
2	528	792	704
3	792	1188	1056
4	1056	1584	1408
5	1320	1980	1760
6	1584	2376	2112
7	1848	2772	2464
8	2112	3168	2816
9	2376	3564	3168
10	2640	3960	3520
11	2904	4356	3872
12	3168	4752	4224
13	3432	5148	4576
14	3696	5544	4928
15	3960	5940	5280
16	4224	6336	5632
17	4488	6732	5984
18	4752	7128	6336

Figure 5-4a

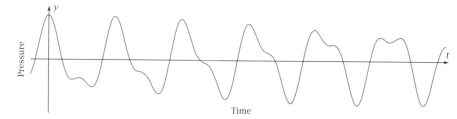

17. *Sum of Two Sinusoids with Nearly Equal Periods Problem:* The graph in Figure 5-4b has a varying amplitude, so you should guess that its equation is the product of two sinusoids with greatly different periods. In this problem you will show that you can also write the function as a *sum* of two sinusoids with *nearly equal* periods.

a. Write a particular equation for y as a product of two sinusoids. Confirm on your grapher that the equation is correct.

b. What are the periods of the two sinusoids in part a?

c. On the same screen as in part a, plot the graph of $y = \cos 10\theta + \cos 8\theta$. What is interesting about the new graph?

d. What are the periods of the two sinusoids in part c?

e. How are the arguments 10θ and 8θ related to the arguments in the equation in part a?

f. It is possible to prove algebraically that the equations in parts a and c are equivalent. Try to do this.

Figure 5-4b

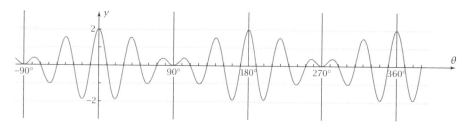

5-5
The Sum and Product Properties

Objective

Transform a sum of two sinusoids into a product of two sinusoids, and vice versa.

Class Time

1 day

Homework Assignment

RA, Q1–Q10, Problems 1–25 odd, 29, 35

Technology Options

 Problem 33: Dynamic Sinusoidal Sums and Products Project

 Presentation Sketch: Piano Present.gsp

 Presentation Sketch: Speed of Light Present.gsp

 Exploration 5-5a: Equivalence of Sinusoid Sums and Products

 Activity: Sum-to-Product Identity for Sines

Important Terms and Concepts

In phase, out of phase

Sum and product properties

Lesson Notes

The point of this section is to show students that the product of two sinusoids and the sum of two sinusoids can be the same function. This leads to the sum and product identities. It is strongly suggested that you do *not* require students to memorize these properties. The important thing is that students be able to *use* the properties. Either give students the properties when they need them or have students derive them.

Examples 1 and 2 illustrate the derivations of the sum and product properties. Here is an alternative solution to Example 1.

$$2 \sin 13° \cos 48°$$

$$= \sin 13° \cos 48° + \sin 13° \cos 48°$$
Split into two identical terms.

$$= (\sin 13° \cos 48° + \cos 13° \sin 48°)$$
$$+ (\sin 13° \cos 48° - \cos 13° \sin 48°)$$
Add a clever form of zero to make the composite argument properties show up.

$$= \sin (13° + 48°) + \sin (13° - 48°)$$
Use the composite argument properties *backward.*

$$= \sin 61° + \sin (-35°)$$

$$= \sin 61° - \sin 35°$$

[Solution provided by students Mary Alice Watkins, Virginia Morales, Jacob Talbot, and Sergio Peña.]

Example 3 ties in harmonic analysis from the previous section. The graphing calculator, as always, is a great aid in verifying the correctness of one's answers. A blackline master of Figure 5-5d is available in the *Instructor's Resource Book.*

Exploration Notes

Exploration 5-5a provides an excellent introduction to the section. You can assign it to groups of students at the beginning of the first day of instruction. Most students will be surprised to find that the graphs for the sum and products are identical. This provides motivation for deriving the properties in the section. Allow students about 20 minutes to complete the Exploration.

Technology Notes

 Problem 33: The Dynamic Sinusoidal Sums and Products Project asks students to use a Dynamic Precalculus Exploration at *www.keymath.com/precalc* to investigate properties of the functions $y = \cos 6x \cdot \sin kx$ and $y = \cos 6x + \sin kx$ as k varies.

 Presentation Sketch: Piano Present.gsp, on the *Instructor's Resource CD,* demonstrates sums of sound waves that are created as you play single notes or chords on a piano keyboard.

Presentation Sketch: Speed of Light Present.gsp, on the *Instructor's Resource CD,* demonstrates the sum of the radio wave being sent from Mars to Earth with another radio wave being sent in the opposite direction.

 Exploration 5-5a: Equivalence of Sinusoid Sums and Products, in the *Instructor's Resource Book,* has students work out how a sum of two sinusoids with nearly equal periods is equivalent to a product of two sinusoids with very different periods. Sketchpad or Fathom could be a useful exploratory tool.

 Activity: Sum-to-Product Identity for Sines, in the *Instructor's Resource Book,* engages students in a study of sounds generated by tuning forks. It is fairly easy and takes about 20 minutes.

Problem Notes

- *Problems 1–16* are similar to Examples 1 and 2.

- *Problems 17–20* are similar to Example 3. A blackline master for those problems is available in the *Instructor's Resource Book.*

- *Problems 21–24* involve solving trigonometric equations using the sum and product properties.

- *Problems 25–30* require students to prove identities.

- *Problems 31, 32, and 34* extend the concepts of the chapter to applications that use the sum and product formulas. These problems work well as extra-credit problems or projects.

- *Problem 33* asks students to investigate what happens when the parameter k changes in the function $f(x) = \cos 6x \sin kx$ using a Dynamic Precalculus Exploration at *www.keymath.com/precalc.* If students want to create their own sketch for this problem, they can learn about sliders in Sketchpad from the document sliders.gsp, which is on the *Instructor's Resource CD* as well as at the previously mentioned Web site.

Supplementary Problems

For Problems 1–4, transform the product into a sum or difference of sines or cosines with positive arguments.

1. $2 \sin 3x \cos 5x$
2. $2 \sin 8x \sin 2x$
3. $2 \cos 4x \cos 7x$
4. $2 \cos 11x \sin 9x$

For Problems 5–8, transform the sum or difference to a product of sines and/or cosines with positive arguments.

5. $\sin 3x + \sin 9x$
6. $\sin 9x - \sin 11x$
7. $\cos 8x - \cos 10x$
8. $\cos 5x + \cos 13x$

For Problems 9 and 10, use harmonic analysis to find an equation of the given graph as a product of two sinusoids. Then transform the equation to a sum of two sinusoids. Confirm graphically that each of your equations produces the given graph.

9.

10.

For Problems 11 and 12, use harmonic analysis to find an equation of the given graph as a sum of two sinusoids. Then transform the equation to a product of two sinusoids. Confirm graphically that each of your equations produces the given graph.

11.

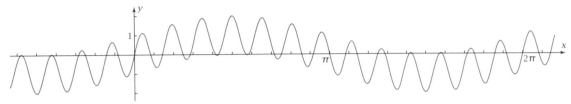

12.

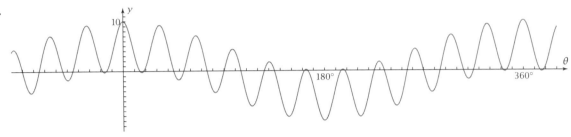

For Problems 13–15, prove that the given equation is an identity.

13. $\sin 5x + \sin 3x = 4 \sin 2x \cos 2x \cos x$

14. $\sin x + \sin 2x + \sin 3x = \sin 2x(1 + 2 \cos x)$

15. $\sin (x + y) \sin (x - y) = \cos^2 y - \cos^2 x$

5-6

Double and Half Argument Properties

Objectives

- Prove that a product of sinusoids with equal periods is also a sinusoid.

- Derive properties for $\cos 2A$, $\sin 2A$, and $\tan 2A$ in terms of functions of A.

- Derive properties for $\cos \frac{1}{2}A$, $\sin \frac{1}{2}A$, and $\tan \frac{1}{2}A$ in terms of functions of A.

Class Time

2 days

Homework Assignment

Day 1: RA, Q1–Q10, Problems 1–3, 5, 11–17 odd

Day 2: Problems 7, 9, 19–43

Important Terms and Concepts

Double argument properties

Half argument properties

Circular reasoning

Lesson Notes

It is recommended that you spend two days on this section. Cover Examples 1–3 on the first day and Example 4 on the second day.

The section opens with a proof that $\sin x \cos x = \frac{1}{2} \sin 2x$. This means that the product of a sine and cosine with equal periods is also a sinusoid. The proof uses a composite argument property for sine from Section 5-3. Figure 5-6d of the student book illustrates that the square of a sine and the square of a cosine are also sinusoids. Specifically, $\cos^2 x = \frac{1}{2} + \frac{1}{2} \cos 2x$ and $\sin^2 x = \frac{1}{2} - \frac{1}{2} \cos 2x$. These identities are very important in calculus. Without them, many integration problems could not be solved algebraically. Students prove these identities in Problem 30 and in Supplementary Problem 3.

Multiplying both sides of $\sin x \cos x = \frac{1}{2} \sin 2x$ by 2 produces the familiar double argument property $\sin 2x = 2 \sin x \cos x$. This property can also be

derived directly from the composite argument property for sine:

$$\sin 2x$$

$$= \sin (x + x)$$

$$= \sin x \cos x + \cos x \sin x \qquad \text{Composite argument property for sine.}$$

$$= 2 \sin x \cos x$$

$$\therefore \sin 2x = 2 \sin x \cos x, \text{ Q.E.D.}$$

The text gives the derivation of one of the double argument properties for cosine, $\cos 2x = \cos^2 x - \sin^2 x$. Students derive the remaining double argument properties for cosine in Problem 28, and they derive the double argument property for tangent in Problem 31.

The half argument properties for sine and cosine can be derived from the double argument properties by using the simple algebraic "trick" of substituting A for $2x$. Go through the derivation with students, and make sure they understand this substitution. It is important that students recognize that the half argument properties are merely an algebraic rearrangement of the double argument properties.

Emphasize that when using the half argument properties for sine and cosine, the sign of the answer is determined by the quadrant that $\frac{1}{2}A$ terminates in, *not* the quadrant that A terminates in. Making a sketch can help students determine which sign to use.

Think about which identities you want students to memorize and which ones you want them to be able to derive. Memorizing all the identities is onerous, while deriving all of them is time-consuming. A reasonable compromise is to ask students to memorize only the double argument properties for sine and cosine and then to be able to derive the rest.

Consider giving a short quiz when you complete this section.

Exploration Notes

Exploration 5-6a helps students work through the steps of deriving the double argument properties for sine and cosine from the composite argument properties. This Exploration is a good activity for introducing double argument properties on Day 1.

Precalculus with Trigonometry: Instructor's Guide
© 2007 Key Curriculum Press

Problem Notes

- *Problems 1 and 2* ask students to explain why $\cos 2x \neq 2 \cos x$ and $\tan \frac{1}{2}x \neq \frac{1}{2} \tan x$. Point out that the distributive property doesn't apply to trigonometric functions.

- *Problems 3–10* require students to illustrate that properties are true by making a table of values. Remind students that a numerical table does *not* constitute a proof.

- *Problems 17 and 18* ask students to investigate the product of two sinusoids.

- *Problems 21–26* emphasize using the formulas and then substituting in the appropriate values. Sketches are very useful for these problems.

- *Problems 27–32* ask students to prove many of the properties introduced in this section.

- *Problems 33–38* involve using double and half argument properties to solve equations algebraically.

- *Problems 39–44* require students to prove identities. Remind students that they cannot work on both sides of the "equation" without using circular reasoning.

Supplementary Problems

1. Explain why $\sin \frac{1}{2}x$ does *not* equal $\frac{1}{2} \sin x$ by considering the differences in the graphs of $y_1 = \sin \frac{1}{2}x$ and $y_2 = \frac{1}{2} \sin x$.

2. Prove by numerical counterexample that $\sin 2x \neq 2 \sin x$.

3. *Squares of Cosine and Sine Problem:* Figure 5-6b in the text suggests graphically that

$$\cos^2 x = \frac{1}{2} + \frac{1}{2} \cos 2x \qquad \text{and}$$

$$\sin^2 x = \frac{1}{2} - \frac{1}{2} \cos 2x$$

Prove algebraically that these properties are true by applying the composite argument properties to $\cos 2x$. The Pythagorean properties might also be useful.

Sinusoid Problems: For Problems 4 and 5, the graph of the function is a sinusoid.

a. Plot the graph of the given function.

b. From the graph, figure out the equation of the sinusoid.

c. Verify algebraically that the equation is sinusoidal.

4. $y = \sin^2 x$

5. $y = \cos^2 x$

6. *Half Argument Interpretation Problem II:* Consider the functions

$$y_1 = \sin \frac{1}{2}x \qquad \text{and} \qquad y_2 = \sqrt{\frac{1}{2}(1 - \cos x)}$$

a. On the same screen, plot the graphs of y_1 and y_2. Use radian mode and a friendly window for y that includes at least two cycles of y_1. Sketch the results.

b. For what intervals of x between 0 and 2π are the graphs the same? For what intervals of x are the graphs reflections of each other across the x-axis?

c. Starting with the double argument property for $\cos 2x$ in terms of $\sin x$ alone, derive the half argument property for sine.

7. *Similar-Looking Properties Problem:* These properties look similar:

$$\cos^2 x - \sin^2 x = \cos 2x \text{ (double argument property)}$$

$$\cos^2 x + \sin^2 x = 1 \text{ (Pythagorean property)}$$

a. Show how the double argument property is derived starting with one of the composite argument properties for cosine.

b. Show how the Pythagorean property follows by applying similar steps to the other composite argument property for cosine.

c. Explain why the steps you took in part b do not constitute a *proof* of the Pythagorean property because of the **circular reasoning** involved.

8. *Cosine Fourier Series Project:* In this project, your objective is to show that a sum of *any* number of cosines can be written in a single, closed-form formula. Specifically, you are to prove that

$$1 + \cos x + \cos 2x + \cos 3x + \cdots + \cos nx$$

$$= \frac{1}{2} + \frac{\sin \frac{2n+1}{2}x}{2 \sin \frac{1}{2}x}$$

for *any* positive integer n. (The cosine terms on the left side of the equation form a partial sum of a **Fourier series**.)

a. By clever use of the double argument property for sine, write an equation expressing $\sin x$ in terms of sines and cosines of $\frac{1}{2}x$.

b. By clever use of the composite argument property for sine, write an equation expressing $\sin x$ in terms of $\frac{3}{2}x$ and $\frac{1}{2}x$.

c. Use the results of parts a and b to prove that

$$1 + \cos x = \frac{1}{2} + \frac{\sin \frac{3}{2}x}{2 \sin \frac{1}{2}x}$$

d. Prove that

$$1 + \cos x + \cos 2x = \frac{1}{2} + \frac{\sin \frac{5}{2}x}{2 \sin \frac{1}{2}x}$$

by starting with the identity you proved in part c and adding cos 2x to both sides. You will find that after you add cos 2x to the big fraction by using a common denominator, the sum and product properties can be used to transform the *product* in the numerator to a very interesting *sum*!

e. Using the technique of part d, prove that

$$1 + \cos x + \cos 2x + \cos 3x = \frac{1}{2} + \frac{\sin \frac{7}{2}x}{2 \sin \frac{1}{2}x}$$

f. Prove that if

$$1 + \cos x + \cos 2x + \cdots + \cos 37x$$
$$= \frac{1}{2} + \frac{\sin \frac{75}{2}x}{2 \sin \frac{1}{2}x}$$

then

$$1 + \cos x + \cos 2x + \cdots + \cos 37x$$
$$+ \cos 38x = \frac{1}{2} + \frac{\sin \frac{77}{2}x}{2 \sin \frac{1}{2}x}$$

g. If you have studied mathematical induction (Appendix B), prove that the property stated at the beginning of this project is true for *any* positive integer value of *n*.

5-7
Chapter Review and Test

Objective

Review and practice the major concepts presented in this chapter.

Class Time

2 days (including 1 day for testing)

Homework Assignment

Day 1: R0–R6, T1–T19

Day 2 (after Chapter 5 Test): Problem Set 6-1

Lesson Notes

Section 5-7 contains a set of Review Problems, a set of Concept Problems, and a Chapter Test. The Review Problems include one problem for each section in the chapter. You may wish to use the Chapter Test as an additional set of review problems.

Encourage students to practice the no-calculator problems without a calculator so they are prepared for the test problems for which they cannot use a calculator.

A blackline master of the Summary of Trigonometric Function Properties is available in the *Instructor's Resource Book.* You may want to give a copy of this to students so that they can keep it in a notebook for reference.

Exploration Notes

Exploration 5-7a contains problems in which students must transform a given expression to another form without being told the exact answer. Supplementary Problems 1–4 are similar.

Problem Note

Blackline masters for Problems R4 and T14 are available in the *Instructor's Resource Book.*

Supplementary Problems

For Problems 1–4, a definition of "simple form" is given. Use that definition to "simplify" the expressions.

1. Simple form involves composite arguments and no arguments that are multiples of a variable. Simplify each expression.

    a. $\cos(\theta - 37°)$

    b. $\cos(x + y + z)$

    c. $\cos 3x$

2. Simple form consists of *one* term, which may be composed of several factors. Simplify each expression.

    a. $\cos 37° \cos \theta + \sin 37° \sin \theta$

    b. $\cos 37° + \cos \theta$

    c. $\cos \theta + \cos 2\theta + \cos 3\theta$

3. Simple form involves *no* products or powers of trigonometric functions but may involve functions with arguments that are multiples of x. Simplify each expression.

    a. $\sin x \cos x$

    b. $\cos^2 x$

    c. $\cos^2 x \sin x$

    d. $\sin^4 x$

4. Simple form involves a *single* cosine or sine term (no products, powers, or sums of functions) but may involve composite arguments or arguments that are multiples of x. Simplify each expression.

    a. $\cos x + \sin x$

    b. $\cos x \sin x$

    c. $\cos x - \sin x$

    d. $\sin x - \cos x$

5. Figure 5-7a shows the graph of $y = 4 \sin \theta \cos \theta$ and the line $y = 1$ as they might appear on your grapher. Solve the equation $4 \sin \theta \cos \theta = 1$ algebraically for $\theta \in [0°, 360°]$. Show that the answers agree with Figure 5-7a.

Figure 5-7a

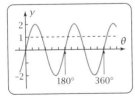

6. *Half Argument Properties Problems:*

    a. Use the half argument properties to find the exact value (no decimals) of $\cos \frac{1}{2}A$ if $\cos A = \frac{2}{3}$ and A is between 0° and 90°.

    b. Use the half argument properties to find the exact value (no decimals) of $\cos \frac{1}{2}B$ if $\cos B = \frac{2}{3}$ and B is between 360° and 450°.

c. Find the measures of angles A and B in parts a and b, and store them without rounding them. Then find decimal values for $\cos \frac{1}{2}A$ and $\cos \frac{1}{2}B$ directly. How do the answers compare with the exact values you found in parts a and b? How does the ambiguous sign ± enter into your answer?

d. Starting with the half argument properties for sine and cosine, derive the following half argument property for tangent. What restrictions are there on the domain of x?

$$\tan \frac{1}{2}x = \frac{1 - \cos x}{\sin x}$$

7. *Triple Argument Property Project:* Figure 5-7b shows the graph of

$$y = 4 \cos^3 \theta - 3 \cos \theta$$

Figure 5-7b

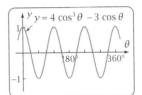

The graph appears to be a sinusoid. Explain how you know that it is indeed a sinusoid. Include graphical, numerical, and algebraic evidence. In particular, show algebraically that the given equation has θ-intercepts at the same places as the sinusoidal graph. Explain why this problem is entitled "Triple Argument Property." As an extension of this problem, derive a triple argument property expressing $\sin 3\theta$ in terms of functions of θ.

8. *Earth and Mars Project Revisited:* In Supplementary Problem Set 4-7, you analyzed the distance between Earth and Mars as a function of time. Refer back to that problem if necessary. In this problem you will use a composite argument property to analyze it further. Figure 5-7c on the following page shows Earth and Mars in orbit around the Sun. A uv-coordinate system is set up with its origin at the Sun. Earth is at (u_1, v_1) and Mars is at (u_2, v_2). The angles in standard position for Earth and Mars are E and M, respectively. Assume that the orbits are circular, with radius r_1 for Earth and r_2 for Mars. Let d be the distance between the two planets.

Figure 5-7c

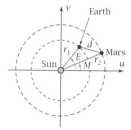

a. Use the distance formula to explain why $d^2 = (u_1 - u_2)^2 + (v_1 - v_2)^2$. Then expand the two squares to get an expression for d^2 that does not involve parentheses.

b. Explain why the expanded expression in part a can be written as

$$d^2 = r_1^2 + r_2^2 - 2(u_1 u_2 + v_1 v_2)$$

c. Use the concept of parametric functions to explain why

$$u_1 = r_1 \cos E \qquad u_2 = r_2 \cos M$$
$$\text{and}$$
$$v_1 = r_1 \sin E \qquad v_2 = r_2 \sin M$$

d. Substitute the parametric equations of part c into the equation of part b. What is interesting about the expression inside the parentheses?

e. Write an equation expressing d^2 in terms of r_1, r_2, and $\cos(E - M)$.

f. Look up the **law of cosines** in the next chapter. How does your answer to part e relate to the law of cosines?

g. The **angular velocity** of Earth is about $\frac{1}{365}$ revolution per day (why?). The angular velocity of Mars is about $\frac{1}{687}$ revolution per day (guess why!). Let t be the number of days that have elapsed since Earth and Mars were closest together, where E and M were both zero. Write angle $(E - M)$ as a function of t.

h. Use the result of part g and the fact that Earth's distance from the Sun is about 93 million miles and Mars' distance from the Sun is about 141 million miles to get a particular equation for d^2 as a function of t alone.

i. From part h you can conclude that d^2 is a sinusoidal function of time. Is d also a sinusoidal function of time? Explain how you reached your conclusion.

6

Triangle Trigonometry

This chapter begins with the law of cosines, first discovered by measurement on accurately drawn graphs and then proven by algebraic methods. Hero's formula allows students to calculate the area of a triangle from three side lengths. The other area formula, "half of side times side times sine of included angle," leads to the law of sines in Section 6-2. This area formula also lays the foundation for the cross product of vectors in Chapter 10. The ambiguous case is approached through a single calculation using the law of cosines. The resulting quadratic equation's solution leads to both possible side lengths and reveals whether there is just one triangle or no triangle. Section 6-6, on vector addition, can be used to introduce students to the unit vectors in the *x*- and *y*-directions, although some instructors prefer to postpone vectors until Chapter 10. The chapter concludes with triangle problems from the real world. The main purpose, other than showing students that trigonometry ("triangle measurement") has applications, is to force students to decide which triangle techniques to use based on the merits of the problem, not on the section in which the problem appears. A cumulative review of Chapters 1 through 6 appears in Section 6-9.

Introduction to Oblique Triangles

Objective

Given two sides and the included angle of a triangle, find by direct measurement the third side of the triangle.

Class Time

$\frac{1}{2}$ day

Homework Assignment

Problems 1–6

Technology Options

 Exploration 6-1a: Introduction to Oblique Triangles

Important Terms and Concepts

Oblique triangle

Lesson Notes

Section 6-1 sets the stage for the development of the law of cosines in Section 6-2. You can assign this section for homework the night of the Chapter 5 test or as a group activity to be completed in class. No classroom discussion is needed before students begin the activity. You may want to adapt the problem set so that it can be done with The Geometer's Sketchpad.

Exploration Notes

Exploration 6-1a may be assigned in place of Problem Set 6-1. It covers much of the same material but includes a grid for students to plot side *a* as a function of angle *A* by hand. Encourage students to plot the points with great care. The Exploration could also be used as a review sheet. Allow students 20 minutes to complete this activity.

Technology Notes

 Exploration 6-1a: Introduction to Oblique Triangles, in the *Instructor's Resource Book,* has students measure the lengths of legs of various triangles and then conjecture the law of cosines. The data they gather can easily be recorded and plotted in Fathom.

Problem Notes

- *Problem 2* asks students to find *a* if *A* is 0°. Students may have trouble understanding why the result is 1 cm rather than 0 cm, because the triangle essentially "collapses" and appears to have no third side. You might suggest that students think of *a* as the segment connecting the endpoints of the other two segments. When *A* is 0°, the 3-cm and 4-cm segments lie on top of one another and *a* connects their right endpoints.

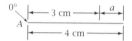

- *Problem 5* encourages students to try to discover the law of cosines on their own.

6-2
Oblique Triangles: Law of Cosines

Objectives

- Given two sides and the included angle of a triangle, derive and use the law of cosines for finding the third side.

- Given three sides of a triangle, find an angle.

Class Time

1 day

Homework Assignment

RA, Q1–Q10, Problems 1, 3, 6, 7–13 odd, 14, 15, 17, 19

Technology Options

 Problem 16: Geometric Derivation of the Law of Cosines Problem

 Presentation Sketch: Law of Cosines Present.gsp

Activity: Law of Cosines

Important Terms and Concepts

Law of cosines

Lesson Notes

In this section, students derive and apply the law of cosines. One goal of this section is to have students see that the law of cosines, which works for *all* types of triangles, is an extension of the Pythagorean theorem, which works only for *right* triangles.

Note that the law of cosines is presented before the law of sines because it is a more reliable technique. The sign of cos *A* indicates whether *A* is obtuse or acute. No such information can be obtained by using the law of sines.

The problems in this section involve using the law of cosines in cases where two sides and an included angle are known (SAS) or where three sides are known (SSS). It can also be used in the *ambiguous case* in which two sides and a *nonincluded* angle are known (SSA). This case will be discussed in Section 6-5.

Example 1 applies the law of cosines to find a missing side when two sides and an included angle are known. In Example 2, the law of cosines is used to find a missing angle when three sides are known.

In Δ*XYZ* you may want to encourage students to write the *Z* with a bar through it, *Ƶ*, so that the *Z* is not confused with a 2.

The lengths given in Example 3 do not form a triangle, so the law of cosines yields no solution. Some students may realize immediately that a triangle cannot be formed because the lengths do not satisfy the triangle inequality.

This section provides an excellent opportunity to review some of the triangle concepts students learned in geometry. Here are some topics you might discuss.

- The fact that the largest angle in a triangle is opposite the longest side and that the smallest angle is opposite the shortest side

- The triangle inequality

- Tests for determining whether an angle is right, acute, or obtuse (see Problem 19)

- Conventions for naming sides and angles (in some texts, angles are denoted by the Greek letters alpha, α, beta, β, and gamma, γ)

Exploration Notes

Exploration 6-2a guides students through the derivation of the law of cosines. You may want to have students work through this Exploration as you derive the law of cosines with them. Allow about 15 minutes for this activity.

Exploration 6-2b has students first find angles by using the law of cosines and then verify their results by measuring. This activity can be done by groups of students in class or assigned for homework. Allow about 15 minutes for this Exploration.

Technology Notes

 Problem 16: Geometric Derivation of the Law of Cosines Problem asks students to experiment with the Dynamic Precalculus Exploration at *www.keymath.com/precalc* in order to derive the law of cosines.

 Presentation Sketch: Law of Cosines Present.gsp, on the *Instructor's Resource CD,* is related to the activity mentioned next.

 Activity: Law of Cosines, in the *Instructor's Resource Book,* provides another visual proof of the law of cosines. Students build a square with side length equal to the length of the longest leg of an obtuse triangle, and then they compare areas of different figures that result.

Problem Notes

Remind students to store intermediate answers without rounding. Only final results should be rounded.

- *Problems 1-12* are straightforward and provide practice with the law of cosines. In Problems 9 and 10, a triangle cannot be formed from the given side lengths. Students may discover this by using the triangle inequality or by attempting to apply the law of cosines.

- *Problems 13 and 14* are ideal to do using The Geometer's Sketchpad. If the program is unavailable, students can use a protractor, compass, and ruler to construct the triangles and find the unknown measures. Students' measurements should agree with the result given by the law of cosines. Centimeter graph paper from the Blackline Masters section in the *Instructor's Resource Book* may be used.

- *Problem 16* gives students an opportunity to explore a geometrical derivation of the law of cosines using a Dynamic Precalculus Exploration at *www.keymath.com/precalc*.

- *Problem 18* poses a test for determining whether an angle of a triangle is acute, right, or obtuse.

Supplementary Problem

1. *Earth and Mars Problem:* Earth orbits the Sun at a distance of about 93 million miles. Mars orbits the Sun at about 142 million miles (Figure 6-2a). The distance *d* between Earth and Mars is a function of angle θ at the Sun.

Figure 6-2a

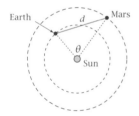

a. With the help of the law of cosines, write an equation for *d* as a function of θ.

b. Plot at least one cycle of the graph. Sketch the result.

c. Write a particular equation of the sinusoid that has the same high and low points as the graph in part b. Plot this sinusoid on the same screen. Sketch the result.

d. As you can tell from your answer to part c, the distance between Earth and Mars does not vary sinusoidally with θ. Does Mars spend more time when it is closest to Earth or when it is farthest from Earth than it would if the graph were sinusoidal? How do you know?

6-3
Area of a Triangle

Objective

Given the measures of two sides and the included angle, find the area of the triangle.

Class Time

1 day

Homework Assignment

RA, Q1–Q10, Problems 1, 3, 7–9, 11, 13, 14

Technology Options

 Problem 11: Variable Triangle Problem

 Exploration 6-3a: Area of a Triangle

Important Terms and Concepts

Hero's formula

Semiperimeter

Lesson Notes

In this section, the traditional formula for the area of a triangle, $A = \frac{1}{2}bh$, is transformed into one involving trigonometry, $A = \frac{1}{2}bc \sin A$. The transformation is straightforward.

The derivation of the area formula given in the student text is for an acute angle *A*. The formula also works if *A* is obtuse. You may want to show students the derivation.

Figure 6-3a

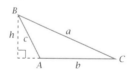

$$\text{Area} = \frac{1}{2}bh$$

$$= \frac{1}{2}b[c \sin(180° - A)]$$

$$= \frac{1}{2}bc(\sin 180° \cos A - \cos 180° \sin A)$$

Composite argument property for sin (*A* − *B*).

$$= \frac{1}{2}bc \sin A \qquad \sin 180° = 0; \cos 180° = -1.$$

This derivation is an ideal opportunity to remind students that an altitude of a triangle may fall outside the triangle.

Example 1 involves direct substitution into the new area formula, whereas Example 2 requires first finding an angle using the law of cosines.

In Example 3, Hero's formula, named after Hero of Alexandria, who lived about 100 B.C., is used to find the area of a triangle given the length of three sides. Hero's formula is a special case of Brahmagupta's formula, which states that the area of a quadrilateral inscribed in a circle is

$$A = \sqrt{(s - a)(s - b)(s - c)(s - d)}$$

where s is the semiperimeter and a, b, c, and d are the lengths of the four sides. Letting one side equal zero makes the quadrilateral degenerate to a triangle, and Hero's formula appears. The formula is sometimes referred to as "Heron's formula," although this is a grammatical error. "Heron" is the genitive (possessive) case of "Hero," so Heron already means "of Hero."

The Additional Class Example following the Technology Notes can be used to demonstrate multiple solutions to a problem.

Exploration Notes

Exploration 6-3a guides students through the derivation of the formula Area = $\frac{1}{2}bc \sin A$ and poses several problems in which students need to apply the formula. You might assign this activity at the beginning of class so that students can derive the formula on their own. Allow 15–20 minutes to complete this activity.

Exploration 6-3b requires students to apply the law of cosines, the formula Area = $\frac{1}{2}bc \sin A$, and Hero's formula and then guides them through the derivation.

Hero's formula: You might use this activity as a take-home assignment or as a group quiz. Allow at least 20 minutes for this Exploration.

Technology Notes

 Problem 11: The Variable Triangle Problem asks students to find the area of a triangle as a function of one angle, when the two legs creating that angle are of fixed lengths. Students are asked to view a Dynamic Precalculus Exploration of this triangle at *www.keymath.com/precalc.* This problem is related to Exploration 6-1a in the *Instructor's Resource Book,* in the sense that both activities begin with a triangle that has two fixed legs and a variable included angle θ, and they express some parameter as a function of θ.

 Exploration 6-3a: Area of a Triangle, in the *Instructor's Resource Book,* guides students

through deriving a formula for area, given the lengths of two sides and the measure of the included angle. Sketchpad can be used to test conjectures about trigonometric formulas against the area as calculated by the software.

Additional Class Example

1. Find the area of $\triangle ABX$ if side $a = 5$ varas, side $b = 12$ varas, and side $c = 13$ varas. (What is a vara?)

Solution

Students will probably apply Hero's formula to this problem, as that's the topic at hand. In doing so, they'll get

$$A = \sqrt{15(15 - 3)(15 - 12)(15 - 13)}$$
$$= \sqrt{15(10)(3)(2)} = 30$$

Perhaps you'll have a student who recognizes that $\triangle ABX$ is a right triangle. The area can be found by the traditional formula, $A = \frac{1}{2}bh$. This is a good example to demonstrate multiple methods of solution for a problem.

Problem Notes

- *Problems 1–7* are straightforward, requiring direct substitution into the area formulas.

- *Problem 8,* the Comparison of Methods Problem, asks students to compare areas calculated via Hero's formula with areas calculated via Area = $\frac{1}{2}bc \sin A$.

Supplementary Problem

1. *Lapel Problem:* Sue Track is making jacket lapels for country western singer Nellie Wilson. Sue must make each lapel triangular, with sides 16 in., 14 in., and 5 in., as shown in Figure 6-3b.

Figure 6-3b

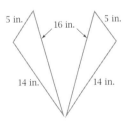

a. What is the area of each lapel?

b. The material for the lapels is a gold fabric that costs $300 per square yard. How much is the material in the two lapels worth?

c. Sue marks up the cost of the fabric by 85% for profit and for material wasted in cutting the fabric. How much does she charge Nellie for the lapels of the jacket?

6-4
Oblique Triangles: Law of Sines

Objective

Given the measure of an angle, the length of the side opposite this angle, and one other piece of information about the triangle, find the other side and angle measures.

Class Time

1 day

Homework Assignment

RA, Q1–Q10, Problems 1–9 odd, 10, 11, 13, 14

Technology Options

 Problem 13: Geometric Derivation of the Law of Sines Problem

 Presentation Sketch: Law of Sines Present.gsp

 Exploration 6-4a: The Law of Sines

 Exploration 6-4b: The Law of Sines for Angles

  Activity: Law of Sines

Important Terms and Concepts

Law of sines

Lesson Notes

The law of sines can be applied when two angles and a nonincluded side of a triangle are known (AAS) or when two angles and an included side are known (ASA). It can also be used with caution in the ambiguous case in which two sides and a non-included angle are known (SSA). The ambiguous case is covered in Section 6-5.

Although the law of sines is an easy and safe way to find side lengths, students must be careful when using it to find angle measures. Problem 11 illustrates the risks involved in using the law of sines to find angle measures. Be sure to discuss this problem in class. It is in handout form as Exploration 6-4b. The risks result from the fact that there are two angles in the interval [0, 180°] with a given sine value. The inverse sine function always gives the first-quadrant angle. To find the correct answer, students must consider the general solution for arcsine.

You might present the table below to summarize what students have learned so far about finding unknown measures in triangles.

Exploration Notes

Exploration 6-4a requires students to measure sides and angles of a triangle, verify the law of sines numerically, and then use the law of sines to find the remaining parts of the triangle. After students have worked with the law of sines, they derive the rule algebraically. Allow 15–20 minutes for this Exploration.

Exploration 6-4b is a worksheet for Problem 11. If you don't want your students to do the problem for homework, this exploration provides a great opportunity for a collaborative effort. By doing this activity, students will discover the pitfalls of using the law of sines to find angle measures. Allow about 20 minutes for this Exploration.

Technology Notes

 Problem 13: The Geometric Derivation of the Law of Sines Problem asks students to use a Dynamic Precalculus Exploration at *www.keymath.com/precalc* and describe how the sketch provides a proof of the law of sines.

What You Are Given	What You Want to Find	Law to Apply
Three sides (SSS)	An unknown angle	Law of cosines
Two sides and an included angle (SAS)	The unknown side	Law of cosines
Two angles and an included side (ASA)	An unknown side	Law of sines (must first find missing angle, using $180° - (A + B)$)
Two angles and an included side (ASA)	The unknown angle	$180° - (A + B)$
Two angles and a nonincluded side (AAS)	An unknown side	Law of sines
Two angles and a nonincluded side (AAS)	The unknown angle	$180° - (A + B)$

Presentation Sketch: Law of Sines Present.gsp, on the *Instructor's Resource CD,* demonstrates a proof of the law of sines. It is related to the Law of Sines activity.

 Exploration 6-4a: The Law of Sines has students derive the law of sines algebraically. Sketchpad can provide a useful exploration tool for students to make and test their conjectures.

 Exploration 6-4b: The Law of Sines for Angles demonstrates the danger of trying to find the measure of an angle using the law of sines. Sketchpad can provide a useful exploration tool. In particular, one page in the presentation sketch Law of Sines Present.gsp, mentioned earlier, visually demonstrates this danger.

 Activity: Law of Sines, in the *Instructor's Resource Book,* has students merge two triangles to see how the sine ratios are equal. On the second page of the provided sketch, students are asked to solve an applied problem using the law of sines. There is a related presentation sketch available. Allow 40–50 minutes.

Problem Notes

- *Problems 1–8* are fairly straightforward and are similar to Examples 1 and 2.

- *Problem 11,* the Law of Sines for Angles Problem, is well worth spending time on. It helps students understand the pitfalls of using the law of sines to find angle measures.

6-5
The Ambiguous Case

Objective

Given two sides and an angle not contained by them in a triangle, calculate the possible values of the third side.

Class Time

1 day

Homework Assignment

Recommended: RA, Q1–Q10, Problems 1–13 odd, 14

Technology Options

 Exploration 6-5a: The Ambiguous Case, SSA

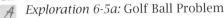 *Exploration 6-5a:* Golf Ball Problem

Important Terms and Concepts

Ambiguous case

Displacement

Directed distance

Lesson Notes

From their geometry courses, students may recall that SSA is not a congruence theorem. So it should not surprise them that there are difficulties associated with the SSA case. Indeed, given two sides and a nonincluded angle, it may be possible to form one triangle, two triangles, or no triangle at all.

Have a volunteer draw $\triangle ABC$ on the board or overhead with $\angle A = 30°$, $b = 10$, and $a = 5$ (Figure 6-5a). Hopefully, students will see that the triangle is a right triangle, because 5 is half of 10 and the triangle has a 30° angle.

Figure 6-5a

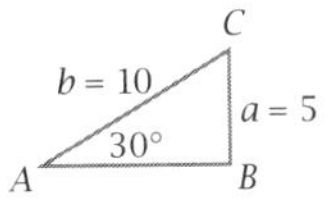

Next, ask a volunteer to draw $\triangle ABC$ with $\angle A = 30°$, $b = 10$, and $a = 4$ (Figure 6-5b). (The student can use $\angle A$ and side b from the previous drawing.) Students should observe that side a is too short and thus that no triangle meets the conditions.

Figure 6-5b

Next, ask a volunteer to draw $\triangle ABC$ with $\angle A = 30°$, $b = 10$, and $a = 6$ (Figure 6-5c). There are two possible triangles in this case, because side a can "swing off" point C toward A or away from A. If students don't notice that two triangles can be drawn, you can ask them if it is possible to draw a second triangle meeting the conditions.

Figure 6-5c

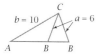

Finally, ask a volunteer to draw $\triangle ABC$ with $\angle A = 30°$, $b = 10$, and $a = 11$ (Figure 6-5d). In this case, side a can only "swing out" away from $\angle A$, so there is only one triangle that meets these conditions.

Figure 6-5d

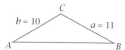

The law-of-cosines technique demonstrated in Example 1 is a more powerful and direct way to find the third side length in the SSA case than the more traditional technique of finding angles first by using the law of sines. The computations involved in the quadratic formula can be done easily with a calculator. If students do not have a quadratic formula program in their calculators, you might suggest that they write or download one so that they can solve the problems efficiently. Using the quadratic formula is preferable to using the solver feature of a grapher because it is easy to miss one of the solutions with the solver feature.

It is worthwhile to go through the steps of the quadratic formula for the cases illustrated in Figures 6-5d and 6-5e in the student text so that students can see how the solutions relate to the figures. The steps are shown in these examples, which could be used to follow Example 1 in the text.

Example 2

In $\triangle XYZ$, $x = 90$ cm, $z = 80$ cm, and $X = 26°$, as in Figure 6-5d in the student text. Find the possible values of side y.

Solution

The problem is the same as in Example 1, except side x is *longer* than side z.

$$90^2 = y^2 + 80^2 - 2 \cdot y \cdot 80 \cos 26°$$
Law of cosines.

$$y^2 - (160 \cos 26°)y + 6400 - 8100 = 0$$

$$y^2 + (-160 \cos 26°)y - 1700 = 0$$

$$y = 154.7896... \text{ or } -10.9826...$$ Use the quadratic formula.

$$y \approx 154.8 \text{ cm}$$ Only the positive solution is a possible side length.

Example 3

In $\triangle XYZ$, $x = 30$ cm, $z = 80$ cm, and $X = 26°$, as in Figure 6-5e in the student text. Find the possible values of side y.

Solution

The problem is the same as in Example 1, except side x is *much shorter* than side z. Again using Figure 6-5c,

$$30^2 = y^2 + 80^2 - 2 \cdot y \cdot 80 \cos 26°$$ Law of cosines.

$$y^2 - (160 \cos 26°)y + 6400 - 900 = 0$$

$$y^2 + (-160 \cos 26°)y + 5500 = 0$$

$$b^2 - 4ac = (-160 \cos 26°)^2 - 4 \cdot 1 \cdot 5500$$
$$= -1319.5331...$$ The discriminant is negative.

No real solution.

No possible triangle.

You may want to give a test or quiz after you complete this section.

Exploration Notes

Exploration 6-5a allows students to investigate the SSA case by measuring and drawing. You could use this activity as a follow-up to Example 1 to reinforce the concept of ambiguity and the use of the quadratic formula. Or you could complete it as a whole-class activity in place of Example 1. Allow 20 minutes for this Exploration.

Exploration 6-5b (inspired by Chris Sollars) shows students a real-world situation involving the ambiguous case for analyzing the position of a golf ball. Allow 20 minutes for this Exploration.

Technology Notes

 Exploration 6-5a: The Ambiguous Case, SSA, in the *Instructor's Resource Book,* asks students to investigate the question of whether

Precalculus with Trigonometry: Instructor's Guide
© 2007 Key Curriculum Press

knowing two side lengths and a nonincluded angle determines a triangle. Sketchpad can be a useful tool in creating constructions for this Exploration. In addition, a page in the Law of Sines Dynamic Precalculus Exploration at *www.keymath.com/precalc* has a sketch that demonstrates the two triangles that can be obtained from a given specification of SSA.

 Exploration 6-5a: Golf Ball Problem, in the *Instructor's Resource Book,* demonstrates the ambiguity of SSA in the context of a golf game. Sketchpad can be useful for constructing a model of the situation and measuring the angles asked for.

Problem Notes

- *Problems 1–8* are straightforward problems in which students must find the unknown side length in SSA situations. Note that when there is only one obtuse triangle, the law of cosines produces a positive solution and a negative solution. The negative solution has a geometric meaning as a directed distance.

- *Problems 9–13* require students to use the law of sines to find missing angles in the SSA case. Students must determine beforehand whether one or two triangles meet the given conditions. Remind students to exercise caution when using the law of sines to find angles. Considering the general solution of arcsine gives two possible angles (the $\sin^{-1}$ value and its supplement). Students must determine whether one or both angles satisfy the problem.

- *Problem 14,* the Six SSA Possibilities Problem, offers a nice summary of the six different possibilities SSA problems present. This is a good problem to discuss in class if you do not want to assign it for homework.

Supplementary Problem

1. *Accurate Drawing Problem:* Triangles *ABC* in Problems 1, 3, and 5 differ only in the length of side *b*. Using computer software such as The Geometer's Sketchpad or a ruler, compass, and protractor, draw side *a* as a horizontal segment of length 4 cm. Then construct angle *B* of measure 34° at one end of the base.

   a. Draw the two possible triangles with side *b* = 3 cm, as in Problem 1. Measure the two possible lengths of side *c*. Your answers should be within ±0.1 cm of the calculated values.

   b. Draw the one triangle with side *b* = 5 cm, as in Problem 3. Measure side *c*. The result should be within ±0.1 cm of the calculated positive solution. Extend the base in the opposite direction and show the point where *b* = 5 cm cuts this line. The length of the segment cut off by this line should agree with the negative value of *c* calculated in Problem 3.

   c. Draw an arc of radius *b* = 2 cm, as in Problem 5, centered at the end of side *a* that is not vertex *B*. Show that this arc misses the other side of angle *B* and thus that no triangle meets the given conditions.

Vector Addition

Objective

Given two vectors, add them to find the resultant vector.

Class Time

2 days

Homework Assignment

Day 1: RA, Q1–Q10, Problems 2, 4, 5, 6

Day 2: Problems 7–17 odd, 18

Technology Options

 Exploration 6-6a: Introduction to Vectors

 Activity: Intersection of Parametric Curves

Important Terms and Concepts

Displacement vector

Vector quantity

Magnitude of a vector

Direction of a vector

Scalar quantity

Head of a vector

Tail of a vector

Absolute value

Equal vectors

Translate a vector

Sum of two vectors

Resultant vector

Unit vector, $\vec{i}$ and $\vec{j}$

Components of a vector

Resolving a vector

Bearing

Opposite of a vector

Commutative

Associative

Zero vector

Closed

Lesson Notes

This section introduces students to vectors in a geometrical context that lays the foundation for the work with three-dimensional vectors in Chapter 10. Theoretical concepts such as commutativity and associativity are touched on in the problem set (Problems 18–22). It is recommended that you spend two days on this section. Cover Examples 1 and 2 on the first day and the remaining examples on the second day.

This section introduces several new terms. Encourage students to use correct terminology when discussing and writing about vectors.

Emphasize to students that a vector has a direction and a magnitude but does *not* have a specific location. This makes it possible to translate vectors in order to add or subtract them.

Example 1 shows how to use triangle trigonometry to find the displacement that results from combining two motions. The resultant displacement is the vector from the beginning of the vector representing the first motion to the end of the vector representing the second motion. This *resultant vector* is the *sum* of the two motion vectors. Having a student act out the scenario in this example might help students gain insight into the resultant vector concept.

Example 1 leads to the definition of the sum of the two vectors. Discuss the definition with students and illustrate it with a drawing (Figure 6-6a).

Figure 6-6a

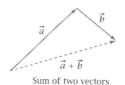

Sum of two vectors

If the two vectors to be added are not already head-to-tail, you can *translate* one of them so that they are. (Figure 6-6b shows an example.) Translation implies that the vector is moved *without* changing its magnitude or direction. Remind students that any two vectors with the same magnitude and direction are equal, so translating a vector does not change its value. Example 2 shows how a tail-to-tail problem can be translated into a head-to-tail problem and then solved by triangle methods.

Figure 6-6b

Two vectors   Translate head-to-tail.   Sum goes from beginning of first to end of last.

Introduce the unit vectors $\vec{i}$ and $\vec{j}$ to students, and explain that any horizontal vector can be written as a *scalar multiple* of $\vec{i}$ and that any vertical vector can be written as a scalar multiple of $\vec{j}$. (See the Supplementary Lesson Notes for more information about scalar multiples of a vector.)

Discuss the airplane situation on pages 268–269 of the student text. In this example, the horizontal and vertical velocities are written as scalar multiples of $\vec{i}$ and $\vec{j}$, respectively, and then these horizontal and vertical vectors are added to get the resultant velocity vector.

Then explain that *any* vector can be written as the sum of a horizontal vector and a vertical vector. For example, if you know a plane's speed and angle of climb, you can calculate the climb velocity and the ground velocity (Figure 6-6c) and then write the velocity vector as the sum of horizontal and vertical components.

Figure 6-6c

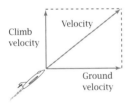

The process of *resolving* a vector into horizontal and vertical components is illustrated in Example 3. The sum of the components is equal to the original vector. The example leads to a general property for resolving a vector into its components.

Note that some texts represent vectors as ordered pairs. The notation $\vec{v} = x\vec{i} + y\vec{j}$ used in this text is conceptually easier for most students. It reminds them that a vector is the sum of a horizontal vector and a vertical vector.

When vectors are written in terms of their components, you can add them by adding the corresponding components. This is illustrated in Figure 6-6h in the student text.

Example 4 shows how to add two vectors by first resolving them into components. In part b, emphasize the importance of making a drawing to determine which value of the arctan to choose.

You might also work with the class to find the sum in Example 4 by using triangle techniques. Most students will find that adding the vectors by first resolving them into components is the easier method.

Example 5 investigates a navigation problem. Make sure students understand that a bearing is measured clockwise from north rather than counterclockwise from the positive horizontal axis. When solving navigation problems, some students may be more comfortable changing the bearings to standard angle measures. The solution for Example 5 uses triangle methods, but you may want to redo it using components. (For more practice using components to solve navigation problems, see Exploration 6-6b.)

Supplementary Lesson Notes

Addition is the only vector operation covered in this chapter. You may also want to show students how to subtract vectors and how to multiply a vector by a scalar, topics covered in Section 10-2.

Subtracting Vectors

Remind students that you subtract a number by adding its opposite. For example, $5 - 2 = 5 + (-2)$. In the same way, you subtract a vector by adding its opposite. The **opposite** of a vector is a vector with the same magnitude that points in the opposite direction. Figure 6-6d illustrates a difference of two vectors.

Figure 6-6d

Vector subtraction $\vec{a} - \vec{b} = \vec{a} + (-\vec{b})$

DEFINITION: Vector Subtraction

The *opposite* of $\vec{b}$, written $-\vec{b}$, is a vector of the same magnitude as $\vec{b}$ that points in the opposite direction.

The *difference* $\vec{a} - \vec{b}$ is the sum $\vec{a} + (-\vec{b})$.

You might present this next example to illustrate how to find the difference of vectors using triangle methods.

Example

Vectors $\vec{a}$ and $\vec{b}$ have magnitudes 5 cm and 9 cm, respectively. The angle between the two vectors when they are placed tail-to-tail is 53° (Figure 6-6e, left side). Find $|\vec{a} - \vec{b}|$ and the angle the resultant vector makes with $\vec{a}$.

Figure 6-6e

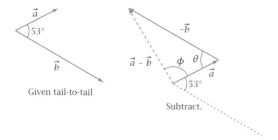

Given tail-to-tail

Subtract.

Solution

To find the difference vector, turn $\vec{b}$ around in the opposite direction, translate $-\vec{b}$ so that its tail is at the head of $\vec{a}$, and draw the resultant vector from the beginning of $\vec{a}$ to the end of $-\vec{b}$ (Figure 6-6e, right). Angle θ is equal to 53° because θ and the original 53° angle are alternate interior angles. Applying the law of cosines,

$$|\vec{a} - \vec{b}|^2 = 5^2 + 9^2 - 2(5)(9)\cos 53° = 51.8366...$$

$$|\vec{a} - \vec{b}| = 7.1997...$$

$$\cos \phi = \frac{5^2 + (7.1997...)^2 - 9^2}{2 \cdot 5 \cdot (7.1997...)} = -0.0578...$$

$$\phi = \cos^{-1}(-0.0578...) = 93.3150...°$$

$\therefore$ $\vec{a} - \vec{b}$ is about 7.2 cm long at an angle of about 93.3° to $\vec{a}$.

Note: If the law of sines had been used to find ϕ, then

$$\sin \phi = \frac{9 \sin 53°}{7.1997...} = 0.9983...$$

Taking the inverse sine gives the principal value, 86.6849...°. This leads to a general solution of 86.6849° and 93.3150°. Because there may be no easy way to tell whether the angle is acute or obtuse, it is safer to use the law of cosines. The negative value of $\cos \phi$ in this example tells you that ϕ is obtuse.

If vectors are written as the sum of components, you can subtract them by subtracting corresponding components. You can illustrate this by revisiting Example 4 and finding the difference $\vec{a} - \vec{b}$ as the sum of two components.

Multiplying a Vector by a Scalar

When you add the real number x to itself, you get twice that number.

$$x + x = 2x$$

It is reasonable to say that when you add a vector to itself, you get *twice* that vector.

$$\vec{a} + \vec{a} = 2\vec{a}$$

When you multiply a real number x by −1, you get the opposite of that number.

$$-1 \cdot x = -x$$

In a similar way, when you multiply a vector by −1, you get the opposite of that vector.

$$-1 \cdot \vec{a} = -\vec{a}$$

This reasoning leads to the definition of the product of a scalar (that is, a real number) and a vector (Figure 6-6f).

Figure 6-6f

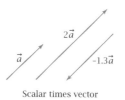

Scalar times vector

DEFINITION: Product of a Scalar and a Vector

The product $x\vec{a}$ is a vector in the direction of $\vec{a}$ if x is positive and in the opposite direction of $\vec{a}$ if x is negative. The magnitude of the product is the magnitude of $\vec{a}$ times the absolute value of x.

Exploration Notes

Exploration 6-6a begins by having students use triangle properties to find the sum of two vectors. Students are then led to discover an "easier" way to find the sum, using components. This is a good activity to assign at the end of Day 1 or the beginning of Day 2 because it reviews the ideas in Examples 1 and 2 and previews the ideas in Examples 3 and 4. Allow students 15 minutes to complete the Exploration.

Exploration 6-6b requires students to use components to solve a navigation problem. You may need to remind students about the difference between a standard-position angle and a bearing and how to get from one to the other. Allow students 20 minutes to complete this activity.

Technology Notes

 Exploration 6-6a: Introduction to Vectors, in the *Instructor's Resource Book,* guides students through the addition of vectors, using properties of triangles. This Exploration can be done with the aid of Sketchpad.

 Activity: Intersection of Parametric Curves, in *Connecting Mathematics with Science,* is a difficult but very engaging experiment in getting a projectile to hit a moving object. Students use parametric functions to represent the components of motion vectors. It will take students at least 45 minutes.

Problem Notes

Encourage students to draw diagrams to accompany their work with vectors. Remind them that a vector *must* include an arrow to indicate direction.

- *Problems 1–4 and Problem 6* are similar to Examples 1 and 2.

- *Problems 7–10* are similar to Example 3.

- *Problems 11 and 12* are similar to Example 4.

- *Problem 5 and Problems 13–16* involve bearings rather than standard-position angles.

- *Problems 18–21* explore the properties of vector addition. In Problem 21 you may need to remind students what *closure* means. For the set of vectors to be closed under addition, the sum of any two vectors must be another vector.

Supplementary Problems

For Problems 1–4,

a. Find the resultant of the two displacement vectors. Express the answer as a distance and a bearing (clockwise from north) from the starting point to the ending point.

b. Give the bearing from the ending point back to the starting point.

1. 11 yd north (0°) followed by 5 yd along a bearing of 70°

2. 8 mi east (90°) followed by 6 mi along a bearing of 210°

3. 6 km west (270°) followed by 14 km along a bearing of 110°

4. 4 m south (180°) followed by 9 m along a bearing of 320°

5. *Accurate Graphing Problem 1:* Construct the vectors in Problem 1 using computer software such as The Geometer's Sketchpad or a ruler and protractor on graph paper. Measure the length of the resultant vector and its bearing from the starting point. The answers should agree with the calculated values to ±0.1 unit of length and to ±1°.

6. *Accurate Graphing Problem 2:* Repeat Problem 5 for the vectors in Problem 2.

7. *Tug-of-War Problem:* Three ropes are tied together at a knot. April pulls on one rope with a force of 60 lb at 110°. Mae pulls the second rope with a force of 40 lb at 230°. June pulls the third rope with a force of 50 lb at 340° (Figure 6-6g).

Figure 6-6g

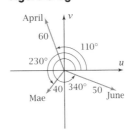

a. What is their resultant force vector as a sum of two components?

b. What is the magnitude of this force?

c. In which direction will the knot move?

6-7
Real-World Triangle Problems

Objective

Given a real-world problem, identify a triangle, and use the appropriate technique to calculate unknown side lengths and angle measures.

Class Time

2 days

Homework Assignment

Day 1: RA, Q1–Q10, Problems 1–9 odd

Day 2: Problems 11–17 odd, 18, plus have students write their own problem (see Problem Notes)

Technology Options

 Exploration 6-7a: The Ship's Path Problem

Lesson Notes

In this section, students solve a variety of triangles. Some real-world problems have been incorporated into earlier sections in this chapter, so two days is a reasonable amount of time to spend on this section.

Remind students that in addition to the new ideas from this chapter—the law of sines, law of cosines, and vector properties—they can use the right triangle properties they learned in Chapter 2. If a problem involves a right triangle, it is easier to use a property such as $\sin A = \frac{\text{opposite}}{\text{hypotenuse}}$ than the law of sines or law of cosines.

The Procedures box on pages 274–275 of the student book summarizes the triangle techniques students studied in this chapter. Students should copy this information into their notebooks, along with the appropriate formulas and any pertinent material from earlier chapters. This activity will help them organize the ideas in this chapter and create a guide they can use when they solve problems.

In addition to the Explorations, students can work collectively on these problems.

You might also consider allowing each group of students to choose a problem from the problem set to present to the class, emphasizing its unique characteristics.

In addition to assigning the problems in the book, consider asking students to write their own problems. The problems students write themselves are often the most interesting and creative ones.

There are also additional supplementary problems that can be used as extra credit and extra projects.

Exploration Notes

There are two Explorations for this section. They can be assigned in class or used as a group project, a group quiz, or an independent homework assignment.

Exploration 6-7a is a real-world triangle problem that involves the ambiguous case. From a verbal description, students are to make a diagram to analyze the situation and solve the problem. Allow about 20 minutes for this activity.

Exploration 6-7b involves the area of regular polygons and uses the idea of a limit as the number of sides increases. This Exploration shows numerically that the limit of the areas of the inscribed *n*-gon approaches the area of the circle (314.1592654...) as *n* increases. Students may need help in writing the program in Problem 6. This screenshot shows a simple TI-83 program, AREGPOLY, that can easily be entered into the calculator.

```
PROGRAM:AREGPOLY
:Degree:Fix 9
:For (X, 3, 1000)
:DISP 50X*sin (360/X)
:END
:
```

The program sets the calculator to degree mode and fixes a 9-digit output. When students are done with the program, they can reset their calculators as desired. The FOR( ) and END commands provide a loop that starts at 3 and continues to 1000. The DISP command will display the area given by the formula.

Technology Notes

 Exploration 6-7a: The Ship's Path Problem, in the *Instructor's Resource Book,* asks students to use the properties they've learned in this chapter to answer questions about a ship's path. Students are asked to construct a diagram to model the ship's movement, and this can easily be done in Sketchpad.

Problem Notes

This problem set is arranged so that, whenever possible, odd- and even-numbered problems are roughly equivalent and so that problems progress from easy to hard. Apart from these criteria, there is no particular pattern to the arrangement. The randomness is deliberate, because students are expected to select the appropriate technique based on the merits of the problem. Assign some problems with diagrams and some without.

Supplementary Problems

This project can be assigned instead of, or as an extension of, Problem 16 in the student book.

1. *Hinged Rulers Project:* Figure 6-7a shows a meterstick (100-cm ruler) with a 60-cm ruler attached to one end by a hinge. The other end of each ruler rests on a horizontal surface. The hinge is pulled upward so that the meterstick makes an angle θ with the surface. In this project you will investigate the distance between the ruler ends as a function of θ.

Figure 6-7a

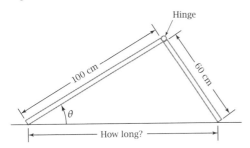

a. Find the two possible distances between the ruler ends if $\theta = 20°$.

b. Find the value of θ that gives just *one* possible distance between the ends.

c. Plot the graph of distance between the ends versus θ. Use a window for x (actually for θ) with a range of $[0°, 180°]$. You should get a graph that resembles the one in Figure 6-7b. The graph shows that in some parts of the domain there are two distance values and that in other parts there are no distance values. Does the graph agree with the distances and angles you calculated in parts a and b?

Figure 6-7b

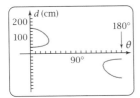

d. If the 60-cm ruler is replaced with a 120-cm ruler, find the possible distances between the ends when $\theta = 20°$.

e. Plot the graph of distance between the ends versus θ for the 120-cm ruler. Use the same screen you used in part c.

f. Each different ruler length gives a different graph. Figure 6-7c shows what happens if you use rulers with lengths 40, 60, 80, 100, and 120 cm and allow θ to range from 0° to 180°. Duplicate this figure on your grapher.

Figure 6-7c

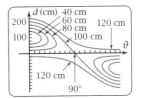

g. How do you interpret the fact that the graphs "end" for the 40-, 60-, and 80-cm rulers? How do you interpret the negative values for the 120-cm ruler? What special curve is the graph for the 100-cm ruler? How do you interpret the graph for values of θ greater than 90°?

2. *Flagpole Problem:* Calvin is waiting outside the school building for his precalculus class to begin. He notices the flagpole casting a shadow on the ground and decides to calculate the height of the pole. He measures the shadow and finds that it is 22 m long. He looks up at the Sun and finds that its angle of elevation is 38° (Figure 6-7d). How tall is the pole?

Figure 6-7d

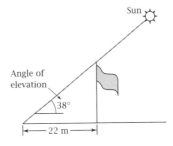

3. *Airplane Problem:* Aloha Airlines Flight 007 is approaching Kahului Airport at an altitude of 7 km. The angle of depression (Figure 6-7e) is 9°.

Figure 6-7e

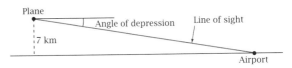

a. What is the plane's ground distance from the airport?

b. If the plane descends straight along the line of sight, how far will it travel along this line before it reaches the airport?

4. *Harbor Problem:* As a ship sails into a harbor, the navigator sights a buoy at an angle of 15° to the path of the ship (Figure 6-7f). The ship sails 1300 m farther, at which point the buoy makes an angle of 29° with the path.

Figure 6-7f

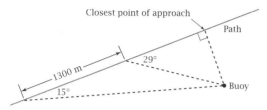

a. How far is the ship from the buoy at the second sighting?

b. What is the closest the ship will come to the buoy if it continues on its straight path?

c. How far must the ship sail from its second sighting point to reach the closest point of approach?

d. When the ship has gone 7000 m beyond the second sighting point, what will be the *obtuse* angle at which the navigator must look back from the ship's path to see the buoy?

5. *Cloud Ceiling Problem:* Ground controllers at airports need to know the "ceiling." That is, they need to know how close the bottoms of the clouds are to the ground. One method for measuring the ceiling involves shining a spotlight straight up at the cloud bottoms and observing the angle of elevation of the spot of light from another point on the ground (Figure 6-7g).

Figure 6-7g

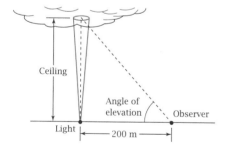

a. If the observer is 200 m from the spotlight, write an equation expressing the ceiling in terms of the angle of elevation.

b. What would the ceiling be if the angle were 73°?

c. What would the angle be if the ceiling were 3000 m?

d. Plot the graph of the equation in part a in the domain [0°, 90°). Sketch the result.

e. Describe how an accurate graph, such as the one from part d, could be used by the observer to calculate the ceiling for any given value of the angle.

6. *Stump Force Problem:* Joe Jamoke and Ivan Hoe are pulling on a tree stump. Joe pulls with a force of 200 lb, and Ivan pulls with a force of 250 lb. A total force of 400 lb is needed to pull up the stump.

a. If they pull at an angle of 25° to each other, will the resultant force be enough to pull up the stump?

b. At what angle must they pull in order to exert *exactly* the 400-lb force needed to pull up the stump?

7. *Torpedo Practice Problem:* Suppose you are aboard a submarine conducting torpedo practice off the Florida coast. At a given time, the target is 7200 m from you on a bearing of 276° and is steaming on a course of 68° (Figure 6-7h). Your long-range torpedoes will go 6400 m, and your short-range torpedoes will go 3200 m. Between what two bearings can you fire torpedoes that will reach the target's path if you use long-range torpedoes? If you use short-range torpedoes?

Figure 6-7h

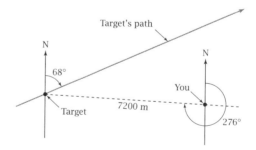

Precalculus with Trigonometry: Instructor's Guide
© 2007 Key Curriculum Press

8. *Castle Height Problem:* Sir Vey wants to find the height of King Arthur's castle. He cannot get right up to the castle because it is surrounded by a moat. From a point on the ground he measures an angle of 37° to the top of the castle (Figure 6-7i). He moves 75 feet closer and measures an angle of 65° to the top of the castle. Calculate the height, *h,* of the castle.

Figure 6-7i

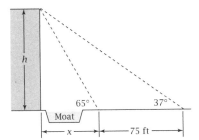

9. *CB Radio Problem:* A CB radio operator has a base station on Farm Road, 8 mi from where it intersects Interstate 30 (Figure 6-7j). Farm Road makes an angle of 32° with I-30. If the radio has a range of 5 mi, between what two distances from the intersection can cars on the highway hear the base station radio?

Figure 6-7j

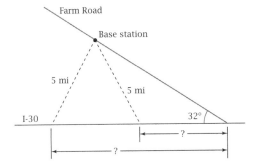

10. *Spider and Clock Problem:* At 4:00 a.m. a spider is sitting at the tip of the minute hand of a clock (Figure 6-7k). The minute hand is 10 in. long, and the hour hand is 7 in. long.

Figure 6-7k

a. At this time, how far would the spider have to jump to reach the tip of the hour hand?

b. How long would the spider have to wait so that it could jump the *minimum* distance from the tip of the minute hand to the tip of the hour hand?

11. *Parade Problem:* A parade goes from Town *A* to Town *B* to Town *C*, then back to Town *A*. These towns are at the vertices of an equilateral triangle. The roads connecting the towns are straight, level, and direct, and the parade goes at a constant speed with no stops. From *A* to *B* takes 80 min, and from *B* to *C* takes 80 min, but from *C* back to *A* takes 1 h 20 min. How do you explain the discrepancy in times?

6-8

Chapter Review and Test

Objective

Review and practice the major concepts presented in this chapter.

Class Time

2 days (including 1 day for testing)

Homework Assignment

Day 1: R0–R7, T1–T21

Day 2 (after Chapter 6 Test): Begin the Cumulative Review (Section 6-9).

Lesson Notes

Section 6-8 contains a set of Review Problems, a set of Concept Problems, and a Chapter Test. The Review Problems include one problem for each section in the chapter. You may wish to use the Chapter Test as an additional set of review problems.

Encourage students to practice the no-calculator problems without a calculator so that they are prepared for the test problems for which they cannot use a calculator.

Supplementary Problems

1. *City Street Problem:* In downtown Clarksville, Alamo Street, Heights Street, and Front Avenue form an acute triangle. Alamo forms an angle of 74° with Front, and Heights forms an angle of 67° with Front. The distance from Alamo to Heights, measured along Front, is 1000 feet.

   a. Make a sketch of the triangular block.

   b. Calculate the lengths of Alamo and Heights from the point where they intersect one another to Front Avenue.

   c. Find the area of the block.

2. Linus and Lucy are quarreling over a bag of Halloween candy. Lucy pulls on the bag with a force of 7 pounds. Linus pulls with a force of 6 pounds at an angle of 160° to Lucy's force. Diagram the situation, and calculate the resultant force on the bag and the angle this force makes with Lucy's vector.

3. True or false: If you add two vectors, the resultant has a magnitude greater than the magnitude of either of the two vectors that were added. Give evidence to support your answer.

4. Figure 6-8a shows a triangle with sides 4 cm, 5 cm, and 7 cm drawn on a centimeter grid.

Figure 6-8a

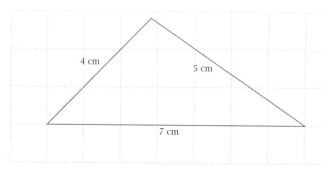

   a. Approximate the area of the triangle by counting squares. To do this, estimate the area of the part of the triangle in each square to the nearest 0.1 cm^2, and then add the estimates.

   b. Use Hero's formula to calculate the area of the triangle. Write all the decimal places your calculator shows. How close is this calculated area to your estimate from part a?

   c. Calculate the measure of the largest angle of the triangle. Store the answer as A in your grapher.

   d. Find the area of the triangle again, using angle A and the two sides that include angle A. Use the stored value of A so that you will be using the precise answer, without round-off. Write all the decimal places your calculator shows.

   e. Does the formula you used in part d give the same area as Hero's formula?

5. A boat in the Gulf of Mexico is traveling 5 mi/h along a bearing of 20°. Meanwhile, the current is flowing 3 mi/h along a bearing of 75°. Figure 6-8b is drawn to scale, with 1 cm representing 1 mi/h.

Figure 6-8b

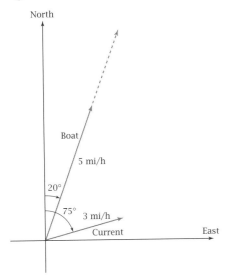

a. The resultant velocity of the boat is the vector sum of the boat's velocity and the current's velocity. Plot this resultant vector.

b. The speed of the boat is the magnitude of the resultant vector. Estimate the boat's speed by measuring the resultant vector.

c. Calculate the boat's speed by appropriate use of the law of cosines or the law of sines. How does the calculated result compare to your estimate from part b?

d. Use a protractor to measure the bearing of the resultant vector. Use the result to write the boat's resultant speed and bearing.

6. Figure 6-8c shows a line crossing the x-axis 6 cm from the origin at an angle of 130° to the axis. A line 5 cm long is drawn to this line from the origin.

Figure 6-8c

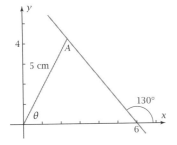

a. Use the law of sines to write an equation expressing sin A in terms of known sides and angles.

b. Write A as a function of θ. Substitute the result for A in your equation from part b.

c. Solve your equation from part c to find the two possible values of θ in the domain [0°, 180°].

7. *Law of Tangents Historical Problem:* In the days before calculators, the law of cosines was hard to use because it could involve products, sums, and square roots of numbers with many decimal places. One alternative method was the **law of tangents,** which involves operations that could be done more easily by hand and with logarithm tables. The law of tangents states that for $\triangle ABC$,

$$\frac{\tan \frac{1}{2}(A - B)}{\tan \frac{1}{2}(A + B)} = \frac{a - b}{a + b}$$

In this problem you will derive the law of tangents.

a. Use the law of sines and the addition property of equality to show that

$$\frac{\sin A + \sin B}{\sin B} = \frac{a + b}{b} \quad \text{and}$$

$$\frac{\sin A - \sin B}{\sin B} = \frac{a - b}{b}$$

b. Divide the two equations in part a (left side by left side and right side by right side). Simplify the result. Then use the sum and product properties from Chapter 5 to express the numerator and denominator on the left side as products.

c. Use the quotient properties of trigonometric functions to arrive at the stated law of tangents.

Cumulative Review, Chapters 1–6

Objective

Review the first six chapters.

Class Time

1 or 2 days

Homework Assignment

Day 1: Keep working on the Cumulative Review.

Day 2: Complete the Cumulative Review and do Problem Set 7-1.

Lesson Notes

At this point in the course, many students will be taking a semester exam. The cumulative review questions in this section will help them rehearse for such an exam. These problems provide an excellent review of the concepts covered so far. Whenever possible, the problems are applied to analyze real-world situations.

A cumulative exam can be quite an ordeal for students. Students working in small groups can have fun with these cumulative review problems and learn a lot from each other. Students should also be encouraged to look over their old tests and quizzes and bring in any problems they still don't understand. You may also want to make up an additional set of practice problems that complement this problem set. Students should consult their journals to aid in the review process.

If you are giving a cumulative test, use this problem set as a guide for the type of problems to include. Use your judgment about the kind of review you will provide and the kind of cumulative exam you will give your students.

Problem Note

* *Problem 4* asks students to sketch the graph of the inverse of a function, given the graph of the function. A blackline master of the graph is available in the *Instructor's Resource Book*.

7 Properties of Elementary Functions

This chapter is the reentry point if you choose to postpone the study of periodic functions in Chapters 2 through 6. Students learn to tell which kind of function might fit a given set of data, by recognizing first the geometric pattern of the graph and then the numerical pattern followed by regularly spaced points. The numerical patterns include the add–multiply property for exponential functions and the multiply–multiply property for power functions. As they study logarithms in Sections 7-4 through 7-6, students learn that logarithmic functions have the multiply–add property, as would be expected for the inverse of an exponential function. Section 7-4 focuses on common logarithms, so that properties can be explored in the familiar context of powers of 10. In Example 1 of 7-5, students learn a verbal way to remember the definition of logarithm, namely that a logarithm is an exponent, that eliminates most mistakes they make here. Natural logarithms and common logarithms are presented so that students will know what $\ln x$ means on their calculator and thus will have heard the words before encountering natural logarithms in calculus. The chapter concludes with the modeling of restrained population growth with the logistic function, whose graph has horizontal asymptotes and points of inflection. Periodic functions are not mentioned in this chapter because it is not assumed that students will have studied Chapters 2 through 6. In the Concept Problems, students encounter semilog and log-log graph paper, which they will learn more about in Section 8-4.

7-1
Shapes of Function Graphs

Objective

Discover patterns in linear, quadratic, power, and exponential function graphs.

Class Time

$\frac{1}{2}$ day

Homework Assignment

Problems 1–4

Important Terms and Concepts

Concavity (concave up, concave down)

Exponential function

Power function

Quadratic function

Linear function

Lesson Notes

In this section, students investigate the shapes and features of the graphs of linear, quadratic, power, and exponential functions. Students will explore these types of functions in more detail in the next two sections. You can assign this section for homework the night of the Chapter 6 test or as a group activity to be completed in class. No classroom discussion is needed before students begin the activity.

Problem Notes

- *Problems 1 and 2* present an exponential function and a power function, respectively. Students sometimes confuse these two types of functions because both involve an exponent. Emphasize that in an exponential function the variable is the *exponent,* whereas in a power function the variable is the *base.* In addition, you may want to discuss these questions with your class.

  a. The $f(x)$-intercept is $f(0)$, the value of $f(x)$ when $x = 0$. What is the graphical significance of the $f(x)$-intercept? Why does the $f(x)$-intercept equal 0.2, not 0, for this function?

b. The word *concave* means "hollowed out." The words *cave* and *cavity* have the same origin. Why do you suppose the graph of f is said to be *concave up*?

c. By calculation, $f(-1) = 0.1$. Why is $f(-1)$ not meaningful in this real-world situation?

d. Why do you suppose the function in this problem is called an *exponential* function?

- *Problem 2* asks students what graphical evidence distinguishes the power function graph in that problem from the exponential function graph in Problem 1. Make sure students realize that the graph of the power function passes through the origin, whereas the graph of the exponential function does not. If you graph the exponential function in Problem 1 and the power function on the same axes, students will see that as x gets big, the exponential function grows faster than the power function. This is an important distinction between the two types of increasing functions. Consider showing them how to use matrices to solve systems. In addition, you may want to discuss these questions with your class.

  a. Based on this mathematical model, how much would you expect a 10-ft snake to weigh?

  b. Why does the domain of g contain only nonnegative numbers?

  c. The equation $g(x) = 0.1x^3$ has an exponent in it. Why do you suppose it is called a *power* function rather than an *exponential* function?

- *Problem 3* presents a quadratic function. It is important for students to recognize that the quadratic function, unlike the exponential and power functions, has a vertex (in this case, a maximum point). In addition, you may want to discuss these questions with your class.

  a. The quadratic function has the *square* of x in it. What other geometrical term do you suppose gives quadratic functions their name?

  b. Describe verbally what the quadratic model indicates about the pattern through time in the sales of this product.

  c. How do you interpret the fact that the quadratic model gives decimal answers for the number of items sold even though the actual number of items sold must be an integer?

- *Problem 4* presents a linear function. The graph of a linear function is neither concave up nor concave down.

Precalculus with Trigonometry: Instructor's Guide
© 2007 Key Curriculum Press

7-2
Identifying Functions from Graphical Patterns

Objective

Given the graph of a function, know whether the function is exponential, power, quadratic, or linear, and find the particular equation algebraically.

Class Time

1–2 days

Homework Assignment

Day 1: RA, Q1–Q10, Problems 1–25 odd

Day 2: Problems 2–10 even, 14–24 even

Technology Options

 Exploration 7-2a: Graphical Patterns in Functions

Important Terms and Concepts

Slope-intercept form

Point-slope form

Slope

Vertex

Vertex form

Parabola

Proportionality constant

Directly proportional

Inversely proportional

Base-10 exponential function

Natural (base-*e*) exponential function

Lesson Notes

In Section 7-1, students plotted equations of exponential, power, quadratic, and linear functions and explored the features of the graphs. In this section, they are given graphs and use what they learned in Section 7-1 to identify the type of function each graph represents. Once they identify the type of function, they use information about points on the graph to find a particular equation.

The student text summarizes the graphs and equations of linear, quadratic, power, and exponential functions. Here is more detailed information about each type of function.

Linear and Constant Functions

The name *linear* comes from the fact that the graph of a linear function is a straight line. Linear functions have no concavity and a constant slope.

In the student text, the slope-intercept form of a linear function is given as $y = ax + b$. In this form, a is the slope of the line and b is the y-intercept. Many texts use m rather than a to represent the slope. The letter m comes from the French *montant*, (as in "mountain"), meaning "the rise."

If $a = 0$, the function $y = ax + b$ becomes the *constant function* $y = b$. The graph of a constant function is a horizontal line. If $a \neq 0$ and $b = 0$, the function is of the form $y = ax$, which represents a line through the origin. If this function is translated so the point at the origin moves to the point (x_1, y_1), then the equation becomes $y - y_1 = a(x - x_1)$. This form is called *point-slope form* because it contains both the coordinates of a point on the graph and the slope. It is important for students to master the point-slope form of a line. This form is more general than the slope-intercept form because *any* point can be used for (x_1, y_1), whereas the slope-intercept calls for a specific point, the y-intercept.

Quadratic Functions

A quadratic function is a second-degree polynomial function (i.e., a polynomial function in which the highest power of x is 2). The graph of a quadratic function is called a *parabola*. The quadratic function is the only function in this group of elementary functions whose graph has a turning point, or vertex.

The left graph in Figure 7-2b in the text shows the parent quadratic function, $y = x^2$. Any other quadratic function is a transformation of this function. The middle graph shows $y = 3 + 0.4(x - 1)^2$, which is a dilation of the parent graph by a factor of 0.4 and a translation of 1 unit horizontally and 3 units vertically. The graph on the right shows $y = 3 - 2(x - 1)^2$, which has the same translations but a dilation factor of −2.

If the vertical dilation is positive, the parabola opens up and is said to be concave up (middle, Figure 7-2b). If the vertical dilation is negative, the parabola opens down and is said to be concave down (right, Figure 7-2b).

The equation $y - 3 = -2(x - 1)^2$ can be solved for y in terms of x.

$$y - 3 = -2(x - 1)^2$$

$$y - 3 = -2(x^2 - 2x + 1) \quad \text{Expand the squared binomial.}$$

$$y = -2x^2 + 4x + 1 \quad \text{Distribute the } -2 \text{ and isolate } y.$$

This equation is now in the polynomial form $y = ax^2 + bx + c$. When a quadratic function is written in this form, a positive value of a indicates that the parabola is concave up and a negative value of a indicates that the parabola is concave down. The y-intercept is c. The polynomial form $y = ax^2 + bx + c$ does not tell us as much about the graph of the quadratic function as the vertex form $y - k = a(x - h)^2$.

About Power Functions

The power function has the general form of $y = ax^b$. Figure 7-2c in the student text shows graphs of three power functions. The graph of $y = 0.002x^3$ contains the origin because $y = 0$ when $x = 0$. The graph is concave up because the y-values increase more and more rapidly as x increases. The graph of $y = 2.5x^{0.6}$ contains the origin, is increasing, and is concave down because the y-values increase at a slower and slower rate as x increases. The graph of $y = 3x^{-1}$ is undefined when $x = 0$ $\left(\text{because } 3x^{-1} = \frac{3}{x}\right)$, so it has no y-intercept. The y-values decrease as x increases because you are dividing by larger and larger numbers.

This list summarizes the features of graphs of functions of the form $y = ax^b$.

- If $a > 0$ and $b > 1$, then the graph contains the origin, is increasing, and is concave up in the first quadrant.

- If $a > 0$ and $0 < b < 1$, then the graph contains the origin, is increasing, and is concave down in the first quadrant.

- If $a > 0$ and $b < 0$, then the graph does not contain the origin and is decreasing and asymptotic to both axes in the first quadrant.

- If $b = 1$, then the function is a linear function.

- If b is a non-integer, then the domain is $x \geq 0$ because of the ambiguity of the solution (for example, $(-8)^{1/3} = -2$, but $(-8)^{3/6} = 2$).

About Exponential Functions

An exponential function has equation $y = ab^x$, where $a \neq 0$, $b > 0$, and $b \neq 1$. Figure 7-2d in the student text shows graphs of three exponential functions. In the function $y = 2 \cdot 1.2^x$, the base is greater than 1. This causes the y-values to increase as x increases. The base in the function $y = 6 \cdot 0.7^x$ is greater than 0 but less then 1. Raising such a number to greater and greater powers gives smaller and smaller results, so the y-values decrease as x increases. Both graphs are concave up—the left graph because y increases at a faster and faster rate and the middle graph because y decreases at a slower and slower

rate. The graph $y = -3 \cdot 1.06^x$ shows what can happen if a is negative.

This list summarizes the features of graphs of functions of the form $y = ab^x$, where $a \neq 0$, $b > 0$, and $b \neq 1$.

- If $a > 0$ and $b > 1$, then the graph is increasing and concave up. The graph is asymptotic to the x-axis and has y-intercept a.

- If $a > 0$ and $0 < b < 1$, then the graph is decreasing and concave up. The graph is asymptotic to the x-axis and has y-intercept a.

- If $a < 0$ and $b > 1$, then the graph is decreasing and concave down. The graph is asymptotic to the x-axis and has y-intercept a.

- If $a < 0$ and $0 < b < 1$, then the graph is increasing and concave down. The graph is asymptotic to the x-axis and has y-intercept a.

Notice that in all four cases the graph is asymptotic to the x-axis and has y-intercept a.

In the examples, students identify the type of function from a given graph and then find the equation.

The function in Example 1 is linear. Part d shows how to find the equation by writing and solving a system of equations. The system is solved by the elimination method, but if your students have studied matrices, you can present the alternative solution given at the end of the example. (Students will study matrices in Chapter 11.)

The equation can also be found by calculating the slope and then writing the equation in point-slope form:

$$\text{slope} = \frac{19 - 6}{5 - 10} = \frac{13}{-5} = -2.6$$

So, using the point $(5, 19)$, the equation is $y - 19 = -2.6(x - 5)$.

The quadratic equation in Example 2 is found by writing and solving a system of three equations in three variables. Part d shows how to find the solution using matrices. While this example is easy to do algebraically, most systems of three equations in three variables are not easy to solve without matrices. If your students have not learned about matrices, you can present this alternative algebraic solution:

$$76 = a + b + c$$

$$89 = 4a + 2b + c$$

$$94 = 9a + 3b + c$$

Subtract the first equation from the second and subtract the second equation from the third to eliminate c and get two equations in two variables:

$$13 = 3a + b$$

$$5 = 5a + b$$

Now solve this system of two equations to find a and b:

$13 - 5 = (3a + b) - (5a + b)$	Subtract the second equation from the first.
$8 = -2a$	Simplify.
$a = -4$	Solve for a.
$13 = 3(-4) + b$	Substitute -4 for a in the first equation.
$b = 25$	Solve for b.

To find c, go back to one of the original equations.

$76 = -4 + 25 + c$	Substitute -4 for a and 25 for b in the original first equation.
$c = 55$	Solve for c.

The curve in Example 3 represents a power function. The shape of the curve is similar to that of an exponential function, but it can be distinguished from an exponential function graph because it passes through the origin. Finding the particular equation for the curve requires the use of logarithms. If students are not familiar with logarithms, you can simply give them the equation and explain that they will learn how to find the equation themselves in Section 7-4.

The curve in Example 4 represents an exponential function. You may need to remind students that they should store intermediate values in the calculator and use them to find the other values.

Exploration Notes

Exploration 7-2a provides practice in finding the particular equation of a linear, quadratic, power, or exponential function from a given graph. You might assign this as a review sheet or use it as a quiz. Allow students 20–25 minutes to complete this activity.

Technology Notes

Exploration 7-2a: Graphical Patterns in Functions, in the *Instructor's Resource Book*, asks students to identify what kinds of functions represent given graphs and to write equations for the graphs. The high-resolution graphing capabilities of either Fathom or Sketchpad would be useful for this Exploration.

Problem Notes

Be sure you discuss all the assigned problems, because they contain key concepts important for students to master and understand.

- *Problems 1–7* help students review the important features of the graphs and equations of the various types of functions.
- *Problem 8* helps students see that there are advantages and disadvantages to both forms of the quadratic-function equation.
- *Problems 9 and 10* require students to find equation models for situations based on written descriptions of the situations.
- *Problems 21–24* help students review the meaning of "directly proportional," "inverse variation," and "direct variation."
- *Problem 25,* the Natural Exponential Function Problem, gives students a natural exponential function and asks them to find an equivalent exponential function with a different base.

Supplementary Problems

1. *Gasoline Consumption Problem:* The number of gallons of gasoline left in your gas tank is (approximately) a linear function of the number of miles you have driven. Suppose you have driven 123 mi since your last fill-up and you have 13 gal left in your tank. Your car uses 0.05 gal/mi (i.e., it gets 20 mi/gal).

   a. Write an equation in point-slope form relating the number of miles driven since you filled the tank and the number of gallons left in the tank. Transform the equation so that gallons is expressed as a function of miles.

   b. Use the answer from part a to determine how many gallons your car's tank holds.

   c. You want to fill up before the amount left drops below 1 gallon. How much farther can you drive before you need to fill up again?

2. *Two Airplanes Problem:* Two airplanes are flying on paths that intersect. At time $t = 0$ min, the planes are 17 mi apart. At time $t = 4$ min, they reach their closest point of approach, 5 mi apart. Thereafter, the distance between the planes increases.

   a. Write an equation in vertex form for the quadratic function expressing the relationship between distance and time. Transform it so that distance is expressed as a function of time.

   b. How far apart were the planes at time $t = 7$ min?

   c. At what time were the planes first 10 mi apart?

7-3
Identifying Functions from Numerical Patterns

Objectives

- Given a set of regularly spaced x-values and corresponding y-values, identify which type of function they fit (linear, quadratic, power, or exponential).
- Find other function values without necessarily finding the particular equation.

Class Time

2 days

Homework Assignment

Day 1: RA, Q1–Q10, Problems 1–23 odd

Day 2: Problems 25–27, 29–32, 35

Technology Options

Explorations 7-3a–7-3c: Numerical Patterns in Functions

Activity: Moore's Law

Activity: Population Growth

Activity: A Watched Cup Never Cools

Important Terms and Concepts

Add–add property

Add–multiply property

Multiply–multiply property

Second differences

Discrete data

Third differences

Quartic function

Lesson Notes

In Section 7-2, students learned to recognize the type of function based on its graph. In this section, students learn to use numerical patterns in the x- and y-values to identify the function type. It is recommended that you spend two days on this section. On the first day, have students do Exploration 7-3a, either in groups or as a guided discovery activity. Introduce the pattern for quadratic functions at the end of the first day or beginning of the second day, using Exploration 7-3b.

Discuss the add–add, add–multiply, multiply–multiply, and second-differences patterns, using the graphs and tables given in the student text. Be sure to emphasize that to use these patterns to identify function type, the x-values must be regularly spaced. The box on page 307 summarizing these four properties should help students as they work on the problems.

Example 1 asks students to identify the pattern and then choose the appropriate model, in this case quadratic. Students do not need to find the particular equation for the function.

Example 2 gives students two function values and asks them to find a third value in three cases— when the function is linear, when it is a power function, and when it is exponential. To find the three values, students must apply the add–add, multiply–multiply, and add–multiply properties, respectively. This example helps students to distinguish between the various properties. As in Example 1, students do not need to find particular equations for the functions.

For Example 3, you will probably need to remind students what "varies directly" and "varies inversely" mean. These ideas were discussed in Section 7-2. In Example 4, you may need to explain what a direct square power function is. Setting up the example using this table might be helpful.

x	$f(x)$
$\times 2\big(\begin{smallmatrix} 5 \\ 20 \end{smallmatrix}$	$\begin{smallmatrix} 1000 \\ ? \end{smallmatrix}\big)\times 4^2$

Example 5 is a radioactive decay problem. The value of $f(12)$ can be found by extending the add–multiply pattern in the table. However, to find the value of $f(25)$, it is necessary to find the particular equation. Part d explains how to do this.

Be sure to discuss the note after Example 5, which emphasizes that there are many functions that fit a particular set of points. Problem 30 also illustrates this point.

Exploration Notes

Exploration 7-3a provides practice in finding a pattern in the y-values for regularly spaced x-values for exponential, power, or linear functions. You might assign this at the beginning of either Day 1 or Day 2 to help students review what they learned the day before. Or you might assign this activity as a review sheet before the chapter test. Allow students 20–25 minutes to complete this activity.

Exploration 7-3b gives students practice identifying the second differences for a quadratic function and finding a particular equation for the function. Problem 2 suggests that students use the MATRX feature on their graphers to find the equation. If your students do not know how to work with matrices, they can solve the system using algebraic methods. You might have students complete this Exploration in class, after you have discussed the add–add, add–multiply, and multiply–multiply patterns. The Exploration could also be used as an extra homework assignment, a review sheet, or a quiz. Allow students 20–25 minutes to complete this activity.

Exploration 7-3c provides practice in finding a particular equation and using it to find other values when a set of regularly spaced *x*- and *y*-values is given. You might assign this Exploration to groups at the end of Day 2 or use it as an extra homework assignment or a review sheet. The problems in the Exploration also make excellent quiz or test questions. Allow students 20–25 minutes to complete this activity.

Technology Notes

Explorations 7-3a–7-3c: Numerical Patterns in Functions, in the *Instructor's Resource Book,* focus on finite differences. Students might benefit from using Fathom's tools for making tables of finite differences.

Activity: Moore's Law, in *Teaching Mathematics with Fathom,* has students use Fathom to fit an exponential curve to data on the number of transistors in Intel processors since 1974. Students are then asked to determine the truth of Moore's Law based on their findings. This would make an excellent project to use now and then to revisit during Section 8-4. Allow 35–50 minutes.

Activity: Population Growth, in *Teaching Mathematics with Fathom,* gives experience with exponential functions based on numerical patterns. Students begin by fitting an exponential growth model to population data, and then they introduce a crowding effect to obtain a logistic function. You could ask students to do only the exponential part, or you could have them do the whole activity to foreshadow the material from Section 7-7. Allow 50 minutes.

Activity: A Watched Cup Never Cools in the book by the same name gives students experience with exponential decay. The activity's mention of calculus can be ignored, or you can

do the activity in conjunction with derivatives in Section 15-5. The full activity may take up to a week.

Problem Notes

- *Problems 1–24* follow the examples and should be routine for students.

- *Problems 25–27* require students to apply the facts that the volumes of similarly shaped objects are directly proportional to the cube of a linear dimension and the areas of similarly shaped objects are directly proportional to the square of a linear dimension.

- *Problems 28 and 29* are application problems that depend on students being able to write the particular equation that meets specific conditions.

- *Problem 30,* the Other Function Fit Problem, emphasizes the point that more than one function fits a set of data points.

- *Problem 32,* the Cubic Function Problem, extends the concept of second differences and quadratics to third differences and cubics.

- *Problems 33–36* guide students through proofs of the properties from this section.

Supplementary Problems

1. Given that $f(x)$ varies linearly with x, $f(-4) = 11$, and $f(0) = 9$, find $f(4)$, $f(8)$, and $f(12)$.

2. Given that $f(x)$ varies directly with x and that $f(2) = 15$, find $f(4)$, $f(8)$, and $f(16)$.

3. Given that $f(x)$ is inversely proportional to x and that $f(7) = 300$, find $f(14)$ and $f(28)$.

4. Given that f is an exponential function with $f(3) = 12$ and that $f(7) = 36$, find $f(11)$ and $f(19)$.

5. *Animal Weight and Area Problem:* The weight of any animal is roughly proportional to the cube of its length. The skin area is roughly proportional to the square of its length. An elephant is roughly 10 times as long as a dog.

   a. How does an elephant's weight compare to a dog's weight?

   b. How does an elephant's skin area compare to a dog's skin area?

   c. Warm-blooded animals lose heat through their skins. How does the skin-to-weight ratio for a dog compare to that for an elephant? Why do you suppose that dogs need fur but elephants do not?

6. *Temperature Problem:* An object not at room temperature cools down or warms up in such a way that the difference between the object's temperature and room temperature decreases exponentially with time.

   a. Suppose a cup of coffee is 70°C above room temperature when it is poured. Five minutes later it is only 50°C above room temperature. How high above room temperature will it be 10 min after it is poured? 15 min after it is poured?

   b. Cold water from the refrigerator is 20°C below room temperature when the glass is filled. Three minutes later it has warmed to 16°C below room temperature. How far below room temperature will the water be 15 min after the glass is filled?

7. *Lizard Mass Problem:* Curators at Scorpion Gulch Zoo measured the masses of lizards of varying lengths, finding these data:

Length (cm)	Mass (g)
3	2.7
6	21.6
9	72.9
12	172.8
15	337.5

   a. What pattern do the data follow? What kind of function has that pattern?

   b. By following the pattern, predict the mass of a 24-cm lizard and of a 30-cm lizard.

   c. Using any two of the data points, find the particular equation for a function that fits the data. (If you are working in groups, each group member should use a different pair of points.) Show that the equation gives you the data in the table.

   d. The largest kind of lizard is the Komodo dragon. Use your equation to predict the mass of a Komodo dragon that is 110 cm long. Does the answer surprise you?

   e. Based on this mathematical model, how long would you expect a 1-kg lizard to be?

8. *Computer Iterations Problem:* When a computer runs a program, it takes a certain fixed amount of time to compile the program and then a variable amount of time to run the program. The running time depends on how many *iterations* are performed (that is, on how many times

the program repeats itself). This table shows the number of seconds it takes a particular computer to run programs with a given number of iterations.

Iterations	Seconds
200	8.7
300	12.2
400	15.7
500	19.2
600	22.7

   a. What pattern do the data follow? What kind of function has this pattern?

   b. By following the pattern, predict how long it would take for 1000 iterations.

   c. Using any two of the data points, find the particular equation for the function that fits the data. (If you are working in groups, each group member should use a different pair of points.) Show that the equation gives you the data in the table.

   d. At what rate (in seconds per iteration) does the computer perform the iterations? What part of the equation gives you this number?

   e. How long does the computer take to compile the program before it starts performing the iterations? What part of the equation gives you this number?

   f. If the program takes 47.3 s to run, how many iterations did the computer perform?

9. *Savings Account Problem:* On Rashid's 10th birthday, his parents started a savings account for him. This table shows the amount of money in the account on several subsequent birthdays.

Age (years)	Amount (dollars)
12	$3630.00
13	3993.00
14	4392.30
15	4831.53

   a. Show that the data have the add–multiply pattern. What kind of function has this pattern?

   b. Follow the pattern forward to find out how much will be in the account on Rashid's 16th and 17th birthdays.

c. Follow the pattern backward to find out how much was invested on Rashid's 10th birthday.

d. By what percentage does your money increase each year? This number is called the *APR*, which stands for *annual percentage rate.*

e. Using any two of the data points, find the particular equation for the function that fits the data. (If you are working in groups, each group member should use a different pair of points.) Show that if you do not round the constants, the equation gives you the data in the table.

f. If Rashid leaves the money in the account and the interest rate remains the same, how much money will be in the account on his 65th birthday? Does the answer surprise you?

7-4
Properties of Logarithms

Objective

Learn the properties of base-10 logarithms.

Class Time

1 day

Homework Assignment

RA, Q1–Q10, Problems 1–47 odd

Important Terms and Concepts

Base-10 logarithm

Logarithm

Logarithm of a product

Logarithm of a quotient

Logarithm of a power

A logarithm is an exponent

Lesson Notes

When discussing the definition and properties of logarithms, the most important idea to stress is that *a logarithm is an exponent,* so logarithms obey the same laws exponents do. Refer to the Additional Class Examples, which can help students see the connection between exponents and logarithms.

Examples 1 and 2 in the student text are direct applications of the definition of logarithm. Examples 3–5 and 7 apply the properties of logarithms, and Example 6 gives the proof of the "logarithm of a product" property. As you work through the examples with students, keep coming back to the idea that a log is an exponent.

This section discusses only base-10 logarithms, which are also called *common logarithms.* The next section introduces base-*e* logarithms, which are called *natural logarithms,* as well as the change-of-base property.

Exploration Notes

Exploration 7-4a enforces the notion that logarithms are exponents by comparing base-10 logarithms with powers of 10. It finishes by considering other bases, so it makes a good transitional activity from Section 7-4 to Section 7-5.

Additional Class Examples

1. Find $x = \log_{10} 37$. Check your answer by showing that $10^x = 37$ for the value of x you found.

   Solution

   $\log_{10} 37 = 1.5682...$ Press log(37) on your calculator.

   $10^{1.5682...} = 37$, which checks   Find 10^{answer} without round-off.

2. Evaluate $10^{-0.375} = 0.4216....$ Use your calculator.

   Log $0.4216... = -0.375$ Take log(answer) without round-off.

   The logarithm is the same as the exponent of 10.

Problem Notes

- *Problems 1–44* are like the examples and give students practice applying the definition and properties of logarithms.

- *Problems 45 and 46* ask students to prove some of the properties of logarithms.

- *Problem 47* gives students an opportunity to see how logarithms were useful in doing long multiplication before calculators.

7-5
Logarithms: Equations and Other Bases

Objective

Use logarithms with base 10 or other bases to solve exponential or logarithmic equations.

Class Time

1 day

Homework Assignment

RA, Q1–Q10, Problems 1–3, 5–49 odd

Technology Options

 Activity: A Sequence Approach to Logs

Important Terms and Concepts

Common logarithm

Natural logarithm

e

Change-of-base property

Exponential equation

Logarithmic equation

Lesson Notes

This section discusses logarithms $\log_b a$, where the base b must satisfy the conditions $b > 0$ and $b \neq 1$. Emphasize to students that the number $\log_b a$ is the exponent to which you raise b in order to get a, a statement that would not make sense if b did not satisfy $b > 0$ and $b \neq 1$.

Examples 1 and 2 in the student text are direct applications of the definition of a logarithm with any base.

Examples 5–8 demonstrate how to use the logarithmic properties to solve logarithmic equations. Examples 6 and 8 emphasize the importance of checking the solutions you find in the original logarithmic equation. Emphasize to students that the work they do in solving a logarithmic (or other type) equation only gives them candidates for solutions and that they need to check these solutions in the original equation.

There are two built-in logarithm bases on a grapher, base 10 and base e. Base-10 logarithms are called *common logarithms,* and base-e logarithms are called *natural logarithms.* Natural logarithms are very important in calculus, so it is necessary for students to become familiar with this new base. The natural logarithm is denoted "ln" and pronounced "el, en." To calculate logarithms with bases other than 10 or *e*, students will need to use the change-of-base property. The student text shows how to calculate $\log_5 17$ in Example 3. Example 4 is another application of the change-of-base property.

One of the main uses of logarithms is in solving exponential equations—equations in which the unknown is an exponent. (In Section 7-2, logarithms were used in this way to find the particular equation for a power function.) When solving an exponential equation, the base of the logarithm used does not affect the answer. However, sometimes choosing a logarithm with a particular base can make solving the equation easier. Show students that the same solution is obtained whether $1000 = 50 \cdot 3^x$ is solved using common logarithms or natural logarithms. Then show them that solving $1000 = 50e^x$ is easier if natural logarithms are used, because $\ln e = 1$.

Technology Notes

 Activity: A Sequence Approach to Logs, in *Exploring Precalculus with The Geometer's Sketchpad,* engages students in examining the identity $\log_c r^n = n \log_c r$. Allow 40–50 minutes.

Additional Class Examples

1. Find the missing value.

   $\ln 72 - \ln 8 = \ln$ —?—

Solution

$$\frac{72}{8} = 9$$

2. Estimate $\log_2 17$. Find $\log_2 17$ using the properties you have learned in this section.

Solution

$\log_2 17 \approx 4$ because $2^4 = 16$ and 16 is close to 17. Use your calculator to get $\log_2 17 = \dfrac{\log 17}{\log 2} = 4.08746....$

3. Solve $\log_2 (x - 2) + \log_2 (x + 3) = 4$.

Solution

$\log_2 (x - 2) + \log_2 (x + 3) = 4$

$\log_2 (x - 2)(x + 3) = 4$

$(x - 2)(x + 3) = 2^4$

$x^2 + x - 22 = 0$

$x = 4.21699...$ or $x = -5.21699...$

Check both solutions in the original equation to see that $-5.21699...$ is extraneous and that the only solution is $4.21699....$

Problem Notes

- *Problems 1–34* give students practice applying the definition and properties of logarithms.

- *Problems 35–48* require students to solve logarithmic and exponential equations.

- *Problems 49 and 50* are real-world problems that can be solved using logarithms.

Supplementary Problems

For Problems 1–4, use the change-of-base property to find the indicated logarithm. Check each answer by finding the logarithm directly.

1. ln 5, using base-10 logarithms

2. ln 0.37, using base-10 logarithms

3. log 0.95, using natural logarithms

4. log 1066, using natural logarithms

7-6

Logarithmic Functions

Objective

Show that logarithmic functions have the multiply–add property, and find particular equations by algebra.

Class Time

1 day

Homework Assignment

Suggested: RA, Q1–Q10, Problems 1–13 odd

Also recommended: Problem 14

Technology Options

 Activity: Properties of Exponential Functions

 Activity: Logarithmic and Exponential Functions

Important Terms and Concepts

Logarithmic function

Multiply–add property

Lesson Notes

This section focuses on the graphs and numerical patterns associated with logarithmic functions.

Emphasize that a logarithmic function is the *inverse* of an exponential function with the same base. In an exponential function, the base must be greater than zero and not equal to 1, and the same is true of a logarithmic function. The range of an exponential function is $y > 0$, so the domain of a logarithmic function is $x > 0$. This makes it easy to explain that one cannot take the log of 0 or a negative number. An exponential function has the add–multiply property, so a logarithmic function has the multiply–add property.

Discuss the graphs of the natural and common logarithmic functions shown in Figures 7-6a and 7-6b of the student text. Emphasize that both of the functions have the same domain, $x > 0$. Moreover, the graphs of both functions are increasing, concave down, and asymptotic to the y-axis and contain the point $(1, 0)$. It is important that students learn to visualize these graphs so that they can sketch translations and dilations of these parent functions.

Figure 7-6a shows the effect of varying the constant a in the natural log function $y = a + \ln x$. As you might expect, the graphs are vertical translations of $y = \ln x$. Note that while $y = \ln x$ has the expected x-intercept of 1, the vertical translations give the other graphs different x-intercepts. Because there was no horizontal translation, the vertical asymptote is still at the y-axis.

Figure 7-6a

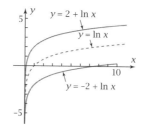

Figure 7-6b shows the effect of varying the constant d for the natural log function $y = \ln (x - d)$. As you might expect, the graphs are horizontal translations of $y = \ln x$. Note that while $y = \ln x$ is asymptotic to the y-axis, the horizontal translations give the other graphs different vertical asymptotes.

Figure 7-6b

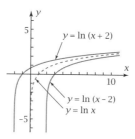

Figure 7-6c shows the effect of varying the multiplicative constant b in $y = b \ln x$. The x-intercept remains at $x = 1$, and the vertical asymptote remains at the y-axis. Note that if b is negative, the graph is reflected across the x-axis.

Figure 7-6c

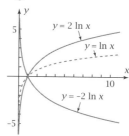

Figure 7-6d

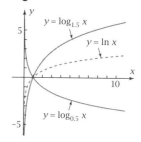

Figure 7-6d shows that changing the base of the logarithmic function has the same effect as a vertical dilation. It is for this reason that it is not necessary to use different bases in order to fit logarithmic functions to various data sets.

The table on page 329 of the student book illustrates the multiply–add property of logarithmic functions. The particular equation for the function is found by first writing x as an exponential function of y and then using logarithms to write y in terms of x. (Part b of Example 1 shows a more direct method for finding a particular logarithmic function that fits a set of points.)

Example 1 demonstrates how to use the multiply–add property to find missing values and how to find the particular equation of a logarithmic function algebraically.

Example 2 involves graphing three logarithmic functions and finding their domains. In parts a and b, have students sketch the graphs by applying transformations to the parent functions and then check their answers with their graphers. The function in part c is more difficult to sketch by hand, so students will want to use their graphers. Because the function involves base-2 logarithms, it must be rewritten in terms of base-10 logarithms (or base-e logarithms) before it can be graphed. (Refer to the Additional Class Example.)

Finding the domain of each function in Example 2 involves finding the values where the argument of the logarithmic function is greater than 0. For part c, this involves solving a quadratic inequality. You may need to remind students how to solve such inequalities. The solution in the text uses the graph of the equation to find out where the quadratic function has positive values (i.e., where the graph of the parabola is above the x-axis). An alternate solution to the problem is to factor $x^2 - 1$ into $(x - 1)(x + 1)$. Then the domain of f is when $(x - 1)(x + 1) > 0$ or when both factors have the same sign.

Technology Notes

 Activity: Properties of Exponential Functions, in *Connecting Mathematics with Science,* allows students to see natural logarithms in the context of straightening an exponential function. This fairly difficult lab will take about 40 minutes.

 Activity: Logarithmic and Exponential Functions, in *Connecting Mathematics with Science,* is somewhat easier than the preceding lab. It concerns logarithmic and exponential functions as inverses and will take about 30 minutes.

Additional Class Example

1. On the same screen, plot $f(x) = 5^x$ and $g(x) = \log_5 x$. Use equal scales on both axes. Show that the graphs are reflections of each other across the line $y = x$.

   Solution

   $$\log_5 x = \frac{\log x}{\log 5} \qquad \text{Use the change-of-base property.}$$

   $$= 1.4306\ldots \log x$$

   Enter $y_1 = 5^x$ and $y_2 = 1.4306\ldots \log x$.

   The graphs are reflections of each other across the line $y = x$, as shown in Figure 7-6e.

Figure 7-6e

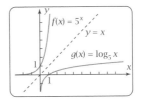

Problem Notes

• *Problems 1–4* require students to find particular equations for logarithmic functions that fit given data sets. They then use the particular equations as mathematical models to make predictions of y for given values of x, and vice versa.

• *Problem 5*, the Logarithmic Function Vertical Dilation and Translation Problem, asks students to express the same function both as a common logarithm function with a dilation and as a log function with a base other than 10.

• *Problem 6*, the Logarithmic and Exponential Function Graphs Problem, asks students to explore the relationship between an exponential function and its inverse.

• *Problem 13* can be used as the basis for an interesting class discussion. The domain of the function is $x > -1$ and $x \neq 0$. However, some graphers may show discrete points to the left of $x = -1$. (The grapher is not familiar with our restriction that if a base is raised to a power, then the base must be positive.) The function has asymptotes at $x = -1$ and $y = 1$ and a removable discontinuity (a hole) at $(0, e)$. You may want to talk informally about the behavior of the function as x approaches -1 and as x approaches infinity. Another interesting aspect of this function is what's happening as x approaches 0. This is a good opportunity for an informal discussion of limits. One of the definitions of e is

$$e = \lim_{x \to 0} (1 + x)^{1/x}$$

- *Problem 14* is a research project that can be assigned for extra credit.

Supplementary Problems

For Problems 1–6, plot the graphs on the same screen. Use equal scales on the two axes. Sketch the result. Show that the graphs are reflections of each other across the line $y = x$.

1. $y = e^x$ and $y = \ln x$

2. $y = 10^x$ and $y = \log x$

3. $y = 6^x$ and $y = \log_6 x$

4. $y = 1.3^x$ and $y = \log_{1.3} x$

5. $y = 0.3^x$ and $y = \log_{0.3} x$

6. $y = 0.8^x$ and $y = \log_{0.8} x$

7. Figure 7-6f shows $y = \log_4 x$. With your grapher in parametric mode, reproduce this graph two ways—first by plotting $x = t$ and $y = \log_4 t$, and then by plotting $x = 4^t$ and $y = t$. Show that the graphs coincide.

8. Figure 7-6g shows $y = \log_{0.7} x$. With your grapher in parametric mode, reproduce this graph two ways—first by plotting $x = t$ and $y = \log_{0.7} t$, and then by plotting $x = 0.7^t$ and $y = t$. Show that the graphs coincide.

Figure 7-6f   **Figure 7-6g**

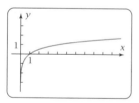   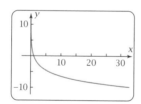

9. *Milk Spoiling Problem:* A rule of thumb used by scientists is that the rate of a biological process such as the spoiling of milk doubles for each 10° increase in the Celsius temperature. Thus, for each 10° increase, milk lasts only half as long.

   a. Explain why the time for milk to spoil is an exponential function of temperature.

   b. Explain why the temperature at which milk must be kept is a logarithmic function of the length of time you want it to last.

c. Suppose that if you want milk to last 192 hours (8 days), you must keep it at 0°C. Write the temperatures at which you would need to keep the milk for it to last 96 hours, 48 hours, and 24 hours.

d. Find the particular equation of the logarithmic function that fits the data points in part c. Make a scatter plot of the data and a graph of the equation on the same screen. Sketch the result.

e. Use the equation to calculate the temperature that would be needed for the milk to keep 144 hours (6 days).

f. Suppose that you took the milk on a hot summer picnic where the temperature is 38°C. How long would you expect the milk to keep?

g. What reasons can you think of that would put upper and lower bounds on the domain of this logarithmic function?

10. *Logarithmic Function Base Problem:* Figure 7-6h shows the graphs of four logarithmic functions, $y = \log_b x$, that differ only in the value of the base, b.

Figure 7-6h

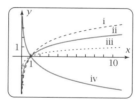

a. Plot several graphs of $y = \log_b x$ on your grapher. From the result, what values of b make the function an increasing function like i, ii, and iii and what values of b make the function decreasing like iv?

b. One of the functions in Figure 7-6h is the common logarithmic function $y = \log_{10} x$. Which one? How can you tell?

c. One of the functions in Figure 7-6h is the natural logarithmic function $y = \ln x$. Which one? How can you tell?

d. Function i contains the point (8, 2). What is the base of the logarithm in this function? Show how you reach your conclusion.

e. Why do all four functions in Figure 7-6h have an x-intercept of 1?

f. True or false: "A function that is increasing is always concave up." Give evidence to support your answer.

7-7

Logistic Functions for Restrained Growth

Objective

Fit a logistic function to data for restrained growth.

Class Time

1 day

Homework Assignment

Suggested: RA, Q1–Q10, Problems 1, 3, 5, 7

Also recommended: Problem 4

Technology Options

 Presentation Sketch: Logistic Present.gsp

 Exploration 7-7a: The Logistic Function for Population Growth

 Activity: The Binomial Theorem and Logistic Functions

 Activity: The Logistic Function

Important Terms and Concepts

Logistic function

Restrained growth

Lesson Notes

A logistic function can be used to model restrained population growth. Moving from the left to right, the graph of a logistic function (with $b > 0$) starts out looking very much like an increasing exponential function. It is asymptotic to $y = 0$ and is increasing and concave up. Then the rate of growth slows, the concavity of the graph changes (that is, the graph has a point of inflection), and the function approaches a horizontal asymptote. The maximum value the function approaches is called the *carrying capacity* of the population, or the *maximum sustainable population.* A logistic function is the only type of function in this chapter that changes concavity. At the point of inflection, the rate of growth of the function is a maximum.

Example 1 shows how to fit a logistic function to a data set using the same methods as for the other types of functions in the chapter. This method is restricted to situations where the maximum sustainable population (the value of c) is known. When you discuss this example, be sure to

emphasize the real-world importance of the point of inflection.

The properties box after the example summarizes the features of logistic functions. Notice that the box includes the case where $b < 0$, in which the logistic function is decreasing. Problem 6 involves a real-world situation that can be modeled with a decreasing logistic function.

Exploration Notes

Exploration 7-7a demonstrates how to fit a logistic function to restricted population growth from two points and the upper horizontal asymptote. Allow approximately 15 minutes for this activity.

Technology Notes

 Presentation Sketch: Logistic Present.gsp, on the *Instructor's Resource CD,* demonstrates the different logistic growth models as the parameters a, b, and c change. Additional pages of the document provide a brief introduction to the iterative approach to logistic growth that is used in the activity The Logistic Function.

 Exploration 7-7a: The Logistic Function for Population Growth, in the *Instructor's Resource Book,* asks students to fit a logistic growth model to dome population data. The data can be plotted and the function can be graphed in Fathom. You might encourage students to use sliders in order to find the best a and b to fit the data and then to compare their values to those they find algebraically, as the Exploration suggests.

 Activity: The Binomial Theorem and Logistic Functions, in the *Instructor's Resource Book,* has students run a classroom simulation of disease spread to verify predictions from the binomial theorem and logistic model. Allow about 45 minutes.

 Activity: The Logistic Function, in *Exploring Precalculus with The Geometer's Sketchpad,* guides students through an exploration of how the initial population size and various parameters affect population growth. This activity uses an iterative approach to the logistic growth model, which is introduced in the Logistic Present.gsp described earlier.

Problem Notes

- *Problems 1 and 2* are similar to the example in the text.

- *Problems 3 and 5* are real-world applications of logistic modeling.

- *Problem 4* is an interesting class simulation experiment. If you have the time, it is worthwhile. If a random number is generated a second time, ignore it and generate another random number.

- *Problem 6,* the Rabbit Overpopulation Problem, presents a real-world situation that is modeled by a *decreasing* logistic function. In part c, there are too many rabbits to be supported in the environment, so they begin to die off, thereby reaching the maximum sustainable population.

- *Problem 7* deals with dilations and translations of the parent logistic function and reviews material from Chapter 1.

Supplementary Problems

1. Given the logistic function $f(x) = \dfrac{c}{1 + ae^{-0.4x}}$

   a. Let $a = 2$. Plot on the same screen the graphs of f for $c = 1, 3,$ and 5. Use a domain of $x \in [-10, 10]$. Sketch the results. How does the value of c affect the graph of f?

   b. Let $c = 3$. Plot on the same screen the graphs of f for $a = 0.2, 1,$ and 5. Sketch the results.

   c. The function $g(x) = \dfrac{3}{1 + ae^{-0.4(x-2)}}$ is a horizontal translation of $f(x)$ by 2 units to the right. Confirm that this is true by plotting f and g on the same screen using $c = 3$ and $a = 1$. Sketch the results.

   d. The graphs in part b are also horizontal translations of f. By how many units and in which direction is the graph of f translated by changing a from 1 to 5?

2. *Transformations of Logistic Functions Problem:* Let f be the logistic function

   $$f(x) = \frac{5 \cdot 2^x}{2^x + 3}$$

   a. Plot the graph of f. Sketch the result, showing the two asymptotes and the point of inflection.

   b. Plot the graph of $g(x) = f(-x)$. Sketch the result. What is the major difference between the graphs of f and g? What transformation of f is function g?

c. Let h be a vertical translation of f by 4 units. Write the particular equation for $h(x)$ in as simple a form as possible. Plot the graph and sketch the results.

d. In part c you should have written $h(x) = f(x) + 4$. Combine the two terms into one fraction. How can you tell the locations of the two horizontal asymptotes from the resulting fraction?

e. Let L be the logistic function

   $$L(x) = \frac{a \cdot 2^x}{2^x + 3}$$

   Plot the graphs of L for $a = 1, 4.5, 9,$ and 12. Sketch the four resulting graphs. Explain how function L is related to function h in part d.

Precalculus with Trigonometry: Instructor's Guide
© 2007 Key Curriculum Press

7-8
Chapter Review and Test

Objective

Review and practice the major concepts presented in this chapter.

Class Time

2 days (including 1 day for testing)

Homework Assignment

Day 1: R0–R7, T1–T28

Day 2 (after Chapter 7 Test): Problem Set 8-1

Lesson Notes

Section 7-8 contains a set of Review Problems, a set of Concept Problems, and a Chapter Test. The Review Problems include one problem for each section in the chapter. You may wish to use the Chapter Test as an additional set of review problems.

Encourage students to practice the no-calculator problems without a calculator so that they are prepared for the test problems for which they cannot use a calculator.

Exploration Notes

Exploration 7-8a may be used as an in-class "rehearsal" for the Chapter Test, or as a review assignment for homework.

Problem Notes

Problems C2 and C3 are good problems for a research project or for extra credit. A blackline master for Problem C3 is available in the *Instructor's Resource Book.*

8 Fitting Functions to Data

In this chapter, students learn the basics of linear regression. They distinguish between deviation and residual (actually, residual deviation). By calculating the sum of the squares of the residuals on their graphers, students learn that the regression line minimizes SS_{res}. The computations that lead to the slope and the intercept of the regression line are left to a course in elementary statistics so that more time will be available in this course for topics leading to calculus. However, Section 8-2 presents the computation of the coefficient of determination as the fraction of SS_{dev} that is removed by the regression, as well as the fact that the correlation coefficient is a square root of the coefficient of determination. Section 8-3 introduces power, exponential, quadratic, logarithmic, and logistic regression. Once students choose the kind of function based on graphical patterns and endpoint behavior, they do the regression on a grapher and verify the result by residual plots. In this way, students avoid the trap of choosing a function simply because it has the correlation coefficient closest to ±1. Section 8-4 introduces logarithmic graph paper and linearization of exponential, logarithmic, and power functions and data.

Several problems and examples relate to data sets that students may want to enter into a grapher. Data sets with ten or more data points are available on the *Instructor's Resource CD* and at *www.keymath.com/precalc*. The data sets can be downloaded onto a TI-83 or TI-84 calculator, into an Excel spreadsheet, or into a Fathom document. Along with the data sets that accompany problems and examples, there are additional data sets that you may find useful for creating extra examples or test questions.

8-1
Introduction to Regression for Linear Data

Objective

Find the equation of the best-fitting linear function for a set of points by running a linear regression on your grapher, and calculate the sum of the squares of the residuals.

Class Time

$\frac{1}{2}$ day

Homework Assignment

Problems 1–6

Technology Options

 Exploration 8-1a: Introduction to Linear Regression

 Activity: Sit-ups

 Activity: Mauna Loa

Important Terms and Concepts

Linear regression, $\hat{y}$

Residual, $y - \hat{y}$

Sum of the squares of the residuals, SS_{res}

Regression line

Lesson Notes

This section sets the stage for Section 8-2, which develops the concept of a regression line. In this section, students use their graphers to find the regression line for a set of data, plot the line on the same screen as the scatter plot of the data, and use the regression equation to make predictions. They also calculate the residuals and the sum of the squares of the residuals, although they will not fully understand the importance of these values until Section 8-2.

Be sure students pay attention to the *order* of the terms when they compute the residuals. A residual is a directed distance and is always equal to the *observed value* minus the *predicted value*. It may be helpful to point out that *observed* comes before *predicted* alphabetically.

A regression line is the best-fitting line for a set of data. It is the line for which the sum of the squares of the residuals is a minimum. If you think it would be helpful for students, show them how to organize their data in a table like the one below. Including both verbal labels and symbols will help students understand and retain the concepts. You may want to have students accurately plot the five points in the table on graph paper. Then have them estimate the best-fit line by using a clear straightedge on the data. They may be surprised at how close their slope and *y*-intercept are to the slope and *y*-intercept on the linear regression line.

Exploration Notes

Exploration 8-1a repeats and reinforces the ideas presented in the exploratory problem set. It provides extra practice for your students. You might assign this Exploration as an additional homework assignment or use it as a group quiz. Allow students about 20–25 minutes to complete this activity.

Technology Notes

 Exploration 8-1a: Introduction to Linear Regression, in the *Instructor's Resource Book,* can be enhanced by using Fathom. Movable

x Observed	*y* Observed	*y* Predicted	Observed Minus Predicted	(Observed Minus Predicted) Squared
x	y	$\hat{y}$	$y - \hat{y}$	$(y - \hat{y})^2$
2	8	7.6	0.4	0.16
4	10	11.8	−1.8	3.24
6	19	16.0	3.0	9.00
8	18	20.2	−2.2	4.84
10	25	24.4	0.6	0.36
		Sums:	0.0	17.60

Precalculus with Trigonometry: Instructor's Guide

lines can help fit data quite easily, and Fathom can display residuals and squares based on them. The activity Sit-ups, described below, provides guidance for how to do these things in Fathom.

 Activity: Sit-ups, in the *Instructor's Resource Book,* has students find the regression line for the data from Section 8-1 of the text. They can use movable lines and see the changing sum of squares to understand the concept of a best-fitting linear equation. This activity can be revisited as a student activity or as a presentation, as more regression concepts are developed in Section 8-2. Estimated time is 25–30 minutes.

 Activity: Mauna Loa, in *Teaching Mathematics with Fathom,* has students fit linear graphs to data on the concentration of CO_2 collected at the Mauna Loa Observatory. Students are then asked to fit other types of graphs to the data and to use their functions to make predictions. The data can be modeled with linear, sinusoidal, and other curves. Allow 35–50 minutes.

8-2
Deviations, Residuals, and the Correlation Coefficient

Objective

Calculate SS_{res}, the sum of the squares of the residuals, and find out how to determine the equation of the linear function that minimizes SS_{res}.

Class Time

1 day

Homework Assignment

RA, Q1–Q10, Problems 1–6

Technology Options

 Figures 8-2e, f: Deviations, Residuals, and the Correlation Coefficient

 Presentation Sketch: Linear Regression Present.gsp

 Explorations 8-2a–8-2c: Sums of Squares of Residuals, and The Correlation Coefficient

 Activity: Linear Regression

Important Terms and Concepts

Average of the y-values, $\overline{y}$

Deviation, $y - \overline{y}$

Residual, $y - \hat{y}$

Sum of the squares of the residuals, SS_{res}

Sum of the squares of the deviations, SS_{dev}

Linear regression equation

Coefficient of determination, $r^2 = \dfrac{SS_{dev} - SS_{res}}{SS_{dev}}$

Correlation coefficient, r

Positive or negative association

Strong or weak correlation

Linear regression line

Lesson Notes

This section illustrates the meaning of *deviation* and of *residual* and explains that the regression line for a set of data is the line that minimizes the sum of the squares of the residuals. Students also learn how to compute and interpret the coefficient of determination and the correlation coefficient.

Explain to students that residual deviations are squared for two reasons: to make the quantity positive and to "punish" points that are far away from the regression line. If a point has a residual with an absolute value greater than 1, squaring the residual gives a result greater than the absolute value of the residual. On the other hand, if a point has a residual with an absolute value less than 1, squaring the residual gives a result less than the absolute value of the residual. Because we want the sum of the squares of the residuals to be a minimum, we would prefer that the points have small residuals in order to get a better fit.

Students may confuse deviations and residuals. The deviation of a point is its directed distance from the horizontal line $y = \overline{y}$, where $\overline{y}$ is the mean of the y-values. The residual of a point is its directed distance from the slanted regression line, $y = \hat{y}$. The deviation of a point is found by calculating $y - \overline{y}$, whereas the residual is found by calculating $y - \hat{y}$. Residuals are what is left of the deviation for that point after regression slants the horizontal line. Figures 8-2c and 8-2d in the student text help clarify the difference between deviations and residuals.

Emphasize that because the residual of a point is the observed value minus the predicted value, points below the regression line have negative residuals and points above the regression line have positive residuals. You may need to explain that the residual represents the *vertical* distance from the point to the line, not some sort of diagonal shortest distance.

Figures 8-2e and 8-2f in the student text provide a nice visual of the sum of the squares of the deviations, SS_{dev}, and the sum of the squares of the residuals, SS_{res}. These figures show that SS_{res} is much smaller than SS_{dev}. If the fit is perfect—that is, if all the points lie on the regression line—then the sum of the squares of the residuals is zero. Fathom can show this dynamically.

The coefficient of determination, r^2, indicates the fraction of SS_{dev} removed by linear regression. If the regression line is a perfect fit, all of SS_{dev} is removed, so r^2 is 1. The correlation coefficient, also known as the Pearson correlation coefficient, is plus or minus the square root of the coefficient of determination. The correlation coefficient is a measure of the *strength* and *direction* of the linear relationship between x and y. An r-value close to 1 or -1 indicates a strong linear relationship. A positive r-value indicates a positive association between the variables (that is, y increases as x increases), whereas a negative r-value indicates a negative association (that is, y decreases as x increases).

Graphers automatically compute the values of r and r^2 when they perform a linear regression. To display these values on a TI-83, for instance, students may have to set the Diagnostics to On. To do this, go to the CATALOG on the calculator (2nd 0), scroll down to DiagnosticOn, press ENTER, and press ENTER again. When the best-fit linear equation is displayed, the r- and r^2-values will also be displayed. Check your calculator manual for more information on r- and r^2-values.

Example 1 demonstrates how to find SS_{res} and SS_{dev} for the sit-ups data. When discussing the example, be sure to emphasize the interpretation of the r^2-value. This example also shows how to enter the data into a grapher to get the lists in an efficient way. Caution students that graphers do not have all the capabilities of a spreadsheet. For example, if students change the y-values in L_2, their graphers will *not* automatically update the values in L_3 and L_4 unless they have been set to do this.

Supplementary Problems 2 and 3 are excellent problems to extend your class discussion on this section.

Exploration Notes

Exploration 8-2a may be used to introduce computing the sum of the squares of the residuals for a best-fit line. Students also compute SS_{res} for a different line and are asked to explain how the value of SS_{res} indicates that the line does not fit the points as well as does the regression line. You can assign this exploration as a group activity or as extra homework or a quiz. Allow students about 20–25 minutes to complete the Exploration.

Exploration 8-2b guides students through the process of computing the values of SS_{res}, SS_{dev}, r^2, and r. This Exploration makes an excellent review sheet or quiz. Allow students about 20–25 minutes to complete the Exploration.

Exploration 8-2c provides students with a formula for finding the correlation coefficient without finding the regression equation first. A grapher is used to verify the result. Students are then led through a step-by-step algebraic proof of this formula. Allow about 20–25 minutes for students to complete this Exploration.

Technology Notes

 Figures 8-2e, f: Deviations, Residuals, and the Correlation Coefficient for Moe's sit-up data are visually demonstrated with a Dynamic Precalculus Exploration at *www.keymath.com/ precalc*. This exploration is not mentioned in the student text, so be sure to point it out to students.

 Presentation Sketch: Linear Regression Present.gsp, on the *Instructor's Resource CD,* demonstrates squares of residuals and their sum, with a movable line and movable data points. It is related to the activity Linear Regression in *Exploring Precalculus with The Geometer's Sketchpad.*

 Explorations 8-2a–8-2c: Sums of Squares of Residuals and The Correlation Coefficient, in the *Instructor's Resource Book,* can be enhanced with the use of Fathom. Students can do their plots in Fathom and then use its calculating abilities to check their calculations.

 Activity: Linear Regression, in *Exploring Precalculus with The Geometer's Sketchpad,* asks students to use a prepared sketch to explore residuals and their squares. Allow 30–40 minutes.

Problem Notes

- *Problems 1 and 2* illustrate that the average-average point $(\bar{x}, \bar{y})$ lies on the regression line. The data sets for these problems are available on the *Instructor's Resource CD* and at *www.keymath.com/precalc.*

- *Problem 2,* the New Subdivision Problem, can be extended as a class discussion or small project as follows: Explore what happens to the slope and *y*-intercept of the regression line if a point near the middle of the data set, say (2500, 207000), is significantly changed to something like (2500, 307000). Then explore what happens to the slope and *y*-intercept if the last point in the original data is changed to (2800, 320000). Ask students to make a conjecture about the relationship between the location of an "outlier" and its effect on the regression line. Students will not be able to prove their conjectures algebraically, but they may be able to give a geometric argument.

- *Problem 3,* the Gas Tank Problem, gives a data set for which the regression line fits the data perfectly.

- *Problem 4,* the Standardized Test Scores Problem, shows a scatter plot for which the correlation between the variables is weak.

- *Problem 5,* the Data Cloud Problem, assesses student understanding of the correlation coefficient.

Supplementary Problems

1. *Deviations and Correlation Problem:* Sketch a graph showing clearly that you understand the difference between the *deviation* of a data point and the *residual* of a data point.

2. *New Subdivision Problem, Part 2: Dependence on Initial Conditions:* Delete the largest house from the data set in Problem 2 in the student text, and do a linear regression with the remaining nine data points. How does this change affect the predictions for the price per square foot and the cost of the lot?

3. *Perfect Correlation vs. Little or No Correlation Problem:*

   a. Suppose a linear function fits a set of data perfectly. What would each residual equal? What would SS_{res} equal? Explain why the coefficient of determination would equal 1. Under what conditions would the correlation coefficient equal 1, and under what conditions would it equal -1?

   b. Suppose the correlation coefficient for a linear regression is 0. What does this fact mean about SS_{res} and SS_{dev}? Explain why r could equal zero if the regression equation has $a = 0$ and $b = \bar{y}$. Would it be possible for r to equal zero if $a \neq 0$? Explain.

   c. Suppose the correlation coefficient for a linear regression is $r = 0.1$. It is tempting to say that the linear relationship between x and y accounts for 10% of SS_{dev} and random variation accounts for the other 90%. Explain why this reasoning is not correct and how you know regression actually accounts for much less than 10% of SS_{dev}.

8-3
Regression for Nonlinear Data

Objective

Given a set of data, make a scatter plot, identify the type of function that could model the relationship between the variables, and use regression to find the particular equation that best fits the data.

Class Time

1 day

Homework Assignment

RA, Q1–Q10, Problems 1–6

Technology Options

 Exploration 8-3a: Violent Crimes Problem

Important Terms and Concepts

Endpoint behavior

Power regression

Exponential regression

Linear regression

Logarithmic regression

Logistic regression

Quadratic regression

Lesson Notes

This section leads students through the process of finding the regression equation that best fits a set of data. To determine which type of equation might fit a data set, students should ask themselves these questions:

* Is the pattern of points curved? If so, is it concave up, or down, or does it change concavity?

* How would or do the data behave at the endpoints of the domain?

Using the answers to these questions and their knowledge about the shapes of function graphs, students should be able to determine which types of regression to try. Once an appropriate model is found, it can be used to make predictions.

The data set for this example, Fish Data Set, is available on the *Instructor's Resource CD* and at *www.keymath.com/precalc.* In general, all data sets in the student text that have ten or more data points are provided on the previously mentioned CD and Web site in three different formats: Microsoft Excel, Fathom, and as TI List files that can be downloaded onto TI-83 and 84 calculators.

Exploration Notes

Exploration 8-3a has students explore the number of arrests for violent crimes each year. Picking only selected points makes the data look linear. Picking other points makes the data look quadratic. Students get practice in several regression analyses, and see that quite different conclusions can be made about crime rates depending on which data points are used. The data are available on the Fathom software CD.

Technology Notes

 Exploration 8-3a: Violent Crimes Problem, in the *Instructor's Resource Book,* asks students to fit various linear models to data and then to analyze them. Fathom can help students find these models quickly, and other models could be found using sliders. The data are available on the Fathom software CD.

Problem Notes

The data sets for Problem 1 and Problems 4–6 are available on the *Instructor's Resource CD* and at *www.keymath.com/precalc.*

* *Problem 1,* the Bacteria Problem, provides a data set that can be modeled with an exponential function. The shape of the scatter plot indicates that either an exponential function or a power function would be appropriate. By considering endpoint behavior, students can predict that an exponential model would be more reasonable. A blackline master for this problem is available in the *Instructor's Resource Book.*

* *Problem 2,* the Printed Paragraph Problem, requires students to use endpoint behavior to conjecture that a decreasing power function rather than a decreasing exponential function would be the more appropriate model for the data set. They confirm their conjecture by running both types of regression and comparing correlation coefficients.

- *Problem 3,* the Bank Interest Problem, provides a data set that can be modeled with a logarithmic function.

- *Problem 4,* the Planetary Period Problem, requires students to find a power function to model the relationship between a planet's distance from the Sun and its period. Data for this problem are on the Fathom software CD.

- *Problem 5,* the Roadrunners Problem, Part 1, involves finding a logistic function to model the growth of a roadrunner population.

- *Problem 6,* the Roadrunners Problem, Part 2, requires students to find a quadratic function to model the relationship between the number of roadrunners at the beginning of a year and the change in the population that year.

8-4
Linearizing Data and Logarithmic Graph Paper

Objectives

Given a set of data that does not follow a linear pattern,

- Transform the data using logarithms, and use linear regression on the transformed data

- Plot the data on log-log graph paper or semilog graph paper.

Class Time

2 days

Homework Assignment

Day 1: RA, Q1–Q10, Problems 1–17 odd

Day 2: Problems 19, 20, 21, 23, 24

Also suggested: Problem 22

Technology Options

 Presentation Sketch: Semilog Present.gsp

 Presentation Sketch: Log-Log Present.gsp

 Activity: Semilog Graphs

 Activity: Log-Log Graphs

 Activity: Moore's Law

Important Terms and Concepts

Linearizing data

Arithmetic graph paper

Log-log graph paper

Semilog graph paper

Add-multiply semilog graph paper

Multiply-add semilog graph paper

Multiple regression, R^2

Lesson Notes

Exponential functions can be very hard to read for points with large y-values and for points near the horizontal asymptote. One way of showing the function more clearly is to change the y-scale to log y. This transforms the unwieldy exponential function into a linear one that is easy to read. Similarly, if you begin with data that appear to grow or decay exponentially, you can take the log of the y-values to linearize the data, do a linear regression on the transformed data, and then transform the line back into an exponential function. In fact, when you run an exponential regression as in Section 8-3, this is the process that the calculator uses.

This section shows how to transform exponential, power, and logarithmic data to become approximately linear. This process is called *linearization*. The text begins by linearizing the exponential function $y = 20 \cdot 1.45^x$, and the resulting equation, $\log y = 1.3010\ldots + 0.1613\ldots x$, shows that $\log y$ is a linear function of x. This process of linearizing an exponential function justifies taking the log of the y-values in exponential-looking data.

Taking the log of both the x- and the y-values linearizes power function data, also known as doing a ($\log x$, $\log y$) transformation. Doing a ($\log x$, y) transformation linearizes a logarithmic function. It should be noted that when you linearize a power function, the slope of the resulting line is equal to the power of the original function, because $y = ax^b$ linearizes as $\log y = \log a + b \log x$. Thus $\log y$ is a linear function of $\log x$, with slope b.

The section also shows how to use semilog or log-log graph paper. Add–multiply semilog paper, with an arithmetic scale on the horizontal axis and a log scale on the vertical axis, is used to graph exponential data as a line. See the left graph in Figure 8-4d. Graph paper that has a logarithmic scale on the horizontal axis and an arithmetic scale on the vertical axis is called multiply-add semilog graph paper; it can be used to linearize logarithmic function data. See the graph on the right in Figure 8-4d. The log-log graph paper shown in Figure 8-4c is used to linearize power function data. It has a logarithmic scale on both the horizontal and vertical axes.

Students should be cautioned that the coefficient of determination r^2 of the linear regression done with linearized data is not the same as the coefficient of determination of the power, log, or exponential regression with the original data. A capital R is used to distinguish between the two. R^2 is used to refer to the latter case, as shown right before Example 1. In this course, students do not need to master how these statistics are calculated, but they do need to understand that r^2 is the coefficient of determination for transformed data that have been linearized. When doing a multiple regression on a calculator, the calculator will not give a value for r^2; it gives R^2 instead.

Example 1 shows how to do a power regression and how to use log-log paper. Relationships between the linear regression equation found using the ($\log x$, $\log y$) data and the constants in the power regression equation are discussed. The data in Example 2 are logarithmic, and they are shown to be linear when plotted on multiply-add semilog graph paper.

Students often have a hard time understanding why they have to do this reexpression of data at all because the calculator will do it for them. See Additional Class Example 1 for a situation where data must be transformed before any of the built-in regression formulas on the calculator will work.

Emphasize to your students that there are multiple criteria for choosing the best fit for a given data set. They should always graph the data first and then consider the shape of the graph, whether the data form a linear pattern on semilog or log-log graph paper, the residual plot (discussed in Section 8-5), and finally r^2 and r. Students tend to think that the value of r is the most important criterion, when, in fact, it can be misleading.

Additional Class Example 2 presents the Anscombe Data Sets. These are four different data sets, each of which has the same linear regression equation with the same correlation coefficient. This example emphasizes the importance of plotting data to get an idea of their shape before deciding what type of regression to do.

Exploration Notes

Exploration 8-4a has students plot points on semilog and log-log graph paper and make connections to the add–multiply (exponential) and multiply–multiply (power) properties. Allow about 20 minutes to complete.

Exploration 8-4b gives students practice in finding which regression best fits their data. The results are then verified by using the appropriate graph paper to show the linear relationship. Allow about 25 minutes for this Exploration.

Technology Notes

 Presentation Sketch: Semilog Present.gsp, on the *Instructor's Resource CD*, demonstrates the add–multiply property of exponential functions on a semilog graph in Sketchpad. This presentation sketch is related to the Semilog Graphs activity.

Presentation Sketch: Log-Log Present.gsp, on the *Instructor's Resource CD,* demonstrates the use of a log-log graph in fitting a power function to data. This presentation sketch is related to the Log-Log Graphs activity.

 Activity: Semilog Graphs, in the *Instructor's Resource Book,* gets students acquainted with semilog graph paper by having them plot points and an exponential function on a semilog graph. They then use the custom tools to solve an exponential decay problem. Allow 50 minutes.

 Activity: Log-Log Graphs, in the *Instructor's Resource Book,* gets students acquainted with log-log graph paper by having them plot points and a power function on a log-log graph. They then use the custom tools to fit a power function to data. Make sure the students do this activity with pencil and paper, because they will be solving an equation by hand. Allow 50 minutes.

Activity: Moore's Law, in *Teaching Mathematics with Fathom,* may be revisited now if you used it in Section 7-3. Allow 25–40 minutes.

Additional Class Examples

Data sets for these examples are available on the *Instructor's Resource CD* and at *www.keymath.com/precalc.*

1. Students in a precalculus class collected these cooling data. They heated water until it was 76°C and allowed it to cool. Make a scatter plot of the data on your grapher. Sketch the graph on your paper, and mark your axes with the variables (t, T), time (min), and temperature (°C).

t (min)	L$_1$	0	10	21	31	41	50	65	78	90	102
T (°C)	L$_2$	76	60	51	45	40	37	33	30	28.5	27

a. The graph appears to be most like an exponential function. However, the function cannot be modeled with an equation in the form $T = ab^t$. Why? Explain this in the context of the problem.

b. Translate the temperature data so they can be modeled by an exponential function. Use the bottom row of the table for the translated data. Assume that the temperature of the room where the data were collected was 23°C.

c. Plot two graphs, one with the transformation $(t, \log T)$ and the other with the transformation $(t, \log (T - 23))$. Which is more linear? Explain.

d. Run a linear regression with the more linear of the transformed data sets from part c, and transform this back into an equation in t and T.

Solution

a. It looks like an exponential function because the graph levels out as t gets bigger. These data are not asymptotic to the t-axis, but the exponential function $T = ab^t$ is. The water won't cool down past room temperature, which is greater than zero.

b. Subtract 23°C from each T-value.

$T - 23$°C	L$_3$	53	37	28	22	17	14	10	7	5.5	4

c. The data are more linear if you plot $(t, \log (T - 23))$ than if you just plot $(t, \log T)$. The data should approach the asymptote $T = 23$, so $T - 23$ should be exponential in t.

Figure 8-4a

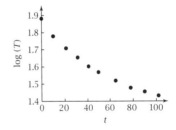

Figure 8-4b

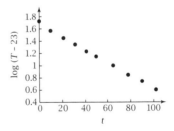

d. $\log (T - 23) = -0.0106\ldots t + 1.6851\ldots$, so $T - 23 = 10^{1.6851\ldots} \cdot (10^{-0.0106\ldots})^t$, or $T - 23 = 48.4301\ldots \cdot (0.9757\ldots)^t$.

This is a vertical translation of an exponential function.

2. *Anscombe Data Sets:* Anscombe's Quartet (F. J. Anscombe, "Graphs in Statistical Analysis," *American Statistician,* 27 [February 1973], 17–21). Sketch a scatter plot of each of the four data sets. Then find the linear regression line and the correlation coefficient for each set. What do you observe about the graphs? The regression lines? The correlation coefficients?

x_1	y_1		x_2	y_2
10	8.04		10	9.14
8	6.95		8	8.14
13	7.58		13	8.74
9	8.81		9	8.77
11	8.33		11	9.26
14	9.96		14	8.1
6	7.24		6	6.13
4	4.26		4	3.1
12	10.84		12	9.13
7	4.82		7	7.26
5	5.68		5	4.74

x_3	y_3		x_4	y_4
10	7.46		8	6.58
8	6.77		8	5.76
13	12.74		8	7.71
9	7.11		8	8.84
11	7.81		8	8.47
14	8.84		8	7.04
6	6.08		8	5.25
4	5.39		19	12.5
12	8.15		8	5.56
7	6.42		8	7.91
5	5.73		8	6.89

Solution

Figure 8-4c

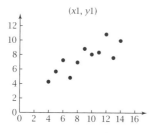
(x1, y1)

Figure 8-4d

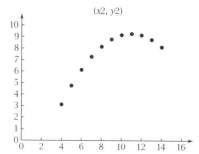
(x2, y2)

Figure 8-4e

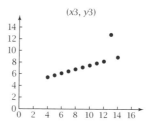
(x3, y3)

Figure 8-4f

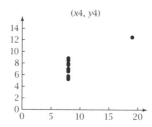
(x4, y4)

The scatter plot of (x_1, y_1) shows relatively linear data. The graph of (x_2, y_2) is quadratic, and the graph of (x_3, y_3) shows data that are exactly linear, except for one point that is above the line. The last graph, of (x_4, y_4), is a group of points on a vertical line, with one point significantly removed from the rest of the plot. All four data sets have the same linear regression equation, $y = 0.5x + 3$, the same correlation coefficient, 0.82, and the same coefficient of determination, 0.67. These data sets show that data with the same linear correlation can have very different shapes. This is why it is always best to plot data and get an idea of their shape before doing a regression.

Problem Notes

- *Problems 1–6* have students graph exponential, power, and logarithmic functions on semilog and log-log paper. If the function is graphed on the correct paper, it forms a straight line.

- *Problems 7 and 8* show that exponential functions are not linear when plotted on log-log graph paper and that power functions are not linear when plotted on semilog graph paper.

- *Problems 9–14* ask students to run regressions based on given graphs on log-log or semilog graph paper.

- *Problems 15 and 16* ask students to linearize exponential functions by graphing log y as a function of x. This essentially creates "add-multiply paper" on the grapher. Problems 17 and 18 are similar, except they involve power functions.

- *Problems 19–22* are real-world applications of the material in this section. A blackline master of the graphs for these problems is available in the *Instructor's Resource Book*. Data sets for Problems 19 and 20 are available on the *Instructor's Resource CD* and at *www.keymath.com/precalc.*

- *Problem 23* asks students to prove relations such as in a power function, log *y* is a linear function of log *x*. This is a good problem to assign to give students more exposure to the theory behind linearization.

- *Problem 24* gives a historical perspective on why log-log and semilog graph paper was used before calculators and computers were available to do regression analysis.

8-5
Residual Plots and Mathematical Models

Objective

Find graphical evidence for how well a given function fits a set of data by plotting and analyzing the residuals.

Class Time

2 days

Homework Assignment

Day 1: RA, Q1–Q10, Problems 1–11 odd

Day 2: Problems 2–10 even

Technology Options

 Exploration 8-5a: Coffee Data Residual Plot

 Exploration 8-5b: Airplane Fuel Problem

Important Terms and Concepts

Residual plot

Lesson Notes

In earlier sections, students saw that the correlation coefficient, *r*, is one measure of how well a function fits a set of data. In this section, they learn how a plot of the residuals gives additional information about fit.

A residual of a point is the observed value minus the value predicted by the regression equation. A residual plot has the same *x*-values as the original data set, but the *y*-values are the residuals. You can get a quick sense of a residual plot simply by looking at the plot of the fitted function and the data. Imagine the fitted function straightened out horizontally like an *x*-axis and the vertical distances to the best-fit function remain fixed. The result will be a residual plot (see Figure 8-5a).

Figure 8-5a

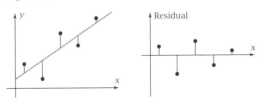

If a function is a good fit, the plot of the residuals will show no identifiable pattern. The points will be randomly scattered above and below the x-axis with approximately the same number of points above as below. If the plot of residuals does show a pattern, it may indicate that there is behavior that is not accounted for by the function model. Any discernible pattern in the residuals is reason to continue the hunt for a better fit.

The student text presents an example involving plant data. You may want to work through this example as a class, having students enter the data, compute the residuals, and create the graphs on their graphers. Some graphers automatically create a list of residuals (RESID) when a regression is done. For graphers without this feature, the residuals can be found by calculating $L_2 - y_1(L_1)$, where y_1 is the regression equation. The residual plot is then $L_2 - y_1(L_1)$ versus L_1. Finding and plotting the residuals this way reinforces the concept of a residual, so it is a good idea to demonstrate this method even if students' graphers have a built-in residual list capability.

In the text example, both the linear model and the exponential model appear to fit the data reasonably well. However, the residual plot for the linear function shows a pattern, indicating that there is behavior that is not accounted for by the linear model. The residual plot for the exponential function shows no discernible pattern, indicating that the exponential model is a better fit. The exponential model is chosen even though the endpoint behavior is not "right." If a function fits but the end behavior is a problem, it's still okay to use the function as a model as long as you are careful when extrapolating beyond the given data.

Be sure to discuss the note after the Conclusion box, which discusses the fact that the residual plot and endpoint behavior can give conflicting information.

To summarize, you may wish to present this list of criteria for students to consider when fitting a function to a data set.

- The shape of the scatter plot

- The behavior of the chosen type of function at the endpoints

- The correlation coefficient

- Whether the residual plot has a pattern

- Whether the data form a linear pattern on semilog or log-log graph paper

It is particularly important to consider the endpoint behavior if the fitted function will be used for extrapolation. Often the residual plot may be acceptable, but the endpoint behavior might be a

problem. In general, it is dangerous to extrapolate very far outside the domain of the original data. Caution your students about relying too heavily on the correlation coefficient. Many of the exercises in the problem set have a correlation coefficient close to 1 or -1, yet other factors, such as endpoint behavior and the residual plot, provide additional information.

Exploration Notes

Exploration 8-5a guides students through the material in Section 8-5 of the student text. You can start the day by having students work through this Exploration in groups, followed by a class discussion of the results. This activity should take students about 15–20 minutes to complete.

Exploration 8-5b may be used as a follow-up group activity or quiz. The airplane fuel data appear on the Fathom software CD.

Technology Notes

 Exploration 8-5a: Coffee Data Residual Plot, in the *Instructor's Resource Book,* asks students to use a residual plot to make conclusions about a cooling cup of coffee. The data plotting and function fitting can easily be done in Fathom.

 Exploration 8-5b: Airplane Fuel Problem, in the *Instructor's Resource Book,* asks students to model the fuel consumption in an airplane with an exponential function and with a power function. The data plotting and function fitting can easily be done in Fathom.

Problem Notes

Data sets for Problems 1–3 and 8, and for Supplementary Problems 1, 2, 3, and 7, are available on the *Instructor's Resource CD* and at *www.keymath.com/precalc.*

- *Problems 1, 2, 4, and 6* present situations for which the correlation coefficients for the function models are close to 1 but where patterns in the residual plots indicate that the models do not account for all of the data's behavior.

- *Problem 3,* the Gas Mileage Problem, has students find both a power model and an exponential model for a set of data. Both models have correlation coefficients close to 1 and residual plots that are fairly random, but the endpoint behavior of the exponential function is more reasonable than that of the power function.

- *Problem 5,* the Population Problem, involves fitting a logistic function to population data.

- *Problem 7,* the Calorie Consumption Problem, requires students to transform a data set by taking logarithms.

- *Problem 8,* the Mile Run Record Times Problem, shows a data set that can be modeled with either a linear function or an exponential function.

- *Problems 9 and 10* focus on using interpolation and extrapolation to make predictions.

Supplementary Problems

For Problems 1 and 2,

a. Do linear regression for both y and z as functions of x. Based on the correlation coefficients, which set of points is fit better by a linear function?

b. Make residual plots for y and z as functions of x. Sketch both plots.

c. Based on the residual plots, which set of points is fit better by a linear function?

d. Find another function that is a better fit for the nonlinear data in part c.

1.

x	y	z
4	64.4	62.2
5	72.5	69.6
6	76.5	76.7
7	81.7	84.4
8	89.7	92.0
9	95.0	98.0
10	104.5	103.6
11	108.6	109.9
12	116.9	115.5
13	123.1	121.0

2.

x	y	z
6	153.6	159.7
7	150.4	156.5
10	137.1	132.8
11	133.4	131.9
13	125.3	120.5
14	120.8	117.3
16	107.7	110.4
20	86.9	79.8
21	78.9	77.6
24	61.0	66.1

3. *Height vs. Age Problem:* These data show the age in months and the height in centimeters of a girl at various times from age 2 to age 14.

Age (months)	Height (cm)	Age (months)	Height (cm)
24	80.6	96	123.2
29	87.0	103	125.7
37	91.4	108	128.6
41	93.0	114	131.1
42	93.7	117	132.7
45	96.5	121	134.3
46	97.2	126	135.6
51	99.7	131	139.1
54	100.3	137	141.6
55	101.9	143	145.7
63	105.1	150	151.4
64	106.4	152	152.4
80	114.6	154	153.4
83	116.2	160	157.8
88	119.1	162	159.4
91	120.6	168	160.0

a. Make a scatter plot of the data.

b. Tell why a linear function would have reasonable endpoint behavior for ages less than 24 months but not for ages much greater than 168 months.

c. Find the best-fitting linear function for the data, and plot it on the same screen as the scatter plot from part a. Sketch the linear function.

d. Use this linear model to predict the girl's height at age 16 years. What assumption must you make for this mathematical-world answer to be representative of the real-world answer?

e. Use this linear model to predict the girl's age when she reached 110.0 cm. Explain why this interpolated answer is probably more accurate than the extrapolated answer in part d.

f. According to the linear model, how tall (actually, "how long") was the girl when she was born? How well does this compare with her actual length of 42 cm? What does the result tell you about using a function model to extrapolate even if it has a high correlation coefficient for points within the data set?

g. Make a residual plot for the linear function. Sketch the result.

h. People usually grow at a steady rate during childhood, slow down a bit as they approach their teens, have a growth spurt during their teens, and then stop growing as they approach adulthood. How do you interpret the residual plot in terms of these observations? For instance, at what age did this girl start her growth spurt?

4. *Learning Curve Problem:* When a product is first manufactured, the cost of making each item is relatively high. As the manufacturer gains experience, the cost per item decreases. The function describing how the cost per item varies with the number of items produced is called the *learning curve*. The table and graph in Figure 8-5b show how the cost to produce each pair of shoes changes as the number of pairs produced increases.

Pairs Produced	Cost per Pair (dollars)
100	60
200	46
500	31
700	26
1000	21

Figure 8-5b

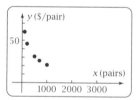

a. Use regression analysis to show that both a logarithmic function and a power function fit the data about equally well.

b. The shoe manufacturer wants to predict the cost per pair of shoes beyond the upper end of the data. Show that the power function has a more reasonable endpoint behavior than the logarithmic function for large values of pairs produced.

c. How many pairs of shoes would you predict must be produced before the cost per pair drops below $10?

d. According to the power function model, what was the cost of manufacturing the first pair of shoes?

e. The learning curve is sometimes described by saying, "Doubling the number manufactured reduces the cost by —?— percent." What is the percent for this kind of shoe? What property of power functions does this fact illustrate?

5. *Pizza Price Project:* You can consider the price you pay for a pizza to be made up of two charges. The first is the cost of the ingredients, which is directly proportional to the square of the diameter. The second is a fixed charge for cooking, service, and so forth. Thus, a reasonable model for the price of a pizza is

$$f(x) = ax^2 + b$$

where $f(x)$ is the price in dollars, x is the diameter in inches, and a and b are constants. These tabulated prices for plain cheese pizzas are from the 2000 menu of a national restaurant chain.

Size	Diameter x (in.)	Price $f(x)$ (dollars)
Extra large	16	7.49
Large	14	6.19
Medium	12	5.09
Small	10	3.99

Figure 8-5c

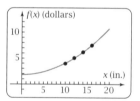

a. Figure 8-5c shows the best-fitting function of the form $y = ax^2 + b$ for the given data. The equation was found by squaring the x-values and then running linear regression on the transformed data. The idea is that y is a *linear* function of x^2. Find this particular equation and use it to duplicate the graph in Figure 8-5c. Write the correlation coefficient for this linear function.

b. Based on the quadratic model, how much do you pay for the fixed costs of producing a pizza?

c. The menu also lists a Kid's Pizza, which has a 7-inch diameter and sells for $2.29. According to the quadratic model, is this pizza overpriced or underpriced?

d. Use the correlation coefficients to show that a linear function fits the (untransformed) data almost as well as the quadratic function but that it has the wrong behavior at the lower endpoint.

e. Get up-to-date menus from one or more local pizzerias. Find the function of the form $y = ax^2 + b$ that best fits the data. Use your mathematical model to determine which pizzas are underpriced and which are overpriced.

6. *Light Intensity Project:* A light sits atop a pole on an island in a lake. The light is h meters from the shore, where h is not known (Figure 8-5d). The accompanying table shows measurements of the intensity of the light at various distances back from the shore.

Figure 8-5d

Water

Distance Back from Shore x (m)	Intensity (candela, cd)
0	126.0
10	93.8
20	72.6
30	57.8
40	47.1

a. The intensity of light from a point source decreases inversely with the square of the distance from the source. The distance in this case is $(x + h)$ meters. Run a power regression for $h = 50$, $h = 60$, $h = 70$, and $h = 80$ m. Based on the results, between what two numbers does the actual distance h lie? How do you know?

b. Perform appropriate calculations to find the actual value of h to the nearest meter. Leave a "trail" so that people can follow your work.

7. *Cost-of-Living Problem:* This table shows the *Consumer Price Index* (CPI-U, where U stands for "urban") from the Bureau of Labor Statistics. This index allows you to compare the cost of living in one year with that in another year. For instance, if a car cost \$12,000 in 1988, then in 1997 an equivalent car would be expected to cost

$$12{,}000 \times \frac{160.5}{118.3} \approx \$16{,}280$$

Year	CPI-U	Year	CPI-U	Year	CPI-U
1961	29.9	1975	53.8	1989	124.0
1962	30.2	1976	56.9	1990	130.7
1963	30.6	1977	60.6	1991	136.2
1964	31.0	1978	65.2	1992	140.3
1965	31.5	1979	72.6	1993	144.5
1966	32.4	1980	82.4	1994	148.2
1967	33.4	1981	90.9	1995	152.4
1968	34.8	1982	96.5	1996	156.9
1969	36.7	1983	99.6	1997	160.5
1970	38.8	1984	103.9	1998	163.0
1971	40.5	1985	107.6	1999	166.6
1972	41.8	1986	109.6	2000	172.2
1973	44.4	1987	113.6	2001	177.1
1974	49.3	1988	118.3	2002	179.9

a. Let y be the CPI-U at a time x years after 1960. Make a scatter plot of the data. Use a window with an x-range of about $[-10, 40]$.

b. Run linear and exponential regressions on the data. Show that the correlation coefficients for the two functions are approximately equal.

c. On the same screen as the scatter plot from part a, plot the linear and exponential functions from part b.

d. How can you tell from the graphs that a linear function would not have the correct endpoint behavior if it were extrapolated backward to years much before 1960? How do you know that an exponential function would have more reasonable behavior for those years?

e. Make a residual plot for the exponential function. Are the residuals randomly scattered, or are there things in the real world that the exponential function does not account for?

f. Extrapolate the linear function and the exponential function to *this* year. What does each model give for the CPI-U? Using the linear model, how much would you expect to pay this year for the car that cost \$12,000 in 1988? Using the exponential model, how much would you expect to pay?

g. Would a logistic function fit the data better than an exponential or a linear function? What would the logistic model tell you about the CPI-U if you extrapolated many years into the future? Do you think this endpoint behavior is reasonable?

h. By performing appropriate operations on your table of data, make a list containing the percentage by which the CPI-U increased each year. Consult your history instructor to find out what happened in 1979 and 1980 to explain the "double-digit inflation rate."

i. Check on the Web at *http://stats.bls.gov* to find these data and the CPI-U for other years.

8. *Shoe Size Problem:* Here are weights and shoe sizes of 10 freshman boys.

Weight (lb)	Shoe Size
90	10
103	11.5
110	9.5
110	10.5
118	12
130	9
133	11.5
145	12
150	10
164	10.5

a. Run a linear regression on the data. Give the regression equation, the coefficient of determination, and the correlation coefficient.

b. Calculate the coefficient of determination and the correlation coefficient again, directly from the definition, by calculating SS_{dev} and SS_{res}. Do the answers agree with those in part a?

c. Give numerical evidence that the linear regression line does *not* fit the data very well. For instance, what percentage of SS_{dev} is removed by the linear regression?

d. Give graphical evidence that the regression line does *not* fit the data very well by making a scatter plot and plotting the regression line on the same screen. On a sketch of the resulting graph, show that the residuals are not much smaller than the original deviations.

8-6
Chapter Review and Test

Objective

Review and practice the major concepts presented in this chapter.

Class Time

2 days (including 1 day for testing)

Homework Assignment

Day 1: R0–R5, T1–T20

Day 2 (after Chapter 8 Test): Problem Set 9-1

Technology Options

 Exploration 8-6a: Carbon Dioxide Follow-Up

Lesson Notes

Section 8-6 contains a set of Review Problems, a set of Concept Problems, and a Chapter Test. The Review Problems include one problem for each section in the chapter. You may wish to use the Chapter Test as an additional set of review problems.

Encourage students to practice the no-calculator problems without a calculator so that they are prepared for the test problems for which they cannot use a calculator.

Exploration Notes

Exploration 8-6a is a follow-up for Review Problem R4. Students use sinusoidal regression on the residuals from the exponential regression to get an equation that models the seasonal fluctuation of carbon dioxide concentration in the atmosphere, as well as the increasing trend over a number of years.

Technology Notes

 Exploration 8-6a: Carbon Dioxide Follow-Up, in the *Instructor's Resource Book,* asks students to fit various models to data and then to analyze them. Fathom can be used to plot the data, and sliders can be created to model the data.

Problem Notes

If you have time and your students have enjoyed this chapter, consider assigning the Concept Problems. They could be used for class discussion or for a project.

The Carbon Dioxide Data Set for Problem R5 is available on the *Instructor's Resource CD* and at *www.keymath.com/precalc.*

Problem R2 asks students questions about SS_{res} and SS_{dev}. A blackline master for part c is available in the *Instructor's Resource Book.*

Supplementary Problems

1. *Word Frequency Problem:* In the University Mathematics Applications Project's Unit 215, Philip Tuchinsky reports on the frequency with which certain words occur in long books. Here are data for James Joyce's *Ulysses.* In the table, x is the number of times a given word occurs and f(x) is the number of words that occur exactly x times.

x	f(x)
1	16432
2	4776
3	2194
4	1285
5	906
6	637
7	483
8	371
9	298
10	222

   Figure 8-6a

   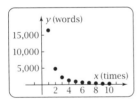

   a. Figure 8-6a shows a scatter plot of the data. Tell why a power function or an exponential function would fit the data reasonably well whereas a linear or quadratic function would not be appropriate.

   b. By regression analysis, find out which type of function, exponential or power, correlates better with the data, and explain how you reached your conclusion. Write the particular equation of this better-fitting function.

   c. Use the function in part b to predict the number of words that occur exactly 20 times. Which process do you use to do this, interpolation or extrapolation?

   d. Suppose a particular word occurs 50 times. Use the function in part b to predict how many other words occur with this frequency. Which process do you use to do this, interpolation or extrapolation?

   e. Transform the data by taking log x and log f(x). Store the results in two more columns in your grapher's data lists. Make a scatter plot of log f(x) versus log x. How does the result confirm your choice of function in part b?

   f. Find the best-fitting linear function for log f(x) versus log x. Use the equation to calculate and plot the residuals. Is there any pattern in the residuals that suggests there is behavior that is not accounted for by the linear model?

2. *Bathtub Problem:* Dwayne pulled the plug on his bathtub. He has studied fluid dynamics and knows that based on theoretical considerations, the depth of water remaining in the tub should be a quadratic function of the time since the plug was pulled. Here are the data that Dwayne collected as the tub drained.

Time (s)	Depth (cm)
30	17.6
60	12.0
90	7.4
120	4.1
150	1.5

   a. Confirm that a quadratic function has a better correlation with the data than a linear, logarithmic, exponential, or power function.

   b. On the same screen, plot the best-fitting quadratic function and a scatter plot of the given data. Use a window with an x-range of [−50, 400] and an appropriate window for y. Sketch the result. Make your sketch dotted for values of x where the model does not fit the real-world situation.

c. Based on the quadratic model, how deep was the water when Dwayne opened the drain?

d. Based on the quadratic model, when will the tub be empty? Show how you reach your conclusion. Tell why the quadratic model would be useless for extrapolating beyond this time.

3. *Atmospheric Pressure Problem:* Atmospheric pressure decreases with increasing altitude because the pressure is caused only by the part of atmosphere remaining *above* you. The table and Figure 8-6b show pressures in psi (pounds per square inch) at various altitudes.

Altitude (ft)	Pressure (psi)
2000	13.50
4000	12.40
6000	11.37
8000	10.46
10000	9.60
12000	8.82

Figure 8-6b

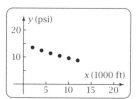

a. Let x be the number of *thousands* of feet. Show by regression that an exponential function fits the data better than a linear or a power function. Write the particular equation of the best-fitting exponential function.

b. Extrapolate the exponential model to predict the air pressure on the top of Mt. Everest, which is at an altitude of 29,000 ft.

c. Blood at body temperature will boil if atmospheric pressure falls below 0.9 psi. At what altitude would you need to start worrying about this phenomenon? Which process do you use to find this number, extrapolation or interpolation?

d. The pressure at sea level (altitude zero) is about 14.7 psi. Does your mathematical model accurately reflect this fact? Explain.

e. Recently, it was discovered that the Mediterranean Sea dried up about 6 million years ago, leaving a "valley" 10,000 ft deep. What do you predict that atmospheric pressure would have been at the bottom of this valley?

f. Run a quadratic regression on the given data. Show that the quadratic function appears to fit the data as well as the exponential function. On the same screen, plot the quadratic regression equation and the exponential function from part a for altitudes from 0 through 100,000 ft. Then explain why the exponential function has the correct endpoint behavior for large values of x and why the quadratic function does not.

g. In part a, you showed that a power function does not fit the data as well as an exponential function. Make residual plots for both of these functions. Sketch the results. Explain how these plots confirm that the exponential function fits better.

9 Probability, and Functions of a Random Variable

This chapter provides a time-efficient way for students to learn the counting principles leading to analysis of permutations and combinations. They learn to calculate probabilities of complex events from the probabilities of the components of those events. The topic fits in with the rest of the course as students learn that probability is the dependent variable in functions of a random (independent) variable. They learn the binomial distribution and touch upon other functions. The chapter concludes with mathematical expectation, a topic that allows students to see more clearly why people would want to study probability theory. A cumulative review of Chapters 7 through 9 appears in Section 9-10.

9-1

Introduction to Probability

Objective

Find the probability of various events in a dice-rolling experiment.

Class Time

$\frac{1}{2}$ day

Homework Assignment

Problems 1–13

Technology Options

 Activity: Rolling Dice

Important Terms and Concepts

Probability

Lesson Notes

In this section, students find probabilities of events in a simple situation in which the outcomes are equally likely. This should be a review for most students. You can assign this section for homework the night of the Chapter 8 test or as a group activity to be completed in class. No classroom discussion is needed before students begin the activity.

To find the number of outcomes in each event, students can simply count, using the chart of all possible outcomes in Figure 9-1a in the student text. Later in this chapter, students will learn shortcuts for calculating numbers of outcomes.

You may want to combine a discussion of the results of this problem set with the discussion of Section 9-2, which introduces vocabulary associated with probability.

Technology Notes

 Activity: Rolling Dice, in *Teaching Mathematics with Fathom,* has students simulate the rolling of one die and of two dice. The histogram they make can help them visualize the probabilities in this section. Allow 50 minutes.

Problem Notes

- *Problems 7 and 9* use the term *inclusive.* You may need to remind some students of the meaning of the word.

- *Problem 13* may be tricky for some students. There are six outcomes for which the black die shows 2 and six outcomes for which the white die shows 5. However, simply adding to get 12 outcomes counts $\boxed{5}\ \boxed{2}$ twice the outcome, so 1 must be subtracted.

9-2

Words Associated with Probability

Objective

Distinguish among various words used to describe probability.

Class Time

1 day

Homework Assignment

Q1–Q10, Problems 1 and 2

Important Terms and Concepts

Random experiment

Outcome

Simple event

Event

Sample space

Probability

Lesson Notes

This section defines several terms associated with probability. You can introduce the new terminology as you review the results of Exploratory Problem Set 9-1. During the discussion, you may want to use an overhead transparency of Figure 9-1a in the student text, which shows the 36 possible outcomes of rolling two dice. If you circle the desired outcomes, students will see patterns and be able to count the outcomes.

Make sure students understand the difference between an *outcome* and an *event*. An outcome is an individual result of a random experiment. An event is a set of one or more outcomes. To help students understand, you might present a situation that is different from the one in the student text. For example, assume you toss a quarter, a dime, and a nickel. Then there are eight possible outcomes:

$H_Q H_D H_N$ $H_Q H_D T_N$ $H_Q T_D H_N$ $H_Q T_D T_N$

$T_Q T_D T_N$ $T_Q T_D H_N$ $T_Q H_D T_N$ $T_Q H_D H_N$

Note that these outcomes are *equally likely*. That is, each one has the same chance of occurring.

One possible event would be "Exactly two tails are tossed." This event is the three-element set

$\{H_Q T_D T_N, T_Q T_D H_N, T_Q H_D T_N\}$

Another event would be "The dime lands heads up." This event is the four-element set

$\{H_Q H_D H_N, H_Q H_D T_N, T_Q H_D T_N, T_Q H_D H_N\}$

Notice that, unlike the individual outcomes, the events are *not* equally likely. The probability of tossing exactly two tails is $\frac{3}{8}$, while the probability the dime lands heads up is $\frac{1}{2}$.

Point out that the definition of probability specifies that the outcomes must be equally likely. You might present an example to illustrate that the probability formula does not work if this is not the case. For example, when you spin the spinner shown here, the possible outcomes, gray and white, are not equally likely. If you try to apply the probability formula in this case, you get $P(\text{gray}) = \frac{1}{2}$, which is clearly not correct.

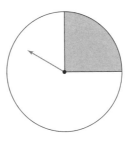

In this lesson, it is best to avoid computational shortcuts for counting outcomes and calculating probabilities because understanding at a concrete level is more important at this point than using abstract formulas students do not fully understand. At this stage, it is perfectly acceptable for students to list and count outcomes.

Problem Notes

- *Problem 1* involves drawing a card from a standard deck of playing cards. Some students may not be familiar with playing cards, so do not assume this problem will be routine for everyone. You may want to bring in decks of cards for students to use when counting outcomes.

- *Problem 2* involves flipping a penny, a nickel, and a dime. Some students may want to use actual coins to find the sample space. To help them keep track of outcomes, students should always list the result for each coin in the same "slot." For example, they could always list the penny first, then the nickel, and then the dime. This will help them understand that THT is different from HTT or TTH. Some students might also find it helpful to use the subscripts P, N, and D (see the Lesson Notes).

- *Problem 3* is a good research problem and can be assigned for extra credit.

9-3
Two Counting Principles

Objective

Calculate the number of outcomes in an event or sample space.

Class Time

1 day

Homework Assignment

RA, Q1–Q10, Problems 1–15 odd, 16, 17

Important Terms and Concepts

Independent events

Mutually exclusive events

Overlapping events

Non-mutually exclusive events

Venn diagram

Lesson Notes

The counting principles presented in this section are essential for counting outcomes in complex probability situations. After learning these principles, students should no longer have to make a list of every outcome. However, they may still find it helpful to start listing outcomes until a pattern becomes clear.

Students should associate addition with the word *or* and multiplication with the words *and* and *and then*. To help students make this connection, you might want to record this information on the board as you discuss the camp situations in the student text:

outdoor AND indoor

$$4 \quad \times \quad 3$$

indoor AND different indoor

$$3 \quad \times \quad 2$$

outdoor OR indoor

$$4 \quad + \quad 3$$

In the first counting principle, $n(B|A)$ means the number of ways event B can happen *after* event A has already occurred. The note after the property box points out that if A and B are independent, then $n(B|A) = n(B)$, so $n(A \text{ and } B) = n(A) \cdot n(B)$. You might want to explain this in terms of the camp examples you just discussed.

- When two different indoor activities are chosen, then the number of outcomes is the number of indoor activities (3) times the number of indoor activities left *after* one has been chosen (2).

- When one outdoor activity and one indoor activity are chosen, the choice of outdoor activity *has no effect* on the choice of indoor activity (that is, the events are independent). So the number of indoor activities remaining *after* the outdoor activity has been chosen is simply the original number of indoor activities. Thus the number of outcomes is simply the number of outdoor activities (4) times the number of indoor activities (3).

In the second principle, it is assumed that events *A* and *B* cannot both happen. That is, they are *mutually exclusive.* You might want to give additional examples of mutually exclusive events and have students suggest others, such as

- Rolling an even number on a die and rolling an odd number

- Drawing a spade and drawing a club in a deck of cards

If events *A* and *B* are mutually exclusive, you find the number of outcomes in event *A* or event *B* by simply adding the number of outcomes in *A* and the number of outcomes in *B*. For example, there are 13 spades and 13 clubs in a deck of cards, so

$$n(\text{spades } or \text{ clubs}) = n(\text{spades}) + n(\text{clubs})$$
$$= 13 + 13 = 26$$

If events *A* and *B* can both happen, they are *over-lapping,* or *non-mutually exclusive,* events. The student text gives the example of drawing a heart *or* drawing a face card from a deck of playing cards. These events are non-mutually exclusive because it is possible to draw a card that is both a heart *and* a face card. Here is another example:

A teacher asks her students which ice cream flavor they like, chocolate or strawberry. Twelve students say they like chocolate and 15 say they like straw-berry. These results include four students who chose both flavors. How many students are in the class? To answer this question, you *cannot* simply add 12 and 15 because this would count the students who chose both flavors twice. To compen-sate, you have to subtract once the number who chose both flavors.

$$n(\text{chocolate or strawberry})$$
$$= n(\text{chocolate}) + n(\text{strawberry})$$
$$- n(\text{chocolate} \cap \text{strawberry})$$
$$= 12 + 15 - 4 = 23$$

Show students how to solve this problem using a *Venn diagram.* Draw two overlapping circles, one for each flavor. Write 4—the number of students who like both flavors—in the intersection. Then figure out what numbers you need to put in the remaining section to get a total of 12 students who like chocolate and 15 who like strawberry. Finally, add the three numbers to get the total number of students.

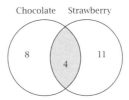

Exploration Notes

Exploration 9-3a reinforces the concepts of this section. You could use this Exploration as a group activity at the beginning of instruction or as extra homework or a review sheet. Allow 15–20 minutes for this activity.

Problem Notes

- *Problems 1–4* are direct applications of the counting principle and should not pose any difficulties.

- *Problems 5–8* require students to extend the first counting principle to situations involving more than two events.

- *Problems 9–12* involve overlapping events.

- *Problems 13 and 14* help introduce the concept of permutations, which is formally introduced in the next section.

Supplementary Problems

1. Ward Robe has 15 pairs of slacks and 23 shirts. Find the number of different ways he could select a pants-and-shirt outfit.

2. Natalie Attired has 20 dresses and 17 pants outfits. In how many different ways could she select a dress or a pants outfit to wear?

3. Sally visits the pet store. There are 37 dogs and 15 cats. Find the number of different ways she could select

   a. A dog or a cat

   b. A dog and a cat

4. A first-grade class has 13 girls and 11 boys. Find the number of different ways the teacher could select these students to go to the office.

   a. A boy and a girl

   b. A boy or a girl

5. A jewelry store has 544 necklaces and 215 pieces containing puka shells. Of the 544 necklaces, 129 are puka shell necklaces. How many pieces does the store have that are necklaces *or* that contain puka shells?

9-4
Probabilities of Various Permutations

Objective

Given a description of a permutation, find the probability of getting that permutation if an arrangement is selected at random.

Class Time

1–2 days

Homework Assignment

Day 1: RA, Q1–Q10, Problems 1–19 odd

Day 2: Selected even-numbered problems or Exploration exercises

Important Terms and Concepts

Permutation

Fixed position

Restricted position

Factorial, !

Circular permutations

Lesson Notes

The next two sections present permutations and combinations in the context of probabilities. They are presented in this way so that students will be less likely to forget the definition of probability while they are learning how to count.

If you find that students are struggling with permutation problems, you may need to spend two days on this section. On the second day, work through some of the even-numbered problems and/or assign the Exploration.

Example 1 demonstrates how to set up and solve a simple permutation problem. Marking a space for each "slot," or position, in the permutation is extremely helpful in keeping track of the possibilities. Point out that you multiply because you select the first book *and then* select the second book *and then* select the third book, and so on.

Example 2 is a more complicated problem because certain positions are *fixed* or *restricted*. Point out that when counting the favorable outcomes, the fixed and restricted positions are filled in first. In this example, the probability is transformed to a percent because the magnitude of an answer such as 12% is easier to comprehend than $\frac{5}{24}$.

As you work through the examples, some students may notice factorial patterns in finding permutations. The formula for computing permutations using factorials has been deliberately delayed until the next section. This allows students to develop an understanding of permutations as arrangements rather than just memorizing and applying a formula.

Exploration Notes

Exploration 9-4a gives students practice in calculating probabilities of events involving different kinds of permutations, including arrangements of elements that "look" the same and circular permutations. This activity is a good follow-up to the homework assignment. Allow students 15–20 minutes to complete this activity.

Problem Notes

- *Problems 1-14* are similar to the examples.

- *Problem 1* involves the Hawaiian alphabet. You may want to ask a couple of students to see if they can find out why the Hawaiian alphabet has only 12 letters.

- *Problems 15 and 16,* Permutations with Repeated Elements Problems, involve permutations in which some of the elements in the set from which the items are selected are the same. When counting permutations, students must count arrangements that look the same only once. For example, when counting two-letter permutations of the letters in POP, the arrangement PO formed by selecting the first P and the O is considered the same as the arrangement PO formed by selecting the second P and the O. Encourage students to read the explanation of these problems carefully before attempting to solve them.

- *Problems 17-20,* Circular Permutation Problems, involve items that are arranged around a circle. In this case, permutations are considered the same if the items have the same positions *with respect to each other.* Again, students should read the explanation of these problems carefully before attempting to solve them.

Supplementary Problems

1. Find the number of different ways you could arrange these numbers of books on a shelf.
   a. 4 books from a set of 9 books
   b. 3 books from a set of 12 books
   c. 5 books from a set of 8 books
   d. 7 books from a set of 7 books

2. Find the number of permutations of the 26 letters in the English alphabet that could be made using these numbers of different letters.
   a. 2 different letters
   b. 3 different letters
   c. 4 different letters
   d. 26 different letters (How many digits are in the answer? Does the answer surprise you?)

3. Suppose that prestige license plates are made using exactly 4 of the 26 letters in the alphabet. How many different prestige plates could be made if all 4 letters are different?

MATH

4. Fifteen people try out for the nine positions on a baseball team.
   a. In how many ways could the pitcher and the catcher be selected?
   b. In how many ways could the three outfielders be selected *after* the pitcher and catcher have been selected?
   c. In how many ways could the first-, second-, and third-base players and the shortstop be selected *after* the pitcher, catcher, and three outfielders have been selected?

5. A five-letter permutation is selected at random from the letters in the word GRATE.
   a. How many permutations are possible?
   b. How many of the permutations begin with G?
   c. What is the probability the permutation selected begins with G? Express the probability as a percent.
   d. What is the probability that the permutation selected is GREAT?

6. A five-letter permutation is selected at random from GRATE. Find the probability of each event.

   a. The second letter is T and the last letter is G.

   b. The second letter is a vowel and the third letter is a consonant.

   c. The second and third letters are both consonants.

   d. The second letter is a consonant and the last letter is E.

   e. The second letter is a consonant and the last letter is R.

7. Find the number of different ways seven first-graders could line up if three of them, April, Mae, and Julie, are identical triplets.

9-5
Probabilities of Various Combinations

Objective

Calculate the number of different combinations containing r elements taken from a set containing n elements.

Class Time

2 days

Homework Assignment

Day 1: RA, Q1–Q10, Problems 1–31 odd

Day 2: Selected even-numbered problems, depending on students' weaknesses

Important Terms and Concepts

Combination

Notation for combinations, $_nC_r$

Notation for permutations, $_nP_r$

Lesson Notes

This section introduces combinations. The important difference between permutations and combinations is that order matters in a permutation, whereas order does *not* matter in a combination. For example, XY and YX are different permutations, but they are the same combination. In both permutations and combinations, elements may not be repeated.

After explaining how to compute numbers of combinations, the book introduces symbolic notation for combinations and permutations. Make sure students write the notations correctly. For instance, in the notation $_nC_r$, the n and r should be written as subscripts, not on the same line with the C.

In Section 9-7, students will learn that the values of $_nC_r$ are equal to the coefficient of the terms in the binomial series for $(a + b)^n$. For instance,

$$(a + b)^9 = {}_9C_0a^9 + {}_9C_1a^8b + \cdots + {}_9C_3a^6b^3$$
$$+ {}_9C_4a^5b^4 + \cdots + {}_9C_8ab^8 + {}_9C_9b^9$$

This text uses the notation $_nC_r$ and $_nP_r$ exclusively. It's worthwhile to point out to students that there are other acceptable notations for combinations and permutations:

$$_nC_r = C(n, r) = \binom{n}{r} \quad \text{and} \quad _nP_r = P(n, r)$$

Example 1 is the same calculation performed earlier in the section—finding the number of combinations of four things taken three at a time—but this time the new notation is used.

Examples 2 and 3 help students recognize patterns that lead to the "factorial formulas" for computing numbers of permutations or combinations. This pattern is summarized in the Technique box after Example 6. Here are the general forms of the equations in that box:

$$_nP_r = \frac{n!}{(n-r)!} \qquad _nC_r = \frac{n!}{r!(n-r)!}$$

Example 4 applies the "factorial formula" to compute the number of three-person committees that could be formed from a group of seven people. Students should recognize that this requires counting *combinations* because the committees are different only if the people on them are different. It does not matter how the people are arranged. You might suggest that students remember the difference between combinations and permutations by associating the words *committee* and *combination*.

Part b of Example 5 uses the first counting principle to simplify the problem. The number of ways of selecting three women *and* two men is the number of ways of selecting three women *times* the number of ways of selecting two men.

Part c of Example 5 uses the second counting principle. A committee with at least three women could have exactly three women *or* exactly four women *or* exactly five women. Because these events are mutually exclusive, one can find the probability of each event and then add the results.

After completing this section, you may want to give a quiz or test on the various counting methods.

Exploration Notes

Exploration 9-5a can give students practice reading the text, either on their own or in cooperative groups. You might start class by having students work through this Exploration in groups. Then discuss the results and work through Examples 4 and 5 in the book. Allow students 20–25 minutes to complete this Exploration.

Problem Notes

- *Problems 1–12* involve computing numbers of combinations and permutations. Make sure your students first use the factorial methods as detailed in the examples and then use the built-in grapher features to verify their answers. In Problems 11 and 12, the grapher returns an answer in scientific notation. Ask your students to evaluate $_{99}P_{96}$ and explain why some graphers give an overflow error.

- *Problems 13–22* provide practice using counting techniques to solve real-life counting problems.

- *Problem 21* leads to the conclusion that $_{10}C_2 = {}_{10}C_8$. That is, the number of ways of selecting 2 things out of 10 things is the same as the number of ways of selecting 8 things out of 10 things.

- *Problem 22* leads students to discover the relationship between the number of elements in a set and the number of subsets. (A set with n elements has 2^n subsets. See Supplementary Problem 5.) After part a is answered, rearrange the answers so that they are in this order: no elements, one element, two elements, and so on. With this arrangement, some students might recognize the answers as the numbers in the fifth row of Pascal's triangle. After students complete Problem 22, you may want to assign Problem 5 from the Supplementary Problems.

- *Problems 23 and 24* have permutation questions mixed in with the combination questions.

- *Problem 31* asks students to update their journals. There have been a lot of new ideas presented, and entering this information will help students assimilate the material.

Supplementary Problems

1. A committee of 5 is to be selected from the 30 students in a freshman English class. In how many ways could the committee be formed? How can you tell that a number of combinations is being asked for, not a number of permutations?

2. Ann goes to the toy store, where her mother will let her buy any 3 different toys. There are 1000 different toys to choose from. How many different selections could Ann make?

3. Ten first-graders—six boys and four girls—are on the playground. Miss Twiddle selects a group of five at random. Find the probability that the group has

  a. Three boys and two girls

  b. Two boys and three girls

  c. Three boys and two girls, or two boys and three girls

  d. Ella Quence, one of the girls

4. The varsity croquet team, which consists of four boys and eight girls, will be traveling to an out-of-town match. The coach will take seven of the team members in her minivan, and the rest will go in a car. The students get into the vehicles at random. Find the probability that the coach's van has

  a. Two boys and five girls

  b. All girls

  c. All boys

  d. Peter Doubt and Manuel Dexterity, two of the boys

5. *Combinations and Powers of 2 Problem:* In Problem 22 in the problem set, you found that

$$_5C_0 + {_5C_1} + {_5C_2} + {_5C_3} + {_5C_4} + {_5C_5} = 2^5$$

This is an example of a general property.

PROPERTY: Sum of All Possible Combinations

$$\sum_{r=0}^{n} {_nC_r} = 2^n$$

---

  a. Show by direct calculation that this property works if $n = 3$.

  b. Use this property in an appropriate manner to find each of the following *quickly.*

    i. The number of combinations of 0 or 1 or 2 or . . . or 10 people that could be made from a set of 10 people

    ii. The number of combinations of 10 people taken at least one at a time, and the number of combinations of 10 people taken at least two at a time

    iii. The number of subsets of a 12-element set

    iv. The number of nonempty subsets of a 12-element set

9-6
Properties of Probability

Objective

Given events A and B, calculate

- $P(A$ and $B)$, the probability of the *intersection* of A and B

- $P(A$ or $B)$, the probability of the *union* of A and B

- $P(\text{not } A)$ and $P(\text{not } B)$, the probabilities of the *complement* of A and the *complement* of B

Class Time

1–2 days

Homework Assignment

Day 1: RA, Q1–Q10, Problems 1–13 odd

Day 2: Selected even-numbered problems, depending on students' weaknesses

Important Terms and Concepts

Intersection of two events

Independent events

Union of two events

Mutually exclusive events

Complementary events

Lesson Notes

In this section, students learn methods for finding the probability of the union and intersection of events and of the complement of an event. These properties should seem familiar to students because they correspond to the counting principles from Section 9-3.

When discussing the playing card examples from the text, make sure students understand the difference between the two cases described.

- In the first case, the first card is *not* replaced before the second card is drawn. Because the result of the first draw affects the choices available for the second, the draws are not independent. After the first draw, only 51 cards remain, and after the first black card is drawn, only 25 black cards remain.

- In the second case, the first card is replaced before the second card is drawn. In this case, the events are independent because the first draw does not affect the choices available for the second draw. On the second draw, just as on the first, there are 52 cards available and 26 of the cards are black.

When discussing the cookie example, make sure students understand the difference between the two cases described.

- In the first case, there are cookies that contain both chocolate *and* oatmeal, so the events are *not* mutually exclusive.

- In the second case, there are no cookies that contain both ginger and macadamia nuts, so the events *are* mutually exclusive.

You might write the below chart on the board to show how the counting principles are related to the probability formulas for intersection and union of events.

The student text shows how the property for the probability of complementary events follows from the probability property for the union of mutually exclusive events.

Example 1 uses the formulas to solve a series of problems. Note that part e shows two solutions. For the first solution, make sure students can explain why the events "at least 1" and "not C and not Ph" are complementary. The second solution uses the fact that "at least one" is the same as "C or Ph" and then applies the probability formula for the union of non-mutually exclusive events.

Exploration Notes

In *Exploration 9-6a,* students calculate probabilities of various events from other events. You may want to begin the instruction for this section by having students work on this activity in groups. Follow up by discussing the results and then working through Example 1 in the text. Allow students about 15 minutes to complete this activity.

Problem Notes

- *Problems 1–13* require students to apply the probability properties to real-world problems. When reviewing these problems, be sure to discuss the fact that "none of the possibilities" and "at least one of the possibilities" are complementary events.

- *Problem 9* may surprise students. Part b of Problem 9 requires the students to use the formula "backwards" and to find the probability of an individual event needed to get a desired overall probability.

- *Problems 12 and 13* require students to decide whether or not the given events are independent, based on the given probabilities.

Supplementary Problems

1. *Grade Problem:* Kara Vann estimates that the probability she will get an A in algebra is 92% and the probability she will get an A in history is 88%. Find the probability of each event.

   a. She gets an A in algebra and history.

   b. She does not get an A in algebra.

   c. She does not get an A in history.

   d. She doesn't get an A in either subject.

   e. She gets at least one A.

	Counting Principle	Probability Formula
A and *B* are *not* independent	$n(A \text{ and } B) = n(A) \cdot n(B|A)$	$P(A \text{ and } B) = P(A) \cdot P(B|A)$
A and *B* are independent	$n(A \text{ and } B) = n(A) \cdot n(B)$	$P(A \text{ and } B) = P(A) \cdot P(B)$
A and *B* are *not* mutually exclusive	$n(A \text{ or } B) = n(A) + n(B) - n(A \cap B)$	$P(A \text{ or } B) = P(A) + P(B) - P(A \cap B)$
A and *B* are mutually exclusive	$n(A \text{ or } B) = n(A) + n(B)$	$P(A \text{ or } B) = P(A) + P(B)$

2. *Menu Problem:* Doc Worker is a regular customer at the Waterfront Coffee Shop. The manager has figured that Doc's probability of ordering ham is 0.8 and his probability of ordering eggs is 0.65. Find the probability of each event.

    a. He does not order ham.

    b. He does not order eggs.

    c. He orders neither ham nor eggs.

    d. He orders ham and eggs.

    e. He orders at least one, either ham or eggs.

9-7
Functions of a Random Variable

Objective

Given a random experiment, find and graph the probabilities of all possible events.

Class Time

2 days

Homework Assignment

Day 1: RA, Q1–Q10, Problems 1, 3, 5

Day 2: Problems 7, 9, 11, 14, and some even-numbered problems

Technology Options

 Calculator Program: BINOMDIS

 Exploration 9-7a: The Binomial Distribution

 Activity: Thumbtacks

Important Terms and Concepts

Function of a random variable

Binomial series

Probability distribution

Binomial distribution

Binomial experiment

Proper divisor

Lesson Notes

The title of the section, Functions of a Random Variable, is used to emphasize the fact that applications of mathematics often take the form of using a function as a mathematical model.

The section in the student text begins by developing an equation for calculating $P(x)$, the probability of getting x heads when a coin is flipped five times. The number of heads, x, is a *random variable,* so $P(x)$ is a *function of a random variable.* By evaluating $P(x)$ for every possible value of x—in this case the integers from 0 through 5—one can find how the 100% probability is distributed among all the possible events. For this reason, $P(x)$ is also called a *probability distribution,* or a *binomial distribution.*

The equation for the coin-flipping experiment is then generalized to any binomial experiment. Emphasize that a *binomial experiment* consists of a number of repetitions of an action that has only *two* possible results. If *E* is one of the results, then the two possibilities can be thought of as *E* and *not E*. In the coin-flipping experiment, the possible results are heads and tails (or heads and not heads). When presenting the general equation for $P(x)$, be sure to discuss what each part of the equation represents.

The terms of the probability distribution—that is, the various values of $P(x)$—are terms in the binomial series for $(a + b)^n$. Students who are not familiar with binomial series can refer to Section 14-3. Explain that a *series* is a sum of terms. A *binomial series* for $(a + b)^n$ is the sum that results from expanding $(a + b)^n$. When you expand $(a + b)^n$, you get

$$_nC_0a^nb^0 + {}_nC_1a^{n-1}b^1 + {}_nC_2a^{n-2}b^2 + \cdots \\ + {}_nC_na^0b^n$$

Emphasize the fact that the coefficients in a binomial series are combination numbers. Students already familiar with Pascal's triangle may recognize that the coefficients of $(a + b)^n$ are the numbers on the *n*th row of Pascal's triangle.

The value of $P(x)$ is the term that includes b^x.

In Example 1, be sure to discuss using the grapher's list feature to compute all the terms in the probability distribution in a time-efficient way. Having the values of *x* and $P(x)$ stored in lists also makes it easy to create the scatter plot in part c. Creating a scatter plot of the probability distribution emphasizes that it is a function. The graph in Example 1 shows six discrete points. Emphasize to students that the points should not be connected, because you can only get integer numbers of heads in five flips.

You may want to work as a class to write a program for calculating binomial distributions (see Supplementary Problem 1). You can check the program by using it to redo part a of Example 1.

Exploration Notes

In *Exploration 9-7a,* students experiment to estimate the probability that a tack will land "point up" on any one flip, and then they use this experimental probability to calculate and plot the binomial

distribution for an experiment consisting of ten tack flips. This Exploration makes an excellent group activity. Allow students about 20 minutes to complete it.

Technology Notes

 Calculator Program: BINOMDIS calculates probabilities of various outcomes in a binomial distribution and may be useful for several problems in this section. The program is available on the *Instructor's Resource CD* and at *www.keymath.com/precalc* for download onto a TI-83 or TI-84 graphing calculator. It also appears in the *Instructor's Resource Book* for students to enter by hand.

Exploration 9-7a: The Binomial Distribution, in the *Instructor's Resource Book,* asks students to calculate and plot probabilities in a binomial distribution. Fathom can be used to generate data and graphs for this Exploration.

Activity: Thumbtacks, in the *Instructor's Resource Book,* has students simulate data on a flipped thumbtack. This activity provides a natural introduction to mathematical expectation.

Problem Notes

Many of these problems are fairly long. Using the grapher's "instant replay" feature, lists, or a program to calculate probabilities will reduce some of the tedium.

- *Problem 8* leads to the conclusion that under certain circumstances a 3-engine plane is more reliable than a 4-engine plane.

- *Problem 9* has an interesting twist because there is a restriction on which team may win the last game.

- *Problems 10–13* involve probability distributions that are not binomial. Be sure to give at least one of these for homework on the second night.

- *Problem 13,* the Same Birthday Problem, makes a good project. Most students will be surprised by the results of this problem. As long as there are more than 22 people, there is a greater than 50% chance that at least 2 people have the same birthday.

Supplementary Problems

1. *Computer Program for Binomial Distributions Problem:* Write or download a program for your grapher to calculate $P(x)$ for each value of x in a binomial distribution. The inputs should be n, the number of times the action is repeated, and b, the probability of success on any one repetition. The appropriate binomial is $(a + b)^n$, where $a = 1 - b$. Note that x will equal the exponent of b in the series. A time-efficient way to calculate the coefficients *recursively* is

$$\frac{(\text{coefficient})(\text{exponent of } a)}{\text{term number}} = \text{next coefficient}$$

The output should be stored in two lists, one for x and the other for $P(x)$. These lists can then be used to plot the distribution.

Test your program using $n = 3$ and $b = 0.3$. The output should be

x	$P(x)$
0	0.216
1	0.432
2	0.288
3	0.064

2. *Graph of Binomial Distribution Problem:* Use the output lists of the program written in Supplementary Problem 1 to make a scatter plot of the binomial distribution given in that problem. You should be able to do this without entering any more data. If you are successful, the result will look something like Figure 9-7a.

Figure 9-7a

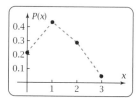

3. *Bull's-Eye Problem:* Mark Wright throws his dart several times and finds that he can hit the bull's-eye 30% of the time. Using this fact, find these probabilities when he throws five darts.

   a. Calculate the probabilities that he gets 0, 1, 2, 3, 4, and 5 bull's-eyes.

   b. Calculate the probability that he makes at least 2 bull's-eyes. Leave a "trail" to show the method you used.

   c. Mark fires nine shots. Compute and graph the probability distribution. Sketch the graph.

4. *Dice Problem:* A game involves rolling a fair die six times. Let x be the number of times you get a 1 or a 2, and let $P(x)$ be the probability you get a 1 or a 2 x times.

   a. If you roll a die once, what is the probability you get a 1 or a 2? What is the probability you do *not* get a 1 or a 2?

   b. Compute $P(x)$ for each value of x in the domain. Use the results to plot the graph of the probability distribution. Sketch the graph.

   c. You win the game if the die comes up 1 or 2 at least twice. What is your probability of winning? Leave a "trail" to show the method you used.

   d. Because the probability of getting a 1 or a 2 on any one roll is $\frac{1}{3}$, you might assume that the probability of getting 1 or 2 on two of six rolls is also $\frac{1}{3}$. Is this assumption true or false? Justify your answer.

5. *Tan Marble Problem:* A bag contains five black marbles and one tan marble. The marbles are drawn one at a time, without replacement, until the tan marble is drawn. Let $P(x)$ be the probability that the tan marble is drawn on the xth draw.

   a. Find $P(1)$.

   b. $P(2)$ is the probability that the tan marble is *not* drawn on the first draw and *is* drawn on the second draw. Find $P(2)$.

   c. Find $P(3)$, $P(4)$, $P(5)$, and $P(6)$.

   d. What is the significance of the fact that the sum of $P(1)$ through $P(6)$ is 1?

   e. Suppose each marble is *replaced* before the next draw. Find $P(1)$ through $P(6)$ under this condition.

   f. Plot the graph of the probability distribution in part e. Sketch the graph.

   g. Show that the sum of the probabilities in part e approaches 1 as x becomes very large.

6. *Lucky Card Problem:* An index card is marked with a lucky number and then shuffled with nine other index cards. Three people play a game in which each, in turn, draws a card at random. If the card drawn is not the marked card, it is replaced, the cards are shuffled, and the next player draws at random. The winner is the first player to draw the marked card. Let $P(x, y)$ be the probability that the xth player (1, 2, or 3) wins on his or her yth turn.

a. What does $P(1, 1)$ equal?

b. $P(2, 1)$ is the probability player 1 does *not* win on his or her first turn and that player 2 *does* win on his or her first turn. Find $P(2, 1)$ and $P(3, 1)$.

c. Show that $P(1, 1)$, $P(1, 2)$, and $P(1, 3)$ are terms in a geometric sequence.

d. The probably that player 1 wins is the sum of the terms in an (infinite) geometric series. Find his or her probability of winning. Find the second and third players' probabilities of winning.

e. Show that the answers to part d are reasonable based on their relative sizes and their sum.

9-8
Mathematical Expectation

Objective

Calculate the mathematical expectation of a given random experiment.

Class Time

2 days

Homework Assignment

Day 1: RA, Q1–Q10, Problems 1, 3, 5, 7

Day 2: Problems 2, 4, 6, 8

Technology Options

 Exploration 9-8a: Mathematical Expectation

 Activity: Random Walk

Important Terms and Concepts

Mathematical expectation

$\sum$ notation

Weighted average

Actuary

Actuarially sound

Mortality table

Lesson Notes

In this section, students learn how to calculate the *mathematical expectation,* or in some cases, the average payoff for a random experiment. If a random experiment is conducted a great number of times, the mathematical expectation is the weighted average of the values associated with the outcomes for the random experiment. The "weights" are the probabilities for each outcome. Mathematical expectation is also sometimes referred to as *expected value.*

In order to calculate the mathematical expectation for an experiment, each mutually exclusive event must have an associated value, or payoff. In the dice-rolling situation in the student text, the "payoff" for each event is the number of points you win if that event occurs. To calculate the mathematical expectation, you multiply the probability of each event by the payoff for that event and then add the result.

Students may need help interpreting the notation in the definition box. Make sure they understand the meaning of the symbol Σ and of A_k and a_k.

Example 1 provides a step-by-step outline of how to calculate mathematical expectation. After solving the problem the "long way," show students how they can use list operations on their graphers to do the computations. In this example, the expectation, E, is -29.705, meaning that if the game is played many times, you can expect to lose about 30¢ each time. The table at the end of the example demonstrates a good structure for calculating mathematical expectation. Encourage students to use this structure for the first several expectation problems they solve.

Exploration Notes

Exploration 9-8a involves calculating expected payoffs for two random experiments. Students should have fun with these problems. As an extension, invite your students to create their own games and payoffs and have other students decide whether they would play. This activity should take about 15–20 minutes for students to complete.

Technology Notes

 Exploration 9-8a: Mathematical Expectation, in the *Instructor's Resource Book,* has students calculate expected outcomes for two different scenarios. If students did the Thumbtacks activity in Section 9-7, they can use similar processes to simulate multiple trials in Fathom and see the expected value in a histogram.

 Activity: Random Walk, in *Teaching Mathematics with Fathom,* gives a gentle introduction to mathematical expectation while having students use moderate Fathom skills. Allow 30–45 minutes.

Problem Notes

• *Problem 1* is the first situation students encounter in which the payoff—in this case the number of neutrons released—is the value of the random variable. In other words, $P(x) \cdot \text{payoff} = P(x) \cdot x$. You may want to discuss this problem in class.

• *Problem 6,* the Expectation for a Binomial Experiment, leads students to prove something that at first seems obvious. For example, if the probability of your making a hit in baseball is 30%, then it seems natural to expect 3 hits in 10 times at bat. However, this result is *not* true in general for experiments other than binomial ones.

• *Problem 7,* the Multiple-Choice Test Problem, gives students the opportunity to discuss guessing and time-management strategies as they relate to SAT-type testing. This problem should lead students to the conclusion that it really does not pay to randomly guess answers on a multiple-choice test on which points are deducted for an incorrect answer. If you can eliminate even one choice, you can expect to add a small number of fractional points. If x is the number of choices that can be eliminated, then the expected numbers of points are given in the table. This means that if you can eliminate only one choice ($x = 1$), then you would have to guess at 16 such questions to get as much expected score as answering one question for which you were sure of the answer. Eliminating choices and then guessing takes time, a valuable commodity. The test taker's time might be better spent on being certain about an answer rather than worrying about eliminating choices and making guesses.

x	$E(x)$
1	1
2	$\frac{3}{8}$
3	$\frac{1}{6}$
4	$\frac{1}{16}$
5	0

• *Problems 9 and 10* are designed to be assigned as projects.

Supplementary Problems

1. *Card Draw Problem:* You pay 26¢ and draw a card at random from a standard 52-card deck, with these payoffs:

   Ace: You win $1.56.

   Face card: You win 65¢.

   Any other card: You win nothing.

   a. What is the mathematical expectation for this game?

   b. In the long run, would you expect to gain money or lose money playing this game? How much money?

2. *Dice Game Problem:* You pay a dollar and roll a die three times. If you roll a 1 at least two of the three times, you get $10.00. Otherwise, you get nothing. What is your mathematical expectation for this game?

9-9
Chapter Review and Test

Objective

Review and practice the major concepts presented in this chapter.

Class Time

2 days (including 1 day for testing)

Homework Assignment

Day 1: R0–R8, T1–T28

Day 2 (after Chapter 9 Test): Section 9-10, Problems 1–13

Lesson Notes

Section 9-9 contains a set of Review Problems, a set of Concept Problems, and a Chapter Test. The Review Problems include one problem for each section in the chapter. You may wish to use the Chapter Test as an additional set of review problems.

Encourage students to practice the no-calculator problems without a calculator so that they are prepared for the test problems for which they cannot use a calculator.

Exploration Notes

Exploration 9-9a is a practice test that reviews the concepts of the chapter. This additional set of review problems can be worked on in small groups in class or as a take-home assignment.

Supplementary Problem

1. *Bingo Project:* In the game of Bingo, each player is given a card similar to the one shown in Figure 9-9a. The B-, I-, G-, and O-columns each contain five different integers. The N-column contains only four different integers, because the middle square is a "free space." In the B-column, the integers range from 1 to 15; in the I-column, they range from 16 to 30; in the N-column, they range from 31 to 46; in the G-column, they range from 46 to 60; and in the O-column, they range from 61 to 75.

Figure 9-9a

B	I	N	G	O
3	19	45	52	67
11	22	37	53	75
7	16		49	66
2	30	38	60	68
13	18	41	47	72

a. How many different groups of five integers could be in each of the B-, I-, G-, and O-columns? How many different groups of four integers could be in the N-column?

b. To reduce the possibility that two people win a game, no two cards should have the same group of integers in the same column. How many different cards meet this requirement?

c. To be *sure* that there are not two winners, no two cards should have the same group of integers in any of the five rows or on the two diagonals, as well as in the columns. How many different cards meet this requirement?

Cumulative Review, Chapters 7–9

Objective

Review the material in Chapters 7–9.

Class Time

1 or 2 days (work in class in groups)

Homework Assignment

Day 1: Problems 14–24

Day 2: Problem Set 10-1

Lesson Notes

The problems in this section constitute review of the topics studied in Chapters 7, 8, and 9. Students should use the class period to work in groups on the assignment. Whatever remains to be completed can be finished as a homework assignment.

There are many options at this point. You may want to wait and assign these problems when you are ready to prepare your students for a final exam. You may want to give a cumulative test on the material covered in these three chapters, for which these problems provide a review. Finally, you may want to assign these problems as a long-term assignment while continuing with topics in the book. You can collect the solutions and explanations to these problems and use that as an assessment of your students' learning.

Always encourage students to practice the no-calculator problems without a calculator so that they are prepared for test problems for which they cannot use a calculator.

Precalculus with Trigonometry: Instructor's Guide
© 2007 Key Curriculum Press

10 Three-Dimensional Vectors

This chapter starts a series of precalculus topics that continues to the end of the book. The topics are tied together as much as possible so that students can feel they are learning a unified body of material. The bonds that tie the topics together are mostly motivational rather than prerequisite. It is possible to select which chapters to include, as well as the sequence in which you present them, without risk of students being ill prepared.

Chapter 10 is a substantive study of three-dimensional vectors. After a brief presentation of two-dimensional vectors, students learn to extend the concept to vectors used to measure the position of points in space. Vector differences measure the change in position, and vector sums measure the effect of consecutive displacements. Dot products allow students to calculate the angle between two vectors and the projection of one vector onto another. The cross products allow students to find a vector perpendicular to two other vectors. The vector techniques enable students to find equations of lines and planes in space. Real-world applications include the forensic analysis of a bullet's path through the wall, ceiling, and roof of a house.

Throughout the chapter, the components format for vectors, $3\vec{i} + 4\vec{j} - 2\vec{k}$, is used rather than the ordered triple format, $(3, 4, -2)$. Although the ordered triple format saves time, using the components format helps students understand the concepts and techniques and ensures that they do not confuse vector notation and point notation.

10-1
Review of Two-Dimensional Vectors

Objective

Given two vectors, find the resultant vector by adding or subtracting them.

Class Time

$\frac{1}{2}$ day

Homework Assignment

Problems 1–8

Important Terms and Concepts

Resultant vector

Position vector

Unit vector

Scalar

Magnitude

Lesson Notes

If students have studied vectors in Chapter 6, this lesson is a review. You can assign this section for homework on the night of the Chapter 9 test. If not, this section may be used for students' introduction to vectors.

Alternatively, you can skip Sections 10-1 and 10-2, and start right away with three-dimensional vectors.

Problem Notes

Problem 3 asks students to visually demonstrate that a vector is the sum of its *x*-component and *y*-component. A blackline master for this problem is available in the *Instructor's Resource Book*.

10-2
Two-Dimensional Vector Practice

Objectives

- Given the components of a two-dimensional position vector, find its length, a unit vector in its direction, a scalar multiple of it, and its direction angle.

- Given two two-dimensional position vectors, find their sum and their difference.

Class Time

1 day

Homework Assignment

RA, Q1–Q10, Problems 1–15 odd, 16

Technology Options

 Activity: Right Triangle Trigonometry: Static Equilibrium

Important Terms and Concepts

Vector quantity

Scalar

Vector

Tail

Head

Magnitude, absolute value, length, $|\vec{v}|$

Unit vector

Equal vectors

Translate a vector

Opposite of a vector

Position vector

Displacement vector

Vector sum

Vector difference, vector subtraction

Triangle inequality

Lesson Notes

This lesson continues the review of two-dimensional vectors. It is important that students master the vocabulary and notation associated with vectors.

As in Chapter 6, emphasize that a vector has a magnitude and direction but not a specific location on the coordinate plane. The exceptions are position vectors, which start at the origin.

The text shows that the difference of two vectors is the vector from the head of the second to the head of the first when the vectors are placed tail-to-tail. You might give an example like this one to illustrate that $\vec{a} + \left(-\vec{b}\right)$ is the same vector as $\vec{a} - \vec{b}$.

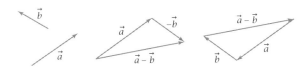

Example 1 shows vector addition graphically, and Example 2 shows vector subtraction graphically.

Part a of Example 2 finds the vector from one point to another. When discussing this part, it is helpful to emphasize finding "where it ends minus where it starts" or "head minus tail." In part b, the position vector of a point $\frac{3}{4}$ of the way from C to D is found. This requires these steps:

1. Find $\overrightarrow{CD}$, the vector from C to D. (This is done in part a.)

2. Find the vector in the same direction as $\overrightarrow{CD}$ but $\frac{3}{4}$ as long. (That is, multiply $\overrightarrow{CD}$ by $\frac{3}{4}$.)

3. Find the desired position vector by adding the vector from step 2 to $\vec{c}$, the position vector for point C.

Exploration Notes

Exploration 10-2a can be used as a guide for students as they read Section 10-2 on their own. You can start class by having students complete the Exploration and then review the results and discuss Examples 1 and 2 in the student text. Allow about 20 minutes for students to complete the Exploration.

Technology Notes

 Activity: Right Triangle Trigonometry: Static Equilibrium, in the *Instructor's Resource Book,* has students use trigonometry to add force vectors. Allow 45 minutes.

Problem Notes

- *Problems 1–4* ask students to demonstrate magnitude, the triangle inequality, vector addition, and vector subtraction on a copy of given vectors. A blackline master for these problems is available in the *Instructor's Resource Book.*

- *Problems 15 and 16* relate to the midpoint formula.

- *Problem 17,* part e, helps students understand that it is necessary to define a zero vector in order for the set of vectors to be closed under addition.

- *Problem 18,* the Triangle Inequality Problem, connects vector sums to the *triangle inequality* students learned in earlier mathematics courses.

10-3
Vectors in Space

Objectives

- Given two three-dimensional vectors, find their lengths, add them, subtract them, and use the results to analyze real-world problems.

- If a position vector terminates in the first octant, sketch it on graph paper.

Class Time

1 day

Homework Assignment

Recommended: RA, Q1–Q10, Problems 1–17 odd, 18

Also suggested: 19

Important Terms and Concepts

Octant

First octant

Unit vectors $\vec{i}, \vec{j}$, and $\vec{k}$

Three-dimensional Pythagorean theorem

Lesson Notes

Some students have a difficult time visualizing things in three dimensions. If possible, designate the front left corner on the floor of your classroom as the origin. Have your students tape index cards marking the origin; the x-, y-, and z-axes; and the unit vectors $\vec{i}, \vec{j}$, and $\vec{k}$. Then rig up a five-foot-long "position vector." Have students estimate the coordinates of the head and tape an index card to the vector indicating its equation. Next, have them compute the magnitude and tape another card to the vector. As you go further in the chapter, have students tape up cards corresponding to the new concepts.

Do not expect students to draw vectors to scale. For most problems in this chapter, a rough sketch is adequate.

Example 1 leads students through the process of drawing a three-dimensional vector in the first octant. When you discuss the example, draw the box, minus the grid, and label its eight corners with letters, using a capital O for the origin. Ask students to find the coordinates of eight corners. As a follow-up, have students trace Figure 10-3a (the helicopter) in the student text and then draw and label the vertices of "the box."

Example 1 also asks students to use the three-dimensional Pythagorean theorem to find the length of the vector. Students may have learned the theorem in geometry. You might ask them if they remember how to prove it. (See Problem 18.)

Examples 2 and 3 extend to three dimensions the displacement vector and position vector concepts learned in the previous section.

Exploration Notes

Exploration 10-3a provides a good introduction to three-dimensional vectors. It can be used as practice similar to the three examples in the section. You can use this activity as an assessment tool to see how well your students are handling the transition from two-dimensional vectors to three-dimensional vectors. Allow about 20 minutes for students to complete the Exploration.

Problem Notes

- *Problems 1–6* are for practicing drawing three-dimensional vectors and doing operations on vectors.

- *Problems 7–10* are like Example 2.

- *Problems 11, 12, and 17* are applications of Example 3.

- *Problems 13–16* provide more practice with position vectors and vector operations.

- *Problem 18*, the Three-Dimensional Distances Problem, asks students to prove the three-dimensional Pythagorean theorem by applying the two-dimensional Pythagorean theorem twice.

- *Problem 19*, the Four-Dimensional Vector Problem, uses ordered quadruple notation and extends vectors to four-dimensional space.

10-4
Scalar Products and Projections of Vectors

Objective

Given two vectors, find their dot product. Use the result to find the angle between the vectors and the projection of one vector on the other.

Class Time

2 days

Homework Assignment

Day 1: RA, Q1–Q10, Problems 1–17 odd

Day 2: Problems 20, 21, 23–25, 27, 29–31

Technology Options

 Problem 21: Dynamic Vector Projection Problem

 Presentation Sketch: Vector Operations Present.gsp

 Activity: Vector Operations

Important Terms and Concepts

Dot product

Scalar product

Inner product

Finding the angle between two vectors

Vector projection of $\vec{a}$ on $\vec{b}$

Scalar projection of $\vec{a}$ on $\vec{b}$

Lesson Notes

In this section, students learn to find the dot product of two vectors. They use the dot product to find the angle between the vectors and the projection of one vector on another. Students need to have a solid understanding of vector and scalar projection for some of the later sections in this chapter. It is recommended that you spend two days on this section. On the first day, cover the text through Example 2. Cover the remaining material on the second day.

The dot product $\vec{a} \cdot \vec{b}$ should be read "$\vec{a}$ *dot* $\vec{b}$," not "$\vec{a}$ *times* $\vec{b}$." Emphasize that $\vec{a} \cdot \vec{b}$ is a scalar, not a vector. For this reason, it is often called the *scalar product.*

Students should learn to distinguish between the *definition* of dot product, $|\vec{a}||\vec{b}| \cos \theta$, and the *technique* for calculating it, $x_1 x_2 + y_1 y_2 + z_1 z_2$. The derivation of the technique in "array" format shown in the Technique box before Example 1 reveals the reason for the name *inner product.*

Example 1 shows how to find the dot product of two vectors, and Example 2 shows how the dot product can be used to calculate the angle between two vectors.

The student text then discusses *vector projection* and *scalar projection.* The text suggests an intuitive way to visualize the vector projection of $\vec{a}$ on $\vec{b}$: Place $\vec{a}$ and $\vec{b}$ tail-to-tail. Imagine that the sun is above $\vec{a}$, shining so the light rays are perpendicular to $\vec{b}$. The vector projection is the shadow cast by $\vec{a}$ on $\vec{b}$ (or on the line containing $\vec{b}$), and the scalar projection is ±(the length of the shadow). You may want to use a flashlight and Popsicle sticks or metersticks to illustrate this idea.

Example 3 finds the vector projection of $\vec{a}$ on $\vec{b}$, where $\vec{b}$ is given as a sum of components and $\vec{a}$ is given in terms of its length and the angle it forms with $\vec{b}$. The solution involves these steps:

1. Find the unit vector $\vec{u}$ in the direction of $\vec{b}$.

2. Find $|\vec{a}| \cos \theta$, the length of the projection of $\vec{a}$ on $\vec{b}$.

3. Multiply $\vec{u}$ by the length of the projection.

These ideas are summarized in the Definition box at the end of Example 3.

Example 4 gives two vectors in terms of their components and asks for the scalar projection and vector projection of one vector on the other. Before the definitions can be applied, you must use the dot product to find the angle between the vectors.

As you present vector and scalar projection in class, you may want to derive and incorporate the formulas found in Problem 24, which provide a shortcut to calculating scalar and vector projections without finding the angle between the vectors.

Exploration Notes

Exploration 10-4a can be used as the basis for your class discussion on dot product. Or consider assigning this Exploration at the end of the first day of instruction so that students will be comfortable with the mechanical aspects of dot product and be prepared for their homework assignment. Allow 15–20 minutes for students to complete this activity.

Exploration 10-4b guides students through the steps of finding vector and scalar projections. You can assign this activity at the beginning of the second day of instruction, following it with a discussion of the results and of Examples 3 and 4 in the student text. Or you can assign the activity as a review *after* discussing Examples 3 and 4. Allow 15–20 minutes for students to complete this activity.

Exploration 10-4c recaps and reinforces vector properties taught up to this point. You can use this Exploration as part of the homework assignment. Students can then use what they've learned to update their journals.

Technology Notes

 Problem 21: The Dynamic Vector Projection Problem asks students to use a Dynamic Precalculus Exploration at *www.keymath.com/ precalc* to explore vector projections and dot products with an interactive sketch.

 Presentation Sketch: Vector Operations Present.gsp, on the *Instructor's Resource CD,* visually demonstrates vector projection. Students can see how the projected vector is affected by changes in either the magnitude or the direction of the original vector. This sketch is related to the Vector Operations activity.

 Activity: Vector Operations, in the *Instructor's Resource Book,* has students use a prepared sketch to investigate dot products and vector projections. Allow 30–40 minutes.

Problem Notes

- *Problems 1–6* involve finding dot products using the definition.

- *Problems 7–12* involve using the definition of dot product to find the angle between two vectors.

- *Problems 13–18* involve finding the dot product of two vectors by using the technique of multiplying coefficients and adding and then using the definition of dot product to find the angle between vectors.

- *Problem 20* is a good applied vector problem. When discussing this problem in class, you may want to sketch in the first floor of the house in the $(+, +, -)$ octant and put letters on the vertices.

- *Problem 21,* the Dynamic Vector Projection Problem, gives students a chance to develop a more visual understanding of vector projection.

- *Problems 22 and 23* are similar to Example 3.

- *Problem 24* is a must. It simplifies the techniques for computing scalar and vector projections. Students frequently mix up scalars and vectors,

so remind them that in the formula $p = \dfrac{\vec{a} \cdot \vec{b}}{|\vec{b}|}$, p is a scalar (a number), as are $\vec{a} \cdot \vec{b}$ and $|\vec{b}|$. Likewise, in the formula $\vec{p} = \dfrac{\vec{a} \cdot \vec{b}}{|\vec{b}|^2}\,\vec{b}$, $\vec{p}$ and $\vec{b}$ are vectors and the coefficient of $\vec{b}$ is a scalar.

- *Problems 26–29* are similar to Example 4. Students can use the techniques from that example or the formulas given in Problem 24.

- *Problem 30* is a good opportunity to strengthen your students' spatial visualization skills.

Supplementary Problems

1. *Staircase Problem:* The staircase in a new house is to go from the point $G(30, 20, 0)$ on the ground floor to the point $U(40, 15, 11)$ upstairs. The origin of the coordinate system is at a bottom corner of the house, and the dimensions are in feet.

   a. Write the displacement vector $\vec{d}$ from G to U.

   b. How long will the staircase be? That is, what is the distance from G to U?

   c. Find the vector projection of $\vec{d}$ on the ground floor.

   d. How steep will the staircase be? That is, what angle will $\vec{d}$ make with the floor?

2. *Work Problem:* The work done by a force in moving an object from one place to another is defined to be the force times the displacement. If the force and displacement are in the same direction, such as 30 pounds moving an object 10 feet, the work is simply the product, 300 foot-pounds. If the force and displacement are in different directions, the work done is the scalar projection of the force vector on the displacement vector. Suppose that force $\vec{F}$ and displacement $\vec{S}$ are

   $$\vec{F} = 20\vec{i} + 15\vec{j} - 3\vec{k} \text{ (in pounds)}$$
   $$\vec{S} = 4\vec{i} + 3\vec{j} + 7\vec{k} \text{ (in feet)}$$

   a. What angle do the force and displacement make with each other?

   b. How much work is done by the force?

   c. Find the magnitudes of the force and displacement vectors.

   d. How much work would be done by the force if it had acted in the same direction as the displacement?

3. *Satellite Acceleration Problem:* Figure 10-4a shows a satellite in an elliptical orbit around Earth. The velocity vector, $\vec{v}$, acts in the direction of motion,

along a tangent to the ellipse. The acceleration vector, $\vec{a}$, acts in the direction of Earth.

Figure 10-4a

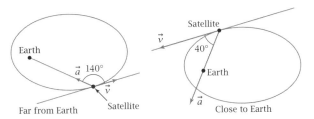

Earth   Satellite $\vec{v}$ 40°
$\vec{a}$ 140°   Earth
$\vec{v}$ $\vec{a}$
Far from Earth   Satellite   Close to Earth

a. At a particular time when the satellite is far from Earth, the velocity vector has a magnitude of 10,000 mi/h and the acceleration vector has a magnitude of 90 (mi/h)/min. The angle between the two vectors is 140°. Sketch the vector projection of the acceleration vector on the velocity vector.

b. The vector projection of acceleration on velocity is the component of acceleration in the direction of motion. This component speeds up or slows down the satellite. Calculate the magnitude of this component at the time in part a. That is, calculate the scalar projection of acceleration on velocity.

c. At the time in part b, is the satellite speeding up or slowing down? What numerical evidence do you have to support your answer?

d. Later, when the satellite is close to Earth, the velocity has a magnitude of 20,000 mi/h, the acceleration has a magnitude of 360 (mi/h)/min, and the angle between the two vectors is 40°. Is the satellite speeding up or slowing down at this time? At what rate?

4. *Dot Product Distributes Over Vector Addition Problem:* Figure 10-4b shows vectors $\vec{a}$, $\vec{b}$, $\vec{c}$, and $(\vec{b} + \vec{c})$. From the figure, explain why the scalar projection of $(\vec{b} + \vec{c})$ on $\vec{a}$ equals the sum of the scalar projections of $\vec{b}$ on $\vec{a}$ and $\vec{c}$ on $\vec{a}$. From this fact, prove that dot product distributes over vector addition. That is, prove that

$$\vec{a} \cdot (\vec{b} + \vec{c}) = \vec{a} \cdot \vec{b} + \vec{a} \cdot \vec{c}$$

Figure 10-4b

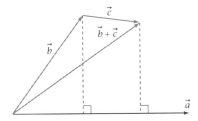

$\vec{c}$
$\vec{b} + \vec{c}$
$\vec{b}$
$\vec{a}$

10-5
Planes in Space

Objective

Given a point on a plane and a vector perpendicular to the plane, find the particular equation of the plane and use it to find other points on the plane.

Class Time

1 day (2 days if you cover the supplementary topic of dihedral angles)

Homework Assignment

RA, Q1–Q10, Problems 1–15 odd

(If dihedral angles are covered, assign Problem 12 and Supplementary Problems 7–13 on Day 2.)

Important Terms and Concepts

Normal vector

Equation of a plane in space

x-, y-, and z-intercepts of a plane

Dihedral angle

Lesson Notes

In this section, students learn to find the equation of a plane given a point on the plane and a vector perpendicular to the plane. The placement of this topic lets the concept of dot product "soak in" before cross products are introduced in the next section.

Use Exploration 10-5a to introduce the topic of planes and their equations. Point out that the graph of the two-variable equation $3x + 5y = 30$ is a one-dimensional line in a two-dimensional plane. Then explain that the graph of the three-variable equation $3x + 5y + 10z = 30$ is a *two*-dimensional plane in *three*-dimensional space. You can easily sketch a "triangular" portion of the plane in the first octant by plotting the x-intercept at 10, the y-intercept at 6, and the z-intercept at 3 and then connecting these points (Figure 10-5a).

Figure 10-5a

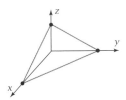

z
y
x

(*Note:* In *three*-dimensional space, the equation $3x + 5y = 30$ represents a plane. Because the coefficient of z is 0, z may assume any value. This plane has x-intercept 10 and y-intercept 6 and is parallel to the z-axis. It stands up "straight" and goes up and down forever.)

If you set up a coordinate system in your classroom in Section 10-3, you can create planes using sheets of oak tag.

Just as a line in two dimensions is uniquely determined by a slope and a point on the line, a plane in three dimensions is uniquely determined by a normal vector and a point on the plane. To demonstrate this, you can use a piece of paper to represent a plane and a pencil to represent the normal vector. Stick the pencil through the paper. Then slide the paper along the pencil, perpendicular to the pencil, to show that there are many planes with the same normal vector. To get a unique plane, we must also specify one point on the plane. When students understand this, move on to the explanation in the text about finding the equation of a plane.

Make sure students see that the coefficients of x, y, and z in the equation of the plane are the same as the coefficients of $\vec{i}, \vec{j}$, and $\vec{k}$ in the equation of the normal vector.

Example 1 shows how to find the equation of a plane given a normal vector and a point on the plane.

Example 2 shows how to find the normal vector to a plane based on the equation of the plane. The solution gives the vector $\vec{n} = 7\vec{i} - 3\vec{j} + 8\vec{k}$, which has coefficients equal to the coefficients of x, y, and z but also points out that any multiple of this vector is also a normal vector.

Example 3 does not give the normal vector or a point on the plane directly. Students must use what they learned in previous sections to find a vector between two points and to find a point 30% of the way from one point to the other.

Example 4 shows how to find a missing coordinate of a point on a plane given the equation of the plane.

Exploration Notes

Exploration 10-5a provides guided discovery for finding the Cartesian equation of a plane given a point on the plane and a vector normal to the plane. You might assign this activity after reviewing the examples in the student text. Allow about 20 minutes for students to complete the Exploration.

Supplementary Lesson Notes

Figure 10-5b shows two intersecting planes. The angle between the planes is called a **dihedral angle.** The prefix *di-* means "two" and the suffix *-hedra* means "faces."

Figure 10-5b

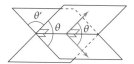

DEFINITION: Dihedral Angle

The dihedral angle between two planes is the angle whose sides lie in the planes and are perpendicular to the line of intersection of the planes.

As Figure 10-5b shows, there are two possible dihedral angles, the acute angle θ and the obtuse angle θ'. Figure 10-5b also shows vectors in the two planes, each perpendicular to the line of intersection, making an angle θ with each other. If these two vectors are rotated 90° with respect to the line of intersection, they become normal vectors to the respective planes. Thus the dihedral angle between two planes is the same as the angle between the normal vectors. Using a manila file folder and sticking pencils through it at a perpendicular will help students see that the dihedral angle is the same as the angle formed by the normal vectors. Alternately, this is shown in Figure 10-5c. Imagine being able to view two intersecting planes, Plane 1 and Plane 2, from a perspective so that you see only the "edges" of the planes. Two normal vectors, $\vec{n}_1$ and $\vec{n}_2$, are drawn to the planes.

Figure 10-5c

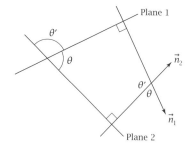

EXAMPLE 5

Find the measures of the two possible dihedral angles between these planes:

Plane 1: $4x + 7y + 13z = -71$

Plane 2: $3x - 5y + 2z = 39$

Solution

Write the normal vectors and find the angle between them.

$$\vec{n_1} = 4\vec{i} + 7\vec{j} + 13\vec{k}$$

$$\vec{n_2} = 3\vec{i} - 5\vec{j} + 2\vec{k}$$

$$|\vec{n_1}| = \sqrt{4^2 + 7^2 + 13^2} = \sqrt{231}$$

$$|\vec{n_2}| = \sqrt{3^2 + 5^2 + 2^2} = \sqrt{38}$$

$$\vec{n_1} \cdot \vec{n_2} = (4)(3) + (7)(-5) + (13)(2) = 3$$

$$\therefore \cos\theta = \frac{3}{\sqrt{231}\,\sqrt{38}} = 0.0320\ldots$$

$$\theta = 88.1650\ldots°$$

$$\theta' = 180° - 88.1650\ldots° = 91.8349\ldots°$$

This box contains a summary of the technique for finding the measure of a dihedral angle.

TECHNIQUE: Computation of Dihedral Angle

To find the measure of the dihedral angle between two planes, find the angle between their normal vectors. This angle and its supplement are measures of the two possible dihedral angles.

Problem Notes

Problem 12, the Roof Valley Problem, helps reinforce spatial visualization skills.

Supplementary Problems

In Problems 1–4, write the equation of a plane with the stated properties.

1. Perpendicular to $\vec{n} = 6\vec{i} + 7\vec{j} - 4\vec{k}$, containing the point $(-2, 8, 17)$.

2. Perpendicular to $\vec{n} = 4\vec{i} - 2\vec{j} + 3\vec{k}$, containing the point $(5, 1, -4)$.

3. Perpendicular to the line segment connecting $(5, 17, 1)$ and $(26, 2, 13)$ and passing through the point $\frac{1}{3}$ of the way from the first point to the second point.

4. Perpendicular to $\vec{n} = \vec{i} - 3\vec{j} + \vec{k}$ and having a z-intercept of -2. (The **z-intercept of a plane** is the value of z when the other two variables are zero.)

5. Find the value of B that makes these two planes perpendicular.

$$2x + By - 5z = 20$$

$$x - y + 2z = 1$$

6. *Attic Problem:* Figure 10-5d shows a triangular room inside the attic of a house. The plane of the roof has the equation $4x + 5y - 6z = -60$ with all measurements in feet.

Figure 10-5d

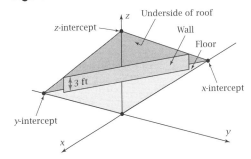

a. Find the three intercepts of the plane of the roof. Explain why your answers are consistent with Figure 10-5d.

b. A wall 3 ft high is to be constructed touching the floor and the underside of the roof. How long is the line segment where the wall and roof intersect?

For Problems 7–13, find the measure of the acute dihedral angle between the two planes.

7. $3x + 2y - 5z = -11$

   $4x + 7y + z = 8$

8. $2x - 7y + 3z = -9$

   $5x + 2y + 8z = -6$

9. $4x - 3y + 2z = 13$

   $x + 5y + 3z = 9$

10. $-2x + 8y - 7z = -1$

    $6x - 3y - 2z = -100$

11. $6x - 7y + 3z = -5$

    the *xy*-plane (the plane for which $z = 0$)

12. $3x + 4y - 2z = -10$

    the *yz*-plane (the plane for which $x = 0$)

13. Draw a sketch showing two intersecting planes in space. Indicate the acute dihedral angle. Show also the two normal vectors. Use your sketch to show why the angle between the normal vectors equals the dihedral angle or its supplement.

Vector Product of Two Vectors

Objective

Be able to calculate cross products of two vectors and use cross products for geometrical computations.

Class Time

2 days

Homework Assignment

Day 1: RA, Q1–Q10, Problems 1–11 odd

Day 2: Problems 13–19, 21–23 odd

Technology Options

 Presentation Sketch: Vector Operations 3D Present.gsp

 Calculator Program: VCROSS

 Calculator Program: PYTHQUAD

 Activity: Vector Operations in Three Dimensions

Important Terms and Concepts

Cross product, $\vec{a} \times \vec{b}$

Finding areas with cross product

Vector product

Outer product

Right-hand rule

Right-handed coordinate system

Determinant

Torque

Pythagorean quadruple

Lesson Notes

In Section 10–4, students learned about the first type of vector product, the dot product. In this section, students learn about the second type, the cross product.

The notation for the cross product of $\vec{a}$ and $\vec{b}$ is $\vec{a} \times \vec{b}$, read "$\vec{a}$ cross $\vec{b}$," *not* "$\vec{a}$ times $\vec{b}$." Emphasize that the cross product is a vector, whereas the dot product is a scalar. The cross product of $\vec{a}$ and $\vec{b}$ is perpendicular to both vectors, has magnitude $|\vec{a}| \, |\vec{b}| \sin \theta$, and points in a direction determined by

the *right-hand rule* described in the text. Point out that because the cross product is perpendicular to both vectors, it is *normal* to the plane containing the two vectors.

The right-hand rule may be clearer to students if you tell them to put their right elbow at the tail of $\vec{a}$ and their right forearm along vector $\vec{a}$ and then to curl their fingers as described in the student text. You can also make a mock-up of three vectors by taping unbent paper clips to the eraser ends of three pencils. Two of the pencils represent $\vec{a}$ and $\vec{b}$. The third, perpendicular to the other two, represents $\vec{a} \times \vec{b}$. Once students understand the right-hand rule, have them get into pairs. With their books closed, ask each pair to come up with the nine cross products of the unit coordinate vectors.

Example 1 shows how to use the cross products of the unit coordinate vectors to compute the cross product of any two vectors. The method will probably seem tedious to students. Explain that using *determinants* makes calculating cross products much easier.

Students who have not seen determinants before will need some background on how to expand a determinant. (See Chapter 11 for a review of matrices.) The technique can be mastered quickly. Use an example with positive elements such as this one, and expand along the top row:

$$\begin{vmatrix} 4 & 8 & 1 \\ 3 & 5 & 7 \\ 11 & 2 & 13 \end{vmatrix} = 4\begin{vmatrix} 5 & 7 \\ 2 & 13 \end{vmatrix} - 8\begin{vmatrix} 3 & 7 \\ 11 & 13 \end{vmatrix} + 1\begin{vmatrix} 3 & 5 \\ 11 & 2 \end{vmatrix}$$

$$= 4(5 \cdot 13 - 7 \cdot 2) - 8(3 \cdot 13 - 7 \cdot 11) + 1(3 \cdot 2 - 5.11)$$

$$= 204 + 304 - 49$$

$$= 459$$

If a clever student argues that a calculator evaluates 3×3 determinants more quickly and accurately, explain that once we replace the top row with $\vec{i}, \vec{j}$, and $\vec{k}$, we will need to evaluate determinants by hand. (In Problem 7, students will write a grapher program for calculating cross products.)

After you have introduced determinants, use the determinant method to compute the cross product in Example 1.

Example 2 shows how to find the equation of a plane given three points in the plane. The solution involves these steps:

1. Find displacement vectors from one of the points to each of the other points.

2. Find the cross product of the two displacement vectors. The cross product is *perpendicular* to *both* vectors and so is *normal* to the plane.

3. Using the cross product as the normal vector and one of the three given points, find the equation of the plane.

The student text then shows that the magnitude of the cross product of $\vec{a}$ and $\vec{b}$ is equal to the area of the parallelogram with $\vec{a}$ and $\vec{b}$ as adjacent sides. The area of a triangle with $\vec{a}$ and $\vec{b}$ as sides is equal to half the magnitude of the cross product. Example 3 shows how this idea can be used to compute the area of a triangle given the coordinates of its vertices.

The remaining sections of this chapter are optional. If you plan to continue in this chapter, you may wish to give a quiz covering the material from Section 10-1 through Section 10-6. Exploration 10-6c provides an excellent review of these sections.

Exploration Notes

Exploration 10-6a is a discovery activity using the vectors from Example 1. It shows the meaning of cross product and methods for computing the cross product. You can assign this Exploration before you demonstrate Example 1, or you can assign it after the example to help students summarize what they've learned. The activity will take about 25–30 minutes if it is used as a discovery exercise and about 20 minutes if it is used as a summarizing tool.

Exploration 10-6b recaps the uses and methods of the dot product and cross product. It provides a good review and will help your students see when it is appropriate to use each type of product. You can use this Exploration as a review sheet or assign it as homework. This activity will take students about 20 minutes to complete.

Exploration 10-6c provides a review of the first six sections. If you are going to continue through the rest of the chapter, you may want to save this activity for later as part of your overall review.

Technology Notes

 Presentation Sketch: Vector Operations 3D Present.gsp, on the *Instructor's Resource CD*, visually demonstrates cross products of three-dimensional vectors as well as colinearity and coplanarity of points in three dimensions. This sketch is related to the activity Vector Operations in Three Dimensions.

 Calculator Program: VCROSS calculates the cross product of two vectors, as asked for in Problem 7. The program is available on the *Instructor's Resource CD* and at *www.keymath.com/precalc* for download onto a TI-83 or TI-84 graphing calculator. It also appears in the *Instructor's Resource Book* for students to enter by hand.

 Calculator Program: PYTHQUAD displays all quadruples of integer values of *x*, *y*, *z*, and *r* satisfying the equation $x^2 + y^2 + z^2 = r^2$, as asked for in Problem 24. The program is available on the *Instructor's Resource CD* and at *www.keymath.com/precalc* for download onto a TI-83 or TI-84 graphing calculator. It also appears in the *Instructor's Resource Book* for students to enter by hand.

 Activity: Vector Operations in Three Dimensions, in *Exploring Precalculus with The Geometer's Sketchpad,* has students use a prepared sketch to investigate cross products and three-dimensional vector properties. Allow 40–50 minutes.

Problem Notes

- *Problem 18,* the Torque Problem, shows a reason why cross product is defined the way it is. Torque, angular velocity, and so on are defined to be vectors along the axis of a rotating object, caused by vectors acting perpendicular to the axis.

- *Problem 19* involves calculating angles between vectors. It is important to stress that cross product should *not* be used to find the angle between two vectors. The dot product formula should be used instead. The reason is that for a given value of sin θ, there may be two possible angles between 0° and 180°, whereas there is only one possible angle between 0° and 180° for a given value of cos θ. To help students understand this, you can assign Supplementary Problem 3.

Supplementary Problems

In Problems 1 and 2, find the indicated cross products.

1. $(4\vec{j} + 3\vec{k}) \times (5\vec{i} - 6\vec{k})$

2. $(8\vec{i}) \times (5\vec{j})$

3. *Cross Product for Angles Problem:* You have found the angle between two vectors by finding the dot product. It is also possible to find the angle using the cross product.
   a. Let $\vec{a} = 3\vec{i} + 5\vec{j} + 4\vec{k}$ and let $\vec{b} = 2\vec{i} + 7\vec{j} + 6\vec{k}$. Find the cross product $\vec{a} \times \vec{b}$. Use the fact

that $|\vec{a} \times \vec{b}| = |\vec{a}| \, |\vec{b}| \sin \theta$ to find the angle between the two vectors. Then find the angle again using the dot product as you have done before. Show that you get the same answer both ways.

b. Let $\vec{c} = \vec{i} + 4\vec{j} - 8\vec{k}$ and let $\vec{d} = 2\vec{i} + 6\vec{j} + 9\vec{k}$. Find the angle between the vectors using the cross product as in part a. Find it again using the dot product as you have done before. Show that the two answers are *not* the same!

c. Explain why the answers to part b are not the same. Then tell why it is dangerous to use the cross product to find the angle between two vectors.

4. *Commuting Products of Vectors Problem:*

a. Explain why scalar multiplication of two vectors is a commutative operation, whereas vector multiplication is not.

b. Prove that $\vec{v} \times \vec{u} = -\vec{u} \times \vec{v}$.

In Problems 5 and 6, find a particular equation of the plane described.

5. Containing (2, 0, 8), (4, 3, 0), and (7, 5, 1)

6. Containing (3, 5, −1) and normal to the line of intersection of the planes $-2x + 7y + 3z = -11$ and $4x - 2y - 6z = -9$

7. Given $\vec{c} = 9\vec{i} - 6\vec{j} + 2\vec{k}$ and $\vec{d} = 8\vec{i} + \vec{j} - 4\vec{k}$,

a. Find $\vec{c} \times \vec{d}$.

b. Use dot products to show that $\vec{c} \times \vec{d}$ really is normal to both $\vec{c}$ and $\vec{d}$.

c. Calculate $\vec{c} \cdot \vec{d}$, and use it to find the angle θ between $\vec{c}$ and $\vec{d}$.

d. Use θ from part c to show that $|\vec{c} \times \vec{d}| = |\vec{c}| \, |\vec{d}| \sin \theta$.

10-7
Direction Angles and Direction Cosines

Objective

Given a vector, find its direction angles and direction cosines, and vice versa.

Class Time

1 day

Homework Assignment

RA, Q1–Q10, Problems 1–23 odd, 24

Important Terms and Concepts

Direction angles

Direction cosines

Pythagorean property of direction cosines

Unit vector property of direction cosines

Azimuth angle

Lesson Notes

From this point on in this chapter, the topics are optional. You must decide whether or not to include them based on your curriculum, the future courses your students will take, and the amount of time you have remaining in the school year.

In this section, students learn to find the direction angles and direction cosines of a vector. The direction angles are the angles the vector makes with the three coordinate axes. The letters α, β, and γ are used to represent the angles a vector forms with the x-, y-, and z-axes, respectively. If you constructed a model of a vector in your classroom earlier in this chapter, you can use it to illustrate the direction angles.

Example 1 uses dot products to find the direction angles for a vector. Ask students if there is anything special about the values of α, β, and γ. There doesn't appear to be. Then ask them if there is anything remarkable about the sum of the values. Again there doesn't appear to be. Finally, ask them about the sum $\cos^2 \alpha + \cos^2 \beta + \cos^2 \gamma$. Most students will be surprised to find that $\cos^2 \alpha + \cos^2 \beta + \cos^2 \gamma = 1$! This is true for any vector.

The Pythagorean property, $\cos^2 \alpha + \cos^2 \beta + \cos^2 \gamma = 1$, is a generalization of the familiar Pythagorean property for trigonometric functions, $\cos^2 \alpha + \sin^2 \alpha = 1$. In two dimensions, the direction angles α and β are *complementary*, so $\cos^2 \alpha + \cos^2 \beta = 1$. This can be rewritten as $\cos^2 \alpha + \cos^2 (90° - \alpha) = 1$, or $\cos^2 \alpha + \sin^2 \alpha = 1$.

Example 2 uses the Pythagorean property of direction cosines to find the direction angles of a vector more efficiently.

Example 3 illustrates that when two direction angles are given, there are two possibilities for the third angle. The two possible angles are supplements of one another.

Exploration Notes

Exploration 10-7a models the three examples in this section. You might begin class by having students work on this Exploration in groups and then have a class discussion summarizing the results. Or you might assign the Exploration at the end of class as a way of summarizing this section. Allow students about 20–25 minutes to complete this activity.

Problem Notes

Problem 22, the Shoe Box Construction Project, can be used as a group exercise or assigned as an extra-credit project.

Supplementary Problems

Problems 1–3 will prepare your students for the next section.

1. If $P_0 = (2, 5, 7)$ and $P_1 = (14, 20, 23)$,
    a. Find the direction cosines of $\overrightarrow{P_0P_1}$.
    b. Find a vector in the direction of $\overrightarrow{P_0P_1}$ that is
        i.   1 unit long
        ii. 75 units long
        iii. *d* units long

2. If $P_0 = (7, 8, 3)$ and $P_1 = (27, 17, 15)$,
    a. Find the direction cosines of $\overrightarrow{P_0P_1}$.
    b. Find a vector in the direction of $\overrightarrow{P_0P_1}$ that is
        i.   1 unit long
        ii. 75 units long
        iii. *d* units long

3. Prove that if $P_0(x_0, y_0, z_0)$ is a fixed point on a line, $P(x, y, z)$ is any other point on that line, and *d* is the directed distance from P_0 to P, then the direction cosines of vector $\overrightarrow{P_0P_1}$ are

$$c_1 = \frac{x - x_0}{d}, \quad c_2 = \frac{y - y_0}{d}, \quad \text{and} \quad c_3 = \frac{z - z_0}{d}$$

10-8
Vector Equations of Lines in Space

Objective

Given information about a line in space, find a vector equation of the line and use it to calculate coordinates of points on the line.

Class Time

1 or 2 days

Homework Assignment

RA, Q1–Q10, Problems 1–15 odd

Technology Options

 Activity: Parametric Functions in Three Dimensions

Important Terms and Concepts

Vector equation of a line

Parameter

Lesson Notes

If you set a rapid pace in this chapter, you may wish to pause and spend two days on this section. Consider assigning Exploration 10-8c and the Supplementary Problems to increase student understanding and comfort.

The general vector equation of a line is $\vec{r} = \overrightarrow{P_0} + d\vec{u}$, where $\overrightarrow{P_0}$ is the position vector to a fixed point P_0 on the line, $\vec{u}$ is a unit vector parallel to the line, and *d* is a *parameter* equal to the directed distance from P_0 to a point on the line. It is important to emphasize that for each value of *d*, $\vec{r}$ is a *position vector to a point on the line*. To demonstrate this, use a copy of Figure 10-8b in the student text. Locate points that the position vector $\vec{r}$ points to for different values of *d*, say, $d = 1, 2, 0, -1,$ and -2. By looking at the set of points traced by the position vector as *d* changes, students will better understand how the vector equation relates to the line.

Example 1 demonstrates how to find the vector equation of a line if you are given a fixed point on a line (P_0) and a unit vector in the direction of the line ($\vec{u}$).

Example 2 uses the fact that *d* is the directed distance from P_0 to find a point on the line from Example 1 that is -21 units from P_0.

Example 3 shows how to find the point where the line from Example 1 intersects the *xy*-plane. The solution uses the fact that the *z*-coordinate of a point on the *xy*-plane is 0. Make sure students can explain why this is true.

Example 4 shows how to find the point where a line intersects a given plane. The solution uses this reasoning:

1. The coefficients of the vector equation represent coordinates of points on the line. So any point on the line has coordinates of the form

$$\left(5 + \frac{6}{11}d,\ 3 - \frac{2}{11}d,\ -1 + \frac{9}{11}d\right)$$

2. Any point on the plane has coordinates that satisfy the equation of the plane, $7x + 4y - 2z = 39$.

3. For a point $(5 + \frac{6}{11}d, 3 - \frac{2}{11}d, -1 + \frac{9}{11}d)$ on the line to also be on the plane, it must satisfy the equation of the plane. That is,

$$7\left(5 + \frac{6}{11}d\right) + 4\left(3 - \frac{2}{11}d\right) - 2\left(-1 + \frac{9}{11}d\right) = 39$$

Make sure students understand these ideas.

You may also want to show students *parametric equations* of a line. These are simply the three equations for the components of $\vec{r}$:

$$x = x_0 + c_1 d$$

$$y = y_0 + c_2 d$$

$$z = z_0 + c_3 d$$

where (x, y, z) are the coordinates of the variable point P; (x_0, y_0, z_0) are the coordinates of the fixed point P_0; c_1, c_2, and c_3 are the direction cosines; and d is the parameter. When you solve the parametric equations for d and set the results equal to one another, you get the *standard equation* of a line in space:

$$\frac{x - x_0}{c_1} = \frac{y - y_0}{c_2} = \frac{z - z_0}{c_3}$$

The Supplementary Problems and Exploration 10-8c involve parametric and standard equations of lines. Many students find the parametric equations and the standard equation of a line in space conceptually easier than the vector equation of a line. These two forms contribute to students' understanding of the vector equation.

Exploration Notes

Exploration 10-8a duplicates the processes in Examples 1–3 for writing vector equations of lines in space. You can use this Exploration in place of the examples or as a review sheet. Allow students about 20 minutes to complete the activity.

Exploration 10-8b provides a guided example of finding the point of intersection of a line and a plane. Unlike Example 4, the Exploration requires students to find the equation of the plane given three points on the plane. You can use this Exploration as additional homework or as a review sheet. Allow students about 20 minutes to complete the activity.

Exploration 10-8c develops the parametric equations and the standard, or symmetric, equation of a line in space. You can assign this activity for extra credit or as additional homework. Allow students about 20 minutes to complete the activity.

Technology Notes

 Activity: Parametric Functions in Three Dimensions, in *Exploring Precalculus with The Geometer's Sketchpad,* has students use Sketchpad to find parametric equations of a line, a helix, and a conic spiral. You could limit students' attention to just the line. This activity may also be saved for use in Chapter 12. Allow 30–50 minutes for the full activity.

Supplementary Problems

1. *Direction Numbers and Equations of Lines Problem:* The coefficients of a vector are sometimes called *direction numbers.* For instance, the vector $\vec{v} = 2\vec{i} + 5\vec{j} + 8\vec{k}$ has direction numbers 2, 5, and 8. The direction cosines of $\vec{v}$ are the direction numbers divided by the length of the vector. Because in this case $|\vec{v}| = \sqrt{93}$, the direction cosines are

$$c_1 = \frac{2}{\sqrt{93}} \qquad c_2 = \frac{5}{\sqrt{93}} \qquad c_3 = \frac{8}{\sqrt{93}}$$

Because direction cosines are often fractions with radicals, it is in some ways simpler to write the equation of a line in space using the direction numbers instead of the direction cosines. If a line parallel to $\vec{v}$ contains the point (6, 1, 4), its vector equation could be written

$$\vec{r} = (6 + 2t)\vec{i} + (1 + 5t)\vec{j} + (4 + 8t)\vec{k}$$

The variable t is used in place of d because the parameter is no longer the distance from the fixed point to the variable point. (It is the number of vector lengths from the fixed point.)

a. Find the value of t for the point on this line for which $x = 100$.

b. Find the coordinates of the point on this line for which $x = 100$.

c. Find the point where the line pierces the xz-plane.

d. Find the point where the line pierces the plane $9x + 3y + 7z = 53$.

e. Find the point on the line 20 units from $(6, 1, 4)$ in the positive direction.

f. Write a few sentences discussing the relative ease of using direction numbers, instead of direction cosines, for the equation of a line in space.

2. *Parametric Equations of a Line in Space:* In the vector equation of a line in space, the coefficients of $\vec{i}, \vec{j}$, and $\vec{k}$ are coordinates of the variable point (x, y, z) on the line. So the vector equation of the line in Supplementary Problem 1 can be written as three *parametric equations:*

$$x = 6 + 2t$$

$$y = 1 + 5t$$

$$z = 4 + 8t$$

a. Find the points on the line for which $t = 1$ and $t = 2$.

b. Show that the points in part a are the same distance apart as the length of vector $\vec{v} = 2\vec{i} + 5\vec{j} + 8\vec{k}$.

c. Find the point on the line for which $z = 52$.

d. Find the point where the line pierces the yz-plane.

3. *Standard Form of the Equation of a Line in Space:*

a. Show the transformations required to write the equations in Supplementary Problem 2 in *standard form,* namely,

$$\frac{x - 6}{2} = \frac{y - 1}{5} = \frac{z - 4}{8}$$

b. Give a point on the line $\frac{x + 3}{11} = \frac{y - 5}{7} = \frac{z - 2.3}{13}$ and a vector parallel to the line.

10-9
Chapter Review and Test

Objective

Review and practice the major concepts of this chapter.

Class Time

2–3 days (including 1 day for testing)

Homework Assignment

Day 1: R0–R8, T1–T27

Day 2 (after Chapter 10 Test): The exploratory problem set in Section 1 of the next chapter you plan to do

Lesson Notes

Section 10-9 contains a set of Review Problems, a set of Concept Problems, and a Chapter Test. The Review Problems include one problem for each section in the chapter. You may wish to use the Chapter Test as an additional set of review problems.

Encourage students to practice the no-calculator problems without a calculator so that they are prepared for the test problems for which they cannot use a calculator.

Strongly consider assigning Explorations 10-9d and 10-9e for review.

Exploration Notes

Explorations 10-9a to 10-9c introduce students to supplementary topics. The first one, *Exploration 10-9a,* introduces the concept of positive and negative normal vectors to a plane. If a normal vector for a plane is translated to the origin, then the positive one points *toward* the plane and the negative one points *away* from the plane.

Exploration 10-9b introduces students to a way to find the perpendicular distance between a plane and a point not on that plane. This is done by projecting onto the normal vector any vector starting in the plane and ending at the point. Coupled with the concept of positive and negative normal vectors from Exploration 10-9a, students can determine algebraically whether the point is on the same side of the plane as the origin, or on the opposite side.

Exploration 10-9c lets students learn how to find the perpendicular distance between a line and a point not on that line by crossing a vector parallel to the line with a vector from a point on the line to the point not on the line.

Exploration 10-9d gives students a review of concepts in the chapter by having them analyze planes and angles formed in the construction of a hip roof. Students actually construct a model of the roof, verifying that the angles and dimensions they calculate are correct.

Exploration 10-9e is a good review of the vector concepts of this chapter.

Problem Notes

- *Problem R1* reviews vector length, vector addition, and vector subtraction. A blackline master for this problem is available in the *Instructor's Resource Book.*

- *Problems T1 and T2* reinforce geometrical understanding of direction angles, cross products, and vector projection. A blackline master for these problems is available in the *Instructor's Resource Book.*

11 Matrix Transformations and Fractal Figures

Multiplication of matrices, the main topic of this chapter, is directed toward applications in which one matrix transforms a pre-image matrix into an image matrix. The dilation, rotation, and translation parts of the transformation matrix are presented in a novel way that is easy for students to remember. By performing a transformation repeatedly (iteratively) and having the grapher do the plotting, students find that the images are attracted to a fixed point. If several transformations are performed iteratively, the images are attracted to an infinite number of fixed points. These *strange attractors* can take the form of various real-world shapes, such as ferns, trees, or snowflakes. The figures are so complex that their dimensions are fractions, not integers. This is why they are called *fractals*. Thus students get an introduction to fractal geometry, one of the newest branches of mathematics, while learning properties of matrices. The Explorations include an introduction to Markov chains, an application of iterative matrix transformations to problems in economics.

11-1
Introduction to Iterated Transformations

Objective

See what happens to the perimeter and area of a square when you perform the same set of transformations repeatedly (iteratively).

Class Time

1 day

Homework Assignment

Problems 1–5

Important Terms and Concepts

Iteration

Pre-image

Sierpiński's carpet

Sierpiński's square

Lesson Notes

In this exploratory problem set, students are introduced to the idea of iteration using Sierpiński's carpet. The results should spark students' curiosity about what is to come in the rest of the chapter. You can assign this section for homework the night of the Chapter 10 test or as a group activity to be completed in class. No classroom discussion is needed before students begin the activity.

Problem Notes

Problem 5 involves finding the total area and perimeter of the image after an *infinite* number of iterations. To find the answers, students can write expressions for the perimeter and area of the *n*th iteration and see what value the expressions approach when greater and greater values are substituted for *n*.

11-2
Matrix Operations and Solutions of Linear Systems

Objectives

- Given two matrices, find their sum and product.

- Given a square matrix, find its multiplicative inverse.

- Use matrices to solve systems of linear equations.

Class Time

1–2 days (2 days if your students have not worked with matrices before or if you want them to perform matrix computations by hand)

Homework Assignment

Day 1: RA, Q1–Q10, Problems 1–23 odd

Day 2: Problems 4, 8, 12, 16, 20

Important Terms and Concepts

Matrix

Elements

Rows

Columns

Dimension of a matrix

Commensurate

Incommensurate

Square matrix

Identity matrix

Inverse matrix

Determinant

Adjoint of a matrix

Matrix solution of a linear system

Lesson Notes

This section covers matrix operations and the solving of linear systems using matrices. If students learned these concepts in an earlier course, you should be able to complete this section in one day.

At first, students are expected to do the matrix operations by hand so that you can be sure they understand how the operations are done. Thereafter, they will do operations on the grapher. Exploration 11-2a is designed for students to gain this knowledge (or refresh their memories) by guided reading of the text, both for grapher techniques and by hand.

Perhaps the most important thing for students to realize about matrix multiplication is that it involves a dot product of a *row* in the first matrix with a *column* in the second matrix. This is why the rows of the first matrix must have the same number of elements as the columns of the second matrix. Presented this way, you preserve the "row, then column" feature that permeates matrix operation. Saying something like, "The number of columns in the first matrix must equal the number of rows in the second matrix," while it is mathematically correct, masks the reason for the concept and contradicts the "row, then column" feature.

When operating with matrices that represent real-world quantities, it is important to think about matrices as more than rectangular arrays of numbers. To add or subtract two matrices, the corresponding rows and columns must represent the same types of quantities—that is, the labels must be the same. For example, in Problem 12, the sum of [P] and [S] has no real-world meaning. To multiply two matrices, the column labels of the left matrix must be the same as the row labels of the right matrix. For example, in Problem 12, the product [P] [S] has a real-world meaning, whereas the product [S] [P] does not.

To help students understand the concepts of identity and inverse matrices, you can compare these concepts to the identity and inverses for real-number multiplication. If you multiply any real number by the multiplicative identity 1, the number is unchanged. Similarly, if you multiply any matrix by the identity matrix, the matrix is unchanged. The multiplicative inverse, or reciprocal, of a real number is the number you multiply it by to get 1, the multiplicative identity. Similarly, the inverse of a matrix is the matrix you multiply it by to get the identity matrix.

In Example 1, graphers are used to find the inverse and determinant of a matrix. If this is the first time students have done matrix computations on their graphers, you will probably need to walk them through the steps of entering a matrix and doing the necessary computations. As the solution to part b states, most graphers do not calculate the adjoint directly. However, students can find the

adjoint using the inverse and determinant they already computed.

Be sure to emphasize that the determinant of a matrix—unlike the adjoint—is a *number*, not a matrix.

$$[M] = \begin{bmatrix} 3 & 2 \\ 8 & 7 \end{bmatrix} \qquad \text{adj } [M] = \begin{bmatrix} 7 & -2 \\ -8 & 3 \end{bmatrix} \qquad \det [M] = 5$$

Being able to use matrices to solve linear systems is a critical skill. Ask questions to make sure students understand each step of the solution process. For example, you might ask: What is the purpose of left-multiplying both sides of the equation by $[C]^{-1}$? Why is it not possible to right-multiply by $[C]^{-1}$?

Exploration Notes

Exploration 11-2a is a guided reading assignment in which students practice learning about a topic (matrix operations, in this case) by reading and rereading the text section.

Exploration 11-2b is an optional activity to show students how to find the determinant of a matrix by hand, using minor determinants. There are other ways that work for 3 × 3 determinants (the "bucket" or "diagonal" method, for instance), but these fail for higher-order determinants and are not presented in conjunction with this text.

Exploration 11-2c leads students stepwise through the process of inverting a 3 × 3 matrix by getting the adjoint matrix (the matrix of cofactors) from the transpose of the given matrix, then multiplying by the reciprocal of the determinant. Some students may be curious enough to wade through this process, thus gaining insight into the nature of the process, and also gaining an appreciation for the fact that they won't have to invert matrices by hand as a career!

Problem Notes

- *Problems 1–10* provide practice with matrix operations. You might also want to make up a few similar problems in which some of the elements of the matrices include variables so that students need to perform the operations by hand.

- *Problem 12* is a nice problem because it requires students to think about what the rows and columns of the matrices represent. Two matrices may be commensurate for addition or multiplication, but this does not mean that the sum or product has a real-world meaning. (See the Lesson Notes.)

11-3
Rotation and Dilation Matrices

Objective

Given a desired dilation and rotation, write a matrix that will perform the transformation when it is multiplied by a matrix representing a geometric figure.

Class Time

1 day

Homework Assignment

RA, Q1–Q10, Problems 1–21 odd, 22

Technology Options

  Problem 21: Dynamic Matrix Transformations Problem

 Presentation Sketch: Matrix Products Present.gsp

 Presentation Sketch: Matrix Transformations Present.gsp

 Calculator Program: ITRANS

Activity: Matrix Transformations

Important Terms and Concepts

Transformation matrix

Image matrix

Image

Pre-image

General dilation matrix

General rotation matrix

Iterated transformations

Lesson Notes

In this section, students learn how to use a transformation matrix to dilate and rotate figures on the coordinate plane.

Emphasize that transformations of figures require that the $2 \times n$ image matrix be *left*-multiplied by the transformation matrix.

Explain to students that when they write a matrix for a given rotation, they must consider the *direction* of the rotation. Counterclockwise rotations are represented by positive angle measures, whereas clockwise rotations are represented by negative angle measures.

Example 1 shows how to find a transformation matrix that will both rotate and dilate a figure. The matrix is then used to transform a triangle.

Example 2 applies a transformation matrix iteratively to obtain a pattern of smaller and smaller spiraling triangles. Be sure to point out that the triangles seem to be attracted to the origin. Also explain that because matrix multiplication is associative, the final answer after four transformations is $[A]^4[M]$.

Exploration Notes

Exploration 11-3a introduces students to dilation and rotation matrices. It is suggested that you use this Exploration as a cooperative group activity following a brief introduction to what they are expected to learn. Allow 15–20 minutes to complete this Exploration.

Exploration 11-3b introduces students to iterated matrix transformations and the concept of fixed point. For this purpose they will need to download the grapher program ITRANS (standing for "Iterated Transformations"). The fixed point can also be found by raising the transformation matrix to a large number, such as 100. This is discussed in greater detail in Section 11-4. This Exploration may be done in cooperative groups. Allow 15–20 minutes to complete this Exploration.

Technology Notes

 Problem 21: The Dynamic Matrix Transformations Problem asks students to use a Dynamic Precalculus Exploration at *www.keymath.com/ precalc* to explore matrix transformations with an interactive sketch.

 Presentation Sketch: Matrix Products Present.gsp, on the *Instructor's Resource CD*, visually demonstrates matrix products as transformations of points in the plane.

 Presentation Sketch: Matrix Transformations Present.gsp, on the *Instructor's Resource CD*, visually demonstrates matrices as transformations. This sketch is related to the Matrix Transformations activity.

 Calculator Program: ITRANS graphically displays iterations of a single matrix transformation, as asked for in Problems 15 and 16. The program is available on the *Instructor's Resource CD* and at *www.keymath.com/ precalc* for download onto a TI-83 or TI-84 graphing calculator. It also appears in the *Instructor's Resource Book* for students to enter by hand.

Activity: Matrix Transformations, in the *Instructor's Resource Book*, helps students understand how matrices can represent rotations and dilations. Students edit matrix transformations and see the effects of applying the transformations to regions in the plane. Allow 30–40 minutes.

Problem Notes

Problem 15 asks students to write or download a grapher program to perform iterative transformations and display the results.

Supplementary Problems

1. Run your program from Problem 15 using the transformation and pre-image in Example 2. Sketch the path followed by the point that is farthest from the origin in the pre-image. Toward what fixed point do the images seem to be attracted?

2. *Three-Dimensional Transformations:* You can also use matrices to transform figures in three-dimensional space.

   a. What transformation of space is produced by multiplying points by this matrix?

   $$\begin{bmatrix} 5 & 0 & 0 \\ 0 & 5 & 0 \\ 0 & 0 & 5 \end{bmatrix}$$

   b. Find a 3×3 matrix that rotates figures in space by 90° counterclockwise about the z-axis.

Supplementary Problem 3 gives students a chance to recall the trigonometric properties they learned in earlier chapters.

3. *Rotation Matrix Problem:* The general rotation matrix you have used has the form

   $$[M_1] = \begin{bmatrix} \cos \theta & \cos (\theta + 90°) \\ \sin \theta & \sin (\theta + 90°) \end{bmatrix}$$

   You may also see the general rotation matrix given in this form.

   $$[M_2] = \begin{bmatrix} \cos \theta & -\sin \theta \\ \sin \theta & \cos \theta \end{bmatrix}$$

   a. Show that $[M_2]$ gives the same image as $[M_1]$ for $\theta = 30°$ when you apply it to the pre-image

   $$[A] = \begin{bmatrix} 5 \\ 7 \end{bmatrix}$$

   b. Use the composite argument properties to show algebraically that $[M_1]$ is equivalent to $[M_2]$.

   c. What advantage can you see to using $[M_2]$ as the general rotation matrix? Which do you think is easier to remember, $[M_1]$ or $[M_2]$?

Translation with Rotation and Dilation Matrices

Objective

Given a desired dilation, rotation, and translation, write a matrix that will perform the transformation when it is multiplied by a pre-image matrix, and find the fixed point to which the images are attracted.

Class Time

2 days

Homework Assignment

Day 1: RA, Q1–Q10, Problems 1, 3

Day 2: Problems 2, 4

Technology Options

 Calculator Program: FIXEDPT

 Activity: Matrix Products

 Activity: Matrix Products in Three Dimensions

Important Terms and Concepts

Translation

Fixed point attractor, or fixed point

Limit

Lesson Notes

In this section, students learn how to represent a translation, a rotation, and a dilation with a single transformation matrix.

A translation can be accomplished by using matrix addition. However, in order to be able to perform a translation, a rotation, and a dilation with one matrix operation, you need to be able to translate a figure using matrix multiplication. The transformation matrix is a 3×3 matrix with the 2×2 identity matrix in the upper-left corner, the x- and y-translations as the top two elements in the third column, and 0 0 1 in the bottom row. To be able to left-multiply by the translation matrix, you need to add a row of 1s to the bottom of the pre-image matrix.

The most effective way to help students understand how the translation matrix works and why the third row of 1s must be in the pre-image matrix is to have them compute $[T] [M]$ *by hand.*

A transformation matrix that combines a translation, a dilation, and a rotation is a 3 × 3 matrix with the dilation and rotation information as the four upper-left entries and the translation information as the top two elements of the last column. The bottom row is always 0 0 1.

After some practice multiplying by hand, students should come to realize that

- The 1 1 1 1 in the pre-image matrix causes the translations to be done.

- The 0 0 1 in the transformation matrix puts the row 1 1 1 1 into the image matrix so that the translations will be done on subsequent iterations.

Example 1 shows how to write a matrix to represent a given rotation, translation, and dilation and then apply it to a pre-image.

If a transformation is applied iteratively a large number of times and the dilation factor has an absolute value less than 1, then the images will be attracted to a fixed point. Emphasize that the fixed point depends *only* on the transformation, *not* on the pre-image. *Any* point in the plane will be attracted to the same fixed point if the transformation is applied repeatedly.

Example 2 applies the transformation from Example 1 iteratively. The images are graphed, so students can see how they spiral toward the fixed point. The example also shows the image matrix after 30 iterations, so students can see that each of the image vertices is attracted to the fixed point.

Example 3 illustrates the algebraic method for finding a fixed point. This method uses the fact that when a transformation is applied to the fixed point, the point does not move. That is, it remains *fixed*.

Example 4 illustrates a numerical method for finding a fixed point. This method involves raising the transformation matrix to a high power. When this is done, the rotation-and-dilation elements of the matrix will be close to 0 and the fixed point will appear as the translation part of the matrix.

The two summaries at the end of the section will help students organize the concepts presented in the examples.

Exploration Notes

Exploration 11-4a covers material similar to that in Examples 1 and 2. Problem 10 of the Exploration will help students see that the fixed point depends on

the transformation, not the pre-image. You can use this Exploration as a discovery activity and then follow it up by discussing Examples 1 and 2. Allow about 20 minutes for groups to complete this Exploration.

Exploration 11-4b gives students an opportunity to further investigate repeated transformations and fixed points. Students write matrices to represent given transformations, apply transformations iteratively, and calculate fixed points both algebraically and numerically. The Exploration also emphasizes that the fixed point depends only on the transformation. This activity makes an excellent group project. You might have each group prepare a written summary of what they have learned and pick a group at random to make an oral presentation of their summary. Allow about 25–30 minutes for groups to complete this activity.

Exploration 11-4c provides practice with the key ideas of the section. It can be assigned as homework or given as a group quiz. Allow about 20 minutes for students to complete this Exploration.

Exploration 11-4d introduces *Markov chains,* one of the most interesting applications of matrices. The activity presents a nongeometric real-world situation involving iterative matrix multiplication. You can use the Exploration as an extra-credit assignment or as a jumping-off point for independent research on Markov chains.

Technology Notes

 Calculator Program: FIXEDPT calculates the fixed point of a transformation consisting of a rotation, a dilation, and translation, and it may be useful for several problems in this section. The program is available on the *Instructor's Resource CD* and at *www.keymath.com/precalc* for download onto a TI-83 or TI-84 graphing calculator. It also appears in the *Instructor's Resource Book* for students to enter by hand.

Activity: Matrix Products, in *Exploring Precalculus with The Geometer's Sketchpad,* gives students the opportunity to create complex transformations, including translations, using products of matrices. The activity is divided into sections that might be used over several days. Allow 50–60 minutes total.

 Activity: Matrix Products in Three Dimensions, in *Exploring Precalculus with The Geometer's Sketchpad,* extends the ideas of translation to three dimensions. Students use three-dimensional transformation matrices to simulate the motion of an orbiting planet. Thanks to custom tools, beginning-to-intermediate students can feel successful with this project. Allow 30–40 minutes.

Problem Notes

- *Problem 3,* the Fixed Point Problem, leads students to determine which matrix determines a fixed point, the transformation matrix or the pre-image matrix. A blackline master for this problem is available in the *Instructor's Resource Book.*

- *Problem 4,* the Third Row Problem, helps students understand how a transformation matrix "works."

11-5

Strange Attractors for Several Iterated Transformations

Objective

Given several different transformations, perform them iteratively, starting with a pre-image, and plot the resulting images.

Class Time

2–3 days

Homework Assignment

Day 1: RA, Q1–Q10, Problems 1, 5, 9

Day 2: Problems 2, 6–8

Day 3: Problems 10, 11

If you decide to spend only two days on this section, skip the Day 2 assignment on the Sierpiński rectangle.

Technology Options

 Problem 12: Sketchpad Fractal Project

 Calculator Program: BARNSLEY

Activity: Barnsley's Fern

Important Terms and Concepts

Strange attractor

Self-similar

Fractal

Barnsley's method

Sierpiński's triangle

Sierpiński's square

Koch's snowflake curve

Lesson Notes

The last section showed how an iterated transformation can cause images to be attracted to a fixed point. This section examines what happens when several different transformations are performed iteratively. It ties into the next section, which discusses fractals.

The study of fractals is comparatively recent. In 1967, Benoit Mandelbrot, a French mathematician born in Poland, published "How Long Is the Coast of Britain?" in *Science* magazine. In this article, he

---

coined the word *fractal* to describe a figure with a dimension that cannot be expressed as an integer. A fractal is self-similar and often resembles things in nature such as trees, ferns, and coastlines. Fractals have unexpected properties, like a boundless perimeter that encloses a finite area.

The "Strange Attractors Geometrically" part of this section starts by applying four different transformations to the same pre-image rectangle. Discuss with students which of the four images corresponds to each transformation. Matrix D is different from transformation matrices students have seen before. It dilates the pre-image by 0 in the x-direction and by 0.3 in the y-direction. This causes the rectangle to "collapse," forming the vertical "stem."

If each of the four transformations is applied to each of the four images from the first iteration, the 16 images shown in Figure 11-5c in the student text result. Rather than simply showing students the results of the second iteration, you might want to have them work in groups on Exploration 11-5a. In this Exploration, students generate the 16 images themselves. After students complete the Exploration, discuss the results as a class.

Explain to students that if the iterative process is continued many times and that in each iteration the four transformations are applied to each image from the previous iteration, the result will look like the fern leaf in Figure 11-5d in the student text.

Barnsley's method is a more efficient way of plotting images created by applying several transformations iteratively. The method begins with one point rather than with a pre-image figure. One of the transformations is selected at random (according to assigned probabilities) and applied to the point. Then another transformation is selected at random and applied to the image. If this process is repeated many, many times, the points are attracted to certain regions, creating an image that approximates the image you would get using the "long" method. This image is known as a *strange attractor*.

Discuss the fact that the fern leaf strange attractor is a fractal. One of the characteristics of fractals is *self-similarity*. This means that if you magnify part of the fractal (in this case a branch or a sub-branch), the magnified portion will look exactly like the whole figure. Students will explore another characteristic of fractals, fractional dimension, in the next section.

In Problem 3, students are asked to write or download a program that will plot a strange

attractor using Barnsley's method. It is essential that students have this program in order to do the homework. Have them test their program in class by using it to generate the fern-shaped strange attractor (see Problem 4). This way you will be certain that each student has a working program and knows how to use it.

Exploration Notes

Exploration 11-5a follows the discussion in the "Strange Attractors Geometrically" part of this section. You can use this Exploration as an alternative to simply presenting the information to students. After briefly running through the process involved, have students work in groups to complete the Exploration. Then discuss the results as a class. Allow students 20–25 minutes to complete this activity.

Exploration 11-5b demonstrates how to generate a strange attractor by using Barnsley's method. In order to do this Exploration, students will need to write or download the Barnsley program (see Problem 3 and the Lesson Notes). Encourage students to play with the program to see what happens when the transformation matrices or pre-image point are changed. Allow students 20–25 minutes to complete this activity.

Technology Notes

 Problem 12: The Sketchpad Fractal Project asks students to use the prepared sketch Barnsley.gsp to investigate the effects of changing transformation matrices and probabilities. Students can download the sketch from *www.keymath.com/precalc,* but they must have access to *The Geometer's Sketchpad* software in order to use it. The sketch is also available on the *Instructor's Resource CD.*

 Calculator Program: BARNSLEY plots fractal images on the calculator screen using Barnsley's method, and it may be useful for several problems in this section. The program is available on the *Instructor's Resource CD* and at *www.keymath.com/precalc* for download onto a TI-83 or TI-84 graphing calculator. It also appears in the *Instructor's Resource Book* for students to enter by hand.

Activity: Barnsley's Fern is on the *Instructor's Resource CD* in the file Fractal Fern.pdf. It is also available for download at *www.keymath.com/precalc.* The activity has students use a prepared sketch, also on the CD and at the Precalculus Resource Center Web site, to randomly iterate transformations and construct a fern with Barnsley's method. This activity uses advanced Sketchpad techniques, so it is recommended that you familiarize yourself with it before assigning it to students. Allow 50 minutes.

Problem Notes

- *Problems 1 and 2* use the "long" method of generating the images created by applying several transformations iteratively to a pre-image.

- *Problems 1 and 5* involve the Sierpiński triangle. Problem 1 shows how to generate the figure the "long" way, and Problem 5 uses Barnsley's method.

- *Problems 2 and 6–8* involve the Sierpiński square. Problem 2 shows how to generate the figure the "long" way, while Problem 6 uses Barnsley's method. Problems 7 and 8 ask students to explore what happens when the dilation factor is changed.

- *Problem 10* introduces the Koch snowflake curve, which is used in the next section to introduce fractal dimension. A blackline master for this problem is available in the *Instructor's Resource Book.*

- *Problem 11* asks students to predict and then compute the fixed point for each transformation involved in generating the fern leaf image.

- *Problem 12* allows students to explore fractals and Barnsley's method with Sketchpad.

11-6
Fractal Dimensions

Objective

Given a figure formed by iteration of several transformation matrices, determine its fractal dimension.

Class Time

2 days

Homework Assignment

Day 1: RA, Q1–Q10, Problems 1, 2, 5

Day 2: Problems 3, 4, 6

Important Terms and Concepts

Fractal

Self-similar

Hausdorff dimension

Lesson Notes

In this section, Hausdorff's definition of dimension is developed using a cube, a shape for which students already know the dimension. The definition is then used to find the dimension of a fractal—the Koch snowflake. Students are often surprised to find that the dimension of the snowflake curve is not an integer. Explain that fractional dimension is one of the characteristics of fractals.

Hausdorff's definition is easy to use to find the dimension of a fractal. An alternate form is $N = m^D$, where N is the number of self-similar pieces, D is the dimension, and m is the magnification factor (the scale factor by which you need to multiply the length of a piece to get the length of the original object). This formula can be rewritten as $D = \frac{\log N}{\log m}$. Some students may find this form easier to remember.

Go through Example 1 carefully. Part b shows that you get the same dimension no matter which iteration you use. Part d looks at the total length of each iteration and explains why the length approaches infinity as more iterations are performed.

This table shows how length, area, and volume are related to the dimension of an object.

Dimension	Length	Area	Volume
$D = 1$	finite	zero	zero
$1 < D < 2$	infinite	zero	zero
$D = 2$	infinite	finite	zero
$2 < D < 3$	infinite	infinite	zero
$D = 3$	infinite	infinite	finite

Exploration Notes

Exploration 11-6a develops Hausdorff's definition of dimension using a cube and then applies it to a square and to Sierpiński's gasket. You might assign this investigation to groups of students at the beginning of class and then have a discussion about the results. Allow students 20–25 minutes to complete the activity.

Exploration 11-6b involves the snowflake curve, which will be used in the next section to introduce fractal dimension. The Exploration is similar to Problem 10, but it requires students to find the transformation matrices themselves. Allow students 20–25 minutes to complete the activity.

Exploration 11-6c is a takeoff on the question posed in Mandelbrot's famous article "How Long Is the Coast of Britain?" Your students will find the results surprising. Allow students 20–25 minutes to complete the activity.

Problem Notes

The problems in this section apply the concept of fractal dimension to various fractal figures. Be sure that students are updating their journal entries.

11-7
Chapter Review and Test

Objective

Review and practice the major concepts of this chapter.

Class Time

2 days (including 1 day for testing)

Homework Assignment

Day 1: R0–R6, T0–T19

Day 2 (after Chapter 11 Test): The exploratory problem set in Section 1 of the next chapter you plan to do

Lesson Notes

Section 11-7 contains a set of Review Problems, a set of Concept Problems, and a Chapter Test. The Review Problems include one problem for each section in the chapter. You may wish to use the Chapter Test as an additional set of review problems.

Encourage students to practice the no-calculator problems without a calculator so that they are prepared for the test problems for which they cannot use a calculator.

Problem Notes

A blackline master for Problems R5 and T11 is available in the *Instructor's Resource Book*.

- *Problem C1* gives students some insight into why Barnsley's method works. A full discussion of Barnsley's method is beyond the scope of this course. However, working with a familiar concrete example is helpful in gaining some intuitive understanding of Barnsley's method.

- *Problem C2*, which asks students to research and write a report on a fractal-related topic, makes an excellent project.

Exploration Notes

Exploration 11-7a reviews the concepts and ideas of this chapter by looking at Foerster's tree. (See Problem 9 in Section 11-5.) You might have students complete this Exploration in class the day before the Chapter Test.

12 Analytic Geometry of Conic Sections and Quadric Surfaces

This chapter concentrates on the similarities and differences in the algebraic and geometric properties of ellipses, circles, and hyperbolas, with a brief treatment of parabolas. Students learn that parametric forms of the equations lead to more satisfactory computer graphs of the conic sections and also refresh their memories on the properties of trigonometric functions. Terminology such as "x-radius" and "y-radius" makes an easy connection with dilations from earlier in the course and avoids the popular misconception that the major or transverse axis is always in the x-direction. Rotation of the conic section graphs about an axis generates quadric surfaces. Inscribing variable cones and cylinders inside these surfaces gives students a taste of three-dimensional sketching and maximum/minimum problems they will later encounter in calculus. For analytic properties of conic sections, the familiar focal radius terminology is extended to include major and minor radius and directrix radius for the ellipse and transverse and conjugate radius for the hyperbola. Ellipse construction on an index with string, included in the Explorations, gives each student a hands-on tool that he or she can file in a notebook for future reference and use.

12-1
Introduction to Conic Sections

Objective

Given a quadratic equation with two variables, plot its graph and formulate conclusions.

Class Time

1 day

Homework Assignment

Problems 1–8

Important Terms and Concepts

Conic section

Circle

Ellipse

Hyperbola

Asymptotes

Parabola

Lesson Notes

In this exploratory problem set, students graph quadratic equations on their graphers and make observations relating the equations and the graphs. You can assign this section for homework the night of the Chapter 11 test or as a group activity to be completed in class. No classroom discussion is needed before students begin the activity.

To graph the equations, students must first solve for y in terms of x. For the equations of the circle, ellipse, and hyperbola, this results in two solutions (a positive square root and a negative square root) that must be entered separately as y_1 and y_2. Remind students to enter Zoom Square after the window has been set. Zoom Square makes the length of 1 unit on the x-axis equal the length of 1 unit on the y-axis. This ensures that the graph of the circle will actually look like a circle rather than like an ellipse.

Problem Notes

Problem 8 requires students to discuss how they can tell what type of conic section an equation represents based on the magnitudes and signs of the coefficients.

12-2
Parametric and Cartesian Equations of the Conic Sections

Objective

Given a Cartesian or parametric equation of a conic section, sketch or plot the graph, and given the graph, find the equation.

Class Time

2–4 days

Homework Assignment

Day 1: RA, Q1–Q10, Problems 1–4, 5–11 odd, 21, 23, 25, 27

Day 2: Problems 13, 15, 17, 19, 28–33

Days 3 and 4: Even-numbered problems and supplementary problems as needed

Technology Options

Presentation Sketch: Parametric Present.gsp

Presentation Sketch: Conics Present.gsp

Presentation Sketch: Ellipse Tour.gsp

Presentation Sketch: Hyperbola Tour.gsp

Presentation Sketch: Parabola Tour.gsp

Calculator Program: CONIC

Calculator Program: CONIC2

Activity: Analytic Conics

Activity: Parametric Functions in Three Dimensions

Important Terms and Concepts

Nappes of a circular cone

Asymptote

x-radius, y-radius

Vertices

Major axis, minor axis

Completing the square

Vertex form of the equation of a parabola

Lesson Notes

This section covers Cartesian and parametric equations of conic sections. If your students studied conics in algebra, then a two-day refresher may be sufficient—one day to review Cartesian equations and one day to cover parametric equations and the connections between the two forms. If students have not studied conics before, spend three or four days on this section. Do not underestimate the amount of material in this section.

Figure 12-2a in the student text shows how a plane slices a cone to form the various conic sections. The names can be remembered based on the "tilt" angle shown in the figure. The tilt angle of the ellipse is small enough so that the plane *leaves out* one nappe of the cone, the same way an ellipsis mark means "something has been left out." The tilt angle of the parabola is just enough to make the plane *parallel* to an element of the cone. (Parabola means, literally, "along the path of a ball.") The tilt angle of the hyperbola is *more* than enough to make a parabola, so the plane slices both nappes of the cone. The prefix *hyper-* means "more than," as in *hypertension* or *hyperspace.*

The equations for the parent conic sections are extremely important. Students should commit both the equations and the graphs to memory. You may need to explain that the unit circle is the parent graph for both circles and ellipses.

When the parent graphs are dilated and translated, the resulting graphs are conics with axes parallel to the *x*- and *y*-axes. Remind students that a dilation in the *x*- or *y*-direction is done by *dividing* x or y by the corresponding dilation factor. Similarly, translations are done by *subtracting* a constant from the respective variable.

Example 1 takes the students through the steps of graphing a translated and dilated conic section, in this case an ellipse.

In Example 2, the equation from Example 1 is rewritten in general form. If the equation were *given* in general form, it could be converted to the form in Example 1 by *completing the square.* Students may have studied this topic in a prior algebra course. (See Problems 31 and 32 and the Supplementary Lesson Notes.) In Example 2, the process of taking the completed square is *reversed* to expand the equation.

Example 3 demonstrates the process of sketching a hyperbola by hand. Make sure students understand how to use the information in the equation to locate the vertices and sketch the asymptotes. After

reviewing the example, have students rewrite the equation in general form.

The student text shows how to solve the general form of the conic section equation for *y* so that it can be graphed. The method is tricky and the result is messy, but students can write or download a program to do the work for them. If students write the program themselves, make sure they realize that because, with the exception of some parabolas, conics are not functions, the program must break the equation into two functions. The input for the program is the six coefficients of the general form of the equation. Emphasize that in this section the equations have no *xy*-term, so students should enter 0 for *B*.

Another way to graph an equation given in general form is first to rewrite it, by *completing the square,* so that it is in the form that shows the dilations and translations (the form in Examples 1 and 3). This technique is discussed in Problems 31 and 32 and in the Supplementary Lesson Notes.

Example 4 uses the grapher program to graph the equation students found in Example 2 (which resulted from expanding the equation in Example 1). Students should verify that the graph matches the sketch they made by hand. Remind students to use Zoom Square so that the conic section has the right proportions. Also have students use the program to verify the graph they sketched in Example 3.

Note that when a grapher is used to graph conics, a disconnected space often appears where y_1 and y_2 should meet. Explain to students that this is merely a limitation of the grapher; the graph is actually a continuous curve.

The student text gives parametric equations for both the unit circle and the unit hyperbolas. Work with students to convert the parametric equations for the circle into Cartesian form: Square both sides of both equations to get $x^2 = \cos^2 t$ and $y^2 = \sin^2 t$. Then add the equations to get $x^2 + y^2 = \cos^2 t + \sin^2 t = 1$, the Cartesian equation for the unit circle. A similar technique can be used to convert the hyperbola equations to Cartesian form, using the identity $\sec^2 t - \tan^2 t = 1$. (As an alternative to presenting this information to students, you can have them work in groups on Exploration 12-2a.)

Example 5 shows how to find parametric equations for the hyperbola in Example 3. Emphasize that with parametric equations, you *multiply* by the dilation factors *and* add the translation constants.

Example 6 shows how to graph the Cartesian equation of a parabola when it is given in the form that shows the dilations and translations. The equation is then transformed into general form and plotted using the grapher program.

Exploration Notes

Exploration 12-2a takes the students through the processes of plotting parametric equations of a circle, an ellipse, and a hyperbola and of transforming the equation into Cartesian form. You can assign this activity as a way of introducing the topic of parametric equations. Allow students about 20 minutes to complete the Exploration.

Exploration 12-2b provides practice with all of the topics from the section: recognizing the type of conic section from an equation, sketching graphs of equations given in the form that shows dilations and translations, writing parametric equations for graphs, transforming equations into general form, and using a grapher program to graph equations given in general form. This Exploration may be used as review, homework, or a quiz. Allow students about 20 minutes to complete the Exploration.

Technology Notes

Presentation Sketch: Parametric Present.gsp, on the *Instructor's Resource CD,* allows you to set a parameter and parametric equations and watch as a particle traces out a parametrically defined graph.

Presentation Sketch: Conics Present.gsp, on the *Instructor's Resource CD,* shows the graph of a conic equation in general form and in the form $\frac{x^2}{A} + \frac{y^2}{B} = 1$. This sketch is related to the activity Analytic Conics. You may wish to use this sketch again in Section 12-5 when discussing the general second-degree equation with nonzero xy-term.

Presentation Sketch: Ellipse Tour.gsp, on the *Instructor's Resource CD,* contains several interactive sketches that show different ways to construct ellipses. You may want to highlight one or two constructions and then allow students to explore the rest on their own. The sketch was taken from *Exploring Conic Sections with The Geometer's Sketchpad.* This book contains activities that guide students through the various constructions of the conics shown in the Tour documents and the proofs that the constructions work.

Presentation Sketch: Hyperbola Tour.gsp, on the *Instructor's Resource CD,* contains several interactive sketches that show different ways to construct hyperboloids. You may want to highlight one or two constructions and then allow students to explore the rest on their own. The sketch was taken from *Exploring Conic Sections with The Geometer's Sketchpad.*

Presentation Sketch: Parabola Tour.gsp, on the *Instructor's Resource CD,* contains several interactive sketches that show different ways to construct parabolas. You may want to highlight one or two constructions and then allow students to explore the rest on their own. The sketch was taken from *Exploring Conic Sections with The Geometer's Sketchpad.*

Calculator Program: CONIC plots the graph of a conic section from the general equation $Ax^2 + Bxy + Cy^2 + Dx + Ey + F = 0$, as needed in Example 4. The program is available on the *Instructor's Resource CD* and at *www.keymath .com/precalc* for download onto a TI-83 or TI-84 graphing calculator. It also appears in the *Instructor's Resource Book* for students to enter by hand.

Calculator Program: CONIC2 plots the graphs of two conic sections from the general equation $Ax^2 + Bxy + Cy^2 + Dx + Ey + F = 0$. The program is available on the *Instructor's Resource CD* and at *www.keymath.com/ precalc* for download onto a TI-83 or TI-84 graphing calculator. It also appears in the *Instructor's Resource Book* for students to enter by hand.

Activity: Analytic Conics, in the *Instructor's Resource Book,* engages students in exploring Cartesian equations of circles, ellipses, and hyperbolas. A second part concerns the general second-degree equation, mostly with the xy-term set to zero. You may wish to revisit this activity in Section 12-4 as you discuss foci and directrices and in Section 12-5 when students explore graphs of general conics with nonzero xy-term. Allow 30–40 minutes.

Activity: Parametric Functions in Three Dimensions, in *Exploring Precalculus with The Geometer's Sketchpad,* has students find parametric equations for a line, a helix, and a conic spiral in Sketchpad. Allow 30–50 minutes.

Problem Notes

- *Problems 1–4* require students to recognize equations of parent conic sections and sketch the graphs.

- *Problems 5–12* involve analyzing and sketching conic sections from their Cartesian equations and then verifying the graphs using the grapher program.

- *Problems 13–20* require students to sketch conic sections based on their parametric equations and then verify the results using their graphers.

- *Problems 21–26* give students graphs of conic sections and ask them to write equations for the graphs in both Cartesian and parametric form.

- *Problems 27 and 28* present applications involving an ellipse and a hyperbola.

- *Problems 29 and 30* require students to transform parametric equations for a hyperbola and an ellipse to Cartesian form.

- *Problem 31,* the Completing the Square Problem, shows students how they can convert an equation from general form to the form that shows dilations and translations by *completing the square.* This allows students to graph equations given in general form without using the grapher program. (See the Supplementary Lesson Notes for more information about completing the square.)

- *Problem 32,* the Ellipse from the Cartesian Equation Problem, requires students to complete the square to transform an ellipse equation from general form into the form that shows translations and dilations.

- *Problem 33,* the *xy*-Term Problem, asks students to observe how adding an *xy*-term to the general equation of a conic affects the graph, in preparation for Section 12-5.

Supplementary Lesson Notes

Completing the Square and Pencil-and-Paper Sketches

To sketch the graph of a conic section whose equation is given in general form, you need to convert the equation to the form that shows the dilations and translations. These additional examples show you how.

1. Sketch the graph of
$9x^2 + 25y^2 - 36x + 200y + 211 = 0$.

Solution

Use the technique of **completing the square.** Associate the *x*-terms and the *y*-terms and then factor out the coefficients of the squared terms.

$$9x^2 + 25y^2 - 36x + 200y = -211$$
Subtract 211 from both sides.

$$9(x^2 - 4x \quad) + 25(y^2 - 8y \quad) = -211$$
Associate the *x*-terms and the *y*-terms and factor out the coefficients of the squared terms. Leave spaces to complete the squares.

$$9(x^2 - 4x + 4) + 25(y^2 - 8y + 16)$$
$$= -211 + 9(4) + 25(16)$$
To complete the square, take half the linear coefficient and square it. Add to the other side also.

$$9(x - 2)^2 + 25(y - 4)^2 = 225$$
Factor each trinomial into a perfect square.

$$\frac{(x - 2)^2}{25} + \frac{(y - 4)^2}{9} = 1$$
Divide both sides by 225 to put 1 on the right. Reduce on the left.

Analysis

- The graph is an ellipse. x^2 and y^2 have coefficients with the same sign.

- The center is at point (2, 4). The *x*- and *y*-translations are 2 and 4, respectively.

- The *x*-radius is 5 and the *y*-radius is 3. The same as the dilation factors.

Figure 12-2a shows the critical features and graph.

Figure 12-2a

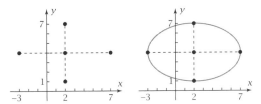

2. Sketch the graph of
$9x^2 - 4y^2 + 90x + 32y + 197 = 0$.

Solution

$$9(x^2 + 10x \quad) - 4(y^2 - 8y \quad) = -197$$
Why $-8y$, not $+8y$?

$$9(x^2 + 10x + 25) - 4(y^2 - 8y + 16)$$
$$= -197 + 9(25) - 4(16)$$
Why $-4(16)$, not $+14(16)$?

$$9(x + 5)^2 - 4(y - 4)^2 = -36$$

$$\frac{9(x + 5)^2}{-36} - \frac{4(y - 4)^2}{-36} = \frac{-36}{-36}$$
Divide by -36 to make the right side equal 1.

$$-\frac{(x + 5)^2}{4} + \frac{(y - 4)^2}{9} = 1$$

Analysis

- The graph is a hyperbola. The squared terms have opposite signs.

- It opens in the *y*-direction. The *y*-containing term is positive.

- The center is at point (−5, 4). The *x*- and *y*-translations are −5 and 4, respectively.

- The asymptotes have slopes $\pm\frac{3}{2}$.

  The slope is $\pm\frac{(y\text{-dilation})}{(x\text{-dilation})}$.

Figure 12-2b shows the critical features and the graph.

Figure 12-2b

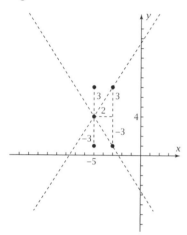

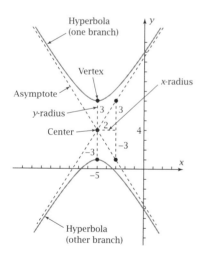

3. Sketch the graph of $y^2 + 2x - 4y - 8 = 0$.

Solution

Note that there is only one squared term, so the graph is a parabola. Because *x* appears only to the first power, solve the equation for *x* in terms of *y* and then complete the square.

$$y^2 + 2x - 4y - 8 = 0$$

$$2x = -y^2 + 4y + 8$$

$$2x = -(y^2 - 4y \quad) + 8$$

Factor out −1 to make the y^2-term have a coefficient of 1.

$$2x = -(y^2 - 4y + 4) + 8 + 4$$

$$2x = -(y - 2)^2 + 12$$

$$x = -\frac{1}{2}(y - 2)^2 + 6$$

Analysis

- The graph is a parabola. The equation has only one squared term.

- The axis of symmetry is horizontal. The equation is $x = \ldots$.

- The graph opens in the negative *x*-direction. The squared coefficient is negative.

- The vertex is at point (6, 2). Substituting 2 for *y* makes the squared term equal zero. When the squared term is zero, *x* is 6.

To find the *x*-intercept, set *y* = 0 and evaluate.

$$x = -\frac{1}{2}(0 - 2)^2 + 6 = -2 + 6 = 4$$

Figure 12-2c shows the critical features and the graph.

Figure 12-2c

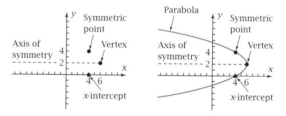

Supplementary Problems

If you have shown students the completing-the-square technique, assign some of the problems from Problems 1–12.

For Problems 1–12,

a. Complete the square and sketch the graph.

b. Confirm that your sketch is correct by plotting the original equation on your grapher. Use a friendly window with an *x*-range that includes the integers as grid points.

1. $9x^2 + 16y^2 - 36x - 160y + 292 = 0$

2. $9x^2 - 25y^2 - 36x + 200y - 589 = 0$

3. $9x^2 - 4y^2 + 54x + 8y + 41 = 0$

4. $25x^2 + 4y^2 - 150x + 8y + 129 = 0$

5. $2x^2 - 4x + y - 4 = 0$

6. $x^2 + 6x - 4y + 17 = 0$

7. $2y^2 - 9x - 16y + 14 = 0$

8. $y^2 - x + 6y + 10 = 0$

9. $x^2 - 9y^2 + 6x = 0$

10. $x^2 + 4y^2 + 16y = 0$

11. $x^2 + y^2 - 6x - 8y = 0$

12. $x^2 + y^2 - 10x - 2y + 10 = 0$

13. *Ellipse Parametric Function Problem:* Here are parametric equations for a particular ellipse.

$$x = 1 + 5 \cos t$$

$$y = 2 + 3 \sin t$$

   a. With your grapher in parametric mode, plot this parametric function. Sketch the result.

   b. From the graph, where does the center seem to be? What do the *x*-radius and *y*-radius seem to be?

   c. How can you identify the center and radii from the parametric equations?

   d. Transform the two equations so that cos *t* and sin *t* are expressed in terms of *x* and *y*, respectively. Then square both sides of each equation and add the two equations to each other. Use the Pythagorean property for cosine and sine to simplify the equation.

   e. How does the answer to part d confirm that the graph really is an ellipse with the features you specified in part b?

14. *Hyperbola Parametric Function Problem:* These are parametric equations for a particular hyperbola.

$$x = 1 + 5 \sec t$$

$$y = 2 + 3 \tan t$$

   a. With your grapher in parametric mode, plot this parametric function. Sketch the result.

   b. From the graph, where does the center seem to be? What does the *x*-radius seem to be?

   c. How can you identify the center and *x*-radius from the parametric equations? What do you conjecture that the *y*-radius is? What then would be the slopes of the asymptotes?

   d. Write equations for the two asymptotes, using the slopes and the center of the

hyperbola. Confirm that the equations are correct by plotting both asymptotes on your grapher. Sketch the result.

   e. Transform the two equations so that sec *t* and tan *t* are expressed in terms of *x* and *y*, respectively. Then square both sides of each equation and subtract the second equation from the first. Use the Pythagorean property for secant and tangent to simplify the equation.

   f. How does the answer to part e confirm that the graph really is a hyperbola with the features you specified in part b?

15. *Dilation Matrix Problem:* Figure 12-2d shows the unit circle $u^2 + v^2 = 1$ and the ellipse $\left(\frac{x}{5}\right)^2 + \left(\frac{y}{3}\right)^2 = 1$, which is a dilation of this circle by 5 in the *x*-direction and 3 in the *y*-direction. In this problem, you will learn why you *divide x* and *y* by the dilation factors.

Figure 12-2d

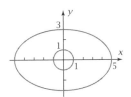

   a. Explain why this matrix will dilate the point (u, v) by a factor of 5 in the *x*-direction and by a factor of 3 in the *y*-direction.

$$\begin{bmatrix} 5 & 0 \\ 0 & 3 \end{bmatrix} \begin{bmatrix} u \\ v \end{bmatrix} = \begin{bmatrix} x \\ y \end{bmatrix}$$

   b. Based on the answer to part a, explain why *u* and *v* in the equation $u^2 + v^2 = 1$ can be replaced by $\frac{x}{5}$ and $\frac{x}{3}$, respectively, to get the equation of the ellipse.

16. *Overpass Problem:* An overpass is to be built to allow train tracks to pass over a highway. For aesthetic reasons, the designers want the underside of the overpass to have the shape of a semi-ellipse, as shown in the vertical cross section in Figure 12-2e. The ellipse will have vertices at points (100, 0) and (300, 0), where *x* and *y* are in feet. The roadway underneath the overpass is 140 ft wide, extending from point (130, 0) to point (270, 0). So that large trucks may go under, the clearance must be 20 ft at the points where the underside of the overpass is closest to the roadway.

Figure 12-2e

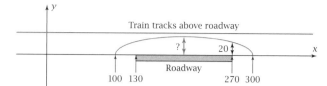

a. Write the particular equation of the ellipse.

b. How much clearance will there be at the center of the overpass, where the ellipse is farthest from the roadway?

c. If a load on a truck is 25 ft high, between what two values of x must the truck pass in order for it not to scrape the underside of the overpass?

17. *I-Beam Problem:* Two steel I-beams being used in the construction of a chemical manufacturing plant are to cross at a 70° angle, as shown in Figure 12-2f. For added strength at the junction of the I-beams, a gusset is to be welded between them. The gusset will be made from a flat plate of steel that fits into the angle between the I-beams. For the proper distribution of stress, the gusset is to be cut into the shape of a hyperbola. The vertex of the hyperbola is 10 in. from the intersection of the I-beams, and the hyperbola ends 25 in. from the intersection of the I-beams.

Figure 12-2f

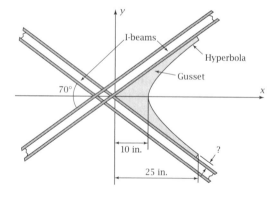

a. Write the particular equation of the hyperbola.

b. In order to make the gusset, the metal workers must know the y-values of the hyperbola at various values of x. Make a table showing these values for every 2 inches, from 10 in. to 22 in.

c. The gusset will be its narrowest at the end where $x = 25$ (see the figure). How narrow is it?

d. Why is an I-beam called an "I-beam"?

12-3
Quadric Surfaces and Inscribed Figures

Objective

Given the equation of a conic section, sketch the surface generated by rotating it about one of its axes, and find the area or volume of a figure inscribed either in the plane region bounded by the graph or in the solid region bounded by the surface.

Class Time

2 days

Homework Assignment

Day 1: RA, Q1–Q10, Problems 1–10

Day 2: Problems 11–17 odd

Technology Options

 Problem 11: Ellipsoids in Sketchpad Problem

 Problem 12: Hyperboloids in Sketchpad Problem

 Presentation Sketch: Surfaces Present.gsp

 Activity: Surfaces

Important Terms and Concepts

Paraboloid

Quadric surface

Major axis

Minor axis

Transverse axis

Conjugate axis

Ellipsoid

Prolate spheroid

Oblate spheroid

Hyperboloid

Hyperboloid of two sheets

Hyperboloid of one sheet

Sample point

Frustum of a cone

Lesson Notes

This section is perhaps the most important one in the chapter for preparing students for calculus. The difficulty many students experience with maximum-minimum, related-rates, and volume problems in calculus is that they must apply newly learned techniques (differentiating and integrating) to unfamiliar situations (three-dimensional figures). This section gives students experience sketching surfaces of revolution and inscribed figures in purely algebraic and geometric settings. Spending adequate time on this section will give students a great advantage when they take calculus. Although calculus software packages can produce three-dimensional figures with ease, students need to develop stronger spatial visualization skills in order to use such programs correctly.

Make sure students understand the terms *surface* and *solid region* and use them correctly. A solid region is the part of three-dimensional space bounded by a surface. Correct use of mathematical language is especially important in three-dimensional work.

Being able to sketch quadric surfaces is central to student understanding, so take your time developing these skills. It is recommended that you devote the entire first day of instruction to this topic. Cover the material up through Example 1 and then have students work on Exploration 12-3a and/or some of the problems from Problems 1–10. Have students make the sketches *by themselves* while you glance at their work. Then choose students to re-create their sketches on the board.

Student sketches don't need to be as nice as those in the text. For instance, in Problem 1, students can simply sketch $y = x^2$ in the xy-plane and indicate that it is rotated around the y-axis by sketching an ellipse at the "top" of the parabola. This will give the appearance of a 3-D surface. Students should keep their sketches simple, with no clutter. They should label the x- and y-axes but include only the essential scale values, such as intercepts.

Example 1 demonstrates how to sketch a hyperboloid of two sheets. After discussing the example, sketch the hyperboloid of one sheet formed by rotating the hyperbola around the x-axis. Hyperboloids of one sheet are remarkably strong structures, even stronger than cylinders. Students have probably seen wicker stools shaped like hyperboloids of one sheet.

When discussing Example 2, explain that selecting a sample point (x, y) in the first quadrant helps avoid errors involving negative signs. Parts c and d show how to solve a maximum-minimum problem numerically and graphically. (You might tell students that they will learn a symbolic method for solving such problems when they take calculus.) Remind students that using the table feature of their graphers is an efficient way to generate numerical data.

Example 3 is a maximum-minimum problem involving volumes. Students may think that the top of the cylinder touches the paraboloid in only two places. Help them understand that the cylinder touches the paraboloid all the way around. If students are having a difficult time visualizing solids and surfaces, encourage them to construct models using modeling clay.

After reviewing Example 3, you might want to make up some similar problems to give students supervised practice making sketches and maximizing volume. Exploration 12-3b also provides practice with maximizing volume.

Exploration Notes

Exploration 12-3a gives students practice in sketching figures formed by rotating conic sections about an axis. You might assign this Exploration after reviewing Example 1. Give students about 20 minutes to complete this activity.

Exploration 12-3b may be used as a cooperative group discovery, or as a follow-up to Examples 2 and 3. It requires students to find the maximum volume of a cylinder that can be inscribed in a given cone. Allow about 20 minutes for students to complete this activity.

Technology Notes

 Problem 11: The Ellipsoids in Sketchpad Problem asks students to use the prepared sketch Surfaces.gsp to view the surfaces they sketched in Problems 3 and 4. Students can download the sketch from *www.keymath.com/precalc,* but they must have access to The Geometer's Sketchpad software in order to use it. Students may also wish to download Surfaces.pdf, an activity that uses the sketch and extends three-dimensional graphing. The sketch and activity are also available on the *Instructor's Resource CD.*

 Problem 12: The Hyperboloids in Sketchpad Problem asks students to use the prepared sketch Surfaces.gsp to view the surfaces they sketched in Problems 5 and 7. Students can download the sketch from *www.keymath.com/precalc,* but they must have access to The Geometer's Sketchpad software in order to use

it. Students may also wish to download Surfaces.pdf, an activity that uses the sketch and extends three-dimensional graphing. The sketch and activity are also available on the *Instructor's Resource CD.*

 Presentation Sketch: Surfaces Present.gsp, on the *Instructor's Resource CD,* graphs surfaces of revolution. You may want to utilize this presentation to familiarize students with the sketch they will use in Problems 11 and 12. This document also includes a sketch of a hyperbolic paraboloid on the second page as well as a general sketch of *z* as a function of *x* and *y* on the third page.

 Activity: Surfaces uses the sketch Surfaces.gsp, described earlier, to graph surfaces of revolution, hyperboloids, and *z* as a function of *x* and *y*. This comes from *Exploring Precalculus with The Geometer's Sketchpad,* but a PDF file of the activity is available on the *Instructor's Resource CD* and at *www.keymath.com/ precalc.*

Problem Notes

• *Problems 1–10* provide practice with sketching quadric surfaces formed by rotating conics.

• *Problems 11 and 12* have students use Sketchpad to construct ellipsoids and hyperboloids. Students compare these sketches with the ones they created by hand for Problems 3, 4, 5, and 7.

• *Problems 13–19* are maximum-minimum problems. Problems 13, 15, and 19 provide figures that will help jump-start students. However, emphasize to students that they still need to understand how to get from the *words* to the *sketch.*

Supplementary Problems

1. *Submarine Problem 2:* The submarine pressure hull in Problem 19 could also be built in the shape of a **frustum of a cone.** As shown in Figure 12-3a, a frustum of a cone is a cone with its vertex cut off. The larger base of the frustum is the base of the half ellipsoid. The smaller base of the frustum touches the half ellipsoid at the sample point (*x, y*).

Figure 12-3a

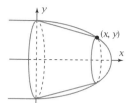

a. Prove that the volume of the frustum of a cone is

$$V = \frac{1}{3}\pi h(R^2 + Rr + r^2)$$

where *h* is the altitude of the frustum (between the two circular bases) and *R* and *r* are the radii of the two bases. You can do this by subtracting from the volume of the entire cone the volume of the small cone that is cut off. Getting the formula in terms of *h*, the difference between the two cones' altitudes, requires clever application of algebra and the geometry of similar triangles.

b. Find a formula for the volume of the frustum in terms of the sample point (*x, y*).

c. Find the maximum volume the frustum can have. What percent greater is this maximum volume than the volume of the maximal cylinder in Problem 19?

2. *Livestock Problem:* A feedlot operator has cattle that weigh an average of 600 lb each and are gaining about 10 lb each week. The price for which they could be sold this week is $0.80 per pound, but this is dropping by 1¢ per pound each week.

a. Show that the total price the operator could get for an average animal is a quadratic function of the number of weeks. Find its particular equation.

b. Plot the graph of the quadratic function. Sketch the result using a reasonable domain.

c. How long should the operator wait in order to get the maximum price per animal?

3. *Ventilator Duct Problem:* A sheet metal duct connects a 20-in. by 60-in. vertical rectangular opening in one wall to a 50-in. by 30-in. vertical rectangular opening in a wall 100 ft away (Figure 12-3b). A cross section is taken through the duct, parallel to the two rectangular openings, at a point *x* in. from the left wall. The lengths *y* and *z* of the cross section are linear functions of *x*.

Figure 12-3b

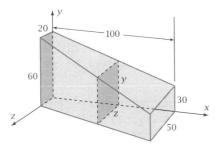

a. Write equations expressing *y* and *z* as functions of *x*.

b. Find the area of the cross section as a function of *x*. What kind of a function is it?

c. At what values of *x* do the maximum and the minimum cross-sectional areas occur? What are these areas?

12-4
Analytic Geometry of the Conic Sections

Objective

Given the equation of a conic section, find the foci, the directrix, and the eccentricity, and vice versa.

Class Time

2–4 days (See the Lesson Notes.)

Homework Assignment

Day 1: RA, Q1–Q10, Problems 1–4

Day 2: Problems 11–31 every other odd

Day 3: Exploration day

Day 4: Some even-numbered problems and/or the remaining odds as needed

Technology Options

 Problem 8: Dynamic Conics Problem

 Presentation Sketch: Ellipse Present.gsp

 Presentation Sketch: Hyperbola Present.gsp

 Presentation Sketch: Parabola Present.gsp

 Activity: Analytic Conics

Important Terms and Concepts

Focus

Directrix

Eccentricity

Major axis

Minor axis

Major radius for an ellipse

Minor radius for an ellipse

Focal radius for an ellipse

Directrix radius for an ellipse

Transverse axis

Conjugate axis

Transverse radius for a hyperbola

Conjugate radius for a hyperbola

Focal radius for a hyperbola

Directrix radius for a hyperbola

Two-foci property of ellipses

Two-foci property of hyperbolas

Pythagorean property for ellipses

Pythagorean property for hyperbolas

Focal distance of a parabola

Latus rectum

Lesson Notes

In the past, teachers spent a week or two on the topics in this section. This material has a beauty of its own and is nice to know. But in today's world, other mathematical concepts have become more important. Covering all the material in this section adequately will require three or four days. If time is short, you might consider one of these options:

• Spend just two days on this section. Focus on having students find analytic features from given equations and skip the reverse process of finding equations from information about the features.

• Skip this section, along with the remainder of this chapter. Sections 12-1 through 12-3 form a sufficient base of knowledge about conic sections. Students will not need the material in the remainder of this chapter for calculus.

There is a lot of terminology in this section. Connecting the terms to the sketches will help students develop a greater understanding of the material and a greater facility with using the relationships. Students may be overwhelmed by all the new concepts when you introduce them. However, working on the problems and explorations will help them understand and absorb the ideas. An excellent summary of the geometric relationships in ellipses and hyperbolas is provided before Example 1 of the student text. Students should find this summary extremely useful as they work on the problems.

Make sure students do not confuse the e used to represent eccentricity with the e used in exponential and logarithmic functions.

This section describes the relationships among axes radii, focal radii, directrix radii, and eccentricity. The two-foci property for ellipses has several applications students may find interesting. For example, suppose a pool table were shaped like an ellipse, with the pocket at one focus. If the ball were placed at the other focus and shot toward *any* spot on the wall, it would bounce off and go into the pocket (a boring game if ever there was one!). Another interesting example is the "whispering chamber" in the U.S. Capitol Building. If a person

stands at one focus of this elliptical room and whispers, she can be heard easily by a person standing at the other focus. Students may want to research an incident involving Daniel Webster in this room.

The text gives the equation $y = \frac{1}{4p}x^2$ for a parabola with vertex at the origin and axis of symmetry along the y-axis. You may want to discuss the relationship between this form and the parabola equation $y = ax^2 + bx + c$ that students learned in algebra. If a parabola has its vertex at the origin and has the y-axis as its axis of symmetry, then $b = 0$ and $c = 0$ and the equation is in the form $y = ax^2$. Hence, $a = \frac{1}{4p}$, or, equivalently, $p = \frac{1}{4a}$, where p is the distance from the vertex to the focus or from the vertex to the directrix.

Example 1 goes through the process of finding all the critical information about a conic section from its equation and then graphing the conic by hand. Students can check their graphs by using the program developed in Section 12-2 or by transforming the Cartesian equation into parametric form and using the parametric mode on the grapher.

Example 2 shows how to find the equation of a conic given its eccentricity and foci. The solution makes use of many of the new concepts and properties from the section. The eccentricity is used to identify the conic as a hyperbola. The center is found by locating the point halfway between the foci. The center and foci are used to find the focal radius. Then the eccentricity and Pythagorean properties are used to find the transverse, conjugate, and directrix radii.

One of the fundamental geometric properties of conic sections is

distance to focus
= (eccentricity)(distance to directrix)

or

$d_2 = ed_1$

Example 3 uses this property to find the equation of an ellipse given a focus, a directrix, and the eccentricity.

Exploration Notes

There are five Explorations for this section. You might want to use Day 3 of the instruction as an Exploration day, during which students work in groups on several of the Explorations. The completed activities can be used for a group grade on this material. Assessing students in this manner will alleviate the stress of memorizing the terminology and formulas and enable students to demonstrate what they know.

Precalculus with Trigonometry: Instructor's Guide
© 2007 Key Curriculum Press

Exploration 12-4a provides introduction to or practice with the properties of ellipses. Students observe by direct measurement and calculation the focus-directrix property, $d_2 = ed_1$, and the two-focus property, $d_3 + d_2 = 2a$, of ellipses. Refer to the Properties box before Example 1 in the student text for a visualization of these properties. Allow students about 15–20 minutes to complete this Exploration.

Exploration 12-4b provides work with the properties of parabolas and hyperbolas. Students use direct measurement to observe that $d_2 = d_1$ for a parabola and then use this property to find a particular equation for the parabola. They also show that $d_2 = ed_1$ for a hyperbola. Allow students about 15 minutes to complete this Exploration.

Exploration 12-4c has students construct an ellipse on an index card using thread and the two-focus property. After completion, students punch the card and file it in their notebooks for future reference. Allow 15–20 minutes for this activity.

Exploration 12-4d leads students through the steps necessary to see that for a hyperbola,

$$(\text{focal radius})^2 = (\text{transverse radius})^2 + (\text{conjugate radius})^2$$

Using words like these, rather than $c^2 = a^2 + b^2$, will help students recall the property and apply it correctly. Allow students about 20 minutes to complete this Exploration.

Exploration 12-4e gives students an opportunity to demonstrate that they know the important properties of this section. Allow students about 20 minutes to complete this Exploration.

Technology Notes

 Problem 8: The Dynamic Conics Problem asks students to explore analytic conics with a Dynamic Precalculus Exploration at *www.keymath.com/precalc.* The page Unified Conics allows students to drag a point to change the eccentricity of a conic and view the effects on the graph.

 Presentation Sketch: Ellipse Present.gsp, on the *Instructor's Resource CD,* shows the ellipse construction with two nails, a string, and a pencil.

 Presentation Sketch: Hyperbola Present.gsp, on the *Instructor's Resource CD,* shows the focus-directrix definition of a hyperbola as well as relationships with the asymptotes.

 Presentation Sketch: Parabola Present.gsp, on the *Instructor's Resource CD,* shows the focus-directrix definition of a parabola.

 Activity: Analytic Conics, in the *Instructor's Resource Book,* allows students to explore conics presented in either standard or general form. If you already assigned the activity in Section 12-2, you may wish to have the students use the second page of the companion sketch, Conics.gsp, to explore graphs of general second-degree equations. Allow 30–40 minutes.

Problem Notes

- *Problems 1–4* review the terminology from this section and require students to verify certain properties. A blackline master for these problems is available in the *Instructor's Resource Book.*

- *Problems 5 and 6* require students to construct conics by using the fact that $d_2 = ed_1$ to plot points.

- *Problems 7 and 8* require students to use The Geometer's Sketchpad to plot conic sections. There are more Sketchpad problems in the Supplementary Problems.

- *Problem 9,* the Mars Orbit Problem, involves exploring the elliptical orbit of Mars about the Sun.

- *Problem 10,* the Comet Path Problem, involves exploring the hyperbolic path of a comet.

- *Problems 11–20* provide practice identifying the features of a conic from its equation. Students also practice sketching graphs and plotting graphs on their graphers.

- *Problems 21–32* provide practice finding the equation of a conic based on information about its features. Students also practice sketching graphs and plotting graphs on their graphers.

- *Problem 33* introduces the term *latus rectum,* which is a chord through the focus of a conic section, parallel to the directrix. "Latus" is Latin for "side" and "rectum" implies right angle.

Supplementary Problems

1. Use a graphing utility such as The Geometer's Sketchpad to plot the conic with focus $(0, 0)$, directrix $x = -6$, and eccentricity $e = \frac{1}{2}$. Sketch the result. How is the graph consistent with the fact that e is between 0 and 1?

2. Use a graphing utility such as The Geometer's Sketchpad to plot a set of conics, each with focus (0, 0) and directrix $x = -6$. Let the eccentricity range from 0.5 to 1.5. Describe what happens to the type of conic and its proportions as the eccentricity increases.

3. Use a graphing utility such as The Geometer's Sketchpad to plot a set of conics, each with focus (0, 0) and directrix $y = -2$. Let the eccentricity range from 0.5 to 1.5. Sketch three of the conics, one with $e = 0.5$, one with $e = 1$, and one with $e = 1.5$. Describe what happens to the type of conic and its proportions as the eccentricity increases.

In Problems 4–9, find the particular equation, name the conic section, and sketch the graph.

4. Focus (0, 0), directrix $x = -3$, eccentricity $\frac{5}{2}$

5. Focus (0, 0), directrix $y = -1$, eccentricity 0.6

6. Focus (0, 25), directrix $y = 9$, eccentricity $\frac{5}{3}$

7. Focus (4, 0), directrix $x = 6.25$, eccentricity $\frac{4}{5}$

8. Focus (0.5, 0), directrix $x = -0.5$, eccentricity 1

9. Focus $(0, -\frac{1}{4})$, directrix $y = \frac{1}{4}$, eccentricity 1

In Problems 10–15, plot the conic section based on the given information and write the particular equation.

10. Ellipse with one vertex at (−15, 6) and foci (10, 6) and (−14, 6)

11. Hyperbola with foci (−3, 1) and (−3, −5), asymptotes with slope $\pm\frac{3}{2}$

12. Conic with center at (−3, −2), one vertex at (−3, −7), and eccentricity $\frac{3}{5}$

13. Conic with foci (−3, 8) and (−3, −4) and eccentricity 1.2

14. Conic with center at (1, 2), directrix $x = 7$, and corresponding focus (3, 2)

15. Ellipse with vertices (3, 10) and (3, −8) and a latus rectum 6 units long (See Problem 33 in the student text.)

16. *Earth's Orbit Problem:* Earth's orbit around the Sun is slightly elliptical, with the Sun at one focus. At its closest, Earth is 147.1 million kilometers from the Sun. At its farthest, it is 152.1 million kilometers from the Sun.

    a. How far is the Sun from the center of the ellipse?

    b. Find the minor radius of the ellipse.

    c. What is the eccentricity of Earth's orbit?

    d. Find the particular equation of the orbit, placing the origin at the center of the ellipse.

    e. How far from the center of the ellipse are the directrices?

    f. How far is Earth from the Sun when Earth is at 90° to the major axis of the ellipse?

17. *Loran Problem:* In the days before the Global Positioning System (GPS), LORAN (an acronym for LOng RAnge Navigation) was used to help planes and ships find their location. Radio pulses from several widely spaced transmitters were broadcast simultaneously. By measuring the difference in time of arrival of the pulses, the difference in distances from two transmitters could be computed. Suppose an airplane is located at a point (x, y), where x and y are in hundreds of miles. Transmitters 1, 2, and 3 are located at points (0, 4), (0, 0), and (6, 0), respectively (Figure 12-4a).

Figure 12-4a

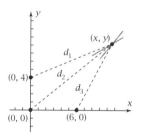

    a. The distances between the airplane and the three stations are related by

$$d_1 - d_2 = 2 \quad\text{and}\quad d_2 - d_3 = 4$$

    Explain why (x, y) is a point on each of two hyperbolas.

    b. Find the particular equations of the two hyperbolas.

    c. Plot the two equations on the same screen. You may modify the grapher program of Section 12-2 so that it plots both graphs, download a program that will do this, or plot the graph on another graphing utility.

    d. Find numerically the four points where the two hyperbolas intersect. How could the airplane's crew determine which of the four points gives their correct location?

Precalculus with Trigonometry: Instructor's Guide
© 2007 Key Curriculum Press

12-5
Parametric and Cartesian Equations of Rotated Conics

Objectives

- Plot a conic section rotated by a specified angle to the coordinate axes.

- Identify a rotated conic from its Cartesian equation.

- Plot a rotated conic using its Cartesian or parametric equations.

Class Time

2 days

Homework Assignment

Day 1: RA, Q1–Q10, Problems 1–11 odd

Day 2:

    Recommended: Problems 13–19 odd, 23

    Also suggested: 21, 22

Technology Options

 Problem 23: Variable *xy*-term Problem

 Activity: Analytic Conics

Important Terms and Concepts

Parametric equations of rotated conic sections

Cartesian equations of rotated conic sections

Discriminant

Lesson Notes

Up to this point, students have worked with conics with horizontal and vertical axes. In this section, they will work with rotated conics.

Example 1 shows how to write parametric equations for a rotated conic. The rotation matrix studied in Chapter 11 is used. After you have discussed the example, you may want to summarize the steps for students.

- Write parametric equations for an unrotated, untranslated conic of the same type and with the same dilation factors as the given conic.

- Write the parametric expressions for *x* and *y* as a 2 × 1 matrix, and left-multiply the matrix by the appropriate rotation matrix.

- Use the resulting matrix to write parametric equations for a rotated conic centered at the origin.

- Add the translations to get the final equations.

The equations in Examples 2–4 differ only in the coefficient of the *xy*-term, yet the three equations give three different types of conics. These examples demonstrate that if the general form of the conic equation contains an *xy*-term, you *cannot* simply use the coefficients of x^2 and y^2 to predict the type of conic. Instead, you can use the *discriminant,* $B^2 - 4AC$. The box after Example 4 in the student text explains how.

Note that in the general equation $Ax^2 + Bxy + Cy^2 + Dx + Ey + F = 0$, if $B = 0$ and $A = C$, the conic is a circle. If you rotate a circle about its center, the graph remains unchanged.

Example 5 shows how to use the discriminant property to identify a conic.

Exploration Notes

Exploration 12-5a is a discovery activity that leads students to discover the discriminant property for determining the type of conic a quadratic with an *xy*-term represents. You may want to start Day 2 by assigning this activity and then review its results and discuss Examples 2–5. Allow students 20–25 minutes to complete this Exploration.

Technology Notes

 Problem 23: The Variable *xy*-term Problem asks students to explore the general equation for a conic with a Dynamic Precalculus Exploration at *www.keymath.com/precalc.* The page General Conic allows students to use sliders to change the coefficients in the equation and view the effects on the graph.

 Activity: Analytic Conics, in the *Instructor's Resource Book,* engages students in exploring Cartesian equations of circles, ellipses, and hyperbolas. A second part concerns the general second-degree equation, mostly with the *xy*-term set to zero. You may wish to use this activity and the accompanying sketch to focus on graphs of general conics with nonzero *xy*-term. Allow 30–40 minutes.

Problem Notes

- *Problems 1–12* give students practice writing parametric equations for rotated conics.

- *Problems 13–18* involve using the discriminant property to determine the type of conic section.

- *Problems 21 and 22* are optional. You may want to assign them as extra-credit projects.

- *Problem 23* asks students to plot the graphs of four conic section equations that differ only in the *xy*-term and to observe the similarities in the four graphs.

12-6
Applications of Conic Sections

Objective

Given a situation from the real world in which conic sections appear, create a mathematical model and use it to make predictions and interpretations.

Class Time

2 days

Homework Assignment

Day 1: Q1–Q10, Problems 1–4

Day 2: Problems 5–8

Lesson Notes

This section includes a set of application problems that make use of the analytic properties from previous sections. It lends meaning to the more abstract work of the last few sections. Jump right in.

Exploration Notes

Exploration 12-6a requires students to create a graph representing the region from which it is cheaper to ship from one warehouse rather than another based on some initial constraints. A verbal description of the problem leads to an algebraic inequality that translates into a graphical picture of a region bounded by a conic section. Allow students about 20 minutes to complete this investigation.

Problem Notes

- *Problem 1*, the Coffee Table Problem, is an essay question that requires students to demonstrate their understanding of the properties of an ellipse.

- *Problem 2*, the Stadium Problem, requires students to find two equations and then use them in clever ways to determine clearances and seating capacity.

- *Problem 3*, the Bridge Problem, lets students apply what they know about parabolas to solve problems about the construction of a bridge.

- *Problem 4*, the Halley's Comet Problem, shows that the orbit of Halley's comet is a highly elongated ellipse. You might ask students to find out the period of Halley's comet and when it was last visible from Earth.

- *Problem 5,* Meteorite Tracking Problem 1, involves solving a system of quadratic equations.

- *Problem 6,* Meteorite Tracking Problem 2, involves parametric equations for a hyperbola.

- *Problems 7 and 8,* Marketing Problems 1 and 2, are fascinating applications of conics to an unexpected field. These problems form the basis for Exploration 12-6a.

- *Problems 9 and 10* provide challenging material for additional assignments. The Hyperboloid Project is a graphing problem in parametric mode. Students may recall doing similar problems in Chapter 4. The Elliptical Pendulum Project requires students to construct a pendulum, set it in motion to form an elliptical path, write the equation of the path, and use the equation to predict the pendulum's position after a specified time.

12-7
Chapter Review and Test

Objective

Review and practice the major concepts of the chapter.

Class Time

2 days (including 1 day for testing)

Homework Assignment

Day 1: R0–R6, T1–T18

Day 2 (after Chapter 12 Test): The exploratory problem set in Section 1 of the next chapter you plan to do

Lesson Notes

Section 12-7 contains a set of Review Problems, a set of Concept Problems, and a Chapter Test. The Review Problems include one problem for each section in the chapter. You may wish to use the Chapter Test as an additional set of review problems.

Encourage students to practice the no-calculator problems without a calculator so that they are prepared for the test problems for which they cannot use a calculator.

Exploration Notes

There are four Explorations in this section that relate to the two concept problems in the chapter review. These Explorations could be assigned as extra-credit projects.

Exploration 12-7a examines the path of a ray of light emanating from one focus of an ellipse. Students who have studied some physics should be able to connect this investigation with the "angle of incidence equals the angle of refraction" property. Allow students about 20 minutes to complete this Exploration.

Exploration 12-7b extends the previous Exploration by leading students to write the equation of the tangent line to a point on an ellipse and then to verify the reflecting property. Allow students 20–25 minutes to complete this Exploration.

Exploration 12-7c uses a geometric definition and much algebra to come up with the equation of a conic section. See if students can connect this activity to the marketing Exploration from the preceding section. Allow students 20–25 minutes to complete this Exploration.

Exploration 12-7d requires students to solve a system of quadratic equations graphically, numerically, and symbolically. Allow students about 20 minutes to complete this Exploration.

Problem Notes

Problems C1 and C2 are concept problems that extend the material in the chapter. They are related to the four Explorations. A blackline master for Problem R4 is available in the *Instructor's Resource Book*.

Supplementary Problems

1. Figure 12-7a shows a part of a conic section graph, with the focus and the directrix labeled.

    Figure 12-7a

    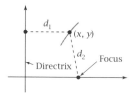

    a. Describe how the distances d_1 and d_2 are related to each other for a hyperbola, a parabola, and an ellipse. Indicate how the eccentricity of the conic section is defined in terms of d_1 and d_2.

    b. Find the particular equation of the conic section with focus (0, 0), directrix $x = 6$, and the given eccentricity. Plot the graphs and sketch the results, showing the focus and directrix.

        i. Eccentricity 1   ii. Eccentricity $\frac{3}{2}$

        iii. Eccentricity $\frac{2}{3}$

2. Figure 12-7b shows a point on the graph of a conic section and the two foci.

    Figure 12-7b

    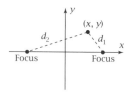

    a. State the relationship between the distances d_1 and d_2 from (x, y) to the two foci for:

        i. An ellipse   ii. A hyperbola

        iii. A circle

    b. Find the particular equation of the ellipse with foci (0, 4) and (0, −4) if the constant sum of the distances is $d_1 + d_2 = 10$. Plot the graph on your grapher. Sketch the result, showing the two foci.

    c. Find the particular equation of the hyperbola with foci (17, 0) and (−17, 0) if the constant difference between the distances is $|d_1 - d_2| = 15$. Plot the graph on your grapher. Sketch the result, showing the two foci.

In Problems 3–5, identify the conic section and specify the center, the important radius lengths, and the eccentricity. Then sketch the graph, showing these features.

3. $y = 0.04x^2$

4. $3x^2 - 7y^2 = -210$

5. $\left(\dfrac{x-2}{6}\right)^2 + \left(\dfrac{y+4}{3}\right)^2 = 1$

In Problems 6–9, find the particular equation of the conic section described. Then sketch the graph, showing the analytic features.

6. Hyperbola with foci (3, 0) and (−3, 0) and constant difference of distances equal to 4

7. Ellipse with center (−6, 8), one vertex at (19, 8), and eccentricity 0.96

8. Parabola with latus rectum (see Problem 33 of Section 12-4 in the student text) between −1 and −9 on the *y*-axis, opening in the negative *x*-direction

9. Hyperbola with foci (2, 7) and (2, −5) and eccentricity $\frac{3}{2}$

10. State the two-foci property for hyperbolas.

11. Sketch an ellipse centered at the origin, with major axis along the *x*-axis. Show one focus and the corresponding directrix. Use the focus-directrix property of ellipses and a clever choice of the point (x, y) on the ellipse to derive the formula $e = \frac{a}{d}$.

12. Consider the equation $9x^2 + 4y^2 + 90x - 8y + 85 = 0$.

    a. Identify which type of conic section the equation represents.

    b. Plot the graph. Sketch the result.

    c. Transform the equation by completing the square. Find the important radii and the eccentricity.

13 Polar Coordinates, Complex Numbers, and Moving Objects

Students first learn about polar coordinates by plotting given points by hand on polar coordinate paper. This seems to be the best way to convey the concept of negative radius. Thereafter, they use their grapher to plot given equations and find intersections of polar curves. Writing complex numbers in polar form gives geometric meaning to products of the numbers. A complex product has modulus equal to the product of the moduli of the factors and argument equal to the sum of the arguments of the factors. The composite argument properties from Chapter 5 are reviewed in the algebraic proof of this property. Extension to powers and roots allows students to discover that any complex number, including any real number, has exactly n distinct nth roots. The chapter concludes with application of polar coordinates, parametric equations, and vectors to analyze some of the classic curves from analytic geometry, such as the involute of a circle. The Explorations provide students with accurate graphs upon which they can make actual measurements to verify the geometric definitions and properties of the curves.

13-1
Introduction to Polar Coordinates

Objective

Given an equation in polar coordinates, plot the graph on polar coordinate paper.

Class Time

$\frac{1}{2}$ day

Homework Assignment

Problems 1–6 (Suggest that students read "Background on Polar Coordinates" in Section 13-2 if they need help plotting points in polar coordinates.)

Each student will need two sheets of polar graph paper, which can be reproduced from the blackline master in the *Instructor's Resource Book*.

Important Terms and Concepts

Polar coordinates

Pole

Polar equation

Lesson Notes

Students are familiar with the Cartesian, or rectangular, coordinate system, in which points are located by *x*- and *y*-coordinates. In this lesson, students plot points using *polar coordinates*, where points are located by an angle θ and a distance r from the origin. You can assign this section for homework the night of the Chapter 12 test or as a group activity to be completed in class. No class-room discussion is needed before students begin the activity.

If students struggle to figure out how to plot polar coordinates, they should read "Background on Polar Coordinates" in Section 13-2.

When you discuss this problem set, point out that θ is the independent variable, and so it appears in the first column of the table, while r, the dependent variable, appears second. Unlike Cartesian coordinates, (x, y), where the independent variable is listed first, it is customary to write polar coordinates in the form (r, θ), with the dependent variable listed first. Also point out that θ can represent an angle in degrees or in radians.

13-2
Polar Equations of Conics and Other Curves

Objectives

- Given a polar equation, plot the graph.
- Given the polar equation of a conic section, transform it into Cartesian coordinates.

Class Time

3 days

Homework Assignment

Day 1: RA, Q1–Q10, Problems 1–9 odd (Students need polar coordinate paper for Problem 1.)

Day 2: Problems 11–23 odd

Day 3: Even-numbered problems as needed

Technology Options

 Figure 13-2f: Polar Graphs

 Figure 13-2l: Polar Conics

 Figure 13-2n: Polar Lines

 Problem 3: Bifolium

 Problem 4: Cissoid of Dioclese

 Presentation Sketch: Polar Present.gsp

 Presentation Sketch: Cartesian Polar Present.gsp

Activity: Cartesian Graphs and Polar Graphs

Activity: Introduction to Polar Coordinates

Important Terms and Concepts

Limaçon of Pascal

Pole

Polar axis

Auxiliary Cartesian graph

Cardioid

Rose

Conic sections in polar coordinates

Relationship between conics and limaçons

Circle in polar coordinates

Line in polar coordinates

Bifolium

Cissoid of Dioclese

Lemniscate of Bernoulli

Spiral

Conchoid of Nicomedes

Lesson Notes

In this section, students plot graphs of polar equations. As students work on this section, encourage them to "play" with their graphers, experimenting with different equations and settings. They will discover all sorts of fascinating things. It is recommended that you spend three days on this section. Start with Exploration 13-2a.

Encourage your students to use the Dynamic Precalculus Explorations for this section to get dynamic, high-resolution polar graphs.

Try to get through Example 1 on the first day and through the remainder of the new material on the second day. The third day can be spent working on problems and/or Explorations.

Before students explore all the nifty graphs in this section, they need to be comfortable with plotting points in polar coordinates. This text follows the convention of writing polar coordinates in the form (r, θ) because this is the way ordered pairs appear on graphers and on standardized tests. Some students may find this notation confusing because the dependent variable r is listed first. Problems 1 and 2 provide practice with plotting points. You may want to have students complete one of these problems in class before you discuss the "Graphs of Polar Equations" part of the section.

Help students plot the graph of the limaçon $r = 1 + 2 \cos \theta$ (in degree mode) on their graphers. Show them that they can trace the graph in either polar or Cartesian coordinates, depending on the setting they choose from the Format menu. If they select polar grid coordinates, the grapher will show the values of θ and r. If they select rectangular grid coordinates, the grapher will show the value of θ and the corresponding values of x and y.

With polar grid coordinates selected, have students trace the graph of $r = 1 + 2 \cos \theta$. They should see that the inner loop corresponds to θ-values between 120° and 140°.

Plotting an auxiliary Cartesian graph can help students connect the familiar Cartesian coordinate system with the unfamiliar polar coordinates. Ask students questions such as "How can you tell from the Cartesian graph of $y = 1 + 2 \cos \theta$ that the polar graph

of $r = 1 + 2 \cos \theta$ will have a loop?" Students should see that the Cartesian graph shows that the function is negative when θ is between 120° and 240°. This means that the points will be plotted in the opposite direction, causing the graph to loop back on itself.

You might also ask students how they could tell from the *equation* (without making an auxiliary graph) that the polar graph of $r = 1 + 2 \cos \theta$ will have a loop. They know that $\cos \theta$ has a range of $[-1, 1]$. Therefore, $2 \cos \theta$ has a range of $[-2, 2]$, and so $1 + 2 \cos \theta$ has a range of $[-1, 3]$. Because r can be negative, the graph will loop back. Students should be able to use similar reasoning to explain why the graph of $r = 2 + \cos \theta$ does not have a loop and why the graph of $r = 2 + 2 \cos \theta$ has a cusp. The definition of a limaçon in the student text generalizes these ideas.

Example 1 refers to a five-leaved rose. Show how to find the solution to this problem numerically, algebraically, and graphically. This is a good place to review the steps in finding a general solution to a trigonometric equation:

$6 \sin 5\theta = 0$ Set r equal to zero and solve for θ.

$5\theta = 0° + 360n°$ or $5\theta = 180° + 360n°$
                Write the general solution for θ.

$\theta = 0° + 72n°$ or $\theta = 36° + 72n°$

$\theta = 0°, 36°, 72°, 108°, \ldots$ Write the particular values.

r is first negative for $36° < \theta < 72°$
           Pick the correct interval by tracing.

Confirmation: see Figure 13-2j in the text.
           Set the θ-range to $[36, 72]$.

Most polar graphs fail the vertical-line test that is used to determine whether a Cartesian equation is a function. Explain that for the polar equations in this section, there is exactly one r-value for a given θ-value; thus the equations are indeed functions. An exception would be an equation like

$$r^2 = 9 + 12 \cos \theta + 4 \cos^2 \theta$$

In this case,

$$r = \pm\sqrt{9 + 12 \cos \theta + 4 \cos^2\theta}$$

so there are two values of r for a given θ-value.

Surprisingly, graphs of the reciprocals of limaçon equations are conic sections. Example 2 plots the polar equation of an ellipse. The results lead to the properties of the conic sections in polar coordinates as well as the relationship between conics and limaçons.

The text then develops polar equations for horizontal and vertical lines and for special circles.

Note: Most of the equations in this section involve a trigonometric function of θ. In this situation, θ may be in either degrees or radians. However, when an equation does not involve a trigonometric function of θ, for example, $r = \frac{2\theta}{\pi}$ in Problem 13, then θ must be in radians, because r has to be a real number.

Exploration Notes

Exploration 13-2a asks students to plot a limaçon both on paper (by plotting and connecting points) and on their graphers. They then investigate the graph. This Exploration can be assigned as a group activity either before or after Example 1. It can also be used as a review sheet or homework assignment. Allow students 15–20 minutes to complete this activity.

Exploration 13-2b has students investigate graphs of roses and make a conjecture about the relationship between the coefficient n and the number of leaves in the rose. This can be assigned any time after Example 1 and may be used as a group activity or an additional homework assignment. Allow students 15–20 minutes to complete this activity.

Technology Notes

 Figure 13-2f: Polar Graphs is a Dynamic Precalculus Exploration at *www.keymath.com/precalc* that allows students to compare polar and Cartesian graphs.

 Figure 13-2l: Polar Conics is a Dynamic Precalculus Exploration at *www.keymath.com/precalc* that has students explore polar equations of conic sections.

 Figure 13-2n: Polar Lines is a Dynamic Precalculus Exploration at *www.keymath.com/precalc* that has students explore polar equations of vertical and horizontal lines.

 Problem 3: Bifolium asks students to graph the equation $r = 20 \cos \theta \sin^2 \theta$ and explore this graph with the Bifolium Dynamic Precalculus Exploration at *www.keymath.com/precalc*.

 Problem 4: Cissoid of Dioclese asks students to graph the equation $r = 2 \sin \theta \tan \theta$ and explore this graph with the Cissoid Dynamic Precalculus Exploration at *www.keymath.com/precalc*.

 Presentation Sketch: Polar Present.gsp, on the *Instructor's Resource CD,* demonstrates polar coordinates in Sketchpad. Students can see

how points have infinitely many polar representations as well as how to plot a point with a negative r-value. This sketch is related to the activity Introduction to Polar Coordinates.

 Presentation Sketch: Cartesian Polar Present.gsp, on the *Instructor's Resource CD,* demonstrates polar graphs and their connection to Cartesian graphs. You can enter any equation and watch as the Cartesian and polar graphs of the equation are graphed simultaneously. This presentation is related to the activity Cartesian Graphs and Polar Graphs.

 Activity: Cartesian Graphs and Polar Graphs, in the *Instructor's Resource Book,* has students compare Cartesian and polar graphs of equations in a prepared Sketchpad document. The sketch shows a simultaneous trace of both the Cartesian and the polar graphs of equations, an excellent tool in demonstrating polar graphs. Students start by exploring the circle $r = a \cos b\theta$ and the line $r = 2 \sec \theta$, and then move on to a sketch where they can graph any equation. Allow 20–30 minutes.

 Activity: Introduction to Polar Coordinates, in *Exploring Precalculus with The Geometer's Sketchpad,* demonstrates the basics in polar coordinates and their relations to Cartesian coordinates. The *Exploring Precalculus with The Geometer's Sketchpad CD* also contains the sketch Intro to Polar.gsp, in which students can move a "target" point around the plane and guess several polar coordinate pairs representing the point. This is good familiarization practice for students who are new to polar coordinates. Allow 25–35 minutes for the activity.

Additional Class Example

This example shows how you can use the technique of completing the square, along with the polar equation of a vertical line, to extend Example 2 in the student text.

1. For the ellipse in Example 2,
   a. Find the center and the lengths of the major and minor radii.
   b. Show that one focus is at the pole.
   c. Find the eccentricity.
   d. Find the polar equation of the directrix corresponding to the focus at the pole, and plot the directrix.

Solution

a. $9x^2 + 25y^2 - 72x - 81 = 0$ Start with the Cartesian equation.

$9(x^2 - 8x + 16) + 25y^2 = 81 + 9(16)$

                      Complete the square.

$9(x - 4)^2 + 25y^2 = 225$

$\left(\dfrac{x-4}{5}\right)^2 + \left(\dfrac{y}{3}\right)^2 = 1$ Make the right side equal 1.

major radius = 5, minor radius = 3

b. Focal radius $c = \sqrt{5^2 - 3^2} = 4$ See Section 12-4.

One focus is at $x = 4 + 4 = 8$, the other is at $x = 4 - 4 = 0$, so one focus is at the pole.

c. $e = \dfrac{\text{focal radius}}{\text{major radius}} = \dfrac{4}{5} = 0.8$ See Section 12-4.

d. $d = \dfrac{\text{major radius}}{\text{eccentricity}} = \dfrac{5}{0.8} = 6.25$ See Section 12-4.

Directrix is $6.25 - 4 = 2.25$ units from the pole.

Directrix has polar equation $r = -2.25 \sec \theta$.

                  The polar equation for a vertical line.

Figure 13-2a shows graphs of the ellipse and the directrix.

Figure 13-2a

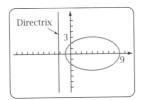

Problem Notes

In this problem set, students will investigate many interesting polar curves. With the exception of *limaçon*, students should not be expected to learn the names of these curves.

- *Problems 1 and 2* require students to plot points given in polar coordinates and connect them to form a curve. Students will need polar coordinate paper.

- *Problems 3 and 4* connect the graphs in Problems 1 and 2 with their equations and ask students to plot and trace the graphs on their graphers.

- *Problems 5 and 6* involve three- and four-leaved roses.

- *Problems 7–10* involve polar equations of circles and lines.

- *Problems 11–14* are interesting problems to discuss in class. In Problem 13, students may be surprised at how the function behaves for negative values of θ. Remind students that they must use radian measures for this problem.

- *Problems 15 and 16* ask students to write polar equations for given lines and circles.

- *Problems 17–19* involve connecting the polar and Cartesian forms of conic equations. In these problems, one focus is at the pole. This is easy to demonstrate by following the procedure of the additional class example in the Lesson Notes.

- *Problem 20,* the Rotated Polar Graphs Problem, investigates the polar equation for a rotated ellipse.

- *Problem 21,* the Roller Skating Problem, asks students to write an equation for a roller skating loop based on the loop's dimensions.

- *Problem 22,* the Rose Problem, asks students to make a conjecture about the relationship between the value of n in the rose equation $r = k \cos n\theta$ and the number of leaves the rose has.

- *Problem 23,* the Comparing Graphs Problem, asks students to examine the relationship between a Cartesian graph and the corresponding polar graph.

Supplementary Problems

1. *General Polar Equation of a Conic Section Problem:* The general polar equation of a conic section with focus at the pole is shown in the box.

PROPERTY: General Polar Equation of a Conic Section

A conic section with focus at the pole and one axis parallel to the polar axis has polar equation

$$r = \frac{ep}{1 \pm e \cos \theta} \quad \text{or} \quad r = \frac{ep}{1 \pm e \sin \theta}$$

where e is the eccentricity of the conic and p is the distance between the pole and the directrix.

Starting with $r = \frac{ep}{1 - e \cos \theta}$,

a. Prove that the graph is a conic section by transforming to Cartesian coordinates.

b. Show that one focus of the conic really is at the pole.

c. Show that *e* really is the eccentricity of the conic.

d. Show that *p* really is the distance between the pole and the directrix.

2. *Line in Polar Coordinates Problem:* Figure 13-2b shows the line $r = \sec \theta$.

Figure 13-2b

a. Plot the graph of $r = 7 \sec (\theta - 60°)$. Tell how the 7 and the 60° affect the graph.

b. Write the polar equation of a line containing the Cartesian point $(-24, 7)$ if this is the point on the line that is closest to the pole.

c. Explain how your result relates to the general polar equation of a line, presented in the box.

PROPERTY: *General Polar Equation of a Line*

The polar equation of a line is

$$r = a \sec (\theta - \alpha)$$

where *a* and α are as shown in Figure 13-2c.

Figure 13-2c

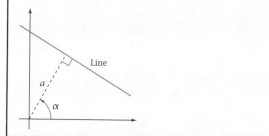

13-3
Intersections of Polar Curves

Objective

Given two polar equations, find the solutions to the system of equations and relate them to the intersections of the polar curves.

Class Time

1 day

Homework Assignment

RA, Q1–Q10, Problems 1–9 odd

Technology Options

Presentation Sketch: Polar Intersect Present.gsp

Important Terms and Concepts

Intersection points of polar graphs

Lesson Notes

The graphs of $r = 3 + \cos 2\theta$ and $r = 5 \sin 2\theta$ in Figure 13-3a in the student text intersect at eight points. In this section, students will discover that only four of these points can be found by solving the system of equations. The others are points where the graphs cross for different values of θ.

In general, finding intersections of polar graphs can be a tedious process. The reason for this goes back to the fact that polar representations of points are not unique. Similarly, a polar curve can be represented by different equations. Therefore, you may have to solve several systems of equations in order to find all points of intersection. For this reason, the emphasis in this section should be on looking at graphs critically and not on finding all points of intersection.

Example 1 shows students how using auxiliary Cartesian graphs to determine intersection points can miss some of the intersections. As an alternative to presenting this example, you can have students work in groups on Exploration 13-3a, which guides them through the process of identifying intersection points. Before students start the Exploration, make sure they know how to plot

---

graphs in simultaneous mode and how to pause the graphing process. On most graphers, you press ENTER to pause and then press ENTER again to resume graphing.

To learn how to identify false intersection points, see Problem 9 and the Supplementary Lesson Notes.

Exploration Notes

Exploration 13-3a guides students through the process described in the text for finding the intersection points of two polar curves. Beginning the section with this activity will lead to fruitful discussions afterward and set your students off on the right foot in their assignment. Allow students 20–25 minutes to complete this Exploration.

Technology Notes

 Presentation Sketch: Polar Intersect Present.gsp, on the *Instructor's Resource CD,* demonstrates how two polar graphs may intersect for different values of θ. The sketch opens with the two functions from Example 1, but the functions can be changed. If possible, give students access to this sketch, possibly even to be used for their homework.

Supplementary Lesson Notes

Figure 13-3a in the student text shows graphs of these two equations.

$$r_1 = 3 + 2 \cos \theta$$

$$r_2 = 5 \sin 2\theta$$

To find the points where the graphs cross for different values of θ, replace r with $-r$ and θ with $(\theta - 180°)$ in one of the two equations. For instance, replace r_2 with $r_3 = -5 \sin 2(\theta - 180°)$. This substitution rotates the graph 180° and then reflects it through the pole. The resulting graph has the same shape as the original polar curve but is generated by values of θ that are 180° further around. Figure 13-3a shows why these transformations give the same figure as the original graph.

Figure 13-3a

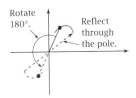

Plot auxiliary Cartesian graphs of the transformed equation, r_3, and the other original equation, r_1. The intersections (Figure 13-3b) will be the missed intersections in Figure 13-3a in the student text.

Figure 13-3b

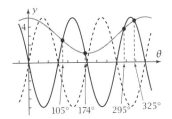

Figure 13-3c

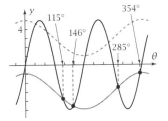

A surprise shows up if you do the replacements in the other original equation. Figure 13-3c shows the result of replacing r_1 with

$$r_4 = -3 - 2 \cos (\theta - 180°)$$

and then plotting auxiliary Cartesian graphs of r_4 and the other original graph, r_2. The missed intersection points have different polar coordinates, but the points are at the same four places on the polar coordinate plane. The angles are 180° apart, and the r-values are opposites of each other.

Missed intersections	*Missed intersections*
(2.4855..., 104.9046...°)	(−3.8511..., 115.1873...°)
(1.0103..., 174.1710...°)	(−4.6529..., 145.7369...°)
(3.8511..., 295.1873...°)	(−2.4855..., 284.9046...°)
(4.6529..., 325.7369...°)	(−1.0103..., 354.1710...°)

A technique for finding intersections of polar curves is summarized in the box.

> **TECHNIQUE:** *Intersections of Polar Curves*
>
> To find the solutions to a system of two polar equations, plot auxiliary Cartesian graphs and solve numerically or graphically for the intersection points. The values of x will be the values of θ, and the values of y will be the values of r.
>
> To find more intersection points, where the graphs cross but do not intersect, replace r with $-r$ and θ with $(\theta - 180°)$ in one of the polar equations. The intersections of this curve and the other given curve will be intersection points of the original polar curves.

Problem Notes

Problem 9 asks students to come up with a method for finding more intersection points. The example should lead them to the realization that if they replace r with $-r$ and θ with $(\theta - 180°)$ in one of the two equations, more intersection points may be found. (For more information on finding intersection points, see the Supplementary Lesson Notes.)

13-4
Complex Numbers in Polar Form

Objective

Operate with complex numbers in polar form.

Class Time

2 days

Homework Assignment

Day 1: Q1–Q10, Problems 1–37 every other odd, 39

Day 2: The remaining odds and, if needed, some of the even-numbered problems

Technology Options

 Presentation Sketch: Complex Multiplication Present.gsp

 Presentation Sketch: Complex Transformations Present.gsp

 Presentation Sketch: Complex Powers Present.gsp

 Activity: Transformations in the Complex Plane

Important Terms and Concepts

Imaginary number

Complex number

Unit imaginary number, i

Complex plane

Polar form of a complex number

Real part of a complex number

Imaginary part of a complex number

Complex conjugate

Modulus

Argument

Product of two complex numbers in polar form

Reciprocal of a complex number in polar form

Quotient of two complex numbers in polar form

De Moivre's theorem

Root of a complex number

Distinct roots of a complex number

Triple argument properties

Lesson Notes

In this section, students learn how to write complex numbers in polar form, which makes it significantly easier to find powers and roots. In the Supplementary Lesson Notes, you will find a brief summary of operations with complex numbers in Cartesian form. You may want to review this material with students before introducing polar form.

The word *imaginary* gives some students the impression that imaginary numbers are somehow "fake." In fact, imaginary numbers are basic to the study of alternating electric current.

The notation used for complex numbers can be confusing. The Cartesian, or rectangular, form is $a + bi$, and the polar form is $r(\cos \theta + i \sin \theta)$, abbreviated r cis θ. Make sure students understand that i is the unit imaginary number, not the unit vector $\vec{i}$.

Example 1 shows how to transform the Cartesian form of a complex number into the polar form. Emphasize the importance of making a sketch in order to determine the correct value of θ.

Example 2 shows how to change the polar form of a complex number to Cartesian form.

Example 3 demonstrates how to find the product of two complex numbers given in polar form. The product is first calculated the "long way," which involves multiplying binomials, combining like terms, and applying composite argument properties. This long solution leads to a shortcut—multiplying the moduli and adding the arguments. Make sure to show both solutions because the "long way" helps students understand why the "short way" works.

Example 4 shows the long and short ways to find the reciprocal of a complex number in polar form. Again, discuss both solutions so students can see how the long way leads to the short way. Note that the long way requires multiplying by 1 in the form $\frac{\text{conjugate}}{\text{conjugate}}$.

Example 5 demonstrates division of complex numbers in polar form. Discuss both solutions. Note that the long way uses both the reciprocal property and the product property.

Example 6 shows how to find the power of a complex number. The short way—raising the modulus to the power and multiplying the argument by the exponent—is known as De Moivre's theorem.

Because a root is simply a fractional exponent, De Moivre's theorem can be used to find the roots of a complex number. This is illustrated in Example 7. The text explains that in general a complex number

has exactly n distinct nth roots. Students usually find roots of complex numbers by finding the obvious one and then adding the appropriate number of degrees to the angle. The n roots of a complex number are equally spaced on a circle with the center at the pole with radius r.

Exploration Notes

Exploration 13-4a guides students as they read Section 13-4 on their own. You can introduce the material in this section by having students work in groups to complete this Exploration. Assign each group one of the properties to present to the class. Allow students about 25 minutes to complete this activity.

Exploration 13-4b demonstrates graphically what happens when two complex numbers are multiplied. Students will be able to observe for themselves that the argument of the product is the sum of the arguments of the factors and the modulus of the product is the product of the moduli of the factors. Allow students about 15–20 minutes to complete this Exploration.

Exploration 13-4c requires students to multiply two complex numbers the long way. This requires students to recall the composite argument properties studied in Chapter 5. The results should verify the shortcut for multiplying two complex numbers in polar form. Allow students about 15–20 minutes to complete this Exploration.

Technology Notes

 Presentation Sketch: Complex Multiplication Present.gsp, on the *Instructor's Resource CD,* demonstrates the multiplication of complex numbers using their polar form. This sketch is related to the activity Multiplication of Complex Numbers, in *Exploring Precalculus with The Geometer's Sketchpad.*

 Presentation Sketch: Complex Transformations Present.gsp, on the *Instructor's Resource CD,* demonstrates the effects of several transformations in the complex plane. There are ten different transformations shown, including $w = 2z$ and $w = iz$. This is related to the activity Transformations in the Complex Plane in *Exploring Precalculus with The Geometer's Sketchpad.*

 Presentation Sketch: Complex Powers Present.gsp, on the *Instructor's Resource CD,* demonstrates the geometric meaning of taking powers of complex numbers. It also demonstrates that the nth roots of a complex number lie on a regular *n*-gon centered at zero. This sketch is related to the activity Powers of Complex Numbers, in *Exploring Precalculus with The Geometer's Sketchpad.*

 Activity: Transformations in the Complex Plane, in *Exploring Precalculus with The Geometer's Sketchpad,* demonstrates the effects of several transformations in the complex plane. Students are challenged to match up algebraic descriptions of the transformations, for example, *w = iz,* with the geometric effect of the transformation, in this case the page in the sketch that shows a rotation by 90°. This activity provides an excellent tie-in to transformations in Chapter 1. You can find four more interesting activities in Chapter 7 of *Exploring Precalculus with The Geometer's Sketchpad,* some related to the presentation sketches described earlier. Allow about 40 minutes for any one activity.

Supplementary Lesson Notes

The following material is provided in case you want to review complex numbers in Cartesian form.

The powers of *i* follow a cyclic pattern.

$i^0 = 1$	Any nonzero number raised to the 0 power equals 1.
$i^1 = i$	Any number raised to the first power equals that number.
$i^2 = -1$	Definition of *i*.
$i^3 = -i$	$i^3 = i^2 \cdot i = -1 \cdot i = -i$
$i^4 = 1$	$i^4 = i^2 \cdot i^2 = (-1)(-1) = 1$
$i^5 = i$	$i^5 = i^4 \cdot i = 1 \cdot i = i$
$i^6 = -1$	Why?
$i^7 = -i$	Why?
$i^8 = 1$	Why?

Note that anytime the exponent is a multiple of 4, the power equals 1. For example, because 76 is a multiple of 4,

$$i^{76} = 1$$

This fact gives an easy way to evaluate powers of *i*.

EXAMPLE 1

Evaluate i^{39} without using a calculator.

Solution

$$i^{39} = i^{36+3} = i^{36} \cdot i^3 = 1 \cdot (-i) = -i$$

Quick way: Divide 39 by 4, get 9 with remainder 3, disregard the 9, write $i^3 = -i$.

A sum or difference of complex numbers is found by combining like terms.

EXAMPLE 2

Subtract and simplify without using a calculator:

$$(4 + 3i) - (5 - 2i)$$

Solution

$$(4 + 3i) - (5 - 2i)$$

$$= 4 + 3i - 5 + 2i \qquad \text{Distribute the implied } -1.$$

$$= -1 + 5i \qquad \text{Combine like terms.}$$

A product of two complex numbers can be found by using the technique for multiplying binomials.

EXAMPLE 3

Multiply and simplify without using a calculator:

$$(4 + 3i)(5 - 2i)$$

Solution

$$(4 + 3i)(5 - 2i)$$

$$= 20 + 7i - 6i^2$$

$$= 20 + 7i + 6 \qquad \text{Because } i^2 = -1.$$

$$= 26 + 7i$$

A quotient of two complex numbers can be found by *rationalizing the denominator.*

EXAMPLE 4

Divide and simplify without using a calculator:

$$\frac{4 + 3i}{5 - 2i}$$

Solution

$$\frac{4 + 3i}{5 - 2i} \cdot \frac{5 + 2i}{5 + 2i} \qquad \text{Multiply by 1 in the form } \frac{\text{conjugate of denominator}}{\text{conjugate of denominator}}.$$

$$= \frac{20 + 23i + 6i^2}{25 - 4i^2} \qquad \text{The product of conjugate binomials in the denominator is a difference of two squares.}$$

$$= \frac{14 + 23i}{29} \qquad \text{Why?}$$

$$= \frac{14}{29} + \frac{23}{29}i \qquad \text{Write in the form } a + bi.$$

EXAMPLE 5

Divide the complex numbers in Example 4 by using your calculator.

Solution

$$\frac{4 + 3i}{5 - 2i} = 0.4827\ldots + 0.7931\ldots i$$

    Put your calculator in complex mode and press the keys.

Note that some calculators operate on complex numbers as *ordered pairs* rather than using $a + bi$ form. For these calculators, you would enter the problem as

$$(4, 3)/(5, -2) =$$

and get the solution

$$(0.4827\ldots, 0.7931\ldots)$$

Problem Notes

- *Problem 37,* the Triple Argument Properties Problem, requires students to use De Moivre's theorem to derive the triple argument properties for expressing $\cos 3\theta$ and $\sin 3\theta$ in terms of sines and cosines of θ.

- *Problem 38* is a research project on De Moivre.

- *Problem 39* is a journal entry. Make sure your students keep their journals up-to-date.

Supplementary Problems

These problems are interesting extensions of De Moivre's theorem.

1. *Quadruple Argument Properties Problem:* By De Moivre's theorem,

   $$(\cos \theta + i \sin \theta)^4 = \cos 4\theta + i \sin 4\theta$$

   Expand the binomial on the left. By equating the real parts and the imaginary parts on the left and right sides of the resulting equation, derive **quadruple argument properties** expressing $\cos 4\theta$ and $\sin 4\theta$ in terms of sines and cosines of θ.

2. *Negative Numbers to Fractional Powers Problem:* Although $\frac{2}{6} = \frac{1}{3}$, the power $(-8)^{2/6}$ is *not* necessarily equal to $(-8)^{1/3}$. This situation arises because

   $$(-8)^{2/6} = [(-8)^2]^{1/6} = 64^{1/6} = 2$$

   but

   $$(-8)^{1/3} = -2$$

With De Moivre's theorem, you can make some sense out of this seeming paradox.

a. Write -8 as a complex number in polar form. Then write the three distinct cube roots of -8 in polar form.

b. Show that one of the cube roots in part a is equal to -2.

c. Write 64 as a complex number in polar form. Then write the six distinct sixth roots of 64 in polar form.

d. Show that one of the sixth roots in part c is equal to 2 and another is equal to -2.

e. Show that every cube root of -8 is also a sixth root of 64 but *not* vice versa.

f. Enter $(-8)^{1/3}$ and $(-8)^{2/6}$ on your calculator. Based on the result, in which order does your calculator do the operations?

$$(-8)^{a/b} = [(-8)^a]^{1/b} \qquad \text{or} \qquad [(-8)^{1/b}]^a$$

How can you tell?

3. *Negative Numbers to Irrational Powers Problem:*

a. Explain why a negative number to an *irrational* power, such as $(-8)^{\sqrt{3}}$, has an *infinite* number of distinct values, *none* of which is a real number.

b. Enter $(-8)^{\sqrt{3}}$ on your calculator. Explain the resulting answer.

Parametric Equations of Moving Objects

Objective

Given a geometrical description of the path followed by a moving object, write parametric equations for the path and plot it on your grapher.

Class Time

2–5 days

Homework Assignment

Day 1: RA, Q1–Q10, Problems 1–4

Day 2: Problems 7, 9

Day 3: Problems 5, 11

Days 4 and 5: The remaining problems and Explorations as desired

Technology Options

 Figure 13-5e: Cycloid Example

 Presentation Sketch: Cycloid Present.gsp

 Presentation Sketch: Parametric Present.gsp

 Activity: Parametric Equations

Important Terms and Concepts

Cycloid

Vector equation

Parametric equation

Cusp

Serpentine curve

Prolate cycloid

Epicycloid

Involute of a circle

Curtate cycloid

Hypocycloid

Hypocycloid of three cusps

Conchoid of Nicomedes

Witch of Maria Agnesi

Lesson Notes

This section is optional. The material is elegant and fun to teach, but a lot of time is needed to develop the ideas well. You may just want to touch on the ideas briefly and not test on them. If you decide to cover the topics in this section more thoroughly, be patient and do not expect miracles! If you assign only one or two problems a day over an extended period, students should eventually catch on.

This chapter began with plotting conic sections, limaçons, roses, and other figures in polar coordinates and was followed by a study of complex numbers in polar form. This section ties vectors together with parametric equations so that students can work with graphs that come from moving objects, such as a wheel rolling along a line.

Example 1 is fairly simple. It involves writing parametric equations for the straight-line path of a ship and then using the equations to make a prediction about the ship's position.

After discussing Example 1, have students work in groups on Exploration 13-6a, which walks them through the process of writing parametric equations for the path of a baseball. Save Example 2 until the second day of instruction. This will give students time to absorb the material from Example 1 and the Exploration and ensure that you have adequate time to discuss Example 2.

Example 2 shows how to write both vector and parametric equations for a *cycloid*, the path traced by a fixed point on the rim of a wheel as the wheel rolls along a straight line. You may want to draw a cycloid by taping chalk to the edge of a circular piece of foam board and rolling the circle along the chalk tray. You will need a couple of student volunteers to help you. The trick is to keep the foam board from slipping as you roll it.

Take your time and go through Example 2 very carefully. Make sure students understand how the equations for $\vec{v_1}$, $\vec{v_2}$, and $\vec{v_3}$ are derived. The key to deriving the equation for $\vec{v_1}$ is to realize that the distance the wheel travels when it rolls t radians is the length of an arc with central angle measure t radians.

To understand the equation for $\vec{v_3}$, students must see that θ, the standard-position angle for $\vec{v_3}$, is equal to $1.5\pi - t$. To help students understand this relationship, draw a vector from the center of the foam-board circle to the edge of the circle and label the point where the vector meets the edge of the circle P. Place the circle so that point P touches the chalk tray, and discuss the fact that in this position $t = 0$ and $\theta = 1.5\pi$. Roll the circle a quarter turn. Help students see that t is now $\frac{\pi}{2}$ (a quarter of a revolution) and θ is π. Roll the circle another quarter turn, and point out that $t = \pi$, while θ is $\frac{\pi}{2}$. Continue this process until you have made one complete revolution.

Exploration Notes

There are seven Explorations for this section. Choose the ones you want to use in class, and assign some of the others as projects.

Exploration 13-5a guides students as they derive parametric equations for the path of a ball. This is a good activity to assign after discussing Example 1 in class. You can then assign Problem 3, the Projectile Motion Problem, for homework. Allow about 20 minutes for students to complete the Exploration.

Exploration 13-5b requires students to write parametric equations for a hyperbola based on a description of its geometric construction. You might follow this Exploration by assigning Problem 5, which requires students to write parametric equations for an ellipse. Allow about 20 minutes for students to complete the Exploration.

The remaining Explorations require students to write parametric equations for various curves. Consider assigning a different Exploration to each group of students, and have the groups report back to the class. Each Exploration will take students 20–25 minutes to complete.

Exploration 13-5c involves the *witch of Maria Agnesi.*

Exploration 13-5d involves the *conchoid of Nicomedes.*

Exploration 13-5e involves a *cardioid.*

Exploration 13-5f involves *hypocycloids.*

Exploration 13-5g involves ellipses and provides additional practice in writing parametric equations for a given path or construction.

Technology Notes

 Figure 13-5e: Cycloid Example shows students the cycloid and its vector equation. Students can use an interactive Dynamic Precalculus Exploration at *www.keymath.com/precalc* to investigate cycloids further.

 Presentation Sketch: Cycloid Present.gsp, on the *Instructor's Resource CD,* shows the cycloid as the path of a point on a moving wheel as well as a parametric representation of the path.

 Presentation Sketch: Parametric Present.gsp, on the *Instructor's Resource CD,* allows you to set a parameter and parametric equations and watch as a particle traces out a parametrically defined graph. Later pages in the sketch show polar curves that are defined parametrically.

 Activity: Parametric Equations, in *Connecting Mathematics with Science,* has students use parametric equations to describe the motion of a steel ball projected off a table so that they can place a cup to catch it. Allow about 30 minutes.

Problem Notes

A blackline master for Problems 5–10 is available in the *Instructor's Resource Book.*

- *Problem 1,* the Airplane's Path Problem, is like Example 1 and should pose no difficulty.

- *Problems 2 and 4* require students to use trigonometry to find equations for the *x*- and *y*-components.

- *Problem 3* should be done in conjunction with Exploration 13-5a.

- *Problem 5* works well when assigned after Exploration 13-5b.

- *Problems 6–10* are difficult but enough alike to give students an opportunity to practice the concepts of combining vectors with parametric equations.

13-6

Chapter Review and Test

Objective

Review and practice the major concepts of this chapter.

Class Time

2 days (including 1 day for testing)

Homework Assignment

Day 1: R0–R5 (if you covered all five sections), T1–T17

Day 2 (after Chapter 13 Test): The exploratory problem set in Section 1 of the next chapter you plan to do

Lesson Notes

Section 13-6 contains a set of Review Problems, a set of Concept Problems, and a Chapter Test. The Review Problems include one problem for each section in the chapter. You may wish to use the Chapter Test as an additional set of review problems.

Encourage students to practice the no-calculator problems without a calculator so that they are prepared for the test problems for which they cannot use a calculator.

Do not test on Section 13-5 unless you spent several days on it and feel your students are comfortable with parametric equations for moving objects.

Problem Notes

The Concept Problems can be assigned as projects.

Exploration Notes

Exploration 13-6a introduces the equation of the curve for a hanging chain and compares it to a parabola. This Exploration can be assigned for extra credit. Allow 20–25 minutes to complete the Exploration.

14 Sequences and Series

In this chapter students are taught to distinguish between a sequence, such as 1, 3, 5, 7, ..., and a series, such as $1 + 3 + 5 + 7 + \cdots$, which is the indicated sum of the terms of a sequence. Students learn that under favorable conditions, geometric series may approach limits as the number of terms becomes infinite, thus strengthening the exposure to limits from earlier in the course and preparing for limits at the beginning of calculus. On a graphing calculator, students experience convergence by watching more and more decimal places in the partial sum remain fixed as the number of terms increases. Binomial series and sequences representing area and length give students a review of probability from Chapter 9 and fractal figures from Chapter 11.

14-1

Introduction to Sequences and Series

Objectives

- Given a few terms in a sequence or series of numbers, find more terms.

- Given a series, find the sum of a specified number of terms.

Class Time

$\frac{1}{2}$ day

Homework Assignment

Problems 1–10

Important Terms and Concepts

Continuous

Discrete

Sequences

Series

Arithmetic sequence

Arithmetic series

Partial sum

Geometric sequence

Geometric series

Lesson Notes

In this exploratory problem set, students are introduced to sequences and series. You can assign this section for homework the night of the Chapter 13 test or as a group activity to be completed in class. No classroom discussion is needed before students begin the activity.

If you did not cover Chapter 8 in your class, you will need to spend time showing students how to use a grapher to

- Enter data as a list.

- Create a scatter plot.

- Find a regression model.

You may need to explain the meaning of *discrete data points.* Viewed intuitively, data points would seem discrete if they are *disconnected.* For a set of points on the number line, this means there is an interval surrounding each point that contains no other points in the set. The integers are an example of a discrete set. For any integer z, the interval $(z - 0.5, z + 0.5)$ contains no other integer but z. The rational numbers are not discrete. No matter how small an interval around a rational number, it will always contain another rational number. Data points on the coordinate plane are discrete if you can find a circle around each point that contains no other data point. The data points for a sequence are of the form (n, t_n), where n is a positive integer. Because the positive integers are a discrete set, the points of a sequence are also discrete.

Exploration Notes

Exploration 14-1a is a nice introduction to sequences. It requires students to find a pattern in a sequence of numbers and to use the pattern to find more terms in the sequence. In Problem 3, students should plot the points by hand. You may need to explain that the points should not be connected with a solid curve because the in-between points are not part of the function. Allow students about 20 minutes to complete this activity.

Problem Notes

- *Problems 2 and 6* ask students to sketch a scatter plot. Students should sketch only the points in the sequence, not the curve that contains them.

- *Problems 4–6* preview Section 14-3. Problem 5 helps students discover a shortcut for computing partial sums of an arithmetic series.

- *Problem 8* asks students to find the tenth *term* of a geometric *sequence. Problem 9* asks them to find the tenth *partial sum* of the corresponding geometric *series.* Make sure students understand the distinction between these problems. A sequence is an ordered list, separated by commas, and the tenth term is the tenth item on the list. A series is a sum of terms, and the tenth partial sum is the sum of the first ten terms.

14-2
Arithmetic, Geometric, and Other Sequences

Objectives

• Represent sequences explicitly and recursively.

Given information about a sequence,

• Find a term when given its term number.

• Find the term number of a given term.

Class Time

1–2 days

Homework Assignment

Day 1: RA, Q1–Q10, Problems 1–6, 16, 17, 23, 24

Day 2: Problems 6–13, 15, 18, 19

Technology Options

 Presentation Sketch: Sequences Present.gsp

 Activity: Arithmetic Sequences

 Activity: Geometric Sequences

 Activity: Generating Arithmetic and Geometric Sequences Numerically

 Activity: Compound Interest

 Activity: Sequence of Squares

Activity: Geometric Sequences

Important Terms and Concepts

Discrete function

Continuous function

Sequence, t_n

Arithmetic sequence

Common difference

Recursion formula

Sequence mode

Explicit formula

Compound interest

Geometric sequence

Common ratio

Fibonacci sequence

Fibonacci numbers

Golden ratio

Arithmetic means

Geometric means

Lesson Notes

In this section, students learn how to represent sequences both recursively and explicitly. They also learn to find a term given its term number and to find a term number given its term.

A *sequence* is defined as a function whose domain is the set of positive integers. Using the word *function* to describe a sequence may confuse students because up to this point all the functions they have worked with are continuous. Point out that for each term number there is exactly one term, so a sequence does satisfy the definition of *function*.

Arithmetic sequences are linear functions, and geometric sequences are exponential functions. The graphs in Examples 1 and 2 provide visual evidence of these facts. The sequence in Example 3 is a quadratic function. Examining a scatter plot can help students determine what type of function fits a particular sequence.

Emphasize that students should *not* connect the points for a discrete function with a solid curve because this implies that the in-between points are also part of the function. Students may instead use a dashed curve if they wish to show the pattern created by points.

Example 1 involves an arithmetic sequence. In part a, students observe that the sequence is a linear function. Students should notice that the table in part b shows the add–add pattern they learned about in Chapter 7.

The equation found in part c of Example 1, $t_n = 53 + 13(n - 1)$, is the *explicit formula* for the sequence. It allows you to find the value of any term without knowing the value of the terms before it. When you work with students to find an explicit formula for an arithmetic sequence, you may find it helpful to use this language:

$t_n =$ first term plus $(n - 1)$ common differences

The text after the example gives the *recursion formula*, $t_n = t_{n-1} + 13$. A recursion formula tells you how to compute the value of a term based on the value of the term before it. Work with students to help them enter the recursive equation into their graphers.

Example 2 uses the idea of compounding interest to introduce geometric sequences. Students should observe that the table in part a shows the add–multiply pattern for exponential functions. Part b shows how to make a scatter plot by entering the recursion formula into a grapher. When you work with students to find an explicit formula for a geometric sequence, you may find it helpful to use this language:

t_n = first term times $(n - 1)$ factors of the common ratio

Part e of Example 2 requires students to find the term number corresponding to a given term value. Because the function is exponential, finding an algebraic solution involves using logarithms. Most students will find the numerical solution easier, but encourage them to practice using both methods so that they will become comfortable with logarithms. Note that the real-world answer to part e is 43, not 42.1522..., because n must be a natural number. Because the interest is compounded at the beginning of any year, the sum of money will not increase until after the 42nd birthday, which will be on the 43rd birthday.

The sequence in Example 3 is neither arithmetic nor geometric. Often so much time is spent discussing arithmetic and geometric sequences that students get the false impression that *every* sequence is either arithmetic or geometric.

The text after Example 3 summarizes the main ideas of this section. Make sure students understand that a recursion formula is an easy way to find the next few terms of a sequence, whereas an explicit formula is useful for finding terms later in the sequence or for finding the term number for a given term.

Exploration Notes

Exploration 14-2a introduces arithmetic and geometric sequences and asks students to find an explicit formula for a sequence that is neither arithmetic nor geometric. This Exploration makes an excellent introduction to Section 14-2. It can also be used at the end of the section to summarize the main ideas. Allow students about 20 minutes to complete this activity.

Exploration 14-2b applies arithmetic and geometric sequences to a real-world problem. This Exploration requires more time than Exploration 14-2a because students must analyze the written information to answer the questions. Students may need your guidance to write the algebraic formulas required for Problems 5 and 6. You may want to stop the class

after most groups have completed Problem 5 and discuss how students found the formula. Allow students about 30 minutes to complete this Exploration.

Technology Notes

 Presentation Sketch: Sequences Present.gsp, on the *Instructor's Resource CD,* shows arithmetic and geometric sequences on a number line.

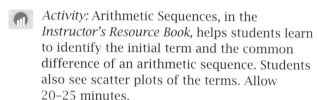 *Activity:* Arithmetic Sequences, in the *Instructor's Resource Book,* helps students learn to identify the initial term and the common difference of an arithmetic sequence. Students also see scatter plots of the terms. Allow 20–25 minutes.

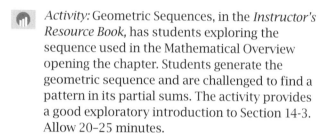 *Activity:* Geometric Sequences, in the *Instructor's Resource Book,* has students exploring the sequence used in the Mathematical Overview opening the chapter. Students generate the geometric sequence and are challenged to find a pattern in its partial sums. The activity provides a good exploratory introduction to Section 14-3. Allow 20–25 minutes.

Activity: Generating Arithmetic and Geometric Sequences Numerically, in *Exploring Precalculus with The Geometer's Sketchpad,* allows students to construct sequences in Sketchpad and see them plotted on a number line. This activity is related to the presentation sketch Sequences Present.gsp mentioned earlier. Allow 25–35 minutes.

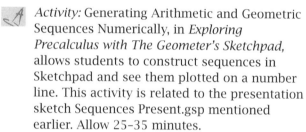 *Activity:* Compound Interest, in *Exploring Precalculus with The Geometer's Sketchpad,* could be used to relate Example 2 and related problems to the exponential growth of Chapter 7. Allow 30–40 minutes.

Activity: Sequence of Squares, in *Teaching Mathematics with Fathom,* is a simple yet open-ended activity in which students make and test conjectures about rules governing the sequence of square numbers. Allow 30–55 minutes.

Activity: Geometric Sequences, in *Connecting Mathematics with Science,* has students model data they collect on the conductivity of a salt solution with both recursive and closed-form equations and also with exponential regression. The experiment takes about 30 minutes.

Problem Notes

- *Problem 13,* the Grain of Rice Problem, gives an example of a geometric series. Carl Sagan wrote an entertaining article, "The Secret of the Persian Chessboard," for the February 5, 1989, issue of *Parade Magazine.* In the article's introduction, Sagan outlines a story similar to the Grain of Rice Problem and explains geometric sequences and exponential growth in words. Then he describes three significant real-world examples involving AIDS, global population growth, and the discovery of nuclear fission. This article can be used to stimulate a class discussion about the role of mathematics in solving critical problems facing humanity.

- *Problem 15,* the Depreciation Problem, compares and contrasts arithmetic and geometric sequences.

- *Problem 18,* the Ancestors Problem, asks students to compute the number of ancestors they have in various generations. This topic is also addressed in Sagan's article, "The Secret of the Persian Chessboard" (see the note for Problem 13).

- *Problem 19,* the Fibonacci Sequence Problem, helps develop intuitive understanding of limits. Part b demonstrates that the limit of the ratio of consecutive terms of the Fibonacci sequence is the *golden ratio.*

- *Problem 20,* the Factorial Sequence Problem, can serve as a review question about factorials.

- *Problem 23,* the Credit Card Problem, is an eye-opening problem. Students will be astounded how long it takes to pay off a credit card with minimum payments.

- *Problem 24* introduces the concepts of arithmetic and geometric means.

14-3
Series and Partial Sums

Objectives

- Given a series, find a specified partial sum, or find the number of terms if the partial sum is given.

- Use sigma notation to write partial sums.

- Given a power of a binomial, expand it as a binomial series.

Class Time

2–3 days

Homework Assignment

Day 1: RA, Q1–Q10, Problems 1–2, 5, 11–27 odd

Day 2: Problems 3–4, 9, 12, 29–51 odd, 53–55

Day 3: Even-numbered problems and Explorations as desired

Technology Options

 Problem 53: Dynamic Geometric Series Problem

 Presentation Sketch: Area Models Present.gsp

 Presentation Sketch: Geometric Staircase Present.gsp

 Calculator Program: SERIES

 Activity: Area Models of Geometric Series

 Activity: A Geometric Series Staircase

 Activity: Harmonic Series

Important Terms and Concepts

Series

Partial sum

Binomial series

Sigma notation

Term index

Arithmetic series

Geometric series

Telescope

Convergent series

Divergent series

Limit

Binomial series

Binomial expansion

Pascal's triangle

Binomial coefficients

Binomial formula (theorem)

Harmonic sequence

Harmonic series

Lesson Notes

This section focuses on series, developing understanding of partial sums, sigma notation, convergence, divergence, and limits. It is recommended that you spend at least two days on this section. Try to cover the material through Example 3 on the first day. Start with Exploration 14-3a so students will see both arithmetic and geometric series on the first day.

Although limits of *functions* are usually studied early in the first semester of college calculus, limits of *sequences and series* are often not studied until the second semester. The problems in Section 14-3 develop intuitive understanding of limits and form a foundation for formal limit problems in calculus, whether the limits involve functions or series and sequences.

An nth partial sum, S_n, of a series is the sum of the first n terms. The sum of a series with an infinite number of terms is defined to be the *limit* of the partial sums as n approaches infinity. A series whose partial sums approach a limit is said to *converge.*

For Example 1, students need to write or download a program to compute partial sums. Students also need to find an explicit formula for the sequence of terms. This skill was developed in Section 14-2.

The piggy bank problem after Example 1 develops an algebraic method for finding a partial sum of an arithmetic series. The method is the same one used by 9-year-old Karl Friedrich Gauss (1777–1855) when asked by his teacher to find the sum of the first 100 natural numbers. Students find this method fascinating and usually want to try it on their own algebraic sequence of numbers. Emphasize that this method works *only* for algebraic sequences. So, for example, it could not be used to find the partial sum in Example 1.

Example 2 uses the algebraic method to find the 100th partial sum of an arithmetic series. To find the 100th term of the sequence, it is necessary to find an explicit formula for the sequence and then to substitute 100 for n. You may want to formalize the ideas from the last section by presenting this formula for the nth term of an arithmetic sequence:

$$t_n = t_1 + (n - 1)d$$

where n is the term number and d is the common difference.

The textbook discussion prior to Example 3 derives a formula for the nth partial sum of a geometric series. When showing the step in which $3S_6$ is subtracted from S_6, you may want to align the terms as shown here:

$$S_6 = 7 + 21 + 63 + 189 + 675 + 1701$$
$$\underline{3S_6 = \qquad 21 + 63 + 189 + 675 + 1701 + 5103}$$

This will help students see why the middle terms cancel out, or *telescope* (collapse like a pirate's spyglass). It is worth taking the time to go through this proof so that students can see why the middle terms telescope. This technique comes up in other situations. In calculus, for example, the proof of the fundamental theorem of calculus also involves middle terms that telescope.

Example 3 applies algebraic methods to find a partial sum for a geometric series. As in Example 2, it is necessary to find an explicit formula for the sequence of terms. You may want to formalize the ideas from the previous section by presenting this formula for the nth term of a geometric sequence:

$$t_n = t_1 r^{n-1}$$

where n is the term number and r is the common ratio. This result is summarized at the end of this section.

Part b involves finding the number of terms in a given partial sum. The algebraic solution involves using logarithms. Make sure students understand why the solution $n = 251.1784...$ must be rounded up to get the real-world answer. (n represents the number of months, and because interest is computed monthly and not for partial months, n must be a whole number. The amount first exceeds \$50,000 on the 252nd month.)

The student text introduces convergent and divergent geometric series using a problem about a person who starts out 200 m from another person and then takes steps, each of which is half the remaining distance, to a second person. Theoretically, the person will never reach his destination. (Sometimes a student will point out that eventually the remaining distance will be less than the size of the foot of the person approaching the stationary person.) The total distance covered is given by the infinite geometric series

$$100 + 50 + 25 + 12.5 + 6.25 + \cdots$$

Although this series is infinite, the partial sums *converge* to the *limit* 200. The text uses the formula for the partial sum S_n to explain why this is true. Make sure students understand why an infinite geometric series converges only if $|r| < 1$.

Example 4 asks students to find the limit of a series. Students are also asked how many terms must be added to be within a given amount of the limit. You may also want to present this example, which involves a divergent geometric series.

EXAMPLE

Consider the geometric series

$$30 - 36 + 43.2 - 51.84 + \cdots$$

a. Tell whether or not the series converges.

b. If it does converge, find the limit to which it converges.

Solution

a. The common ratio is $\frac{-36}{30}$, or -1.2. Because $|-1.2| > 1$, the series does not converge.

b. Because the series does not converge, it has no limit.

The discussion of binomial series mentions several patterns in the binomial expansion. You may want to give your students a few of the expansions and let them describe the relationships they see. You can give them hints to steer them toward uncovering the remaining relationships.

Example 5 asks students to expand a binomial. Rewriting $(x - 2y)^4$ as $(x + (-2y))^4$ will help students avoid making errors involving the negative sign.

In Example 6, make sure students see that because the first term of the expansion of $(3 - 2x)^{12}$ contains $(-2x)^0$ and because the power of $-2x$ increases by 1 with each term, the eighth term contains $(-2x)^7$, not $(-2x)^8$.

Exploration Notes

Exploration 14-3a requires students to find partial sums by hand and by using a grapher program. (The grapher program will also be needed for Explorations 14-3b, c, and e.) This Exploration makes a nice introduction to Section 14-3. If you want students to download the program, allow about 20 minutes for this activity. If you want students to write the program, allow 45–60 minutes.

Exploration 14-3b leads students to discover a shortcut for finding the sum of an arithmetic series. You might assign this Exploration instead of presenting the introductory material in the "Finding Partial Sums of Arithmetic Series Algebraically" part of Section 14-3. You can also use it as a review sheet or homework assignment. Students will need a grapher program for computing partial sums. Allow students about 20 minutes to complete this activity.

Exploration 14-3c leads students to discover a shortcut for finding the sum of a geometric series. Students will need a grapher program for computing partial sums. You might assign this Exploration instead of presenting the introductory material in the "Finding Partial Sums of Geometric Series Algebraically" part of Section 14-3. You can also use it as a review sheet or homework assignment. Allow students about 20 minutes to complete this activity.

Exploration 14-3d helps students discover how the coefficients of the terms in a binomial expansion can be found recursively and by using factorials. Allow students about 20 minutes to complete this activity.

Exploration 14-3e requires students to find terms and partial sums of arithmetic or geometric series both numerically and algebraically. Students will need a grapher program for computing partial sums. You can use this activity as a quiz, as extra homework, or as a review sheet. Allow students 20–25 minutes to complete this Exploration.

Technology Notes

 Problem 53: The Dynamic Geometric Series Problem asks students to use the Geometric Series Dynamic Precalculus Exploration at *www.keymath.com/precalc* to explore a derivation of the formula for the sum of a geometric series.

 Presentation Sketch: Area Models Present.gsp, on the *Instructor's Resource CD,* demonstrates geometric series as sums of areas inside a square. It is related to the activity Area Models of Geometric Series.

 Presentation Sketch: Geometric Staircase Present.gsp, on the *Instructor's Resource CD,* demonstrates geometric series as sums of areas of squares that are bounded by two intersecting lines. It is related to the activity A Geometric Series Staircase.

 Calculator Program: SERIES calculates the partial sums of a series $\sum_{n=1}^{N} t_n$, as in Examples 1–3. The program is available on the *Instructor's Resource CD* and at *www.keymath.com/precalc* for download onto a TI-83 or TI-84 graphing calculator. It also appears in the *Instructor's Resource Book* for students to enter by hand.

 Activity: Area Models of Geometric Series, in the *Instructor's Resource Book,* leads students to dissect a square to represent geometric series and to investigate their sums. This is for advanced Sketchpad users and will take 40–50 minutes.

 Activity: A Geometric Series Staircase, in *Exploring Precalculus with The Geometer's Sketchpad,* gives students a visual model of the sum of an infinite geometric series. The activity A Geometric Series Coil in the same book uses a different visual model. Each activity involves a prepared sketch and will take 40–50 minutes.

 Activity: Harmonic Series, in *Connecting Mathematics with Science,* helps students to gain experience with partial sums of a series as they stack metersticks or tiles hanging over the edge of a table. Allow 30 minutes.

Problem Notes

• *Problem 4,* the Harmonic Series Divergence Problem, associates the terms of the harmonic series into groups of fractions, each with a sum greater than or equal to $\frac{1}{2}$. Students may need guidance to realize that the sum of the harmonic series grows without bound because it is greater than the sum of an infinite number of $\frac{1}{2}$s.

• *Problem 9,* the Thumbtack Binomial Series Problem, illustrates the connection between binomial probabilities and a binomial expansion. Students solved problems similar to this in Chapter 9. Note that in the expression $(0.4 + 0.6)^5$, 0.6 is the probability that the tack will land point up on any one toss and 0.4 is the probability that it will land point down. Because these are the only possible outcomes, the probabilities add to 1.

• *Problem 10,* the Snowflake Curve Series Problem, revisits Koch's snowflake curve from Chapter 11.

• *Problems 11–52* are routine problems designed to provide drill and practice.

• *Problems 47 and 48* are a little tricky. For instance, in Problem 47, students need to recognize that x^{18} is equivalent to $(x^3)^6$; thus the x^{18}-term is actually the eighth term in the expansion of $(x^3 - y^2)^{13}$.

14-4
Chapter Review and Test

Objective

Review and practice the major concepts of this chapter.

Class Time

2 days (including 1 day for testing)

Homework Assignment

Day 1: R0–R3, T1–T24

Day 2 (after Chapter 14 Test): The exploratory problem set in Section 1 of the next chapter you plan to do

Important Terms and Concepts

Power series

Taylor Series

Maclaurin Series

Lesson Notes

Section 14-4 contains a set of Review Problems, a set of Concept Problems, and a Chapter Test. The Review Problems include one problem for each section in the chapter. You may wish to use the Chapter Test as an additional set of review problems.

Encourage students to practice the no-calculator problems without a calculator so that they are prepared for the test problems for which they cannot use a calculator.

Problem Notes

The concept problems are an excellent source of material for extra credit, extensions of the material, or an extra group assignment.

- *Concept Problem C1* connects geometric sequences and series with limits and fractals.

- *Concept Problem C2* introduces an empirical pattern in the spacing of the planets from the Sun. Bode's law, first published by Johann Titus in 1766, was not widely known until Johann Bode republished it. Search the Internet for Bode's law. One good Web site is *www.theeel.com/~bruce/histastro/Bode.html.*

- *Concept Problem C4* introduces the idea of a power series, which students will study in calculus.

Exploration Notes

Exploration 14-4a introduces the concept of power series. By calculating the partial sums at different x-values, students are led to recognize that these partial sums give estimated values for the $f(x) = e^x$ function. Allow 20–25 minutes to complete this Exploration.

Exploration 14-4b gives the power series expansions for the $f(x) = \sin x$, $g(x) = \cos x$, and $h(x) = e^x$ functions. Using these power series, students discover the exponential form of complex numbers. Allow 20–25 minutes for the Exploration.

Supplementary Lesson Notes

Problem C4 presents power series for e^x, $\sin x$, and $\cos x$. There are eight basic power series students will learn in calculus. They are summarized here for your information and for extension of the concept of power series.

Eight Well-Known Power Series

$$e^x = 1 + x + x^2 + x^3 + x^4 + \cdots$$

$$\sin x = x - x^3 + x^5 - x^7 + \cdots$$

$$\cos x = 1 - x^2 + x^4 - x^6 + \cdots$$

$$\sinh x = x + x^3 + x^5 + x^7 + \cdots \text{ (Hyperbolic sine)}$$

$$\cosh x = 1 + x^2 + x^4 + x^6 + \cdots \text{ (Hyperbolic cosine)}$$

$$\ln x = (x - 1) - \tfrac{1}{2}(x - 1)^2 + \tfrac{1}{3}(x - 1)^3 - \tfrac{1}{4}(x - 1)^4 + \cdots$$

$$\frac{1}{1 - x} = 1 + x + x^2 + x^3 + x^4 + \cdots \text{ (A geometric series)}$$

$$\tan^{-1} x = x - x^3 + x^5 - x^7 + \cdots$$

The hyperbolic cosine and sine are defined as

$$\cosh x = 0.5(e^x + e^{-x})$$

$$\sinh x = 0.5(e^x - e^{-x})$$

They bear the same relation to the unit hyperbola $u^2 - v^2 = 1$ as the circular functions bear to the unit circle $u^2 + v^2 = 1$, as shown in Figures 14-4a and 14-4b.

Figure 14-4a

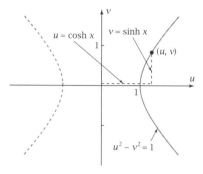

Figure 14-4b

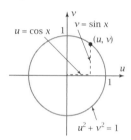

The graphs of cosh and sinh are shown in Figure 14-4c.

Figure 14-4c

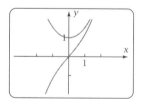

The hyperbolic cosine graph is a *catenary,* the shape taken by a chain hanging under its own weight.

With the aid of these series, you can show such properties as

$$e^{ix} = \cos x + i \sin x = \operatorname{cis} x$$

$$e^{i\pi} = -1$$

$\cos(ix) = \cosh x$, so that, for example, $\cos 2i = \cosh 2 = 3.762\ldots$, a number greater than 1.

15 Polynomial and Rational Functions, Limits, and Derivatives

This concluding chapter ties together much of what students have learned and gives them a push toward calculus. Regression is reviewed by having students fit polynomial functions to data. The properties of polynomial functions, possibly previously studied by students, are combined with operations on algebraic fractions to get rational functions representing the average rate of change over a given interval. By taking the limit as the width of the interval approaches zero, students learn to compute the instantaneous rate of change, or the derivative.

A cumulative review of Chapters 10–15 appears in Section 15-7. Following recommendations of the College Board, calculus itself is not treated in this text. Although the words *limit* and *derivative* appear in this chapter, the concepts are not stressed with the rigor required in a calculus course.

15-1
Review of Polynomial Functions

Objective

Discover some properties of cubic functions and their graphs.

Class Time

$\frac{1}{2}$ day

Homework Assignment

Problems 1–11

Technology Options

 Activity: Exploring the Roots of Quadratics

Important Terms and Concepts

Zeros

Double zero

Complex zeros

Lesson Notes

This exploratory problem set introduces students to cubic functions and their graphs. You can assign this section for homework the night of the Chapter 14 test or as a group activity to be completed in class. No classroom discussion is needed before students begin the activity.

The functions in the problem set illustrate the characteristics of cubic functions with three distinct real zeros, with a double zero, and with two nonreal complex zeros. In addition to these examples, you might want to present a function with a triple zero, such as $j(x) = x^3 - 6x^2 + 12x - 8 = (x - 2)^3$. As the graph approaches the triple zero, it flattens out, becomes tangent to the x-axis, and then crosses the x-axis at the point of tangency.

$$j(x) = (x - 2)^3$$

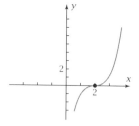

When graphing polynomial functions, students often have trouble choosing an appropriate viewing window. (For this problem set, students can choose the window settings by examining Figure 15-1a in the student text.) Fortunately, most graphers have a built-in feature that automatically adjusts the window so that it includes the minimum and maximum y-values of the function between the specified x-min and x-max values. Students may still have to adjust the x-min, x-max, and scale settings to see all the important characteristics of the graph, but this feature should make their work significantly easier.

Some graphers allow the user to enter multiple variations of the same basic equation by enclosing in braces the values of the term that varies. For instance, f, g, and h in this problem set could be entered as $y_1 = x^3 - 4x^2 - 3x + \{2,18,54\}$. The grapher will plot all three variations on the same axes in the order listed within the braces. Another way to see the effect of changing just one term is to enter $y_1 = x^3 - 4x^2 - 3x + A$. The grapher will use whatever value is stored in A when it graphs y_1. Changing the value of A is a quick way to see the results of varying a particular term.

Exploration Notes

Exploration 15-1a is essentially the same set of problems as those in the exploratory problem set of Section 15-1. Allow students 20–25 minutes to complete this activity.

Technology Notes

 Activity: Exploring the Roots of Quadratics, in *Exploring Precalculus with The Geometer's Sketchpad,* will provide students with a review of quadratic functions and finding their zeros. Allow 40–50 minutes.

Problem Notes

Problem 4 requires students to rewrite $f(x)$ in the form

$$f(x) = (x + 1)(\text{unknown factor})$$

To find the unknown factor, students need to use long division of polynomials (or synthetic substitution if they have learned this method in an earlier course).

15-2
Graphs and Zeros of Polynomial Functions

Objectives

Given a polynomial function,

- Tell from the graph what degree it might be, and vice versa.
- Find the zeros from the equation or graph.

Class Time

1–2 days (see Lesson Notes)

Homework Assignment

Day 1: RA, Q1–Q10, Problems 1–17 odd, 27, 29–32

Day 2: Problems 19–25 odd, 34, 37

Technology Options

 Calculator Program: SYNSUB

Important Terms and Concepts

Polynomial

Polynomial operations

Degree of a polynomial

Leading coefficient

Zeros

Extreme point

Vertex

Critical point

Synthetic substitution

Nested form

Remainder theorem

Factor theorem

Double zero

Fundamental theorem of algebra

Real zeros

Sums and products of the zeros of cubic functions

Lesson Notes

In this section, students explore the relationship between the graph of a polynomial function and the degree of the function and learn to find the zeros of a polynomial function from its equation or graph. You can shorten this section if time is limited. Synthetic substitution, the remainder theorem, the factor theorem, and various other theorems were once necessary to find or approximate solutions and to draw graphs for polynomials. Now complex equations can be solved and graphed by using a grapher. The techniques in this section are useful (but not required) for investigating discontinuities and limits in Section 15-4. If you choose to cover the entire section, it is recommended that you spend at least two days on it. Cover the material up to (but not including) "Sums and Products of Zeros" on the first day and the remaining material on the second day.

The text introduces *synthetic substitution* as a method for evaluating a polynomial function for a specific value and for dividing a polynomial by a linear binomial. Make sure students understand that to use synthetic substitution to divide by a linear binomial, you must substitute the value of x for which the linear binomial is equal to 0. So, for example, to divide by $(x + 3)$, substitute -3, not 3. After demonstrating synthetic substitution, present and discuss the remainder theorem and its corollary, the factor theorem.

Example 1 revisits the three cubic functions from Section 15-1. One zero of each function is found by using synthetic substitution, and the remaining zeros are found by factoring or using the quadratic formula. Each of the cubic functions has three zeros.

- Function f has three distinct real zeros. The graph crosses the x-axis at each zero.

- Function g has a *double zero,* meaning that two of the zeros are the same number. The graph touches but does not cross the x-axis at the double zero and crosses the x-axis at the other zero.

- Function h has one real-number zero and two nonreal complex zeros. The nonreal complex zeros are complex conjugates. The graph intersects the x-axis at the real-number zero.

When doing synthetic substitution, you may want to "box off" the remainder. For example, write the bottom line of the solution in Example 1a as $1\ {-5}\ 2\ \boxed{0}$. This will help students avoid putting the remainder in with the coefficients of the quotient.

Example 1 leads to the fundamental theorem of algebra and its corollaries. Make sure students understand that the n zeros of an nth-degree polynomial include multiple zeros and nonreal complex zeros. Therefore, an nth-degree polynomial does *not* necessarily have n x-intercepts.

Finding a double zero with the CALC: intersect feature on a calculator can be problematic. For example, if you graph $y = x^3 - 4x^2 - 3x + 18$ and $y = 0$ in a nonfriendly graphing window, you will not be able to find the zero $x = 3$ using the intersect feature. However, the CALC: zero feature will find the double zero $x = 3$ as well as the zero $x = -2$.

Example 2 presents a graph of a polynomial function and asks students to identify the degree of the function and the number of real and nonreal complex zeros that the function could have.

More examples involving finding the zeros of a polynomial can be found in the Additional Class Examples.

When the leading coefficient is factored from a cubic function, there are relationships between the coefficients of the resulting cubic and the sums and products of the zeros of the function. In the text, these relationships are illustrated using the function $f(x) = 5x^3 - 33x^2 + 58x - 24$ and summarized in the property box before Example 3. When discussing the text in the property box, you may want to rewrite the general cubic function as

$$p(x) = a\left(x^3 + \frac{b}{a}x^2 + \frac{c}{a}x + d\right)$$

so that students can better see how the property relates to the specific function they just investigated.

In Example 3, students find the zeros of a cubic function and then verify that the sum, the sum of pairwise products, and the product correspond to the coefficients of the equation.

Example 4 shows how to find an equation of a cubic function given the sum, sum of pairwise products, and product of its zeros.

Exploration Notes

Exploration 15-2a shows students how to use synthetic substitution to evaluate and factor a function. Allow students about 20 minutes to complete this activity.

Exploration 15-2b leads students to discover the relationships between the coefficients of a cubic polynomial function and the sums and products of its zeros. After discovering the patterns, students must apply them to write an equation of a cubic function given the zeros of the function. You might assign this activity at the beginning of the second day of instruction. Allow 20–25 minutes for this Exploration.

Technology Notes

 Calculator Program: SYNSUB calculates the value of a function for a particular input value using the synthetic substitution technique, as asked for in Problem 33. The program is available on the *Instructor's Resource CD* and at *www.keymath.com/precalc* for download onto a TI-83 or TI-84 graphing calculator. It also appears in the *Instructor's Resource Book* for students to enter by hand.

Additional Class Examples

1. Find the zeros of $g(x) = 6x^3 + 17x^2 - 24x - 35$ algebraically. Write $g(x)$ in factored form.

   Solution

   Figure 15-2a shows the graph of g. By tracing the graph, $x = -1$ appears to be a zero. Confirm this algebraically by synthetic substitution.

   Figure 15-2a

   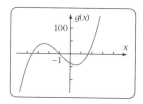

   $$\begin{array}{r|rrrr} -1 & 6 & 17 & -24 & -35 \\ & & -6 & -11 & 35 \\ \hline & 6 & 11 & -35 & 0 \end{array}$$ Synthetically substitute -1 for x. The remainder is 0.

   $\therefore -1$ is a zero of $g(x)$. $g(-1) = 0$ because it equals the remainder.

   $g(x) = (x + 1)(6x^2 + 11x - 35)$ $(x + 1)$ is a factor of $g(x)$ because it is 0 when $x = -1$.

   $\qquad = (x + 1)(2x + 7)(3x - 5)$ Factor the quadratic by inspection.

   $g(x) = 0 \leftrightarrow x + 1 = 0$ or
   $2x + 7 = 0$ or $3x - 5 = 0$

   Zeros are $x = -1$, $x = -\frac{7}{2}$, and $x = \frac{5}{3}$.

2. Show that $x - 5$ is a factor of $f(x) = x^3 - 9x^2 - x + 105$. Write $f(x)$ in factored form.

   Solution

   $$\begin{array}{r|rrrr}
   5 & 1 & -9 & -1 & 105 \\
     &   & 5 & -20 & -105 \\
   \hline
     & 1 & -4 & -21 & 0
   \end{array}$$

   Synthetically substitute 5 for x.

   The remainder is 0. So $(x - 5)$ is a factor of $f(x)$.

   $\therefore f(x) = (x - 5)(x^2 - 4x - 21)$ $(x - 5)$ is a factor of $f(x)$ because it is 0 when $x = 5$.

   $= (x - 5)(x + 3)(x - 7)$ Factor the quadratic by inspection.

3. *Double Zeros:* Plot the graph of the quartic function

   $$P(x) = (x + 2)(x - 1)(x - 3)(x - 3)$$

   Describe the difference in behavior at the double zero $x = 3$ compared to that at the single zeros $x = -2$ and $x = 1$. Does the number of zeros agree with the corollary to the fundamental theorem of algebra?

   Solution

   The graph (Figure 15-2b) shows that at the double zero $x = 3$, the graph is *tangent* to the x-axis. That is, the graph touches the x-axis but does not cross it. The graph does cross the x-axis at the single zeros -2 and 1 because $P(x)$ changes sign at those points.

   Although the graph touches the x-axis only three times, there are still *four* zeros, counting the double zero at $x = 3$. This fact agrees with the corollary to the fundamental theorem of algebra.

   Figure 15-2b

   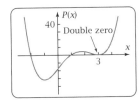

   Note that a double zero is also called a *zero of multiplicity 2*. Similarly, a triple zero has multiplicity 3, and so on.

4. Find all zeros, real and nonreal, of $f(x) = x^3 - 4x^2 + 22x + 68$.

   Solution

   The graph (Figure 15-2c) indicates that there is a real zero at $x = -2$.

   Figure 15-2c

   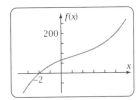

   By synthetic substitution of $x = -2$, write $f(x)$ in factored form.

   $$\begin{array}{r|rrrr}
   -2 & 1 & -4 & 22 & 68 \\
      &   & -2 & 12 & -68 \\
   \hline
      & 1 & -6 & 34 & 0
   \end{array}$$

   $f(x) = (x + 2)(x^2 - 6x + 34)$

   $x = 3 \pm 5i$ Use the quadratic formula.

   Zeros are -2, $3 + 5i$, and $3 - 5i$.

Problem Notes

- *Problems 1–6* model and reinforce the concepts covered in Examples 1 and 2.

- *Problems 7–18* ask students to sketch graphs of polynomial functions given information about their zeros, leading coefficients, and extreme points. Make sure students understand that the term *complex zero* is used to mean a *nonreal complex zero*.

- *Problems 19–26* provide practice with the properties of the sums and products of zeros demonstrated in Examples 3 and 4.

- *Problems 27 and 28* require students to use synthetic substitution to evaluate a polynomial function and to write the quotient of the polynomial and a linear binomial in mixed-number form.

- *Problems 29–32* require students to state the properties studied in this section.

- *Problem 33*, the Synthetic Substitution Program Problem, asks students to write a grapher program that does synthetic substitution.

- *Problems 34–37* can be used as group problems or projects. They require students to investigate the zeros of a polynomial from different perspectives.

- *Problem 34* requires excellent algebra skills to demonstrate the properties for sums and products of zeros of quadratic functions.

- *Problem 35* extends the properties of sums and products of zeros of cubic functions to functions of degree greater than 3.

- *Problem 36* proves that the zeros of $p(x) = ax^3 + bx^2 + cx + d$ are reciprocals of the zeros of $q(x) = dx^3 + cx^2 + bx + a$.

- *Problem 37* requires students to find the equation of the translation of a given function by 1 unit. Students must then show that each zero of the translated function is 1 greater than the corresponding zero of the given function.

15-3
Fitting Polynomial Functions to Data

Objective

Given a set of points, find the particular equation of the polynomial function that fits the data exactly or fits the best for a given degree.

Class Time

1 day

Homework Assignment

Recommended: RA, Q1–Q10, Problems 1, 3, 4, 6–8, 11, 14

Also suggested: Problem 12

Important Terms and Concepts

Third differences

Constant-nth-differences property

Dominant highest-degree term

Technology Options

 Presentation Sketch: Polynomial Fit Present.gsp

Activity: Fitting Polynomial Functions

Lesson Notes

In this section, students fit polynomial functions to data. If you did not cover Chapter 8, you will need to show students how to enter data in lists, create scatter plots, and run regression analyses.

Example 1 goes through the steps for finding a cubic function containing a given set of points. (In this case, we are looking for a function that fits the points *exactly.*) You may need to review how to solve a system of equations using matrices.

The property box after Example 1 extends the constant-second-differences property of quadratics to all polynomial functions.

The data in Example 2 are not as "nice" as those in Example 1. In other words, the points do not fall exactly along the graph of a cubic function. Students will need to use the built-in regression feature of their graphers to find the polynomial that best fits the data. The example illustrates that looking at the coefficient of determination is not sufficient for choosing the best model. In this case, the quartic model has a greater R^2-value than the cubic model. However, the quartic function has the wrong endpoint behavior, so the cubic model is the better choice. Use this example to emphasize to students that they should not apply the regression capabilities of their calculators indiscriminately.

Exploration Notes

Exploration 15-3a requires students to find the equation for a cubic function that fits a given set of points, both by using matrices and by using the regression feature of their graphers. Students then factor the equation and show that the zeros of the equation agree with the graph. You can assign this Exploration as a group activity to be completed in class or as a homework assignment or review sheet. Allow students about 20 minutes to complete this Exploration.

Technology Notes

Presentation Sketch: Polynomial Fit Present.gsp, on the *Instructor's Resource CD,* demonstrates how any *n* points can be fit to a polynomial of degree $n - 1$. This sketch is related to the activity Fitting Polynomial Functions.

Activity: Fitting Polynomial Functions, in *Exploring Precalculus with The Geometer's Sketchpad,* has students use matrices to fit a polynomial function to three arbitrary points in the plane. Allow 30 minutes.

Problem Notes

• *Problems 1 and 2* ask students to explore the zeros, extreme points, and constant differences of polynomial functions.

• *Problems 3 and 4* require students to find algebraically the equations of polynomials that fit given data points.

• *Problem 6,* the Two-Stage Rocket Problem, models the position of a moving object and is similar to problems students will encounter in calculus.

• *Problem 8c* demonstrates the significance of initial conditions in real-world problems.

• *Problem 11,* the Behavior of Polynomial Functions for Large Values of *x* Problem, illustrates why most of the fluctuations that create zeros and vertices in the graph of a polynomial function occur relatively near the origin. Knowing that fluctuations occur near the origin applies to setting the window on a grapher. The *x*-minimum and *x*-maximum usually can be between −10 and 10, even when the *y*-minimum and *y*-maximum are extremely large or small.

• *Problem 12,* the Constant-*n*th-Differences Proof Project, requires good algebraic skills and is appropriate for group work or as a graded take-home quiz.

• *Problem 13* provides a refresher on the coefficient of determination.

15-4

Rational Functions: Discontinuities, Limits, and Partial Fractions

Objective

Find discontinuities in the graph of a rational algebraic function, and identify what kind of discontinuities they are.

Class Time

1–2 days

Homework Assignment

Day 1: RA, Q1–Q10, Problems 1, 2, 3–11 odd, 24

Day 2:

   Recommended: Problems 13–25 odd

   Also suggested: Problem 26

Technology Options

 Presentation Sketch: Limits by Table Present.gsp

 Activity: Limits with Tables

 Activity: Printing Paragraphs

Activity: Lines and Circles and Limits, Oh My!

Important Terms and Concepts

Rational algebraic function

Discontinuous function

Removable discontinuity

Vertical asymptote

Indeterminate form

Infinite form

Limit

Partial fractions

Lesson Notes

In this section, students work with rational functions. The topics covered—discontinuities, limits, and partial fractions—are important in calculus. The problems in this section help students develop an intuitive understanding of these concepts.

The examples in this section use synthetic substitution. If you did not cover synthetic substitution

in Section 15-3, instruct students to use long division wherever the textbook instructions indicate synthetic substitution.

Because division by 0 is undefined, rational functions are *discontinuous* at values of x for which the denominator is equal to 0. Figure 15-4a in the student text illustrates two types of discontinuity—a removable discontinuity and a vertical asymptote.

The behavior of a function near a discontinuity can be described using the idea of a limit. You can keep the discussion of limits somewhat informal and intuitive; the topic will be covered more formally in calculus. Students need to know that a limit is a *y-value.* For the function f, as the x-values get closer and closer to 3, the y-values get closer and closer to 5. That is, *the limit of $f(x)$ as x approaches 3 is 5.* The discontinuity could be "removed" by defining $f(3) = 5$. Intuitively, this is like filling in the "hole" in the graph. For the function g, as the x-values get closer and closer to 3, the y-values decrease or increase without bound. That is, *the limit of $g(x)$ as x approaches 3 is infinite.* In this case, the discontinuity cannot be removed.

To "remove" a removable discontinuity, you need to find the limit of the function at the discontinuity. Example 1 illustrates how this is done. The numerator of the rational function is factored (with the help of synthetic substitution) and then the common factors in the numerator and denominator are reduced, eliminating the factor in the denominator that is causing the problem. The limit can then be found by substituting the x-value at the discontinuity, in this case 3, into the resulting polynomial.

Example 2 also involves finding the limit of a function at a discontinuity. As in Example 1, the solution starts by using synthetic substitution to divide the numerator by the denominator, $x - 3$. In this case, however, the denominator is *not* a factor of the numerator. When the quotient is written in mixed-number form, students can see that the limit is infinite. That is, the discontinuity *cannot* be removed.

The symbol ∞ is used for infinity. Another way to say ∞ is *increasing without bound* and to say $-\infty$ is *decreasing without bound.* This method avoids the misconception that ∞ is a number called infinity. The phrases *increasing without bound* and *decreasing without bound* also create mental images of vertical asymptotes.

It is a good idea to present one or two more examples in which you find limits graphically, numerically, and algebraically. Investigating the same problem using all three methods will give students a clearer understanding of limits. For example, you might explore this function:

$$f(x) = \frac{x^3 - 2x^2 - 5x + 6}{x + 2}$$

Graphically

Use an overhead grapher to demonstrate how to locate the discontinuity in the curve. Plot the function using a window that includes integers as grid points. You should be able to see a gap in the graph where the discontinuity occurs. Use the TRACE feature to trace the curve from both sides of $x = -2$. Ask students to watch how the y-value changes as the x-value gets closer and closer to -2. At $x = -2$, the y-value will disappear from the screen. At $x = -1.9$, $y \approx 14.21$; at $x = -2.1$, $y \approx 15.81$.

Numerically

Now use the TABLE feature of the overhead grapher to demonstrate how to find the limit numerically. Choose "Ask" for the independent variable. Enter values for x that are smaller than and larger than $x = -2$ and that get increasingly close to $x = -2$.

x	y_1
-2.1	15.81
-2.01	15.08
-2.001	15.008
-2	Error
-1.999	14.992
-1.99	14.92
-1.9	14.21

Algebraically

After examining the graph and the table, students know that $(x + 2)$ is a factor of the numerator. They can use synthetic substitution or long division to find the other factor.

$$f(x) = \frac{x^3 - 2x^2 - 5x + 6}{x + 2}$$

$$= \frac{(x + 2)(x^2 - 4x + 3)}{x + 2}$$

$$= x^2 - 4x + 3, \qquad provided\ x \neq -2$$

$$\lim_{x \to -2} f(x) = (-2)^2 - 4(-2) + 3$$

$$\therefore \lim_{x \to -2} f(x) = 15$$

If the denominator of a rational function is the product of linear factors, then you can rewrite the function as the sum of *partial fractions* with linear denominators. Example 3 shows two methods for

doing this. The first method uses matrices. The second method is the Heaviside method, which is a clever way mentally to resolve a function into partial fractions. Point out that this shortcut works only for rational functions with no repeated linear factors in the denominator (that is, with no double zeros). You can present these additional examples to give students more practice with the shortcut. The Heaviside method is quick and easy, but students must understand it in order to remember it correctly.

1. $\dfrac{x + 1}{x^2 + x - 2}$ *Answer:* $\dfrac{\frac{2}{3}}{x - 1} + \dfrac{\frac{1}{3}}{x + 2}$

2. $\dfrac{2x + 1}{x^2 + x - 6}$ *Answer:* $\dfrac{1}{x - 2} + \dfrac{1}{x + 3}$

3. $\dfrac{3x + 18}{x^2 + 5x + 4}$ *Answer:* $\dfrac{-2}{x + 4} + \dfrac{5}{x + 1}$

4. $\dfrac{5x - 10}{x^2 - x - 6}$ *Answer:* $\dfrac{1}{x - 3} + \dfrac{4}{x + 2}$

Exploration Notes

Exploration 15-4a introduces the concepts of asymptotes and removable discontinuities. Assigning this Exploration as a small-group activity is an excellent way to begin Section 15-4. The function $f(x)$ in Problem 5 has both an asymptote *and* a removable discontinuity. Allow students 20–25 minutes to complete this investigation.

Exploration 15-4b extends the lesson to parabolic asymptotes. If you spend two days on Section 15-4, there should be enough time for students to spend about 30 minutes at the beginning of Day 2 on this Exploration. There are no problems with curved asymptotes in the text. Exploration 15-5b could also be assigned as a project. Problem 9 provides significant guidance to students by showing what the first two graphs should look like. If you assign this Exploration as a project, emphasize that the answers to questions that ask for written analyses and summaries should be thorough and clearly stated.

Technology Notes

Presentation Sketch: Limits by Table Present.gsp, on the *Instructor's Resource CD,* allows you to demonstrate the limit of a function by keeping a table of values. This sketch is related to the activity Limits with Tables.

Activity: Limits with Tables, in *Exploring Precalculus with The Geometer's Sketchpad,* has students investigate a limit of a function with a removable discontinuity by creating a table of values. Allow 30–40 minutes.

Activity: Printing Paragraphs, in *Teaching Mathematics with Fathom,* lets students work with a rational (inverse variation) function relating the length of a paragraph as it is printed with varying widths. It is fairly elementary, but it may take 45–55 minutes.

Activity: Lines and Circles and Limits, Oh My!, in *A Watched Cup Never Cools,* considers some nonintuitive limits related to lines tangent to conics. The activity gives students practice in calculating some limits algebraically and can be done over a week or more.

Problem Notes

• *Problems 1–8* provide practice with finding limits and discontinuities graphically, numerically, and algebraically. All of these problems should be assigned because subsequent problems depend on the answers from previous problems.

• *Problems 9 and 10* involve the transformations studied earlier in the year. These kinds of questions reinforce the idea that math is a unified study. Students who realize this will be able to approach problem solving using multiple strategies.

• *Problems 11–16* integrate graphing, partial fractions, and transformations.

• *Problems 17–22* give students practice on resolving rational expressions into partial fractions.

• *Problems 23 and 24* are writing questions that develop understanding of vocabulary.

• *Problem 25,* the Step Discontinuity Problem, introduces students to another type of discontinuity that will be studied further in calculus. The problem examines step discontinuities graphically. You might ask students to also look at the discontinuities numerically. Dot mode is used so that the grapher does not connect the ends of the discontinuities. Talk to students about the open circles in the graph of Figure 15-4c in the student text and about where the open and closed circles should be in the graph in Figure 15-4d in the student text.

• *Problem 26* is a research project.

15-5

Instantaneous Rate of Change of a Function: The Derivative

Objective

Given the particular equation of a polynomial function, find the instantaneous rate of change at a given point (the derivative), and interpret the answer graphically.

Class Time

1–2 days

Homework Assignment

Day 1: RA, Q1–10, Problems 1–5

Day 2:

　　Recommended: Problems 6, 7, 8, 9–25 odd

　　Also suggested: Problem 26

Technology Options

 Problem 7: Door Closer Problem

 Presentation Sketch: Instantaneous Rate Present.gsp

 Activity: Instantaneous Rate

 Activity: Rates of Change

 Activity: Slopes of Exponential Functions

Important Terms and Concepts

Derivative

Instantaneous rate of change

Average rate of change

Tangent

$f'(x)$, "f prime of x"

Derivative function

Calculus

Lesson Notes

This section provides students with a preview of one of the main topics of calculus. It is fine if you do not get to it. The section opens with a function that represents the height of a bird as a function of time. To introduce the idea of derivative, the text asks, "At what rate is the bird climbing at the *instant* $x = 2$?"

This real-world context is used so that students can develop an understanding of the concept of derivative before practicing skill problems.

The "shortcut" for finding the derivative function of a polynomial function is introduced in the problem set and in Exploration 15-5a. If you prefer not to teach your students the shortcut, spend only one day on Section 15-5, covering the material through Example 1 and assigning the problems listed for Day 1. Otherwise, spend two days on this section. On the first day, cover all the material through Example 1 and assign the Day 1 problems. On the second day, assign Exploration 15-5a and Problems 7, 8, 13, and 17 as group problems in class, and assign the remaining Day 2 problems as homework.

The text shows how to find the instantaneous rate, or *derivative*, numerically, algebraically, and graphically. It is a good idea to work through all three methods as a class. After you have found the derivative numerically and algebraically, have students work in groups on parts a and b of Problem 1. After discussing the results, continue on to the graphical method. Summarize the conclusions about the definition and graphical property of the derivative this way:

> The value of the derivative of $f(x)$ at $x = c$ *is* the instantaneous rate of change of $f(x)$ at $x = c$. It *equals* the slope of the tangent line to the graph at that point.

This physical definition of derivative, its geometrical interpretation, and the distinction between the two are the most important concepts in preparing students for calculus. It is the foundation for understanding the concept of derivative. When you feel students understand what the statement says, have them work in groups on part c of Problem 1. Discuss the results and then summarize the entire discussion by reviewing all the statements in the definition box.

You might explain to students that the average rate of change,

$$r(x) = \frac{f(x) - f(c)}{x - c}$$

is the slope of the *secant* line through the points $(x, f(x))$ and $(c, f(c))$, whereas the *instantaneous rate* is the slope of the *tangent* line at point $(c, f(c))$. Point out that the formula for the average rate of change is the slope formula from Algebra I, $m = \frac{y_2 - y_1}{x_2 - x_1}$, in disguise.

If you feel your students need to see another example involving an instantaneous rate, you can work through the Supplementary Problem. Then present Example 1.

Example 1 asks students to find the equation of the tangent line to the graph at the point where $x = 2$. As students have seen, the slope of this line is the derivative of the function at $x = 2$. To find the y-intercept, students need the coordinates of one other point on the graph. The example uses the point (2, 20).

On the second day of instruction, assign Exploration 15-5a as a group activity. After discussing the results, have students work on textbook Problems 7, 8, 13, and 17 to reinforce the concepts from the exploration. Discuss the results in class, and summarize using the text in the property box before Problem 9.

Exploration Notes

Exploration 15-5a is best saved for the second day of instruction. Make a transparency of the graph so that you can plot the line requested in Problem 6 and display it on the overhead for students to see. Be sure to discuss why the answer in Problem 7 is negative. Problems 8–11 require students to make a conjecture about the shortcut for finding the equation of the derivative of a polynomial. Check students' progress before they work Problem 12, in which they must apply the shortcut. Allow 20–25 minutes for groups to complete this activity.

Technology Notes

 Problem 7: Door Closer Problem asks students to use a Dynamic Precalculus Exploration at *www.keymath.com/precalc* to investigate the average and instantaneous rate of change of a function modeling a closing door. Students use sliders to change the interval over which the average rate of change is being calculated, in order to make a conjecture about the instantaneous rate of change.

 Presentation Sketch: Instantaneous Rate Present.gsp, on the *Instructor's Resource CD,* allows you to demonstrate average or instantaneous rate of change as the slope of a secant or tangent line. It is initially set to analyze the door closer function of Problem 7, but this function may be changed to anything. This sketch is related to the activity Instantaneous Rate.

 Activity: Instantaneous Rate, in the *Instructor's Resource Book,* helps students connect instantaneous rate of change with the slope of a graph's tangent line. The function explored in this activity is the one presented in Problem 7. Allow 30–40 minutes.

 Activity: Rates of Change, in *Teaching Mathematics with Fathom,* helps students relate average rate of change, instantaneous rate of change, and derivatives. Students work both numerically and graphically with prepared sketches of power functions. Allow about 30 minutes.

 Activity: Slopes of Exponential Functions, in *Exploring Precalculus with The Geometer's Sketchpad,* is an excellent activity for students to use in preparation for or concurrently with Problem 25. Students are asked to make inferences about how exponential functions relate to their derivatives, based on their graphs. Allow 30 minutes.

Problem Notes

A blackline master for Problems 3–6 is available in the *Instructor's Resource Book.*

- *Problems 1 and 2* are practice problems for finding instantaneous rates of change numerically and algebraically. Part c of each problem asks students to write an equation of a tangent line and plot both the polynomial and tangent line using a grapher, as in Example 1.

- *Problems 3 and 4* require students to estimate graphically the derivative of a function whose graph is given. Good derivative estimates depend on accurately drawn tangent lines.

- *Problem 5,* Tim and Lum's Board Pricing Problem, applies derivatives to the price of lumber.

- *Problem 6,* the Bumblebee Problem, applies derivatives to motion and velocity, traditional derivative applications in calculus.

- *Problem 7,* the Derivative Shortcut for Power Function Problem, leads students to discover the shortcut for finding derivative functions for polynomials. The problem also introduces the idea that the tangent to a curve at an extreme point is horizontal and thus that the derivative is 0.

- *Problems 8–16* are practice problems for the shortcut known in calculus as the power rule for derivatives of polynomials. Students should use the notation $f'(x)$ starting in Problem 9.

- *Problems 17–22* give students practice finding the x-coordinates of the extreme points of a polynomial. Because the tangent line is horizontal at an extreme point, its slope is 0. Therefore, to find the x-coordinate of an extreme point, find the deriva-

tive function, $f'(x)$, set $f'(x)$ equal to 0, and solve for x.

- *Problems 23 and 24* give students practice finding the equation of a line tangent to a polynomial at a given value of x.

- *Problem 25,* the Derivative of an Exponential Function Problem, leads students to discover that the shortcut rule for finding the derivative of a polynomial function does not apply to exponential functions.

- *Problem 26,* the Historical Research Problem, is a research problem about Isaac Newton and Gottfried W. Leibniz.

Supplementary Problem

1. *Instantaneous Velocity Problem:* A rocket is launched into space. It speeds up for a while, then slows down until the second stage starts firing, and then speeds up again. Suppose that its altitude as a function of time is given by

    $$d(x) = x^3 - 7x^2 + 40x - 34$$

    where x is time in minutes since the rocket was launched and $d(x)$ is altitude in miles.

    a. Find $d(4)$, the rocket's altitude after 4 minutes.

    b. Find $d(4.1)$. How far did the rocket travel in the 0.1 minute from $x = 4$ to $x = 4.1$? What was its average velocity for this time interval?

    c. Find $d(4.01)$ and $d(4.001)$. What were the average velocities for the time intervals [4, 4.01] and [4, 4.001]? What limit do these average velocities seem to be approaching as the upper end of the time interval approaches 4?

    d. Calculate algebraically the instantaneous velocity at $x = 4$.

15-6
Chapter Review and Test

Objective

Review and practice the major concepts of this chapter.

Class Time

2 days (including 1 day for testing)

Homework Assignment

Day 1: R0–R5, T1–T21 (if you covered all five sections)

Day 2: Section 15-7, Problems 1–17

Important Terms and Concepts

Rational root theorem

Lesson Notes

Section 15-6 contains a set of Review Problems, a set of Concept Problems, and a Chapter Test. The Review Problems include one problem for each section in the chapter. You may wish to use the Chapter Test as an additional set of review problems.

Encourage students to practice the no-calculator problems without a calculator so that they are prepared for the test problems for which they cannot use a calculator.

Test only over the sections you covered in class.

Exploration Notes

There are three Explorations that can be used in place of, or in addition to, the Section 15-6 Review Problems.

Exploration 15-6a includes two functions, with multiple questions per function. Problems 1–8 review polynomials and zeros. Problems 9–14 review derivatives with a motion-and-velocity problem.

Exploration 15-6b reviews the algebraic properties of polynomial functions in Problems 1–9. Problems 10–13 review velocity and derivatives using Problem 6, the Bumblebee Problem, in Section 15-5.

Exploration 15-6c identifies in outline form the types of questions students should be able to solve.

Problem Notes

A blackline master for Problems R5, C1, T6, and T19 is available in the *Instructor's Resource Book.*

- *Problem R2c,* the Stock Market Problem, requires data regression analysis.

- *Problem R5* is a continuation of *Problem R3,* the Train Problem.

- *Concept Problem C1* presents a fascinating and little-known method for finding complex zeros of a cubic function graphically. Students draw a line containing the one line through the x-intercept that is tangent to the graph at some other point. The real part of each complex zero equals the x-coordinate of the point of tangency. The imaginary part equals the positive square root of the slope of the tangent line for one of the zeros, and the negative square root for the other zero. This is a good problem for your stronger students.

- *Concept Problem C2* presents the rational root theorem, which was once important in courses on the theory of equations before technology made it practical to find roots of polynomial and other equations numerically.

Cumulative Review, Chapters 10–15

Objective

The problem set comprises a final exam over the topics of

Three-dimensional vectors

Matrix transformations

Conic sections

Polar coordinates

Parametric functions

Complex numbers

Sequences and series

Polynomial functions

Limits and derivatives

Class Time

2 days

Homework Assignment

Long-term assignment over a period of three to four weeks: Problems 1–46

or

Day 1: Problems 18–32

Day 2: Problems 33–47

Important Terms and Concepts

Cardioid

Epicycloids of one cusp

P-series

Lesson Notes

The recommended time to complete all of the problems is about three hours. This problem set would make a good long-term assignment for students to work on over a period of three to four weeks along with their usual homework assignments. Consider using the problems as a take-home group test, in which groups of three to four students submit one paper per group for a grade. Allot time for discussing questions on the day the papers are returned.

Before assigning the problem set, have a class discussion about time management and how to break a large project into small parts with periodic self-imposed deadlines. If you feel your students are not ready for self-imposed deadlines, create a time schedule for groups to submit designated problems periodically over the three- to four-week period.

Most jobs involve large projects requiring several weeks, months, or years to complete. Yet at the same time, there are small, routine tasks that must be completed daily. Thus, a long-term project such as this serves to provide students an opportunity to develop skills needed for employment.

Problem Notes

A blackline master for Problems 13, 23, and 45 is available in the *Instructor's Resource Book.*

- *Problems 1–8* are three-dimensional vector problems.

- *Problems 9–22* are matrix transformation problems.

- *Problems 23–27* are conic section problems.

- *Problems 28 and 31* are polar coordinate problems.

- *Problems 29 and 30* are complex-number problems.

- *Problem 32* is a parametric equation problem that is related to the cardioid in *Problem 31.*

- *Problems 33–40* are sequence and series problems.

- *Problems 41–44* are polynomial questions.

- *Problems 45 and 46* are limit and derivative problems.

Solutions to Supplementary Problems

Chapter 1

Section 1-2

1. Enter into the y= menu
$y = (x^2 - 8x + 11)/(x \geq 2 \text{ and } x \leq 7)$. Set your
window to the ranges $x \in [-1, 8]$ and $y \in [-6, 6]$.

Section 1-4

1. a. Initial volume is 100 ft^3, and the volume is
decreasing at a constant rate of 5 ft^3/min. So
you can calculate the decrease by $-5t$. So
$V(t) = 100 - 5t$ will give the volume by time.

   b. $\frac{r}{h} = \frac{1}{2}$ (from $r = 5$ ft and $h = 10$ ft). So
$V = \frac{1}{3}\pi\left(\frac{1}{2}h\right)^2 \cdot h = \frac{1}{3}\pi\left(\frac{1}{4}h^2 \cdot h\right) = \frac{1}{12}\pi h^3$.

   c. Solving for h in terms of V:
$V = \frac{1}{12}\pi h^3 \Rightarrow \frac{12}{\pi}V = h^3 \Rightarrow \sqrt[3]{\frac{12}{\pi}V} = h$. So
$h(V) = \sqrt[3]{\frac{12}{\pi}V}$. Substituting $V(t) = 100 - 5t$
gives
$h(V(t)) = \sqrt[3]{\frac{12}{\pi}(100 - 5t)}$.

   d. Empty: Solve for t:
$100 - 5t = 0 \Rightarrow 100 = 5t \Rightarrow t = 20$ s
Full: $100 - 5t = \frac{1}{3}\pi \cdot 25 \cdot 10$ ft^3
$= 261.7993... \Rightarrow -5t \Rightarrow 161.7993... \Rightarrow$
$t = -32.3598...$ Domain: $-32.3598... \leq t \leq 20$

2. a. $V = \frac{4}{3}\pi r^3 \Rightarrow \frac{3V}{4\pi} = r^3 \Rightarrow r = \sqrt[3]{\frac{3V}{4\pi}}$

   b. $100 + 20t$

   c. $r(t) = \sqrt[3]{\frac{3(100 + 20t)}{4\pi}} = \sqrt[3]{\frac{75 + 15t}{\pi}}$

   d.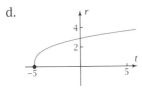

   In the real world, the radius is nonnegative.
   So $r(t) \geq 0$, so $75 + 15t \geq 0 \Rightarrow -15t \geq -75 \Rightarrow$
   $t \geq -5$. So t can be negative. A negative value
   for t corresponds to the time before the
   volume was 100 cm^3.

e. $7 = \sqrt[3]{\frac{75 + 15t}{\pi}} \Rightarrow 343 = \frac{75 + 15t}{\pi} \Rightarrow$
$1077.5662... = 75 + 15t \Rightarrow 15t$
$= 1002.5662... \Rightarrow t = 66.8377...$
So the upper bound for the domain of t is
$t = 66.8377...$ s.

3. a.

   b. $f(g(3)) = f(10 - 6) = f(4) = 4 + 2 = 6$

   c. The values of function g, $g(x)$, have to be
in the domain of $f(x)$. So $3 \leq g(x) \leq 7 \Rightarrow$
$3 \leq 10 - 2x \leq 7 \Rightarrow -7 \leq -2x \leq 7 \Rightarrow$
$3.5 \geq x \geq 1.5$. This is in the domain of g,
so the domain of $f \circ g$ is $1.5 \leq x \leq 3.5$.
You find the range by $3 \leq g(x) \leq 7 \Rightarrow$
$3 + 2 \leq g(x) + 2 \leq 7 + 2 \Rightarrow 5 \leq f(g(x)) \leq 9$.

   d. $g(f(2))$ is undefined because 2 is not in the
domain of f. $g(f(5))$ is undefined because
$f(5) = 7$ and 7 is not in the domain of g.

   e. No graph appears.

   f. The values of f must be in the domain of g.
So $1 \leq f(x) \leq 4 \Rightarrow 1 \leq x + 2 \leq 4 \Rightarrow 1 \leq x \leq 2$.
There are no values in this range that are in
the domain of f, so there is no x for which
$g \circ f$ is defined.

   g. $f(f(4)) = f(6) = 8$;
$g(g(2)) = g(6)$, which is undefined because
$x = 6$ is not in the domain of g.

4. a.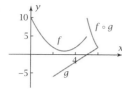

    b. $g(1) = 2 - 10 = -8$, $f(g(1)) = f(8)$ is undefined.
       $f(1) = 1 - 6 + 10 = 5$, $g(f(1)) = g(5) = 0$. $g(f(0))$
       is undefined because $f(0) = 10$ and $x = 10$ is
       not in the domain of g.

    c. $0 \le f(x) \le 5 \Rightarrow 0 \le 2x - 10 \le 5 \Rightarrow$
       $10 \le 2x \le 15 \Rightarrow 5 \le x \le 7.5$. x must also be
       in the domain of g, so the domain is
       $5 \le x \le 6$, which agrees with the graph in
       part a.

    d. $f(g(x)) = f(2x - 10)$
       $= (2x - 10)^2 - 6(2x - 10) + 10$
       $= 4x^2 - 40x + 100 - 12x + 60 + 10$
       $= 4x^2 - 52x + 170$
       The graph is the same as that in part a.

Chapter 2

Section 2-4

1. a. This table shows the length of the segments
       for various values of $\angle BAC$:

	$\overline{AC}$	$\overline{AD}$	$\overline{DC}$	$\overline{BE}$
0°	1	1	0	0
45°	1	$\frac{\sqrt{2}}{2}$	$\frac{\sqrt{2}}{2}$	1
90°	1	0	1	undefined
135°	1	$-\frac{\sqrt{2}}{2}$	$\frac{\sqrt{2}}{2}$	1
180°	1	-1	0	0
225°	1	$-\frac{\sqrt{2}}{2}$	$-\frac{\sqrt{2}}{2}$	-1
270°	1	0	-1	undefined
315°	1	$\frac{\sqrt{2}}{2}$	$-\frac{\sqrt{2}}{2}$	-1

   $\overline{BE}$ gets infinitely longer as $\angle BAC$ goes from
   0° to 90°, while $\overline{DC}$ is bounded by the radius
   of the circle, 1.

    b. $\overline{BE}$ is equal to the tangent of $\angle BAC$.
       $\overline{AD}$ is equal to the cosine of $\angle BAC$.
       $\overline{DC}$ is equal to the sine of $\angle BAC$.

    c. At 90°, the denominator, AD, becomes 0.

2. a. $\sin \theta = -\frac{3}{5}$

       $\cos \theta = \frac{4}{5}$

       $\tan \theta = -\frac{3}{4}$

       $\cot \theta = -\frac{4}{3}$

       $\sec \theta = \frac{5}{4}$

       $\csc \theta = -\frac{5}{3}$

       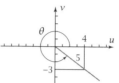

    b. $r = \sqrt{49 + 25} = \sqrt{74}$

       $\sin \theta = \frac{7}{\sqrt{74}}$

       $\cos \theta = \frac{-5}{\sqrt{74}}$

       $\tan \theta = \frac{-7}{5}$

       $\cot \theta = \frac{-5}{7}$

       $\sec \theta = \frac{-\sqrt{74}}{5}$

       $\csc \theta = \frac{\sqrt{74}}{7}$

       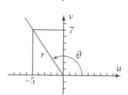

    c. $\sec \theta = 4 \Rightarrow \cos \theta = \frac{1}{4}$

       θ terminates in Quadrant IV.

       $\sin \theta = \frac{-\sqrt{15}}{4}$

       $\tan \theta = -\sqrt{15}$

       $\cot \theta = \frac{-1}{\sqrt{15}}$

       $\csc \theta = \frac{-4}{\sqrt{15}}$

d. $\theta = 60°$

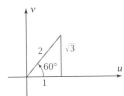

$\sin 60° = \dfrac{\sqrt{3}}{2}$

$\cos 60° = \dfrac{1}{2}$

$\tan 60° = \sqrt{3}$

$\cot 60° = \dfrac{1}{\sqrt{3}}$

$\sec 60° = 2$

$\csc 60° = \dfrac{2}{\sqrt{3}}$

e. $\theta = 135°$

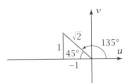

$\sin 135° = \dfrac{1}{\sqrt{2}}$

$\cos 135° = -\dfrac{1}{\sqrt{2}}$

$\tan 135° = -1$

$\cot 135° = -1$

$\sec 135° = -\sqrt{2}$

$\csc 135° = \sqrt{2}$

f. $\theta = 360°$

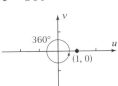

$\sin 360° = 0$
$\cos 360° = 1$
$\tan 360° = 0$
$\cot 360° = $ undefined
$\sec 360° = 1$
$\csc 360° = $ undefined

Section 2-5

1. a. On the domain $-90° \le x \le 90°$ the cosine function isn't a one-to-one function, so it isn't invertible. The cosine function is a one-to-one function on the domain $0° \le x \le 180°$, so it's invertible there.

b. $\cos^{-1}(-0.9) = 154.158...$
The angle for any value of the inverse cosine function is between 0° and 180°, so it's positive.

2. a. Angle $\approx 52°$; hypotenuse ≈ 9.4 cm

b. Angle $= \tan^{-1}\dfrac{7.4 \text{ cm}}{5.8 \text{ cm}} = 51.9112...°$;

hypotenuse $= \sqrt{(7.4 \text{ cm})^2 + (5.8 \text{ cm})^2}$
$= 9.4021...$ cm

3. $325 \text{ m} \cdot \tan 23.6° = 141.9890...$ m

4. $80 \text{ ft} \cdot \cot 0.7° = 6547.7632...$ ft $= 1.2401...$ mi

5. a. $2000 \text{ ft} \cdot \csc 63° = 2244.6524...$ ft

b. $2000 \text{ ft} \cdot \cot 63° = 1019.0508...$ ft

6. a. $\tan^{-1}\dfrac{10{,}000 \text{ ft}}{30{,}000 \text{ ft}} = 18.4349...°$

b. $\sqrt{(10{,}000 \text{ ft})^2 + (30{,}000 \text{ ft})^2}$
$= \sqrt{1{,}000{,}000{,}000} \text{ ft} = 31{,}622.7766...$ ft

7. a. $\tan^{-1}\dfrac{5 \text{ cm}}{33 \text{ cm}} = 8.6156...°$

b. $101 \text{ m} \cdot \sin 8.6156...° = 15.1303...$ m

c. $101 \text{ m} \cdot \cos 8.6156...° = 99.8602...$ m
≈ 100 paces

8. a. Let y be the height and z be the distance from the observer.
$y = 5.2 \tan 31.45° = 3.1803...$ km ≈ 3.2 km;
$z = \dfrac{52}{\cos 31.45°} = 6.0954...$ km ≈ 6.1 km

b. Let a be the angle of elevation.
$\tan a = \dfrac{30}{5.2} \Rightarrow a = \tan^{-1}\dfrac{30}{5.2}$
$= 80.1664...° \approx 80.17°$

Section 2-6

T1. $\sec^{-1} 2.5 = \cos^{-1}\dfrac{1}{2.5} = 66.4218...°$

T2. $\cot^{-1} 0.2 = \tan^{-1}\dfrac{1}{0.2} = 78.6900...°$

T3. $\csc^{-1} 10 = \sin^{-1}\dfrac{1}{10} = 5.7391...°$

Chapter 3

Section 3-3

1. a. $\frac{3}{0.1} = 30$; $\frac{3}{0.01} = 300$; $\frac{3}{0.001} = 3000$; $\frac{3}{-0.1} = -30$;

   $\frac{3}{-0.01} = -300$; $\frac{3}{-0.001} = -3000$; $\frac{3}{-0.001} = -3000$.
   The fraction $\frac{3}{x}$ is undefined if $x = 0$ because
   the equation $\frac{3}{0} = y$ is equivalent to $3 = 0 \cdot y$,
   and there is no value of y that makes this
   true. When the denominator is close to 0, the
   value of the fraction approaches either
   positive infinity or negative infinity.

   b. $\frac{5 \cdot 0.1}{0.1} = 5$; $\frac{5 \cdot 0.01}{0.01} = 5$; $\frac{5 \cdot 0.001}{0.001} = 5$; $\frac{5 \cdot (-0.1)}{-0.1} = 5$;

   $\frac{5 \cdot (-0.01)}{-0.01} = 5$; $\frac{5 \cdot (-0.001)}{-0.001} = 5$. The expression $\frac{5.0}{0}$
   is undefined because the expression $\frac{5.0}{0} = y$
   is equivalent to $5 \cdot 0 = 0 \cdot y$, and *all* values
   of y make this true. The fraction never
   approaches infinity for any value of x.

   c. The tangent graph does not approach any
   finite value near its discontinuities, while the
   $\frac{5x}{x}$ graph stays at 5 near its discontinuity.

2. f. $L = 500 \text{ m} \cdot \sec \theta$

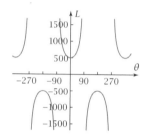

   g. When $90° < \theta < 270°$, the beam at angle θ is
   pointing away from the shore, so the beam
   that hits the shore is represented by
   negative values of L.

   h. The asymptotes occur when θ is a multiple
   of 90°. At these points the light beams are
   parallel to the shore, so L is undefined.

Section 3-5

1. a.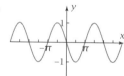

   b. The graphs are identical.

   c. $\sin(-1) = -0.8414\ldots = -\sin 1$;
   $\sin(-x) = -\sin x$

   d. The result looks like $\sin x$;
   $\sin(\pi - 1) = 0.8414\ldots = \sin 1$

   e.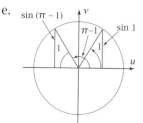

   For any x, the v-coordinate, representing the
   sine, is the same for both x and $\pi - x$.

Section 3-6

1. arcsin $0.7 = 0.7753\ldots, 2.3661\ldots, 7.0505\ldots$,
   $8.6493\ldots, 13.1417\ldots$

2. arctan $4 = 1.3258\ldots, 4.4674\ldots, 7.6090\ldots$,
   $10.7505\ldots, 13.8921\ldots$

3. a. $\sin^{-1} 0.4 = 0.4115\ldots$
   $\Rightarrow x = 0.4115\ldots, 2.7300\ldots, 6.6947\ldots$,
   $9.0132\ldots, 12.9778\ldots, 15.2964\ldots$

   b. $x = 100.9424\ldots$

4. a. $\tan^{-1} 2 = 1.1071\ldots$
   $\Rightarrow x = 1.1701\ldots, 4.2487\ldots, 7.3903\ldots$,
   $10.5319\ldots, 13.6735\ldots, 16.8151\ldots$

   b. $x = 51.3726\ldots$

Section 3-7

1. a.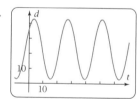

   b. 3 ft. This number must be positive because
   the wheel isn't underground!

   c. $d = 23 + 20 \cos \frac{\pi}{12}(t - 3)$

   d. $d(20) = 23 + 20 \cos \frac{17\pi}{12} = 17.8236\ldots$ ft

   e. $18 = 23 + 20 \cos \frac{\pi}{12}(t - 3)$
   $\Rightarrow t = 3 \pm \frac{12}{\pi}\left(\cos^{-1} \frac{-1}{4} + 2\pi n\right)$
   $= 9.9651\ldots$ s, $20.0348\ldots$ s, $33.9651\ldots$ s

2. a.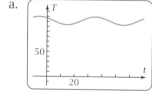

   b. $T = 112 + 8 \cos \frac{\pi}{20}(t - 35)$

   c. $T(0) = 112 + 8 \cos \frac{-35\pi}{20}$
   $= 112 + 8 \cdot \frac{\sqrt{2}}{2}$
   $= 117.6568\ldots°$F

Precalculus with Trigonometry: Instructor's Guide
© 2007 Key Curriculum Press

d. $114 = 112 + 8 \cos \frac{\pi}{20}(t - 35)$

$\Rightarrow t = 35 \pm \frac{20}{\pi}\left(\cos^{-1}\frac{-1}{4} + 2\pi n\right)$
$= 3.3913...$ min,
$26.6086...$ min, $43.3913...$ min

3. a. $d = 9 - 10 \sin \frac{2\pi}{15}t$

t	d
0 min	9 m
2 min	1.5685... m
4 min	−0.9452... m
6 min	3.1221... m
8 min	11.0791... m
10 min	17.6602... m
12 min	18.5105... m
14 min	13.0673... m
16 min	4.9326... m

b. The theoretical minimum depth is −1 m; the actual depth is 0 because the depth cannot be beneath the sea floor.

c. $d(t) = 0 \Rightarrow t = \frac{15}{2\pi}\left(\sin^{-1}\frac{9}{10} + 2\pi n\right)$ or
$\frac{15}{2\pi}\left(\pi - \sin^{-1}\frac{9}{10} + 2\pi n\right)$;
$d = 0$ for $2.6732...$ min $\leq t \leq 4.8267...$ min

d. 300 km

e. The boat rises or falls (trough to crest or vice versa) at an average rate of only 20 m per half-period of $7\frac{1}{2}$ min $= 2\frac{2}{3}$ m/min $= 0.16$ km/h, barely perceptible.

4. a. $y = 4000 \cos \frac{\pi}{45}(t - 10)$

b. $y(25) = 2000$ km; $y(41) = -2236.7716...$ km; $y(163) = 1236.0679...$ km

c. $t = 10 \pm \frac{45}{\pi}\left(\cos^{-1}\frac{-2}{5} + 2\pi n\right) \Rightarrow$
$t = 38.3945...$ min

d. $y(0) = 3064.1777...$ km north of the equator.

e. Cape Canaveral is at 28.45° N latitude, which corresponds to about 3162 km from the equator.

5. a. $y = A \cos \frac{\pi}{600}(200) - A \cos \frac{\pi}{600}(x + 200)$

$= A \cdot \left[0.5 - \cos \frac{\pi}{600}(x + 200)\right]$;
$y(100) = -90$ m $\Rightarrow A = -180$;

$y = -90 + 180 \cos \frac{\pi}{600}(x + 200)$

b. $y(510) = -240.9607...$ m

c. $y_{\min} = 270$ m at $x = 400$ m

d. $y = 90$ m

e. $y = -120 \Rightarrow x = -200 \pm \frac{600}{\pi}\left(\cos^{-1}\frac{-1}{6} + 2\pi n\right)$;
0 m $\leq x \leq 131.9802...$ m and
$668.0197...$ m $\leq x \leq 800$ m

f.

x	y	$\$
50	−43.4125...	3,255.94
100	−90	6,750.00
150	−136.5874...	10,244.06
200	−180	13,500.00
250	−217.2792...	16,295.94
300	−245.8845...	18,441.34
350	−263.8666...	19,790.00
400	−270	20,250.00
450	−263.8666...	19,790.00
500	−245.8845...	18,441.34
550	−217.2792...	16,295.94
600	−180	13,500.00
650	−136.5874...	10,244.06
700	−90	6,750.00
750	−43.4125...	3,255.94

Total cost = $196,804.56

6. a. $P = 100 \cos \frac{2\pi}{23}t$; $E = 100 \cos \frac{2\pi}{28}t$;

$I = 100 \cos \frac{2\pi}{33}t$

b.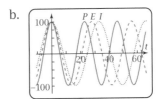

c. $P(33) = 100 \cos \frac{66\pi}{23} = -91.7211...$;

$E(33) = 100 \cos \frac{66\pi}{28} = 43.3883...$

d. $P = 0$ at $t = \frac{23 \text{ days}}{4} = 5.75$ days; $E = 0$ at
$t = \frac{28 \text{ days}}{4} = 7$ days; $I = 0$ at $t = \frac{33 \text{ days}}{4}$
$= 8.25$ days

e. $t =$ the least common multiple of 23, 28, and 33 days $= 23 \cdot 28 \cdot 33 = 21,252$ days $\approx$ 58 years, 2 months from now.

f. Biorhythm theory originated at the end of the 19th century with Viennese doctors Wilhelm Fliess and Hermann Swoboda.

7. a. $i = 5 \cos 120\pi t$

b. $v = 180 \cos 120\pi(t + 0.003)$

c. $v(0) = 76.6402... \text{ V} \approx 77 \text{ V}$

d. $i(-0.003) = 2.1288... \text{ A} \approx 2.13 \text{ A}$

e. $180 \cos 120\pi(t + 0.003) = 170 \Rightarrow$
$$t = -0.003 \pm \frac{1}{120\pi}\left(\cos^{-1}\frac{170}{180} + 2\pi n\right),$$
for which $t = 0.0127...$ s is the first positive value.

8. a. $E = -5 + 60 \cos \dfrac{\pi}{12}(t - 12.75)$

b.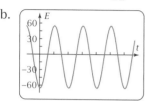

c. The t-intercepts correspond to sunrise and sunset. The sinusoid is below the t-axis at night.

d. $E\left(9\frac{27}{60}\right) = 33.9668...° \approx 34.0°$

$E\left(14\frac{30}{60}\right) = 48.8123...° \approx 48.8°$

e. $E = 0$ at sunrise; $t = 7.0686... \approx 7{:}04$ a.m.

f. Make the sinusoidal axis a function of the date.

Chapter 4

Section 4-2

1. $\csc x = \dfrac{1}{\sin x}$

2. $\sec x = \dfrac{1}{\cos x}$, so $\cos x \cdot \sec x = \cos x \cdot \dfrac{1}{\cos x} = 1$

3. $\cot x = \dfrac{\cos x}{\sin x}$

4. $\tan x = \dfrac{\sin x}{\cos x} = \dfrac{1/\cos x}{1/\sin x} = \dfrac{\sec x}{\csc x}$

5.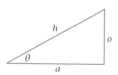

$\sin\theta = \dfrac{o}{h}$, $\cos\theta = \dfrac{a}{h}$, $a^2 + o^2 = h^2$, so

$(\cos\theta)^2 + (\sin\theta)^2 = \left(\dfrac{a}{h}\right)^2 + \left(\dfrac{o}{h}\right)^2$

$= \dfrac{a^2 + o^2}{h^2} = \dfrac{h^2}{h^2} = 1$

6. $\cos^2 x + \sin^2 x = 1 \Rightarrow$
$$\frac{1}{\cos^2 x} \cdot (\cos^2 x + \sin^2 x) = \frac{1}{\cos^2 x} \Rightarrow$$
$$\frac{\cos^2 x}{\cos^2 x} + \frac{\sin^2 x}{\cos^2 x} = \frac{1}{\cos^2 x} \Rightarrow$$
$$1 + \left(\frac{\sin x}{\cos x}\right)^2 = \left(\frac{1}{\cos x}\right)^2 \Rightarrow 1 + \tan^2 x = \sec^2 x$$

7.

8.

x	$\cos^2 x$	$\sin^2 x$	$\cos^2 x + \sin^2 x$
0	1	0	1
1	0.2919...	0.7080...	1
2	0.1731...	0.8268...	1
3	0.9800...	0.0199...	1
4	0.4272...	0.5727...	1
5	0.0804...	0.9195...	1

Note that $\cos^2 x + \sin^2 x = 1$ for all x, in accordance with the Pythagorean property.

9. $\cos^2 x + \sin^2 x = 1 \Rightarrow$
$\cos^2 x + \sin^2 x - \sin^2 x = 1 - \sin^2 x \Rightarrow$
$\cos^2 x = 1 - \sin^2 x$

10. $1 + \tan^2 x = \sec^2 x \Rightarrow 1 + \tan^2 x - 1$
$= \sec^2 x - 1 \Rightarrow \tan^2 x = \sec^2 x - 1$

11. $\sin x = \sin x$
$\cos x = \pm\sqrt{1 - \sin^2 x}$
$\tan x = \pm\dfrac{\sin x}{\sqrt{1 - \sin^2 x}}$
$\cot x = \pm\dfrac{\sqrt{1 - \sin^2 x}}{\sin x}$
$\sec x = \pm\dfrac{1}{\sqrt{1 - \sin^2 x}}$
$\csc x = \dfrac{1}{\sin x}$

12. $\sin x = \pm\sqrt{1 - \cos^2 x}$
$\cos x = \cos x$
$\tan x = \pm\dfrac{\sqrt{1 - \cos^2 x}}{\cos x}$
$\cot x = \pm\dfrac{\cos x}{\sqrt{1 - \cos^2 x}}$
$\sec x = \dfrac{1}{\cos x}$
$\csc x = \pm\dfrac{1}{\sqrt{1 - \cos^2 x}}$

Section 4-3

1. $\cot^2 A \csc^2 A - \cot^2 A = \cot^2 A \cdot (\csc^2 A - 1)$
$= \cot^2 A \cdot (\cot^2 A) = \cot^4 A$

2. $\sec^4 t - \tan^4 t = (\sec^2 t + \tan^2 t)(\sec^2 t - \tan^2 t)$
$= (\sec^2 t + \tan^2 t) \cdot 1$
$= \sec^2 t + \tan^2 t + (\tan^2 t - \tan^2 t)$
$= (\sec^2 t - \tan^2 t) + \tan^2 t + \tan^2 t$
$= 1 + 2 \tan^2 t$

3. $\dfrac{\sec x}{\sin x} - \dfrac{\sin x}{\cos x} = \dfrac{1/\cos x}{\sin x} - \dfrac{\sin x}{\cos x} \cdot \dfrac{\sin x}{\sin x}$
$= \dfrac{1}{\cos x \sin x} - \dfrac{\sin^2 x}{\cos x \sin x}$
$= \dfrac{1 - \sin^2 x}{\cos x \sin x} = \dfrac{\cos^2 x}{\cos x \sin x}$
$= \dfrac{\cos x}{\sin x} = \cot x$

4. $\dfrac{1}{\sec^2 x} + \dfrac{1}{\csc^2 x} = \dfrac{1}{(1/\cos x)^2} + \dfrac{1}{(1/\sin x)^2}$
$= \cos^2 x + \sin^2 x = 1$

5. $\dfrac{1}{1 - \sin r} = \dfrac{1 + \sin r}{(1 - \sin r)(1 + \sin r)} = \dfrac{1 + \sin r}{1 - \sin^2 r}$
$= \dfrac{1 + \sin r}{\cos^2 r} = \dfrac{1}{\cos^2 r} + \dfrac{\sin r}{\cos^2 r}$
$= \sec^2 r + \dfrac{1}{\cos r} \cdot \dfrac{\sin r}{\cos r}$
$= \sec^2 r + \sec r \tan r$

6. $\dfrac{\sin x}{1 - \cos x} + \dfrac{1 - \cos x}{\sin x}$
$= \dfrac{\sin x(1 + \cos x)}{(1 - \cos x)(1 + \cos x)} + \dfrac{1 - \cos x}{\sin x}$
$= \dfrac{\sin x(1 + \cos x)}{1 - \cos^2 x} + \dfrac{1 - \cos x}{\sin x}$
$= \dfrac{\sin x(1 + \cos x)}{\sin^2 x} + \dfrac{1 - \cos x}{\sin x}$
$= \dfrac{1 + \cos x}{\sin x} + \dfrac{1 - \cos x}{\sin x}$
$= \dfrac{2}{\sin x} = 2 \csc x$

7. $\dfrac{\sec x}{\sec x - \tan x} = \dfrac{\sec x(\sec x + \tan x)}{(\sec x - \tan x)(\sec x + \tan x)}$
$= \dfrac{\sec^2 x + \sec x \tan x}{\sec^2 x - \tan^2 x} = \dfrac{\sec^2 x + \sec x \tan x}{1}$
$= \sec^2 x + \sec x \tan x$

8. $\sin^3 z \cos^2 z = \sin^2 z \cos^2 z \sin z$
$= (1 - \cos^2 z)\cos^2 z \sin z$
$= \cos^2 z \sin z - \cos^4 z \sin z$

9. a. $\theta = 150°, 390°, 510°, 750°$;
$\sin^{-1} 0.5 = 30° + 360n°$ or $150° + 360n°$

b. $\theta = 240°, 420°, 600°, 780°$;
$\tan^{-1} \sqrt{3} = 60° + 180n°$

Section 4-4

1. The graphs coincide. You can conclude that the right side is also a sinusoid.

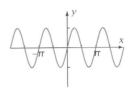

Section 4-5

1. a. The graph should agree.

b. $x = \sec t, y = \tan t$. So $\sec^2 t - \tan^2 t = 1 \Rightarrow$ $x^2 - y^2 = 1$

c. $x = -2 + 5 \tan t, y = 1 + 3 \sec t$

d.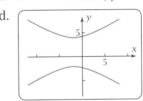

2. a.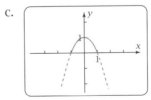

b. $\cos^2 t + \sin^2 t = 1 \Rightarrow x_1^2 + y_1^2 = 1 \Rightarrow y_1 = -x_1^2 + 1$

c.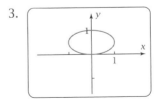

cos t and sin t are restricted to $[-1, 1]$, so x_1 and y_1 are also restricted. But there is no such restriction for x_2 or y_2.

3.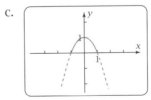

4.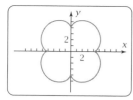

5.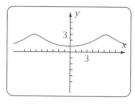

6.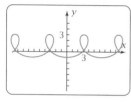

7.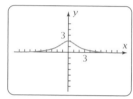

8.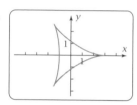

9. a. By the Taylor series,
   $\tan^{-1} 0.3 \approx 0.29145475714286....$
   The actual value of $\tan^{-1} 0.3$ is
   $0.29145679447787...$, a difference of
   $-0.00000203733501...$, or about $\frac{2}{10,000}\%$.

   b. $y = \cos^{-1} x \Rightarrow x = \cos y \Rightarrow$
   $$\tan y = \frac{\sin y}{\cos y} = \frac{\pm\sqrt{1 - \cos^2 y}}{\cos y} = \frac{\pm\sqrt{1 - x^2}}{x} \Rightarrow$$
   $$y = \arctan\frac{\pm\sqrt{1 - x^2}}{x} = n\pi + \tan^{-1}\frac{\pm\sqrt{1 - x^2}}{x}.$$
   Case 1 $x \in (0, 1]$:
   Then $\cos^{-1} x \in \left[0, \frac{\pi}{2}\right)$.
   If $\tan^{-1}(x) \in \left(0, \frac{\pi}{2}\right]$, then $x \in [0, \infty)$.
   But because $x > 0$, $\dfrac{+\sqrt{1 - x^2}}{x} \in [0, \infty)$.
   $\therefore \cos^{-1} x = \tan^{-1}\dfrac{\sqrt{1 - x^2}}{x}$
   Case 2 $x \in [-1, 0)$:
   Then $\cos^{-1} x \in \left(\frac{\pi}{2}, \pi\right]$.
   Never is $\tan^{-1}(x) \in \left(\frac{\pi}{2}, \pi\right]$.

   But $\pi + \tan^{-1}(x) \in \left(\frac{\pi}{2}, \pi\right]$
   if $\tan^{-1}(x) \in \left(-\frac{\pi}{2}, 0\right]$,
   that is, if $x \in (-\infty, 0]$.
   But because $x < 0$, $\dfrac{+\sqrt{1 - x^2}}{x} \in [-\infty, 0)$.
   $\therefore \cos^{-1} x = \pi + \tan^{-1}\dfrac{\sqrt{1 - x^2}}{x}$

   c. The graphs coincide on $(0, 1]$, showing that
   the equation is true there. They don't
   coincide on $[-1, 0)$ because, as explained in
   part b, Case 2, a different equation must be
   used there.

   d. $y = \sin^{-1} x \Rightarrow x = \sin y \Rightarrow$
   $$\tan y = \frac{\sin y}{\cos y} = \frac{\sin y}{\pm\sqrt{1 - \sin^2 y}} = \frac{x}{\pm\sqrt{1 - x^2}} \Rightarrow$$
   $$y = \arctan\frac{x}{\pm\sqrt{1 - x^2}} = n\pi + \tan^{-1}\frac{x}{\pm\sqrt{1 - x^2}}.$$
   Now, $x \in (-1, 1) \Rightarrow \sin^{-1} x \in \left(-\frac{\pi}{2}, \frac{\pi}{2}\right)$. But
   $\tan^{-1}(x) \in \left(-\frac{\pi}{2}, \frac{\pi}{2}\right)$ if $x \in (-\infty, \infty)$, that is, for
   all x.

   You only need to make sure that $\sin^{-1} x$ and
   $\tan^{-1}(x)$ have the same sign. But $\sin^{-1}(x)$
   and $\tan^{-1}(x)$ are in either Quadrant I or
   Quadrant IV, and in those quadrants, sine
   and cosine have the same sign if their
   arguments have the same sign and x and
   $\frac{x}{+\sqrt{1 - x^2}}$ always have the same sign.
   $\therefore \sin^{-1} x = \tan^{-1}\dfrac{x}{\sqrt{1 - x^2}}$

   e. The graphs coincide, showing that the
   equation is true.

Section 4-6

1. $y = \sec^{-1} x$

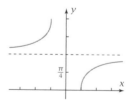

$y = \csc^{-1} x$

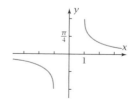

Incorrect graph of $y = \cot^{-1} x$, as given by the calculator:

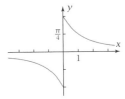

The correct graph of $y = \cot^{-1} x$ is

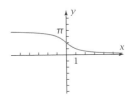

2. Graphs should match those in Figure 4-6d of the student text.

3. $\sin^{-1}$ has negative domain in Quadrant IV, so opp $= -\sqrt{2}$ and hyp $= 2$, so adj $= \sqrt{2}$, so $\cot\left[\sin^{-1}\left(-\frac{\sqrt{2}}{2}\right)\right] = \frac{\sqrt{2}}{-\sqrt{2}} = -1$.

4. arcsec has negative domain in Quadrants II and III, so hyp $= \sqrt{2}$ and adj $= -1$, so opp $= \pm 1$, so $\tan\left[\text{arcsec}\left(-\sqrt{2}\right)\right] = \frac{\pm 1}{-1} = \pm 1$.

5. arccot has positive domain in Quadrants I and III, so adj $= \pm 3$ and opp $= \pm 1$ (same sign as adj), so hyp $= \sqrt{10}$, so $\csc(\text{arccot } 3) = \frac{\sqrt{10}}{\pm 1} = \pm\sqrt{10}$.

6. $\tan^{-1}$ has positive domain in Quadrant I, so opp $= 1$ and adj $= 2$, so hyp $= \sqrt{5}$, so $\csc\left(\tan^{-1}\frac{1}{2}\right) = \frac{\sqrt{5}}{1} = \sqrt{5}$.

7. arccsc has positive domain in Quadrants I and II, so hyp $= 2$ and opp $= 1$, so $\csc(\text{arccsc } 2) = \frac{2}{1} = 2$.

8. $\sin^{-1}$ has positive domain in Quadrant I, so opp $= 2$ and hyp $= 3$, so $\sin\left(\sin^{-1}\frac{2}{3}\right) = \frac{2}{3}$.

9. Domain of $\cos^{-1}$ is in Quadrants I and II; adj $= x$ and hyp $= 1$; opp ≥ 0 in Quadrants I and II, so opp $= \sqrt{1 - x^2}$, so $\tan(\cos^{-1} x) = \frac{\sqrt{1 - x^2}}{x}$.

10. See Problem 9. Then $\sin(\cos^{-1} x) = \frac{\sqrt{1 - x^2}}{1} = \sqrt{1 - x^2}$.

11. a. $m = 3$, $b = 2$, $y = 0 \Rightarrow x = -\frac{2}{3}$

    b. $y = \frac{x - 2}{3} = \frac{1}{3}x - \frac{2}{3}$; yes, no x-value goes to more than one y-value. The graph passes the vertical line test.

c. $m = \frac{1}{3}$, $b = -\frac{2}{3}$, $y = 0 \Rightarrow x = 2$; slopes are reciprocals, x- and y-intercepts are interchanged.

d. They are reflections of each other over that line.

e. $f(f^{-1}(x)) = f\left(\frac{1}{3}x - \frac{2}{3}\right) = 3\left(\frac{1}{3}x + \frac{2}{3}\right) + 2$
   $= (x - 2) + 2 = x$; $f^{-1}(f(x)) = f^{-1}(3x + 2)$
   $= \frac{1}{3}(3x + 2) - \frac{2}{3} = \left(x + \frac{2}{3}\right) - \frac{2}{3} = x$

12. a. $x = y^2 \Rightarrow y = \pm\sqrt{x}$

    b.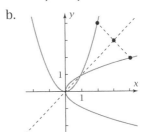

For the graph of the inverse, use $Y_2 = \sqrt{X}$ and $Y_3 = -\sqrt{X}$.

c. A point $(x, y) = (x, f(x)) = (x, x^2)$ on the graph of $y = f(x)$ corresponds to the point (x^2, x) on the graph of $y = f^{-1}(x)$. The midpoint of the line joining them is $\left(\frac{x + x^2}{2}, \frac{x^2 + x}{2}\right)$, which is on the line $y = x$ because its x- and y-coordinates are the same. Thus the two points are located symmetrically about the line.

d. No, because any $x > 0$ goes to the *two* y-values $+\sqrt{x}$ and $-\sqrt{x}$. The graph does not pass the vertical line test.

Chapter 5

Section 5-2

1. $y = \cos 5\theta + \sin 5\theta = \sqrt{2} \cos(5\theta - 45°)$; horizontal dilation by 5

2. $\cos\frac{\pi}{5}x + 4 \sin\frac{\pi}{5}x = \sqrt{17} \cos\left(\frac{\pi}{5}x - \cos^{-1}\frac{\sqrt{17}}{17}\right)$
   $= \sqrt{17} \cos\left(\frac{\pi}{5}x - 1.3258...\right)$

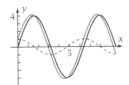

3. a. $y = 50 \cos \left(1.5\pi \times 10^{15}\right)x$
        $+ 70 \sin \left(1.5\pi \times 10^{15}\right)x$

        $= 10\sqrt{74} \cos \left[\left(1.5\pi \times 10^{15}\right)x - \cos^{-1}\dfrac{5}{\sqrt{74}}\right]$

        $= 10\sqrt{74} \cos \left[(1.5\pi \times 10^{15})x - 0.9505\ldots\right]$

    b. No. Amplitude $= \sqrt{50^2 + 70^2} = 10\sqrt{74}$
        $= 86.02232\ldots$

    c. 3×10^8 m/s $\cdot \dfrac{1}{10^{-10}\text{ m}} \cdot \dfrac{2\pi}{4000}$
        $= 1.5\pi \times 10^{15}$ radians/s

4. $\cos 15° = \cos (45° - 30°)$
    $= \cos 45° \cos 30° + \sin 45° \sin 30°$
    $= \dfrac{\sqrt{2}}{2} \cdot \dfrac{\sqrt{3}}{2} + \dfrac{\sqrt{2}}{2} \cdot \dfrac{1}{2} = \dfrac{\sqrt{6} + \sqrt{2}}{4}$

Section 5-3

1. $\cos (A - B) = \cos A \cos B + \sin A \sin B$
    $= \dfrac{7}{25} \cdot \dfrac{15}{17} + \dfrac{24}{25} \cdot \dfrac{8}{17} = \dfrac{297}{425}$

2. $\sin (A - B) = \sin A \cos B - \sin B \cos A$
    $= \dfrac{24}{25} \cdot \dfrac{15}{17} - \dfrac{8}{17} \cdot \dfrac{7}{25} = \dfrac{304}{425}$

3. $\tan (A - B) = \dfrac{\tan A - \tan B}{1 + \tan A \tan B}$
    $= \dfrac{\frac{24}{7} - \frac{8}{15}}{1 + \frac{24}{7} \cdot \frac{8}{15}} = \dfrac{304}{297}$

4. $\cos (A + B) = \cos A \cos B - \sin A \sin B$
    $= \dfrac{7}{25} \cdot \dfrac{15}{17} - \dfrac{24}{25} \cdot \dfrac{8}{17} = -\dfrac{87}{425}$

5. $\sin (A + B) = \sin A \cos B + \sin B \cos A$
    $= \dfrac{24}{25} \cdot \dfrac{15}{17} + \dfrac{8}{17} \cdot \dfrac{7}{25} = \dfrac{416}{425}$

6. $\tan (A + B) = \dfrac{\tan A + \tan B}{1 - \tan A \tan B}$
    $= \dfrac{\frac{24}{7} + \frac{8}{15}}{1 - \frac{24}{7} \cdot \frac{8}{15}} = -\dfrac{416}{87}$

Section 5-4

1. $y = \cos \theta + 3 \sin 12\theta$

2. $y = 3 \cos \theta \cos 10\theta$

3. $y = 5 \cos \dfrac{\pi}{3}x + \cos 2\pi x$

4. $y = 4 \sin \dfrac{\pi}{4}x + \cos 2\pi x$

5. $y = 4 \sin \theta \sin 12\theta$

6. $y = -5 \cos \theta + \cos 15\theta$

7. $y = 2 \cos \theta + 3 \sin 20\theta$

8. $y = 6 \sin \theta \cos 17\theta$

9. $y = 4 \sin \theta \sin 5\theta$

10. $y = 3 \sin 2\theta + \sin 30\theta$

11. $y = 2 \sin \dfrac{\pi}{4}x \cos \dfrac{15\pi}{4}x$

12. $y = 2 \cos \pi x + \sin 11\pi x$

13. $y = 3 \sin \theta + \cos 19\theta$

14. $y = 5 \cos \theta \cos 15\theta$

15. $y = 3 \cos 2\theta + 2 \cos 25\theta$

16. a. $y = \sin 528\pi t$

    b. $y_2 = 0.4 \sin 2112\pi t$

    c.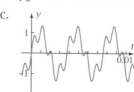

    d. i. 792, 1584, 2376, 3168, 3960, 4752, . . .
        ii. 1056, 2112, 3168, 4224, 5280, . . .
        iii. 3168, 6336, . . .

    e. C should harmonize well with either G or F, but G and F should not harmonize well with each other.

    f. The graph is not periodic, and the "harmonic" does not have many smaller-frequency overtones in common with the fundamental. (*Note:* Actually, the graph *is* periodic, but the period is much, much longer than the length shown here, and in particular, much longer than the period of the fundamental.)

    g. False. (For example, consider part e.)

    h. Student project

17. a. $y = 2 \cos \theta \cos 9\theta$

    b. 360° and $\dfrac{360°}{9} = 40°$

    c. The graphs are the same.

    d. $\dfrac{360°}{10} = 36°$ and $\dfrac{360°}{8} = 40°$

    e. $10\theta = 9\theta + \theta$ and $8\theta = 9\theta - \theta$

    f. $\cos 10\theta + \cos 8\theta$
        $= \cos (9\theta + \theta) + \cos (9\theta - \theta)$
        $= \cos 9\theta \cos \theta - \sin 9\theta \sin \theta$
        $\quad + \cos 9\theta \cos \theta + \sin 9\theta \sin \theta$
        $= 2 \cos 9\theta \cos \theta$

Section 5-5

1. $2 \sin 3x \cos 5x = \sin 8x - \sin 2x$

2. $2 \sin 8x \sin 2x = \cos 6x - \cos 10x$

3. $2 \cos 4x \cos 7x = \cos 11x + \cos 3x$

4. $2 \cos 11x \sin 9x = \sin 20x - \sin 2x$

5. $\sin 3x + \sin 9x = 2 \sin 6x \cos 3x$

6. $\sin 9x - \sin 11x = -2 \cos x \sin 10x$

7. $\cos 8x - \cos 10x = 2 \sin 9x \sin x$

8. $\cos 5x + \cos 13x = 2 \cos 9x \cos 4x$

9. $y = 2 \sin \theta \cos 7\theta = \sin 8\theta - \sin 6\theta$

10. $y = 6 \sin x \cos 12x = 3 \sin 13x - 3 \sin 11x$

11. $y = \sin x + \sin 13x = 2 \sin 7x \cos 6x$

12. $y = 5 \cos \theta + 5 \cos 11\theta = 10 \cos 6\theta \cos 5\theta$

13. $\sin 5x + \sin 3x = 2 \sin 4x \cos x$
$\qquad\qquad\qquad = 2 \sin (2 \cdot 2x) \cos x$
$\qquad\qquad\qquad = 2(2 \sin 2x \cos 2x) \cos x$
$\qquad\qquad\qquad = 4 \sin 2x \cos 2x \cos x$

14. $\sin x + \sin 2x + \sin 3x = \sin 2x + (\sin x + \sin 3x)$
$\qquad\qquad\qquad\qquad = \sin 2x + (2 \sin 2x \cos x)$
$\qquad\qquad\qquad\qquad = \sin 2x (1 + 2 \cos x)$

15. $\sin (x + y) \sin (x - y)$
$= -\dfrac{1}{2} \cos [(x + y) + (x - y)] + \dfrac{1}{2} \cos [(x + y) - (x - y)]$
$= -\dfrac{1}{2} \cos 2x + \dfrac{1}{2} \cos 2y$
$= -\dfrac{1}{2} (\cos 2x + 1) + \dfrac{1}{2} (\cos 2y + 1)$
$= -\dfrac{1}{2} [\cos (x + x) + \cos (x - x)]$
$\quad + \dfrac{1}{2} [\cos (y + y) + \cos (y - y)]$
$= -\dfrac{1}{2} (2 \cos x \cos x) + \dfrac{1}{2} (2 \cos y \cos y)$
$= \cos^2 y - \cos^2 x$

Section 5-6

1. $\sin \frac{1}{2}x$ has period 4π and amplitude 1, but $\frac{1}{2} \sin x$ has period 2π and amplitude $\frac{1}{2}$.

2. $\sin 2 \cdot \dfrac{\pi}{2} = \sin \pi = 0$, but $2 \sin \dfrac{\pi}{2} = 2 \cdot 1 = 2$.

3. $\frac{1}{2} + \frac{1}{2} \cos 2x = \frac{1}{2} + \frac{1}{2}(2 \cos^2 x - 1) = \cos^2 x$;
$\frac{1}{2} - \frac{1}{2} \cos 2x = \frac{1}{2} - \frac{1}{2}(1 - 2 \sin^2 x) = \sin^2 x$;
another method, using the sum and difference properties:
$1 + \cos 2x = \cos 0 + \cos 2x$
$= \cos (x - x) + \cos (x + x)$
$= 2 \cos x \cos x = 2 \cos^2 x \Rightarrow$
$\cos^2 x = \frac{1}{2} + \frac{1}{2} \cos 2x$;
$1 - \cos 2x = \cos 0 - \cos 2x$
$= \cos (x - x) \cos (x + x)$
$= 2 \sin x \sin x = 2 \sin^2 x \Rightarrow \sin^2 x = \frac{1}{2} - \frac{1}{2} \cos 2x$

4. a.

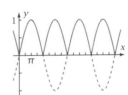

b., c. $y = \dfrac{1}{2} - \dfrac{1}{2} \cos 2x$
See Problem 3.

5. a.

b., c. $y = \dfrac{1}{2} + \dfrac{1}{2} \cos 2x$
See Problem 3.

6. a. $y = \sin \dfrac{1}{2}x$ (dotted), $y = \sqrt{\dfrac{1}{2}(1 - \cos x)}$ (solid)

b. The graphs are the same on $[0, 2\pi]$ and $[4\pi, 6\pi]$, and reflections on $(2\pi, 4\pi)$ and $(6\pi, 8\pi)$.

c. $\cos 2x = 1 - 2 \sin^2 x \Rightarrow$
$2 \sin^2 x = 1 - \cos 2x \Rightarrow$
$\sin^2 x = \dfrac{1}{2} - \dfrac{1}{2} \cos 2x \Rightarrow$
$\sin^2 \dfrac{1}{2}x = \dfrac{1}{2} - \dfrac{1}{2} \cos x \Rightarrow$
$\sin \dfrac{1}{2}x = \pm\sqrt{\dfrac{1}{2} - \dfrac{1}{2} \cos x}$

7. a. $\sin x = 2 \sin \dfrac{x}{2} \cos \dfrac{x}{2}$

b. $\sin \dfrac{3x}{2} = \sin \left(\dfrac{x}{2} + x \right)$

$= \sin \dfrac{x}{2} \cos x + \cos \dfrac{x}{2} \sin x$

c. $\dfrac{1}{2} + \dfrac{\sin \frac{3x}{2}}{2 \sin \frac{x}{2}} = \dfrac{1}{2} \left(1 + \dfrac{\sin \frac{3x}{2}}{\sin \frac{x}{2}} \right)$

$= \dfrac{1}{2} \left(1 + \dfrac{\sin \frac{x}{2} \cos x + \cos \frac{x}{2} \sin x}{\sin \frac{x}{2}} \right)$

$= \dfrac{1}{2} \left(1 + \dfrac{\sin \frac{x}{2} \cos x + \cos \frac{x}{2} \cdot 2 \sin \frac{x}{2} \cos \frac{x}{2}}{\sin \frac{x}{2}} \right)$

$= \dfrac{1}{2} \left(1 + \cos x + 2 \cos^2 \dfrac{x}{2} \right)$

$= \dfrac{1}{2} \left(2 + \cos x + 2 \cos^2 \dfrac{x}{2} - 1 \right)$

$= \dfrac{1}{2} (2 + \cos x + \cos x)$

$= 1 + \cos x$

d. $1 + \cos x + \cos 2x = \dfrac{1}{2} + \dfrac{\sin \frac{3x}{2}}{2 \sin \frac{x}{2}} + \cos 2x$

$= \dfrac{1}{2} + \dfrac{\sin \frac{3x}{2} + 2 \sin \frac{x}{2} \cos 2x}{2 \sin \frac{x}{2}}$

$= \dfrac{1}{2} + \dfrac{\sin \frac{3x}{2} + \sin \left(2x + \frac{x}{2} \right) - \sin \left(2x - \frac{x}{2} \right)}{2 \sin \frac{x}{2}}$

$= \dfrac{1}{2} + \dfrac{\sin \frac{5x}{2}}{2 \sin \frac{x}{2}}$

e. $1 + \cos x + \cos 2x + \cos 3x$

$= \dfrac{1}{2} + \dfrac{\sin \frac{5x}{2}}{2 \sin \frac{x}{2}} + \cos 3x$

$= \dfrac{1}{2} + \dfrac{\sin \frac{5x}{2} + 2 \sin \frac{x}{2} \cos 3x}{2 \sin \frac{x}{2}}$

$= \dfrac{1}{2} + \dfrac{\sin \frac{5x}{2} + \sin \left(3x + \frac{x}{2} \right) - \sin \left(3x - \frac{x}{2} \right)}{2 \sin \frac{x}{2}}$

$= \dfrac{1}{2} + \dfrac{\sin \frac{7x}{2}}{2 \sin \frac{x}{2}}$

f. If $1 + \cos x + \cos 2x + \cdots + \cos 37x$

$= \dfrac{1}{2} + \dfrac{\sin \frac{75x}{2}}{2 \sin \frac{x}{2}}$, then

$1 + \cos x + \cos 2x + \cdots + \cos 37x + \cos 38x$

$= \dfrac{1}{2} + \dfrac{\sin \frac{75x}{2}}{2 \sin \frac{x}{2}} + \cos 38x$

$= \dfrac{1}{2} + \dfrac{\sin \frac{75x}{2} + 2 \sin \frac{x}{2} \cos 38x}{2 \sin \frac{x}{2}}$

$= \dfrac{1}{2} + \dfrac{\sin \frac{3x}{2} + \sin \left(38x + \frac{x}{2} \right) - \sin \left(38x - \frac{x}{2} \right)}{2 \sin \frac{x}{2}}$

$= \dfrac{1}{2} + \dfrac{\sin \frac{77x}{2}}{2 \sin \frac{x}{2}}$

g. The property is true for $n = 1$. Suppose
$1 + \cos x + \cos 2x + \cdots + \cos (k - 1)x$

$= \dfrac{1}{2} + \dfrac{\sin \frac{(2k - 1)x}{2}}{2 \sin \frac{x}{2}}$ for $k \geq 1$.

Then $1 + \cos x + \cos 2x + \cdots + \cos (k - 1)x$
$\quad + \cos kx$

$= \dfrac{1}{2} + \dfrac{\sin \frac{(2k - 1)x}{2}}{2 \sin \frac{x}{2}} + \cos kx$

$= \dfrac{1}{2} + \dfrac{\sin \frac{(2k - 1)x}{2} + \sin \left(kx + \frac{x}{2} \right) - \sin \left(kx - \frac{x}{2} \right)}{2 \sin \frac{x}{2}}$

$= \dfrac{1}{2} + \dfrac{\sin \frac{(2k + 1)x}{2}}{2 \sin \frac{x}{2}}$

Therefore, the property is true for all n.

8. a. $\cos 2x = \cos (x + x)$
$\qquad = \cos x \cos x - \sin x \sin x$
$\qquad = \cos^2 x - \sin^2 x$

b. $1 = \cos 0 = \cos (x - x)$
$\qquad = \cos x \cos x + \sin x \sin x$
$\qquad = \cos^2 x + \sin^2 x$

c. The Pythagorean property is used in the proof of the composite argument properties.

Section 5-7

1. a. $\cos (\theta - 37°) = \cos \theta \cos 37° + \sin \theta \sin 37°$

b. $\cos (x + y + z) = \cos x \cos (y + z)$
$\qquad - \sin x \sin (y + z)$
$\qquad = \cos x(\cos y \cos z - \sin y \sin z)$
$\qquad - \sin x(\sin y \cos z + \cos y \sin z)$
$\qquad = \cos x \cos y \cos z - \cos x \sin y \sin z$
$\qquad - \sin x \cos y \sin z - \sin x \sin y \cos z$

c. $\cos 3x = \cos (x + 2x) = \cos x \cos 2x$
$\qquad - \sin x \sin 2x$
$\qquad = \cos x(\cos^2 x - \sin^2 x) - \sin x(2 \sin x \cos x)$
$\qquad = \cos^3 x - 3 \sin^2 x \cos x$

2. a. $\cos 37° \cos \theta + \sin 37° \sin \theta = \cos (\theta - 37°)$

b. $\cos 37° + \cos \theta = 2 \cos \dfrac{\theta + 37°}{2} \cos \dfrac{\theta - 37°}{2}$

c. $\cos \theta + \cos 2\theta + \cos 3\theta$
$= \cos 2\theta + (\cos \theta + \cos 3\theta)$
$= \cos 2\theta + 2 \cos \dfrac{2\theta}{2} \cos \dfrac{4\theta}{2}$
$= \cos 2\theta(1 + 2 \cos \theta)$

3. a. $\sin x \cos x = \dfrac{1}{2} \sin 2x$

b. $\cos^2 x = \dfrac{1}{2} + \dfrac{1}{2} \cos 2x$

c. $\cos^2 x \sin x = \cos x(\sin x \cos x)$
$\qquad = \dfrac{1}{2} \cos x \sin 2x$
$\qquad = \dfrac{1}{4} \sin 3x + \dfrac{1}{4} \sin x$

d. $\sin^4 x = (\sin^2 x)^2 = \left(\dfrac{1}{2} - \dfrac{1}{2}\cos 2x\right)^2$

$\quad = \dfrac{1}{4} - \dfrac{1}{2}\cos 2x + \dfrac{1}{4}\cos^2 2x$

$\quad = \dfrac{1}{4} - \dfrac{1}{2}\cos 2x + \dfrac{1}{4}\left(\dfrac{1}{2} + \dfrac{1}{2}\cos 4x\right)$

$\quad = \dfrac{3}{8} - \dfrac{1}{2}\cos 2x + \dfrac{1}{8}\cos 4x$

4. a. $\cos x + \sin x = \sqrt{2}\cos\left(x - \dfrac{\pi}{4}\right)$

b. $\cos x \sin x = \dfrac{1}{2}\sin 2x$

c. $\cos x - \sin x = \sqrt{2}\cos\left(x + \dfrac{\pi}{4}\right)$

d. $\sin x - \cos x = -\sqrt{2}\cos\left(x + \dfrac{\pi}{4}\right)$

5. $4\sin\theta\cos\theta = 2\sin 2\theta = 1 \Rightarrow$

$2\theta = \arcsin\dfrac{1}{2} = 30° + 360n°$ or $150° + 360n° \Rightarrow$

$\theta = 15° + 180n°$ or $75° + 180n°$
$= 15°, 75°, 195°, 255°$

This agrees with the intersections of the two graphs.

6. a. $0° \le \dfrac{1}{2}A \le 45°$, so $\cos\dfrac{1}{2}A = +\sqrt{\dfrac{1 + \cos A}{2}}$

$\quad = \sqrt{\dfrac{1 + \frac{2}{3}}{2}} = \sqrt{\dfrac{5}{6}} = 0.9128\ldots$

b. $180° \le \dfrac{1}{2}A \le 225°$, so $\cos\dfrac{1}{2}A = -\sqrt{\dfrac{1 + \cos A}{2}}$

$\quad = \sqrt{\dfrac{1 + \frac{2}{3}}{2}} = -\sqrt{\dfrac{5}{6}} = 0.9128\ldots$

c. $\arccos\dfrac{2}{3} = \pm\cos^{-1}\dfrac{2}{3} + 360n°$

$\quad = \pm 48.1896\ldots° + 360n°,$

$\Rightarrow A = 48.1896\ldots°$ and $B = 408.1896\ldots°,$

$\Rightarrow \cos\dfrac{1}{2}A = \cos 24.0948\ldots° = 0.9128\ldots$

and $\cos\dfrac{1}{2}B = \cos 204.0948\ldots° = -0.9128\ldots$

The choice between + and − is determined by the quadrant in which the half-angle lies, which in turn is determined by the value of the original angle.

d. $\tan\dfrac{1}{2}x = \dfrac{\sin\frac{1}{2}x}{\cos\frac{1}{2}x} = \dfrac{\pm\sqrt{\dfrac{1 - \cos x}{2}}}{\pm\sqrt{\dfrac{1 + \cos x}{2}}} = \pm\sqrt{\dfrac{1 - \cos x}{1 + \cos x}}$

$\quad = \pm\sqrt{\dfrac{1 - \cos x}{1 + \cos x} \cdot \dfrac{1 - \cos x}{1 - \cos x}} = \pm\sqrt{\dfrac{(1 - \cos x)^2}{1 - \cos^2 x}}$

$\quad = \pm\sqrt{\dfrac{(1 - \cos x)^2}{\sin^2 x}} = \pm\dfrac{1 - \cos x}{\sin x}$

However, a quadrant-by-quadrant analysis of x reveals that $\dfrac{1 - \cos x}{\sin x}$ always has the same sign as $\tan\frac{1}{2}x$, so $\tan\frac{1}{2}x = \dfrac{1 - \cos x}{\sin x}$. The restriction is $\sin x \ne 0 \Rightarrow x \ne n\pi$ (or $180n°$).

7. a. The first formula is found by squaring $d = \sqrt{(u_1 - u_2)^2 + (v_1 - v_2)^2}$ or more directly just from the Pythagorean theorem. Then $d^2 = u_1^2 - 2u_1u_2 + u_2^2 + v_1^2 - 2v_1v_2 + v_2^2$.

b. $d^2 = (u_1^2 + v_1^2) + (u_2^2 + v_2^2) - 2u_1u_2 - 2v_1v_2$
$= r_1^2 + r_2^2 - 2(u_1u_2 + v_1v_2)$

c. The parametric equation of a circle with center at the origin and radius r is $x(\theta) = r\cos\theta$, $y(\theta) = r\sin\theta$, so $u_1 = r_1\cos E$ and $v_1 = r_1\sin E$ for the circular orbit of Earth, and $u_2 = r_2\cos M$ and $v_2 = r_2\sin M$ for the circular orbit of Mars.

d. $d^2 = r_1^2 + r_2^2$
$\quad - 2(r_1\cos E \cdot r_2\cos M + r_1\sin E \cdot r_2\sin M)$
$= r_1^2 + r_2^2 - 2r_1r_2(\cos E \cos M + \sin E \sin M).$
The expression inside the parentheses is the composite angle formula for $\cos(E - M)$.

e. $d^2 = r_1^2 + r_2^2 - 2r_1r_2\cos(E - M)$

f. The law of cosines says that the unknown side c of a triangle with known sides a and b and known angle C included between a and b is found by $c^2 = a^2 + b^2 - 2ab\cos C$. Here the unknown side is d, the known sides are r_1 and r_2, and the known included angle is $E - M$.

g. $\omega_E \approx \dfrac{1}{365}$ revolutions per day, where ω (omega) is the conventional symbol for angular velocity, because Earth revolves once in 365 days (approximately). Similarly, Mars revolves once in about 687 days. $E(t) = \dfrac{t}{365} \cdot 2\pi = \dfrac{2\pi t}{365}$ and $M(t) = \dfrac{t}{687} \cdot 2\pi = \dfrac{2\pi t}{687}$, so $(E - M)(t) = \dfrac{2\pi t}{365} - \dfrac{2\pi t}{687} = 2\pi\left(\dfrac{1}{365} - \dfrac{1}{687}\right)t.$

h. $d^2 = 93^2 + 141^2$

$$-2 \cdot 93 \cdot 141 \cos 2\pi \left(\frac{1}{365} - \frac{1}{687}\right)t$$

$$= 28{,}530 - 26{,}226 \cos \frac{644\pi}{250{,}755}t$$

i. $d = \sqrt{28{,}530 - 26{,}226 \cos \frac{644\pi}{250{,}755}t}$ is not sinusoidal. This is most easily seen from the graph:

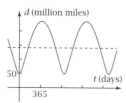

The parts of the graph above and below the midline have different shapes. (The graph shows that the planets spend more time far apart than they do close together.)

8. The graph of $y = \cos 3\theta$ is the same as Figure 5-7c.

θ	$\cos 3\theta$	$4 \cos^3 \theta - 3 \cos \theta$
0°	1	1
15°	0.70711	0.70711
30°	0	0
45°	−0.70711	−0.70711
60°	−1	−1
75°	−0.70711	−0.70711
90°	0	0

$\cos 3\theta = \cos (\theta + \theta + \theta)$

$\quad = \cos \theta \cos \theta \cos \theta - \cos \theta \sin \theta \sin \theta$
$\qquad - \sin \theta \cos \theta \sin \theta - \sin \theta \sin \theta \cos \theta$
$\quad = \cos^3 \theta - \cos \theta \sin^2 \theta - \cos \theta \sin^2 \theta$
$\qquad - \cos \theta \sin^2 \theta$
$\quad = \cos^3 \theta - \cos \theta (1 - \cos^2 \theta)$
$\qquad - \cos \theta (1 - \cos^2 \theta) - \cos \theta (1 - \cos^2 \theta)$
$\quad = \cos^3 \theta - \cos \theta - \cos^3 \theta - \cos \theta - \cos^3 \theta$
$\qquad - \cos \theta - \cos^3 \theta$
$\quad = 4 \cos^3 \theta - 3 \cos \theta$

Chapter 6

Section 6-2

1. a. $d = \sqrt{93^2 + 142^2 - 2 \cdot 93 \cdot 142 \cos \theta}$
$\quad = \sqrt{28{,}813 - 26{,}412 \cos \theta}$ million miles

b.
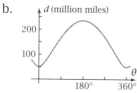

c. $142 - 93 \cos \theta$

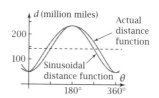

d. The horizontal line represents 142 million miles, the average of the closest (49 million miles) and farthest (235 million miles) distances. The actual distance function spends more time above the line than below it, so Mars spends more time farther from Earth.

Section 6-3

1. a. $s = \dfrac{16 + 14 + 5}{2} = 17.5$ in.

$\sqrt{(17.5)(17.5 - 16)(17.5 - 14)(17.5 - 5)}$
≈ 33.89 in.^{2}

b. $\dfrac{33.89}{36^2} \cdot 300 \approx \$7.84$

c. $(1.85)(7.84) \approx \$14.50$

Section 6-5

1. Algebraic solutions for c:

a. $3^2 = 4^2 + c^2 - (2)(4)(c) \cos 34° \Rightarrow$
$c^2 - (8 \cos 34°)c + 7 = 0 \Rightarrow$

$c = \dfrac{8 \cos 34° \pm \sqrt{(-8 \cos 34°)^2 - 4 \cdot 1 \cdot 7}}{2} \Rightarrow$

$c = 1.3169\ldots$ or $5.3153\ldots$

b. $5^2 = 4^2 + c^2 - (2)(4)(c) \cos 34° \Rightarrow$
$c^2 - (8 \cos 34°)c - 9 = 0 \Rightarrow$

$c = \dfrac{8 \cos 34° \pm \sqrt{(-8 \cos 34°)^2 - 4(-9)}}{2} \Rightarrow$

$c = 7.7879\ldots$

c. $2^2 = 4^2 + c^2 - (2)(4)(c) \cos 34° \Rightarrow$
$c^2 - (8 \cos 34°)c + 12 = 0 \Rightarrow$

$c = \dfrac{8 \cos 34° \pm \sqrt{(-8 \cos 34°)^2 - 4(12)}}{2}$

But $(-8 \cos 34°)^2 - 4(12) = -4.0125\ldots$, so there are no solutions.

Section 6-6

1. a. $\phi = 180° - 70° = 110°$;

   $|\vec{r}| = \sqrt{11^2 + 5^2 - 2 \cdot 11 \cdot 5 \cos 110°}$
   $= 13.5507...$ yd

   Bearing $= \alpha = \cos^{-1} \dfrac{11^2 + (13.5507...)^2 - 5^2}{2 \cdot 11 \cdot (13.5507...)}$
   $\approx 20.29°$

   b. Return bearing $\approx 20.29° + 180° = 200.29°$

2. a. $\phi = 270° - 210° = 60°$;

   $|\vec{r}| = \sqrt{8^2 + 6^2 - 2 \cdot 8 \cdot 6 \cos 60°}$
   $= 7.2111...$ mi

   $\alpha = \cos^{-1} \dfrac{8^2 + (7.2111...)^2 - 6^2}{2 \cdot 8 \cdot (7.2111...)} \approx 46.10°$
   Bearing $= 90° + \alpha \approx 136.10°$

   b. Return bearing $\approx 180° + 136.10° = 316.10°$

3. a. $\phi = 110° - 90° = 20°$

   $|\vec{r}| = \sqrt{6^2 + 14^2 - 2 \cdot 6 \cdot 14 \cos 20°}$
   $= 8.6099...$ km

   $\alpha = \cos^{-1} \dfrac{6^2 + (8.6099...)^2 - 14^2}{2 \cdot 6 \cdot (8.6099...)} \approx 146.21°$
   Bearing $= 270° - \alpha \approx 123.79°$

   b. Return bearing $\approx 180° + 123.79° = 302.79°$

4. a. $\phi = 360° - 320° = 40°$;

   $|\vec{r}| = \sqrt{4^2 + 9^2 - 2 \cdot 4 \cdot 9 \cos 40°}$
   $= 6.4687...$ m

   $\alpha = \cos^{-1} \dfrac{4^2 + (6.4687...)^2 - 9^2}{2 \cdot 4 \cdot (6.4687...)} \approx 116.58°$
   Bearing $= 180° + \alpha \approx 296.58°$

   b. Return bearing $\approx 360° - 296.58° = 63.42°$

5. Resultant should be 13.6 cm $\pm$ 0.1 cm [assuming 1 cm represents 1 yd], and bearing should be $200° \pm 1°$.

6. Resultant should be 7.2 cm $\pm$ 0.1 cm [assuming 1 cm represents 1 mi], and bearing should be $136° \pm 1°$.

7. a. $(60 \cos 110° + 40 \cos 230° + 50 \cos 340°)\vec{i}$
   $+ (60 \sin 110° + 40 \sin 230° + 50 \sin 340°)\vec{j}$
   $= 0.7519...\vec{i} + 8.6387...\vec{j}$

   b. $|\vec{r}| = \sqrt{(0.7519...)^2 + (8.6387...)^2}$
   $= 8.6714...$ lb

   c. $\theta = \tan^{-1} \dfrac{8.6387...}{0.7519...} - 85.0255...°$

Section 6-7

1. a. $60^2 = x^2 + 100^2 - 2 \cdot x \cdot 100 \cos 20° \Rightarrow$

   $x = \dfrac{200 \cos 20° \pm \sqrt{(-200 \cos 20°)^2 - 4 \cdot 1 \cdot 6400}}{2 \cdot 1}$
   ≈ 143.27 cm or 46.67 cm

   b. The 60-cm ruler must be perpendicular to the surface, making the 100-cm ruler the hypotenuse of a right triangle. Then $\frac{60}{100} = \sin\theta$, so $\theta = \sin^{-1}\frac{60}{100} \approx 36.87°$.

   c. $f(\theta)$

   $= \dfrac{200 \cos\theta \pm \sqrt{(-200 \cos\theta)^2 - 4 \cdot 1 \cdot 6400}}{2}$

   $= 100 \cos\theta \pm 20\sqrt{25 \cos^2\theta - 16}$

   The graph should agree with Figure 6-7b. The results of parts a and b do appear on the graph.

   d. $120^2 = x^2 + 100^2 - 2 \cdot x \cdot 100 \cos 20° \Rightarrow$

   $x = \dfrac{200 \cos 20° \pm \sqrt{(-200 \cos 20°)^2 - 4 \cdot 1 \cdot (-4400)}}{2 \cdot 1}$

   ≈ 208.99 cm or -21.05 cm (21.05 cm to the left)

   e. $f(\theta)$

   $= \dfrac{200 \cos\theta \pm \sqrt{(-200 \cos\theta)^2 - 4 \cdot 1 \cdot (-4400)}}{2}$

   $= 100 \cos\theta \pm 20\sqrt{25 \cos^2\theta + 11}$

   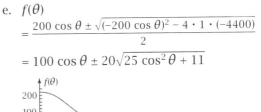

   f. The graph should match Figure 6-7c.

   g. If θ is too large, the 60-cm ruler can't reach the surface. Because the 120-cm ruler is longer than the meterstick, two triangles can be created. The negative values are for the triangles where the end of the 120-cm ruler is placed to the left of the origin.

   $100^2 = x^2 + 100^2 - 2 \cdot x \cdot 100 \cos\theta$
   $x^2 - 200x \cos\theta = 0$
   $x(x - 200 \cos\theta) = 0$
   $x = 200 \cos\theta$ (or $x = 0$)

   It is a cosine function dilated by 200 cm in the y-direction.

   When $\theta > 90°$, the entire triangle is to the left of the origin, so the distances are negative.

2. $22 \tan 38° \approx 17.19$ m

3. a. $7 \cot 9° \approx 44.20$ km

   b. $7 \csc 9° \approx 44.75$ km

4. Let A be the point of the initial sighting, B be the point of the second sighting, C be the point of closest approach, and D be the buoy.

   a. $\angle ABD = 180° - 29° = 151°$
   $\angle BDA = 180° - 15° - 151° = 14°$
   $$BD = \frac{1300 \sin 15°}{\sin 14°} \approx 1390.8 \text{ m}$$

   b. $CD = BD \sin 29° = \dfrac{1300 \sin 15° \sin 29°}{\sin 14°}$
   ≈ 674.3 m

   c. $BC = BD \cos 29° = \dfrac{1300 \sin 15° \cos 29°}{\sin 14°}$
   ≈ 1216.4 m

   d. Let E be the point 7000 m beyond the second sighting.
   $CE = BE - BC \approx 7000 - 1216.4 = 5783.6$ m
   $$\angle E = \tan^{-1} \frac{CD}{CE} \approx \tan^{-1} \frac{674.3}{5783.6} \approx 6.65°$$
   Obtuse angle $\approx 180° - 6.65° = 173.35°$

5. a. $c = 200 \tan \theta$

   b. $200 \tan 73° \approx 654.2$ m

   c. $\theta = \tan^{-1} \dfrac{3000}{200} = 86.2°$

   d.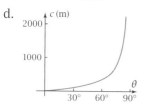

   e. Find the angle on the horizontal axis, and go directly up to the graph and then directly left to the vertical axis to read the ceiling.

6. a. $\theta = 180° - 25° = 155°$
   $|\vec{r}| = \sqrt{200^2 + 250^2 - 2 \cdot 200 \cdot 250 \cos 155°}$
   ≈ 439.5 lb, which is more than enough.

   b. $\theta = \cos^{-1} \frac{200^2 + 250^2 - 400^2}{2 \cdot 200 \cdot 250} \approx 125.1°$. The angle between them must be approximately $180° - 125.1° = 54.9°$.

7. Let A be you, B be the target, and C be the farthest point where the torpedo will still hit the target. AB is at $276° - 180° = 96°$ to North, so $\angle ABC = 96° - 68° = 28°$.

   Long-range: $\angle ACB = \sin^{-1} \frac{7200 \sin 28°}{6400} \approx 31.9°$ or $148.1°$. $\angle BAC \approx 180° - 28° - 31.9° = 120.1°$ or $180° - 28° - 148.1° = 3.9°$. Bearing $\approx 276° + 3.9° = 279.9°$ or $276° + 120.1° - 360° = 36.1°$.

The target will be in range for bearings from $279.9°$ through $360° \Leftrightarrow 0°$ to $36.1°$.

Short-range: $\sin \angle ACB = \frac{7200 \sin 28°}{3200} \approx 1.06$, which is not the sine of any angle. The 3200-m distance is too short to form a triangle. The target is in range.

8. Let A be the point of the $37°$ sighting, B be the point of the $65°$ sighting, C be the foot of the castle, and D be the top of the castle. By the theorem about the exterior angles of a triangle, $\angle CBD = \angle BAD + \angle ADB$, so $\angle ADB = \angle CBD - \angle BAD = 65° - 37° = 28.$
$\frac{BD}{\sin 37°} = \frac{75}{\sin 28°}$, so $BD = \frac{75 \sin 37°}{\sin 28°}$. $\frac{h}{BD} = \sin 65°$, so $h = BD \sin 65° = \frac{75 \sin 37° \sin 65°}{\sin 28°} \approx 87.1$ ft.

9. $5^2 = x^2 + 8^2 - 2 \cdot x \cdot 8 \cos 32°$
   $x^2 + (-16 \cos 32°)x + 39 = 0$
   $$x = \frac{16 \cos 32° \pm \sqrt{(-16 \cos 32°) - 4 \cdot 1 \cdot 39}}{2 \cdot 1}$$
   ≈ 9.4 mi or 4.1 mi

10. a. $\sqrt{10^2 + 7^2 - 2 \cdot 10 \cdot 7 \cos 120°}$
    $= \sqrt{219} \approx 14.8$ in.

    b. The hour hand moves one-twelfth as fast as the minute hand, so after x minutes the hour hand points to $\frac{x}{12} + 20$.

    To find when the two hands are together, solve: $x = \frac{x}{12} + 20 \Rightarrow x = \frac{12}{11} \cdot 20 = \frac{240}{11}$
    $= 21.8181\ldots$ min

    The spider should wait about 21 min 49 s.

11. One hour 20 minutes is the same as 80 minutes.

Section 6-8

1. a.

   Alamo St. / Heights St. triangle with angles 74° and 67° at Front Ave.

   b. Alamo $= \dfrac{1000 \sin 67°}{\sin 39°} \approx 1463$ ft

   Heights $= \dfrac{1000 \sin 74°}{\sin 39°} \approx 1527$ ft

   c. $A = \dfrac{1}{2} \cdot \dfrac{1000 \sin 67°}{\sin 39°} \cdot \dfrac{1000 \sin 74°}{\sin 39°} \cdot \sin 39°$
   $= \dfrac{1}{2} \cdot 1000^2 \cdot \dfrac{\sin 67° \sin 74°}{\sin 39°} \approx 703{,}017 \text{ ft}^2$

2.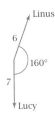

$\theta = 180° - 160° = 20°$;

$|\vec{r}| = \sqrt{7^2 + 6^2 - 2 \cdot 7 \cdot 6 \cos 20°} = 2.4628...$ lb;

$\phi = \cos^{-1} \dfrac{7^2 + (2.4628...)^2 - 6^2}{2 \cdot 7 \cdot (2.4628...)} = 56.4306...°$

3. False. The magnitude of the sum can be anything from 0 (if the two vectors are equal and opposite) to the sum of their magnitudes (if they are parallel).

4. a. Estimates should be around 9.8 cm^2.

   b. $s = \dfrac{4 \text{ cm} + 5 \text{ cm} + 7 \text{ cm}}{2} = 8$ cm;

   Area $= \sqrt{8(8-4)(8-5)(8-7)} = \sqrt{96}$ cm^2
   $= 4\sqrt{6}$ cm$^2 = 9.797958971...$ cm^2

   c. $\angle A = \cos^{-1} \dfrac{4^2 + 5^2 - 7^2}{2 \cdot 4 \cdot 5} = 101.5369...°$

   d. Area $= \frac{1}{2} \cdot 4 \cdot 5 \cdot \sin A = 9.797958971...$ cm^2

   e. Yes.

5. a. The resultant vector should point from the origin to the tip of the dotted vector.

   b. Estimates should be around 7.2 mi/h.

   c. $\theta = 180° - (75° - 20°) = 125°$;
   $|\vec{r}| = \sqrt{5^2 + 3^2 - 2 \cdot 3 \cdot 5 \cos 125°}$
   $= 7.1559...$ mi/h

   d. Bearing $\approx 40°$; actual value is

   $20° + \cos^{-1} \dfrac{5^2 + (7.1559...)^2 - 3^2}{2 \cdot 5 \cdot (7.1559...)} = 40.0851...°$

   The angle in standard position $\approx 90° - 40°$
   $= 50°$, so $\vec{r} \approx (7.2$ mi/h, $50°)$.

6. a. $180° - 130° = 50°$; $\dfrac{\sin A}{6 \text{ cm}} = \dfrac{\sin 50°}{5 \text{ cm}} \Rightarrow$

   $\sin A = \dfrac{6 \sin 50°}{5}$

   b. $A = 130° - \theta$; $\sin(130° - \theta) = \dfrac{6 \sin 50°}{5}$

   c. $\theta = 130° - \sin^{-1} \dfrac{6 \sin 50°}{5} = 63.1828...°$ or
   $16.8171...°$

7. a. $\dfrac{\sin A}{a} = \dfrac{\sin B}{b}$

   $\dfrac{\sin A}{\sin B} = \dfrac{a}{b}$

   $\dfrac{\sin A}{\sin B} + 1 = \dfrac{a}{b} + 1$

   $\dfrac{\sin A + \sin B}{\sin B} = \dfrac{a + b}{b}$

   And similarly, by subtracting 1, we get

   $\dfrac{\sin A - \sin B}{\sin B} = \dfrac{a - b}{b}$

   b. $\dfrac{\left(\frac{\sin A - \sin B}{\sin B}\right)}{\left(\frac{\sin A + \sin B}{\sin B}\right)} = \dfrac{\left(\frac{a - b}{b}\right)}{\left(\frac{a + b}{b}\right)} \Rightarrow$

   $\dfrac{\sin A - \sin B}{\sin A + \sin B} = \dfrac{a - b}{a + b} \Rightarrow$

   $\dfrac{2 \cos \frac{1}{2}(A + B) \sin) \frac{1}{2}(A - B)}{2 \sin \frac{1}{2}(A + B) \cos \frac{1}{2}(A - B)} = \dfrac{a - b}{a + b}$

   c. $\dfrac{\tan \frac{1}{2}(A - B)}{\tan \frac{1}{2}(A + B)} = \dfrac{a - b}{a + b}$

Chapter 7

Section 7-2

1. a. $y - 13 = -0.05(x - 123) \Rightarrow y = -0.05x + 19.15$

   b. $y(0) = b = 19.15$ gal

   c. $y = -0.05x + 19.15 = 1$ gal $\Rightarrow$
   $x = \frac{1 - 19.15}{-0.05} = 363$ mi; you can drive
   363 mi − 123 mi = 240 mi farther.

2. a. Let d be the distance. $d = 0.75t^2 - 6t + 17$

   b. $d(7) = 11.75$ mi

   c. $10 = 0.75t^2 - 6t + 17 \Rightarrow$
   $0.75t^2 - 6t + 7 = 0 \Rightarrow$
   $t = \dfrac{6 \pm \sqrt{6^2 - 4(0.75)(7)}}{2} \Rightarrow$
   $t = 1.0635...$ min

Section 7-3

1. $f(4) = 7$, $f(8) = 5$, $f(12) = 3$

2. $f(4) = 30$, $f(8) = 60$, $f(16) = 120$

3. $f(14) = 150$, $f(28) = 75$

4. $f(11) = 108$, $f(19) = 972$

5. a. The elephant should weigh $10^3 = 1000$ times as much as the dog.

   b. The elephant should have $10^2 = 100$ times as much skin as the dog.

   c. The dog's skin : weight ratio is 10 times that of the elephant. For each pound of weight, the dog has 10 times as much skin area through which to lose heat.

6. a. $T(10) = \frac{5}{7} \cdot 50°C = 35.7142...°C$ above room temperature

      $T(15) = \frac{5}{7} \cdot \frac{5}{7} \cdot 50°C = 25.5102...°C$ above room temperature

   b. $T(15) = 0.8^5 \cdot 20°C = 6.5536°C$ below room temperature

7. a. Multiply-multiply property; power function

   b. $M(24) = 8 \cdot (172.8\ g) = 1382.4\ g$, $M(30) = 8 \cdot (337.5\ g) = 2700\ g$

   c. $M(L) = 0.1L^3$

   d. $M(110) = 133{,}100\ g \approx 292.82\ lb!$

   e. $1000\ g = 0.1L^3 \Rightarrow L = \sqrt[3]{10{,}000}$ $= 21.5443...\ cm$

8. a. Add-add property; linear function

   b. $T(1000) = 36.7\ s$

   c. $T(I) = 1.7 + 0.035I$

   d. 0.035 second per iteration, given by the coefficient of I.

   e. 1.7 second, given by the constant term.

   f. $47.3\ s = 1.7 + 0.035I \Rightarrow I \approx 1303$ iterations

9. a. $\dfrac{D(13)}{D(12)} = \dfrac{3993.00}{3630.00} = 1.1$

      $\dfrac{D(14)}{D(13)} = \dfrac{4392.20}{3993.00} = 1.1$

      $\dfrac{D(15)}{D(14)} = \dfrac{4831.53}{4392.20} = 1.1$

   b. $D(16) = 1.1D(15) \approx \$5314.68$ $D(17) = 1.1D(16) \approx \$5846.15$

   c. $D(10) = \$3000.00$

   d. 10%

   e. $D(t) = \$3000 \cdot 1.1^{t-10}$

   f. $D(65) \approx \$567{,}177.43$

Section 7-5

1. $\ln 5 = \dfrac{\log 5}{\log e} = 1.6094...$

2. $\ln 0.37 = \dfrac{\log 0.37}{\log e} = -0.9942...$

3. $\log 0.95 = \dfrac{\ln 0.95}{\ln 10} = -0.0222...$

4. $\log 1066 = \dfrac{\ln 1066}{\ln 10} = 3.0277...$

Section 7-6

1.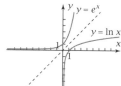

2.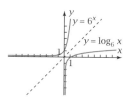

3.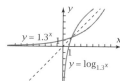

4.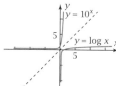

5.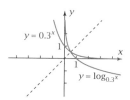

6.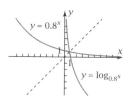

7. The graphs coincide and match Figure 7-6f.

8. The graphs coincide and match Figure 7-6g.

9. a. It has the add-multiply property. When you add 10°C to the temperature, you multiply the freshness time by $\frac{1}{2}$.

   b. Temperature as a function of time is the inverse function of time as a function of temperature. It has the multiply-add property.

Precalculus with Trigonometry: Instructor's Guide
© 2007 Key Curriculum Press

c. Let c be the temperature and t be time.

t	c
192 h	10°C
96 h	10°C
48 h	20°C
24 h	30°C

d. $c = 75.8496... - 14.4269... \ln t$

e. $c(144) = 4.1503...°C \approx 4.2°C$

f. $c = 75.8496... - 14.4269... \ln t = 38°C \Rightarrow$
$t = e^{\frac{38 - 75.8496...}{-14.4269...}} = 13.7843... \text{ h} \approx 14 \text{ h}$

g. The function predicts that the freshness time would approach infinity as the temperature approaches 0, which is unrealistic. So the model is not appropriate for low temperatures. An upper limit for the domain would be some highest temperature that it would be reasonable to expect in real life.

10. a. Increasing: $b > 1$
   Decreasing: $0 < b < 1$

   b. Function iii, because $y = 1$ when $x = 10$ and $\log_{10} 10 = 1$.

   c. Function ii, because $y = 1$ when $x = 2.7182...$ and $\ln e = 1$

   d. Base 3: $\log_b 8 = 2 \Rightarrow 2^b = 8 = 2^3 \Rightarrow b = 3$

   e. Any number raised to the zero power is 1.

   f. False; functions i, ii, and iii are counterexamples.

Section 7-7

1. a. c is a vertical dilation factor.

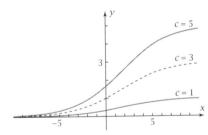

   b.

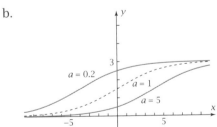

c.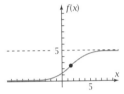

d. $\dfrac{3}{1 + 5e^{-0.4x}} = \dfrac{3}{1 + e^{-0.4(x-k)}} \Rightarrow$
$5e^{-0.4x} = e^{-0.4(x-k)} \Rightarrow$
$\ln 5 - 0.4x = -0.4(x - k) = -0.4 + 0.4k \Rightarrow$
$k = \dfrac{\ln 5}{0.4} = 4.0235...$; horizontal translation by 4.0235... units right

2. a.

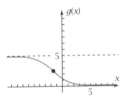

b. Whereas f is increasing, g is decreasing. g is the reflection of f across the vertical axis.

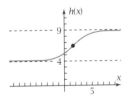

c. $h(x) = f(x) + 4 = \dfrac{5 \cdot 2^x}{2^x + 3} + 4$

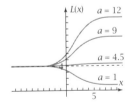

d. $h(x) = \dfrac{5 \cdot 2^x}{2^x + 3} + 4 = \dfrac{9 \cdot 2^x + 12}{2^x + 3}$

Asymptotes at $y = \frac{12}{3} = 4$ and $y = 9$

e. $h(x)$ is $L(x)$ with $a = 9$.

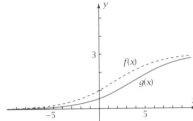

Chapter 8

Section 8-2

1.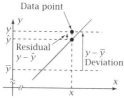
Data point

y
$\hat{y}$
Residual
$y - \hat{y}$
$\bar{y}$
$y - \bar{y}$
Deviation
$\bar{x}$ x x

2. The new equation is $\hat{y} = 64.7023...x + 32{,}779.7619...$, compared to the old equation, $\hat{y} = 67.6358...x + 26{,}139.5007...$. When graphed, the two lines are virtually indistinguishable over the domain covered by the data.

3. a. Each residual would equal 0; $SS_{res} = 0$.
$$r^2 = \frac{SS_{dev} - SS_{res}}{SS_{dev}} = \frac{SS_{dev} - 0}{SS_{dev}} = 1$$
$r = 1$ if y generally increases as x increases, and $r = -1$ if y generally decreases as x decreases.

   b. SS_{res} must equal SS_{dev} so that
$$r^2 = \frac{SS_{dev} - SS_{res}}{SS_{dev}} = \frac{SS_{dev} - SS_{dev}}{SS_{dev}} = 0.$$
If $\hat{y} = 0x + \bar{y}$, then for each x the corresponding residual is $y - \hat{y} = y - (0x - \bar{y}) = y - \bar{y}$, so $SS_{res} = SS_{dev}$. If $a \neq 0$, then there is some perceptible trend (slope) to the data, so there is some perceptible correlation, so $r \neq 0$.

   c. It is r^2, not r, that gives the amount of explained variation. $r^2 = 0.01$, so regression accounts for only 1% of SS_{dev}.

Section 8-5

1. a. $\hat{y} = (6.5048...)x + 37.9987...$
$r^2 = 0.9959...$
$r = 0.9979...$
$\hat{z} = (6.5460...)x + 37.6484...$
$r^2 = 0.9960...$
$r = 0.9980...$
The z-data are fit slightly better by a linear equation.

   b. y-residuals:
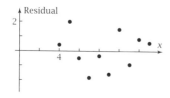
Residual
2
4
x

z-residuals:
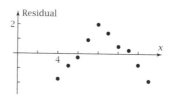
Residual
2
4
x

   c. The y-data are fit better by a linear equation.
   d. The power equation $\hat{z} = (27.8457...)x^{0.5719...}$ fits best, with $r^2 = 0.9992...$ or $r = 0.9996...$.

2. a. $\hat{y} = (-5.1508...)x + 188.6521...$
$r^2 = 0.9911...$
$r = -0.9955...$
$\hat{z} = (-5.3333...)x + 190.9942...$
$r^2 = 0.9905...$
$r = -0.9952...$
The y-data are fit slightly better by a linear equation.

   b. y-residuals:
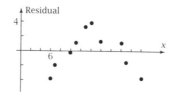
Residual
4
6
x

z-residuals:
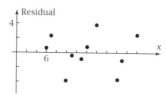
Residual
4
6
x

   c. The z-data are fit better by a linear equation.
   d. The logistic equation $\hat{y} = \dfrac{179.0704...}{1 + (0.0766...)e^{(0.1334...)x}}$ fits best, with $r^2 = 0.9987...$ or $r = 0.9993...$.

3. a.
y
20
20
x

   b. For times below 24 months, a linear function would indicate the girl's height was positive and greater than about 70 cm, which is reasonable. For times much greater than 168 months, the girl will eventually stop growing taller. A linear function would indicate the girl grows taller at the same rate as long as she lives, which is unreasonable.

c. Letting x = months and y = cm,
$\hat{y} = (0.5268\ldots)x + 71.7632\ldots$
$r^2 = 0.9969\ldots$
$r = 0.9984\ldots$

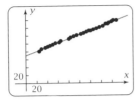

d. $\hat{y}(16 \cdot 12) \approx 172.9$ cm (about 5′8″). You must assume that growth continues past 168 months at the same linear rate.

e. $\frac{110.0 - (71.7632\ldots)}{0.5268\ldots} \approx 72.58$ months (about 6 years). Interpolation is probably safe because the function is fairly linear, having a high correlation coefficient in the region of known data.

f. $\hat{y}(0) \approx 71.8$ cm, much longer than her actual length. The extrapolation is not safe.

g.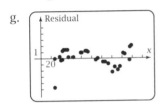

h. The growth spurt started at 137 months.

4. a. Logarithmic:
$\hat{y} = (136.6412\ldots) - (16.8782\ldots)\ln x$ has $r = -0.9979\ldots$.
Power: $\hat{y} = (488.0261\ldots) \cdot x^{-0.4494\ldots}$ has $r = -0.9970\ldots$.

b. The logarithmic model approaches negative infinity; the power function approaches 0.

c. $ax^b = 10 \Rightarrow x = \left(\frac{10}{a}\right)^{\frac{1}{b}}$

$= \left(\frac{10}{488.0261\ldots}\right)^{\frac{1}{-0.4494\ldots}} \approx 5715$ pairs

d. $\hat{y}(1) \approx \$488$

e. $\frac{\hat{y}(2x)}{\hat{y}(x)} = \frac{a(2x)^b}{ax^b} = \frac{2^b ax^b}{ax^b} = 2^b = 2^{-0.4494\ldots}$
$= 0.7323\ldots$. It is reduced by approximately 27%. Multiply-multiply.

5. a. $\hat{y} = (0.0222\ldots)x^2 + 1.8165\ldots$; $r = 0.9993\ldots$

b. $\hat{y}(0) \approx \$1.82$

c. $\hat{y}(7) \approx \$2.91$; underpriced

d. For the quadratic model, $r = 0.9993\ldots$. Using linear regression, $\hat{y} = 0.58x - 1.85$, with $r = 0.9991\ldots$. However, the linear regression model predicts $\hat{y}(0) = -\$1.85$. This is not reasonable because it implies that the pizzeria actually pays you to take a sufficiently small pizza.

e. Answers will vary.

6. a. $h = 50$: $\hat{y} = 88{,}417x^{-1.6737\ldots}$
$h = 60$: $\hat{y} = 335{,}293x^{-1.9259\ldots}$
$h = 70$: $\hat{y} = 1{,}303{,}323x^{-2.1764\ldots}$
$h = 80$: $\hat{y} = 5{,}184{,}379x^{-2.4258\ldots}$

60 m $< h <$ 70 m. For $h = 60$, the power is greater than -2. For $h = 70$, it is less than -2. Somewhere in between it is exactly -2.

b.
h(m)	Power
60	$-1.9259\ldots$
70	$-2.1764\ldots$
65	$-2.0513\ldots$
62	$-1.9761\ldots$
63	$-2.0012\ldots$

$h \approx 63$ m

7. a.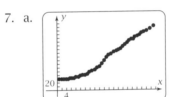

b. Linear:
$\hat{y} = (4.1266\ldots)x + 3.8126\ldots$
$r^2 = 0.9727\ldots$
$r = 0.9862\ldots$

Exponential:
$\hat{y} = (25.6029\ldots) \cdot (1.0530\ldots)^x$
$r^2 = 0.9725\ldots$
$r = 0.9861\ldots$

c. Linear:

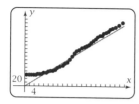

Exponential:

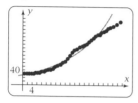

d. The linear function goes to 0 shortly before 1960. The exponential function approaches an asymptote, 25.6029....

e.

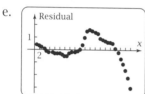

There is still a pattern not explained by the exponential function.

f. Answers will vary according to year. Here are the predictions for 1999–2003:

	Lin CPI	Exp CPI	Lin Car	Exp Car
2002	177.1	224.0	17,964	22,722
2003	181.3	235.9	18,391	23,929
2004	185.4	248.4	18,806	25,197
2005	189.5	261.6	19,222	26,536
2006	193.6	275.4	19,638	27,905

g. The logistic function fits the data better.

$$\hat{y} = \frac{222.9142...}{1 + (10.9191...) \cdot e^{-(0.0905...)x}}$$

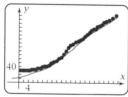

$$\frac{SS_{dev} - SS_{res}}{SS_{dev}} = 0.9914...$$

This function approaches 222.9142... as an asymptote. If inflation continues without bound, then this is not a reasonable endpoint behavior.

h.

Year	% Increase
1961 to 1962	$\frac{30.2 - 29.9}{29.9} \cdot 100\% \approx 1.00\%$
1962 to 1963	$\frac{30.6 - 30.2}{30.2} \cdot 100\% \approx 1.32\%$
1963 to 1964	$\frac{31.0 - 30.6}{30.6} \cdot 100\% \approx 1.31\%$
1964 to 1965	$\frac{31.5 - 31.0}{31.0} \cdot 100\% \approx 1.61\%$
1965 to 1966	$\frac{32.4 - 31.5}{31.5} \cdot 100\% \approx 2.86\%$
1966 to 1967	$\frac{33.4 - 32.4}{32.4} \cdot 100\% \approx 3.09\%$
1967 to 1968	$\frac{34.8 - 33.4}{33.4} \cdot 100\% \approx 4.19\%$
1968 to 1969	$\frac{36.7 - 34.8}{34.8} \cdot 100\% \approx 5.46\%$
1969 to 1970	$\frac{38.8 - 36.7}{36.7} \cdot 100\% \approx 5.72\%$
1970 to 1971	$\frac{40.5 - 38.8}{38.8} \cdot 100\% \approx 4.38\%$
1971 to 1972	$\frac{41.8 - 40.5}{40.5} \cdot 100\% \approx 3.21\%$
1972 to 1973	$\frac{44.0 - 41.8}{41.8} \cdot 100\% \approx 6.22\%$
1973 to 1974	$\frac{49.3 - 44.4}{44.4} \cdot 100\% \approx 11.04\%$
1974 to 1975	$\frac{53.8 - 49.3}{49.3} \cdot 100\% \approx 9.13\%$
1975 to 1976	$\frac{56.9 - 53.8}{53.8} \cdot 100\% \approx 5.76\%$
1976 to 1977	$\frac{60.6 - 56.9}{56.9} \cdot 100\% \approx 6.50\%$
1977 to 1978	$\frac{65.2 - 60.6}{60.6} \cdot 100\% \approx 7.59\%$
1978 to 1979	$\frac{72.6 - 65.2}{65.2} \cdot 100\% \approx 11.35\%$
1979 to 1980	$\frac{82.4 - 72.6}{72.6} \cdot 100\% \approx 13.50\%$
1980 to 1981	$\frac{90.9 - 82.4}{82.4} \cdot 100\% \approx 10.32\%$
1981 to 1982	$\frac{96.5 - 90.9}{90.9} \cdot 100\% \approx 6.16\%$

i. Answers will vary.

8. a. $\hat{y} = 0.0036...x + 10.1958...$
$r^2 = 0.0063..., r = 0.0796...$

b. $\bar{y} = 10.65$

$y - \bar{y}$	$(y - \bar{y})^2$	$y - \hat{y}$	$(y - \hat{y})^2$
−0.65	0.4225	−0.5220...	0.2725...
0.85	0.7225	0.9308...	0.8664...
−1.15	1.3225	−1.0945...	1.1980...
−0.15	0.0225	−0.0945...	0.0089...
1.35	1.8225	1.3764...	1.8946...
−1.65	2.7225	−1.6670...	2.7790...
0.85	0.7225	0.8220...	0.6758...
1.35	1.8225	1.2785...	1.6348...
−0.65	0.4225	−0.7395...	0.5468...
−0.15	0.0225	−0.2902...	0.0842...

$SS_{dev} = 10.025$, $SS_{res} = 9.9613...$

$$r^2 = \frac{10.025 - 9.9613...}{10.025} = 0.0063...$$

$$r = \sqrt{0.0063...} = 0.0796...$$

c. *r* is close to zero; less than 1% is removed.

d.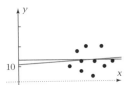

Section 8-6

1. a. $\hat{y} = ax^b$, $b < 0$, and $\hat{y} = ab^x$, $0 < b < 1$, both approach 0 asymptotically as x approaches infinity. The other two functions do not.

   b. The power function $\hat{y} = 16{,}809.4737...x^{-1.8408...}$ has the better correlation, $r = -0.9996...$ (exponential has $r = -0.9560...$) and less pattern in the residuals.

   c. $\hat{y}(20) = 67.6960... \approx 68$ words. Extrapolation.

   d. $\hat{y}(50) = 12.5319... \approx 13$ words (12 more words). Extrapolation.

   e.

log x	log f(x)
0	4.2157
.30103	3.6791
.47712	3.3412
.60206	3.1089
.69897	2.9571
.77815	2.8041
.8451	2.6839
.69897	2.9571
.77815	2.8041
.8451	2.6839
.90309	2.5694
.95424	2.4742
1	2.3464

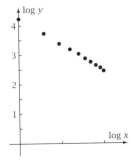

The scatterplot appears very linear.
$\log \hat{y} = a \log x + b \Leftrightarrow \hat{y} = 10^b x^a = Bx^a$, a power function.

   f. $\log \hat{y} = -1.8408... \log x + 4.2255...$
   The residuals are good, with only the slightest hint of a pattern:

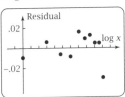

2. a. Quadratic: $R^2 = 0.9998...$
   Linear: $r^2 = 0.9767...$
   Exponential: $r^2 = 0.9620...$
   Power: $r^2 = 0.8386...$

   b. $\hat{y} = 0.0005...x^2 - 0.2379...x + 24.2$

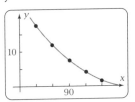

   [0, 180, 30, 0, 20, 5]
   The model fits all values quite well.

   c. $\hat{y}(0) = c = 24.2$ cm

   d. $x = \dfrac{-b \pm \sqrt{b^2 - 4ac}}{2a} = 185.3230...$ s
   or 225.3884... s. At about 185 seconds, the tub empties, but the model predicts negative values, which are meaningless, and then that the tub would spontaneously refill itself after 225 s.

3. a. $\hat{y} = 14.6969... \cdot 0.9583...^x$, $r = -0.9999...$
   Linear: $r = -0.9979...$
   Power: $r = -0.9679...$

   b. $\hat{y}(29) = 4.2767... \approx 4.28$ psi

   c. $ab^x = 0.9 \Rightarrow \ln a + x \ln b = \ln 0.9 \Rightarrow$
   $x = \dfrac{\ln 0.9 - \ln a}{\ln b} = \dfrac{\ln 0.9 - \ln 14.6959...}{\ln 0.9583...}$
   $= 65.6155... \approx 65{,}600$ ft

d. Yes. $\hat{y}(0) = a = 14.6959... \approx 14.7$ psi

e. $\hat{y}(-10) = 22.4934... \approx 22.49$ psi

f. $\hat{y} = 0.0101...x^2 - 0.6097x + 14.676$ has $R^2 = 0.99997....$ The exponential function (solid) correctly shows the pressure dropping toward 0 at high altitudes, while the quadratic function (dotted) shows it reaching a minimum and then increasing.

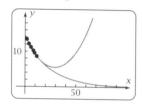

[0, 100, 10, 0, 20, 1]

g. Residuals for exponential function:

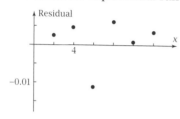

$(-0.0169... < y < 0.0085...)$

Residuals for power function:

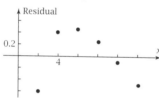

$(-0.7574... < y < 0.6436...)$

The exponential function residuals are smaller, with less of a pattern.

Chapter 9

Section 9-3

1. $15 \cdot 23 = 345$

2. $20 + 17 = 37$

3. a. $37 + 15 = 52$

   b. $37 \cdot 15 = 555$

4. a. $13 \cdot 11 = 143$

   b. $13 + 11 = 24$

5. $544 + 215 - 129 = 630$

Section 9-4

1. a. $9 \cdot 8 \cdot 7 \cdot 6 = 3024$

   b. $12 \cdot 11 \cdot 10 = 1320$

   c. $8 \cdot 7 \cdot 6 \cdot 5 \cdot 4 = 6720$

   d. $7! = 5040$

2. a. $26 \cdot 25 = 650$

   b. $26 \cdot 25 \cdot 24 = 15,600$

   c. $26 \cdot 25 \cdot 24 \cdot 23 = 358,800$

   d. $26! = 403,291,461,126,640,000,000,000,000$; more than 26 digits.

3. $26 \cdot 25 \cdot 24 \cdot 23 = 358,800$

4. a. $15 \cdot 14 = 210$

   b. $13 \cdot 12 \cdot 11 = 1716$

   c. $10 \cdot 9 \cdot 8 \cdot 7 = 5040$

5. a. $5! = 120$

   b. $1 \cdot 4! = 24$

   c. $\frac{24}{120} = \frac{1 \cdot 4!}{5!} = \frac{1 \cdot 4!}{5 \cdot 4!} = \frac{1}{5}$. Or because G is 1 of 5 possible letters with which the permutation could start, $\frac{1}{5}$ of the permutations will start with G. 20%.

   d. $\frac{1}{120}$

6. a. $\frac{3 \cdot 1 \cdot 2 \cdot 1 \cdot 1}{5!} = \frac{6}{120} = \frac{1}{20}$

   b. $\frac{3 \cdot 2 \cdot 3 \cdot 2 \cdot 1}{5!} = \frac{36}{120} = \frac{3}{10}$

   c. $\frac{3 \cdot 3 \cdot 2 \cdot 2 \cdot 1}{5!} = \frac{36}{120} = \frac{3}{10}$

   d. $\frac{3 \cdot 3 \cdot 2 \cdot 1 \cdot 1}{5!} = \frac{18}{120} = \frac{3}{20}$

   e. $\frac{3 \cdot 2 \cdot 2 \cdot 1 \cdot 1}{5!} = \frac{12}{120} = \frac{1}{10}$

7. $\frac{7!}{3!} = \frac{5040}{6} = 840$

Section 9-5

1. $_{30}C_5 = 142,506$; all members of a committee have equal roles, so order is not important.

2. $_{1000}C_3 = 166,167,000$

3. a. $\frac{_6C_3 \cdot _4C_2}{_{10}C_5} = \frac{20 \cdot 6}{252} = \frac{10}{21} \approx 48\%$

   b. $\frac{_6C_2 \cdot _4C_3}{_{10}C_5} = \frac{15 \cdot 4}{252} = \frac{5}{21} \approx 24\%$

Precalculus with Trigonometry: Instructor's Guide
© 2007 Key Curriculum Press

c. $\dfrac{10}{21} + \dfrac{5}{21} = \dfrac{5}{7} \approx 71\%$

d. $\dfrac{{}_1C_1 \cdot {}_9C_4}{{}_{10}C_5} = \dfrac{1 \cdot 126}{252} = \dfrac{1}{2} = 50\%$

4. a. $\dfrac{{}_4C_2 \cdot {}_8C_5}{{}_{12}C_7} = \dfrac{6 \cdot 56}{792} = \dfrac{14}{33} \approx 42\%$

 b. $\dfrac{{}_4C_0 \cdot {}_8C_7}{{}_{12}C_7} = \dfrac{1 \cdot 8}{792} = \dfrac{1}{99} \approx 1\%$

 c. 0, because there aren't seven boys.

 d. $\dfrac{{}_2C_2 \cdot {}_{10}C_5}{{}_{12}C_7} = \dfrac{1 \cdot 252}{792} = \dfrac{7}{22} \approx 32\%$

5. a. ${}_3C_0 + {}_3C_1 + {}_3C_2 + {}_3C_3$
 $= 1 + 3 + 3 + 1 = 8 = 2^3$

 b. i. $2^{10} = 1024$

 ii. $2^{10} - {}_{10}C_0 = 1024 - 1 = 1023$;
 $2^{10} - {}_{10}C_0 - {}_{10}C_1 = 1024 - 1 - 10 = 1013$

 iii. $2^{12} = 4096$

 iv. $2^{12} - {}_{12}C_0 = 4096 - 1 = 4095$

Section 9-6

1. a. $(0.92)(0.88) = 0.8096 = 80.96\%$

 b. $1 - 0.92 = 0.08 = 8\%$

 c. $1 - 0.88 = 0.12 = 12\%$

 d. $(0.08)(0.12) = 0.0096 = 0.96\%$

 e. $1 - 0.0096 = 0.9904 = 99.04\%$

2. a. $1 - 0.8 = 0.2 = 20\%$

 b. $1 - 0.65 = 0.35 = 35\%$

 c. $(0.2)(0.35) = 0.07 = 7\%$

 d. $(0.8)(0.65) = 0.52 = 52\%$

 e. $1 - 0.07 = 0.93 = 93\%$

Section 9-7

1. Answers should match those in the text.

2. Graph should match that in the text.

3. a.

x	$P(x)$
0	0.16807
1	0.36015
2	0.30870
3	0.12320
4	0.02835
5	0.00243

b. $P(2) + P(3) + P(4) + P(5)$
 $= 0.30870 + 0.13230 + 0.02835 + 0.00243$
 $= 0.47178$; or
 $1 - [P(0) + P(1)] = 1 - (0.16807 + 0.36015)$
 $= 0.47178$

c.

x	$P(x)$
0	0.0403…
1	0.1556…
2	0.2668…
3	0.2668…
4	0.1715…
5	0.0738…
6	0.0210…
7	0.0035…
8	0.0004…
9	0.00001…

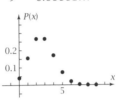

4. a. $\dfrac{2}{6} = \dfrac{1}{3}; \dfrac{4}{6} = \dfrac{2}{3}$

 b.

x	$P(x)$
0	0.0877…
1	0.2633…
2	0.3292…
3	0.2194…
4	0.0823…
5	0.0164…
6	0.0013…

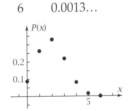

 c. $P(2) + P(3) + P(4) + P(5) + P(6) = 0.6488…$;
 or $1 - [P(0) + P(1)] = 0.6488…$

 d. False. $P(2) = {}_6C_2\left(\dfrac{1}{3}\right)^2\left(\dfrac{2}{3}\right)^4 = 0.3292…$

5. a. $\dfrac{1}{6}$

   b. $\dfrac{5}{6}\cdot\dfrac{1}{5}=\dfrac{1}{6}$

   c. $P(3)=\dfrac{5}{6}\cdot\dfrac{4}{5}\cdot\dfrac{1}{4}=\dfrac{1}{6}$

   $P(4)=\dfrac{5}{6}\cdot\dfrac{4}{5}\cdot\dfrac{3}{4}\cdot\dfrac{1}{3}=\dfrac{1}{6}$

   $P(5)=\dfrac{5}{6}\cdot\dfrac{4}{5}\cdot\dfrac{3}{4}\cdot\dfrac{2}{3}\cdot\dfrac{1}{2}=\dfrac{1}{6}$

   $P(6)=\dfrac{5}{6}\cdot\dfrac{4}{5}\cdot\dfrac{3}{4}\cdot\dfrac{2}{3}\cdot\dfrac{1}{2}\cdot\dfrac{1}{1}=\dfrac{1}{6}$

   d. They are the only possibilities.

   e. $P(1)=\dfrac{1}{6}=0.1666...$

   $P(2)=\dfrac{5}{6}\cdot\dfrac{1}{6}=0.1388...$

   $P(3)=\left(\dfrac{5}{6}\right)^2\cdot\dfrac{1}{6}=0.1157...$

   $P(4)=\left(\dfrac{5}{6}\right)^3\cdot\dfrac{1}{6}=0.0964...$

   $P(5)=\left(\dfrac{5}{6}\right)^4\cdot\dfrac{1}{6}=0.0803...$

   $P(6)=\left(\dfrac{5}{6}\right)^5\cdot\dfrac{1}{6}=0.0669...$

   f.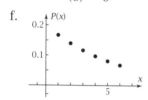

   g. $s_1=\dfrac{1}{6}=1-\dfrac{5}{6}$

   $s_2=\dfrac{1}{6}+\dfrac{5}{36}=\dfrac{11}{36}=1-\left(\dfrac{5}{6}\right)^2$

   $s_3=\dfrac{1}{6}+\dfrac{5}{36}+\dfrac{25}{216}=\dfrac{91}{216}=1-\left(\dfrac{5}{6}\right)^3$

   $\vdots$

   $s_n=1-\left(\dfrac{5}{6}\right)^n$

   As $n\to\infty$, $\left(\dfrac{5}{6}\right)^n\to0$, so the sum approaches 1.

6. a. $P(1,1)=0.1$

   b. $P(2,1)=(0.9)(0.1)=0.09$

   $P(3,1)=(0.9)^2(0.1)=0.081$

   c. $P(1,1)=0.1$

   $P(1,2)=(0.9)^3(0.1)=(0.729)(0.1)$

   $P(1,3)=(0.9)^6(0.1)=(0.729)^2(0.1)$

   $a_0=0.1,\ r=0.729$

   d. $P(1\text{st})=\displaystyle\sum_{i=0}^{\infty}(0.729)^i(0.1)=\dfrac{0.1}{1-0.729}$

   $=0.3690...$

   $P(2\text{nd})=\displaystyle\sum_{i=0}^{\infty}(0.9)(0.729)^i(0.1)=\dfrac{0.09}{1-0.729}$

   $=0.3321...$

   $P(3\text{rd})=\displaystyle\sum_{i=0}^{\infty}(0.9)^2(0.729)^i(0.1)=\dfrac{0.081}{1-0.729}$

   $=0.2988$

   e. The first probability is higher than the second, which is higher than the third, which makes sense because player 1 has the first chance to win. Their sum is 1 = 100%.

Section 9-8

1. a. Let x be the card and a be the payoff.

x	$P(x)$	a	$P(x)\cdot a$
Ace	$\frac{4}{52}$	1.30	0.10
Face	$\frac{12}{52}$	0.39	0.09
Other	$\frac{36}{52}$	−0.26	−0.18
		(Total) $E(x)$ =	$0.01

   b. In the long run, you expect to win 1¢ for each game played.

2. Your probability of getting a 1 on any particular roll is $\frac{1}{6}$. Let k = number of 1s:

   $P(k\ge2)=P(k=2)+P(k=3)$

   $=\,_3C_2\left(\dfrac{1}{6}\right)^2\left(\dfrac{5}{6}\right)^1+\,_3C_3\left(\dfrac{1}{6}\right)^3\left(\dfrac{5}{6}\right)^0=\dfrac{5}{72}+\dfrac{1}{216}$

   $=\dfrac{2}{27}=0.\overline{074}$; let x = winnings:

   $E(x)=(\$10-\$1)\cdot\dfrac{2}{27}+(\$0-\$1)\cdot\dfrac{25}{27}$

   $\approx-\$0.26$

Section 9-9

1. a. $_{15}C_5=3003$; $_{15}C_4=1365$

   b. If there are more than 1365 cards, then at least 2 will have the same group of numbers in the middle (third) column, so the maximum number of cards in a set is 1365.

   c. Again, the maximum number of cards is 1365.

Precalculus with Trigonometry: Instructor's Guide
© 2007 Key Curriculum Press

Chapter 10

Section 10-4

1. a. $\vec{d} = (40\vec{i} + 15\vec{j} + 11\vec{k}) - (30\vec{i} + 20\vec{j} + 0\vec{k})$
   $= 10\vec{i} - 5\vec{j} + 11\vec{k}$

   b. $|\vec{d}| = \sqrt{10^2 + 5^2 + 11^2}$ ft $= \sqrt{246}$ ft ≈ 15.7 ft

   c. You can do this without using the formula for vector projection because we are looking for the "shadow" of the displacement vector, its horizontal components with no vertical component. So it is $\vec{p} = 10\vec{i} - 5\vec{j} + 0\vec{k}$.

   d. $\theta = \cos^{-1} \dfrac{\vec{d} \cdot \vec{p}}{|\vec{d}| \cdot |\vec{p}|}$
   $= \cos^{-1} \dfrac{(10\vec{i} - 5\vec{j} + 11\vec{k}) \cdot (10\vec{i} - 5\vec{j} + 0\vec{k})}{\sqrt{246} \cdot \sqrt{10^2 + 5^2 + 0^2}}$
   $= \cos^{-1} \dfrac{100 + 25 + 0}{\sqrt{246} \cdot \sqrt{125}} \approx 44.5°$

2. a. $\theta = \cos^{-1} \dfrac{\vec{F} \cdot \vec{S}}{|\vec{F}||\vec{S}|}$
   $= \cos^{-1} \dfrac{(20\vec{i} + 15\vec{j} - 3\vec{k}) \text{ lb} \cdot (4\vec{i} + 3\vec{j} + 7\vec{k}) \text{ ft}}{|20\vec{i} + 15\vec{j} - 3\vec{k}| \text{ lb} |4\vec{i} + 3\vec{j} + 7\vec{k}| \text{ ft}}$
   $= \cos^{-1} \dfrac{20 \cdot 4 + 15 \cdot 3 - 3 \cdot 7}{\sqrt{20^2 + 15^2 + 3^2}\sqrt{4^2 + 3^2 + 7^2}}$
   $= \cos^{-1} \dfrac{104}{\sqrt{634} \cdot \sqrt{74}} \approx 61.3°$

   b. $W = \vec{F} \cdot \vec{S} = 104$ ft-lb (from part a)

   c. $|\vec{F}| = \sqrt{634}$ lb ≈ 25.2 lb and $|\vec{S}| = \sqrt{74}$ ft ≈ 8.6 ft (from part a)

   d. $W_{\text{hypoth}} = |\vec{F}||\vec{S}| = \sqrt{634}$ lb $\cdot \sqrt{74}$ ft ≈ 216.6 ft-lb (from part a)

3. a.

   Not to scale, because the units for $\vec{a}$ and $\vec{p}$ are not the same as those for $\vec{v}$.

   b. $p = |\vec{a}| \cos \theta = 90$ mi/h/min $\cdot \cos 140°$
   $= -68.9439...$ mi/h/min

   c. Slowing down. The acceleration is negative.

   d. $p = |\vec{a}| \cos \theta = 30$ mi/h/min $\cdot \cos 40°$
   $= 275.7759...$ mi/h/min. Speeding up at that rate.

4. Let O be the common tail of $\vec{b}$, $\vec{b} + \vec{c}$, and $\vec{a}$, let B be the foot of the perpendicular from the head of $\vec{b}$ to $\vec{a}$, and let C be the foot of the perpendicular from the head of $\vec{b} + \vec{c}$ to $\vec{a}$. Let p_1 be the scalar projection of $\vec{b} + \vec{c}$ onto $\vec{a}$, p_2 be the scalar projection of $\vec{b}$ onto $\vec{a}$, and p_3 be the scalar projection of $\vec{c}$ onto $\vec{a}$.

$$p_1 = \dfrac{\vec{a} \cdot (\vec{b} + \vec{c})}{|\vec{a}|} = OC = OB + BC = p_2 + p_3$$

$$= \dfrac{\vec{a} \cdot \vec{b}}{|\vec{a}|} + \dfrac{\vec{a} \cdot \vec{c}}{|\vec{a}|}, \text{ so multiplying through by } |\vec{a}|,$$

$$\vec{a} \cdot (\vec{b} + \vec{c}) = \vec{a} \cdot \vec{b} + \vec{a} \cdot \vec{c}.$$

Section 10-5

1. $6x + 7y - 4k = D$;
   $D = 6(-2) + 7(8) - 4(17) = -24$;
   $6x - 7y - 4z = -24$

2. $4x - 2y + 3z = D$; $D = 4(5) - 2(1) + 3(-4) = 6$;
   $4x - 2y + 3z = 6$

3. $\vec{n} = (26 - 5)\vec{i} + (2 - 17)\vec{j} + (13 - 1)\vec{k}$
   $= 21\vec{i} - 15\vec{j} + 12\vec{k}$;
   $\vec{p} = \dfrac{2}{3}(5, 17, 1) + \dfrac{1}{3}(26, 2, 13) = (12, 12, 5)$;
   $21x - 15y + 12z = D$;
   $D = 21(12) - 15(12) + 12(5) = 132$;
   $21x - 15y + 12z = 132$

4. $x - 3y + z = D$; $D = 1(0) - 3(0) + 1(-2) = -2$;
   $x - 3y + z = -2$

5. $\vec{n_1} = 2\vec{i} + B\vec{j} - 5\vec{k}$; $\vec{n_2} = \vec{i} - \vec{j} + 2\vec{k}$;
   $\vec{n_1} \cdot \vec{n_2} = 0 \Rightarrow 2 \cdot 1 + B(-1) - 5 \cdot 2 = -B - 8 = 0 \Rightarrow$
   $B = -8$

6. a. $4x = -60 \Rightarrow x = -15$;
   $5y = -60 \Rightarrow y = -12$;
   $-6z = -60 \Rightarrow z = 10$
   Figure 10-5d has $x \le 0$, $y \le 0$, and $z \ge 0$ at the three corners.

   b. The upper-left corner has $(x, y, z) = (0, y, 3) \Rightarrow$
   $4(0) + 5y + 6(3) = -60 \Rightarrow y = -8.4 \Rightarrow$
   $(x, y, z) = (0, -8.4, 3)$. The upper-right corner has $(x, y, z) = (x, 0, 3) \Rightarrow$
   $4x + 5(0) - 6(3) = -60 \Rightarrow x = -10.5 \Rightarrow$
   $(x, y, z) = (-10.5, 0, 3)$.
   Length $= \sqrt{(8.4 \text{ ft})^2 + (10.5 \text{ ft})^2} = \sqrt{180.81 \text{ ft}^2}$
   ≈ 13.45 ft.

7. $\vec{n_1} = 3\vec{i} + 2\vec{j} - 5\vec{k}; \vec{n_2} = 4\vec{i} + 7\vec{j} + \vec{k};$

$$\theta = \cos^{-1} \frac{\vec{n_1} \cdot \vec{n_2}}{|\vec{n_1}| \cdot |\vec{n_2}|}$$

$$= \cos^{-1} \frac{3 \cdot 4 + 2 \cdot 7 - 5 \cdot 1}{\sqrt{3^2 + 2^2 + 5^2} \cdot \sqrt{4^2 + 7^2 + 1^2}}$$

$$= \cos^{-1} \frac{21}{\sqrt{38} \cdot \sqrt{66}} = 65.2077...^\circ$$

8. $\vec{n_1} = 2\vec{i} - 7\vec{j} + 3\vec{k}; \vec{n_2} = 5\vec{i} + 2\vec{j} + 8\vec{k}$

$$\theta = \cos^{-1} \frac{\vec{n_1} \cdot \vec{n_2}}{|\vec{n_1}| \cdot |\vec{n_2}|}$$

$$= \cos^{-1} \frac{2 \cdot 5 - 7 \cdot 2 + 3 \cdot 8}{\sqrt{2^2 + 7^2 + 3^2} \cdot \sqrt{5^2 + 2^2 + 8^2}}$$

$$= \cos^{-1} \frac{20}{\sqrt{62} \cdot \sqrt{93}} = 74.7289...^\circ$$

9. $\vec{n_1} = 4\vec{i} - 3\vec{j} + 2\vec{k}; \vec{n_2} = \vec{i} + 5\vec{j} + 3\vec{k}$

$$\theta = \cos^{-1} \frac{\vec{n_1} \cdot \vec{n_2}}{|\vec{n_1}| \cdot |\vec{n_2}|}$$

$$= \cos^{-1} \frac{4 \cdot 1 - 3 \cdot 5 + 2 \cdot 3}{\sqrt{4^2 + 3^2 + 2^2} \cdot \sqrt{1^2 + 5^2 + 3^2}}$$

$$= \cos^{-1} \frac{-5}{\sqrt{29} \cdot \sqrt{35}} = 99.0293...^\circ$$

The acute angle is $80.9706...^\circ$.

10. $\vec{n_1} = -2\vec{i} + 8\vec{j} - 7\vec{k}; \vec{n_2} = 6\vec{i} - 3\vec{j} - 2\vec{k};$

$$\theta = \cos^{-1} \frac{\vec{n_1} \cdot \vec{n_2}}{|\vec{n_1}| \cdot |\vec{n_2}|}$$

$$= \cos^{-1} \frac{-2 \cdot 6 + 8(-3) - 7(-2)}{\sqrt{2^2 + 8^2 + 7^2} \cdot \sqrt{6^2 + 3^2 + 2^2}}$$

$$\cos^{-1} \frac{-22}{\sqrt{117} \cdot \sqrt{49}} = 106.8913...^\circ$$

The acute angle is $73.1086...^\circ$.

11. $\vec{n_1} = 6\vec{i} - 7\vec{j} + 3\vec{k}; \vec{n_2} = 0\vec{i} + 0\vec{j} + \vec{k}$ because any normal to the xy-plane is parallel to the z-axis;

$$\theta = \cos^{-1} \frac{\vec{n_1} \cdot \vec{n_2}}{|\vec{n_1}| \cdot |\vec{n_2}|}$$

$$= \cos^{-1} \frac{6 \cdot 0 - 7 \cdot 0 + 3 \cdot 1}{\sqrt{6^2 + 7^2 + 3^2} \cdot \sqrt{0^2 + 0^2 + 1^2}}$$

$$= \cos^{-1} \frac{3}{\sqrt{94}} = 71.9753...^\circ$$

12. $\vec{n_1} = 3\vec{i} + 4\vec{j} - 2\vec{k}; \vec{n_2} = \vec{i} + 0\vec{j} + 0\vec{k}$ because the normal to the yz-plane is the x-axis;

$$\theta = \cos^{-1} \frac{\vec{n_1} \cdot \vec{n_2}}{|\vec{n_1}| \cdot |\vec{n_2}|}$$

$$= \cos^{-1} \frac{3 \cdot 1 + 4 \cdot 0 - 2 \cdot 0}{\sqrt{3^2 + 4^2 + 2^2} \cdot \sqrt{1^2 + 0^2 + 0^2}}$$

$$= \cos^{-1} \frac{3}{\sqrt{29}} = 56.1454...^\circ$$

13.

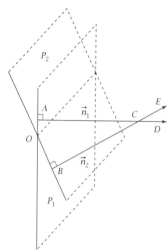

Plane P_1 with normal $\vec{n_1}$ intersecting plane P_2 with normal $\vec{n_2}$.

We will prove that $m\angle ACE = m\angle BOA$:
$m\angle BOA + m\angle OAC + m\angle ACB + m\angle CBO = 360^\circ$ (interior angles of a quadrilateral).
But $m\angle OAC = m\angle CBO = 90^\circ$.
$\therefore m\angle BOA + m\angle ACB = 180^\circ$,
so $m\angle BOA = 180^\circ - m\angle ACB$. Also,
$m\angle ACE = 180^\circ - m\angle DCE$ (supplementary angles). But $m\angle DCE = m\angle ACB$ (vertical angles),
so $m\angle ACE = 180^\circ - m\angle ACB$, so
$m\angle ACE = m\angle BOA$.

Section 10-6

1. $(4\vec{j} + 3\vec{k}) \times (5\vec{i} - 6\vec{k}) = \begin{vmatrix} \vec{i} & \vec{j} & \vec{k} \\ 0 & 4 & 3 \\ 5 & 0 & -6 \end{vmatrix}$

$$= \vec{i} \begin{vmatrix} 4 & 3 \\ 0 & -6 \end{vmatrix} - \vec{j} \begin{vmatrix} 0 & 3 \\ 5 & -6 \end{vmatrix} + \vec{k} \begin{vmatrix} 0 & 4 \\ 5 & 0 \end{vmatrix}$$

$$= \vec{i}(-24 - 0) - \vec{j}(0 - 15) + \vec{k}(0 - 20)$$

$$= -24\vec{i} + 15\vec{j} - 20\vec{k}$$

2. $8\vec{i} \times 5\vec{j} = (8 \cdot 5)(\vec{i} \times \vec{j}) = 40\vec{k}$. This is faster than

$$\begin{vmatrix} \vec{i} & \vec{j} & \vec{k} \\ 8 & 0 & 0 \\ 0 & 5 & 0 \end{vmatrix} = \vec{i} \begin{vmatrix} 0 & 0 \\ 5 & 0 \end{vmatrix} - \vec{j} \begin{vmatrix} 8 & 0 \\ 0 & 0 \end{vmatrix} + \vec{k} \begin{vmatrix} 8 & 0 \\ 0 & 5 \end{vmatrix}$$

$$= \vec{i}(0 - 0) - \vec{j}(0 - 0) + \vec{k}(40 - 0) = 40\vec{k}.$$

3. a. $\vec{a} \times \vec{b} = (3\vec{i} + 5\vec{j} + 4\vec{k}) \times (2\vec{i} + 7\vec{j} + 6\vec{k})$
$= 2\vec{i} - 10\vec{j} + 11\vec{k};$

$$\theta = \sin^{-1} \frac{|\vec{a} \times \vec{b}|}{|\vec{a}| \cdot |\vec{b}|}$$

$$= \sin^{-1} \frac{\sqrt{2^2 + 10^2 + 11^2}}{\sqrt{3^2 + 5^2 + 4^2} \cdot \sqrt{2^2 + 7^2 + 6^2}}$$

$$= \sin^{-1} \frac{\sqrt{225}}{\sqrt{50} \cdot \sqrt{89}} = 12.9946...^\circ$$

$$\theta = \cos^{-1} \frac{\vec{a} \cdot \vec{b}}{|\vec{a}| \cdot |\vec{b}|}$$

$$= \cos^{-1} \frac{3 \cdot 2 + 5 \cdot 7 + 4 \cdot 6}{\sqrt{50} \cdot \sqrt{89}}$$

$$= \cos^{-1} \frac{65}{\sqrt{50} \cdot \sqrt{89}} = 12.9946...°$$

b. $\vec{c} \times \vec{d} = (\vec{i} + 4\vec{j} - 8\vec{k}) \times (2\vec{i} + 6\vec{j} + 9\vec{k})$
$$= 84\vec{i} - 25\vec{j} - 2\vec{k};$$

$$\theta = \sin^{-1} \frac{|\vec{c} \times \vec{d}|}{|\vec{c}| \cdot |\vec{d}|}$$

$$= \sin^{-1} \frac{\sqrt{84^2 + 25^2 + 2^2}}{\sqrt{1^2 + 4^2 + 8^2} \cdot \sqrt{2^2 + 6^2 + 9^2}}$$

$$= \sin^{-1} \frac{\sqrt{7685}}{\sqrt{81} \cdot \sqrt{121}} = 62.3126...°$$

$$\theta = \cos^{-1} \frac{\vec{c} \cdot \vec{d}}{|\vec{c}| \cdot |\vec{d}|}$$

$$= \cos^{-1} \frac{1 \cdot 2 + 4 \cdot 6 + (-8) \cdot 9}{\sqrt{81} \cdot \sqrt{121}}$$

$$= \cos^{-1} \frac{-46}{\sqrt{81} \cdot \sqrt{121}} = 171.6873...°$$

c. The answers are the supplements of each other. The value of $\frac{\vec{a} \times \vec{b}}{|\vec{a}| \cdot |\vec{b}|}$ will always be positive, so the inverse sine function will return answers only in the range $0 \le \theta < 90°$, while the actual angle between the two vectors can be in the range $0 \le \theta < 180°$. The inverse cosine function will give correct values in this range because $\frac{\vec{a} \cdot \vec{b}}{|\vec{a}| \cdot |\vec{b}|}$ can be positive or negative.

4. a. $\vec{b} \cdot \vec{a} = |\vec{b}| \cdot |\vec{a}| \cdot \cos \theta = |\vec{a}| \cdot |\vec{b}| \cdot \cos \theta$
$$= \vec{a} \cdot \vec{b}$$

Scalar multiplication is commutative because multiplication of real numbers is commutative. Vector multiplication is not commutative because the right-hand rule gives an opposite direction when the fingers curl from $\vec{b}$ to $\vec{a}$ than when they curl from $\vec{a}$ to $\vec{b}$.

b. $|\vec{v} \times \vec{u}| = |\vec{v}| \cdot |\vec{u}| \cdot \sin \theta = |\vec{u}| \cdot |\vec{v}| \cdot \sin \theta = |\vec{u} \times \vec{v}|$, but, as mentioned in part a, the directions of the products are opposite. In more detail, if $\vec{u} = a\vec{i} + b\vec{j} + c\vec{k}$ and $\vec{v} = d\vec{i} + e\vec{j} + f\vec{k}$, then

$$\vec{u} \times \vec{v} = \begin{vmatrix} \vec{i} & \vec{j} & \vec{k} \\ a & b & c \\ d & e & f \end{vmatrix}$$

$$= (bf - ce)\vec{i} - (af - cd)\vec{j} + (ae - bd)\vec{k}$$

$$\vec{v} \times \vec{u} = \begin{vmatrix} \vec{i} & \vec{j} & \vec{k} \\ d & e & f \\ a & b & c \end{vmatrix}$$

$$= (ce - bf)\vec{i} - (cd - af)\vec{j} + (bd - ae)\vec{k}$$

$$= -(\vec{u} \times \vec{v})$$

5. $\vec{l}_{1,2} = (4 - 2)\vec{i} + (3 - 0)\vec{j} + (0 - 8)\vec{k}$
$$= 2\vec{i} + 3\vec{j} - 8\vec{k}$$
$\vec{l}_{1,3} = (7 - 2)\vec{i} + (5 - 0)\vec{j} + (1 - 8)\vec{k} = 5\vec{i} + 5\vec{j} - 7\vec{k}$
$\vec{n} = \vec{l}_{1,2} \times \vec{l}_{1,3} = 19\vec{i} - 26\vec{j} - 5\vec{k} \Rightarrow$
$19x - 26y - 5z = D \Rightarrow$
$D = 19(2) - 26(0) - 5(8) = -2 \Rightarrow$
$19x - 26y - 5z = -2$

6. $\vec{n}_1 = -2\vec{i} + 7\vec{j} + 3\vec{k}; \vec{n}_2 = 4\vec{i} - 2\vec{j} - 6\vec{k}$
$\vec{l} = \vec{n}_1 \times \vec{n}_2 = -36\vec{i} - 24\vec{k} = -12(3\vec{i} + 2\vec{k}) \Rightarrow$
$3x + 2z = D \Rightarrow D = 3(3) + 2(-1) = 7 \Rightarrow$
$3x + 2z = 7$

7. a. $\vec{c} \times \vec{d} = (9\vec{i} - 6j + 2\vec{k}) \times (8\vec{i} + \vec{j} - 4\vec{k})$
$$= 22i + 52\vec{j} + 57\vec{k}$$

b. $\vec{c} \cdot (\vec{c} \times \vec{d})$
$$= (9\vec{i} - 6\vec{j} + 2\vec{k}) \cdot (22\vec{i} + 52\vec{j} + 57\vec{k})$$
$$= 9.22 + (-6) \cdot 52 + 2 \cdot 57 = 0;$$
$\vec{d} \cdot (\vec{c} \times \vec{d}) = (8\vec{i} + \vec{j} - 4\vec{k}) \cdot (22\vec{i} + 52j + 57\vec{k})$
$$= 8.22 + 1.52 + (-4) \cdot 57 = 0$$

c. $\vec{c} \cdot \vec{d} = (9\vec{i} - 6\vec{j} + 2\vec{k}) \cdot (8\vec{i} + \vec{j} - 4\vec{k})$
$$= 9.8 + (-6) \cdot 1 + 2 \cdot (-4) = 58;$$

$$\theta = \cos^{-1} \frac{\vec{c} \cdot \vec{d}}{|\vec{c}| \cdot |\vec{d}|}$$

$$= \cos^{-1} \frac{58}{\sqrt{9^2 + 6^2 + 2^2} \cdot \sqrt{8^2 + 1^2 + 4^2}}$$

$$= \cos^{-1} \frac{58}{\sqrt{121} \cdot \sqrt{81}} = \cos^{-1} \frac{58}{99}$$

$$= 54.1363...°$$

d. $|\vec{c} \times \vec{d}| = \sqrt{22^2 + 52^2 + 57^2} = \sqrt{6437}$
$$= 80.2309...; |\vec{c}| \cdot |\vec{d}| \cdot \sin \theta$$
$$= 11.9 \cdot \sin 54.1363...°$$
$$= 80.2309...$$

Section 10-7

1. a. $\vec{P_0P_1} = (14 - 2)\vec{i} + (20 - 5)\vec{j} + (23 - 7)\vec{k}$
$$= 12\vec{i} + 15\vec{j} + 16\vec{k};$$
$\sqrt{12^2 + 15^2 + 16^2} = \sqrt{625} = 25;$

$$\alpha = \cos^{-1} \frac{12}{25} = 61.3145...°;$$

$$\beta = \cos^{-1} \frac{15}{25} = \cos^{-1} \frac{3}{5} = 53.1301...°;$$

$$\gamma = \cos^{-1} \frac{16}{25} = 50.2081...°$$

b. i. $\vec{u} = \dfrac{12}{25}\vec{i} + \dfrac{3}{5}\vec{j} + \dfrac{16}{25}\vec{k}$

   ii. $75\vec{u} = 36\vec{i} + 45\vec{j} + 48\vec{k}$

   iii. $d\vec{u} = \dfrac{12}{25}d\vec{i} + \dfrac{3}{5}d\vec{j} + \dfrac{16}{25}d\vec{k}$

2. a. $\overrightarrow{P_0P_1} = (27 - 7)\vec{i} + (17 - 5)\vec{j} + (15 - 3)\vec{k}$
$= 20\vec{i} + 9\vec{j} + 12\vec{k}$;
$\sqrt{20^2 + 9^2 + 12^2} = \sqrt{625} = 25$;

$\alpha = \cos^{-1}\dfrac{20}{25} = \cos^{-1}\dfrac{4}{5} = 38.8698...°$;

$\beta = \cos^{-1}\dfrac{9}{25} = 68.8998...°$;

$\gamma = \cos^{-1}\dfrac{12}{25} = 61.3145...°$

  b. i. $\vec{u} = \dfrac{4}{5}\vec{i} + \dfrac{9}{25}\vec{j} + \dfrac{12}{25}\vec{k}$

   ii. $75\vec{u} = 60\vec{i} + 27\vec{j} + 36\vec{k}$

   iii. $d\vec{u} = \dfrac{4}{5}d\vec{i} + \dfrac{9}{25}d\vec{i} + \dfrac{12}{25}d\vec{k}$

3. $\overrightarrow{P_0P} = (x - x_0)\vec{i} + (y - y_0)\vec{j} + (z - z_0)\vec{k}$

$c_1 = \cos\alpha = \dfrac{\vec{i} \cdot \overrightarrow{P_0P}}{|\vec{i}| \cdot |\overrightarrow{P_0P}|} = \dfrac{x - x_0}{d}$, and similarly for c_2 and c_3.

Section 10-8

1. a. $x = 6 + 2t = 100 \Rightarrow t = 47$

  b. $\vec{r} = (6 + 2 \cdot 47)\vec{i} + (1 + 5 \cdot 47)\vec{j} + (4 + 8 \cdot 47)\vec{k}$
$= 100\vec{i} + 236\vec{j} + 380\vec{k}$; $(100, 236, 380)$

  c. $z = 4 + 8t = 0 \Rightarrow t = -\dfrac{1}{2}$

$\vec{r} = \left[6 + 2\left(-\dfrac{1}{2}\right)\right]\vec{i} + \left[1 + 5\left(-\dfrac{1}{2}\right)\right]\vec{j}$
$+ \left[4 + 8\left(-\dfrac{1}{2}\right)\right]\vec{k}$

$= 5\vec{i} - \dfrac{3}{2}\vec{j} + 0\vec{k}$; $\left(5, -\dfrac{3}{2}, 0\right)$

  d. $9(6 + 2t) + 3(1 + 5t) + 7(4 + 8t) = 53 \Rightarrow$

$89t = -32 \Rightarrow t = -\dfrac{32}{89}$;

$\vec{r} = \left[6 + 2\left(-\dfrac{32}{89}\right)\right]\vec{i} + \left[1 + 5\left(-\dfrac{32}{89}\right)\right]\vec{j}$
$+ \left[4 + 8\left(-\dfrac{32}{89}\right)\right]\vec{k}$

$= \dfrac{470}{89}\vec{i} - \dfrac{71}{89}\vec{j} + \dfrac{100}{89}\vec{k}$

$= (5.2808...)\vec{i} - (0.7977...)\vec{j} + (1.1235...)\vec{k}$;

$\left(\dfrac{470}{89}, -\dfrac{71}{89}, \dfrac{100}{89}\right)$

$= (5.2808..., -0.7977..., 1.1235...)$

  e. $\vec{u} = \dfrac{2}{\sqrt{93}}\vec{i} + \dfrac{5}{\sqrt{93}}\vec{j} + \dfrac{8}{\sqrt{93}}\vec{k}$;

$\vec{P_0} + 20\vec{u} = \left(6 + \dfrac{40}{\sqrt{93}}\right)\vec{i} + \left(1 + \dfrac{100}{\sqrt{93}}\right)\vec{j}$
$+ \left(4 + \dfrac{160}{\sqrt{93}}\right)\vec{k}$

$= (10.1478...)\vec{i} + (11.3695...)\vec{j}$
$+ (20.5912...)\vec{k}$;
$(10.1478..., 11.3695..., 20.5912...)$

  f. Answers will vary. The principal advantage is that if the coefficients of the vector are integers, you will not have to use fractions, and if they are rational, you will not have to use radicals.

2. a. For $t = 1$: $x = 6 + 2 \cdot 1 = 8$, $y = 1 + 5 \cdot 1 = 6$, $z = 4 + 8 \cdot 1 = 12$; $(8, 6, 12)$
For
$t = 2$: $x = 6 + 2 \cdot 2 = 10$, $y = 1 + 5 \cdot 2 = 11$, $z = 4 + 8 \cdot 2 = 20$; $(10, 11, 20)$

  b. $d = \sqrt{(10 - 8)^2 + (11 - 6)^2 + (20 - 12)^2}$
$= \sqrt{2^2 + 5^2 + 8^2} = |\vec{v}|$

  c. $z = 4 + 8t = 52 \Rightarrow t = 6$; $x = 6 + 2 \cdot 6 = 18$;
$y = 1 + 5 \cdot 6 = 31$; $(18, 31, 52)$

  d. $x = 6 + 2t = 0 \Rightarrow t = -3$; $y = 1 + 5(-3) = -14$,
$z = 4 + 8(-3) = -20$; $(0, -14, -20)$

3. a. $x = 6 + 2t \Rightarrow \dfrac{x - 6}{2} = t$; $y = 1 + 5t \Rightarrow \dfrac{y - 1}{5} = t$;

$z = 4 + 8t \Rightarrow \dfrac{z - 4}{8} = t$; so $\dfrac{x - 6}{2} = \dfrac{y - 1}{5}$

$= \dfrac{z - 4}{8} \ (= t)$

  b. $\dfrac{x + 3}{11} = t \Rightarrow x = -3 + 11t$;

$\dfrac{y - 5}{7} = t \Rightarrow x = 5 + 7t$; $\dfrac{z - 2.3}{13} = t \Rightarrow$

$z = 2.3 + 13t$

One point on the line is $(-3, 5, 2.3)$, and one vector parallel to it is $11\vec{i} + 7\vec{j} + 13\vec{k}$.

Precalculus with Trigonometry: Instructor's Guide
© 2007 Key Curriculum Press

Chapter 11

Section 11-3

1. The images seem to converge to the origin.

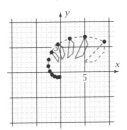

2. a. Dilation by 5.

   b. $[M] = \begin{bmatrix} 0 & -1 & 0 \\ 1 & 0 & 0 \\ 0 & 0 & 1 \end{bmatrix}$

3. a. $[M_1] = \begin{bmatrix} \cos 30° & \cos 120° \\ \sin 30° & \sin 120° \end{bmatrix} = \begin{bmatrix} \frac{\sqrt{3}}{2} & \frac{-1}{2} \\ \frac{1}{2} & \frac{\sqrt{3}}{2} \end{bmatrix}$;

   $[M_1][A] = \begin{bmatrix} \frac{\sqrt{3}}{2} & \frac{-1}{2} \\ \frac{1}{2} & \frac{\sqrt{3}}{2} \end{bmatrix}\begin{bmatrix} 5 \\ 7 \end{bmatrix} = \begin{bmatrix} \frac{5\sqrt{3}}{2} - \frac{7}{2} \\ \frac{5}{2} + \frac{7\sqrt{3}}{2} \end{bmatrix}$

   $= \begin{bmatrix} 0.8301\ldots \\ 8.5621\ldots \end{bmatrix}$;

   $[M_2] = \begin{bmatrix} \cos 30° & -\sin 30° \\ \sin 30° & \cos 30° \end{bmatrix} = \begin{bmatrix} \frac{\sqrt{3}}{2} & \frac{-1}{2} \\ \frac{1}{2} & \frac{\sqrt{3}}{2} \end{bmatrix}$;

   $[M_2][A] = \begin{bmatrix} \frac{\sqrt{3}}{2} & \frac{-1}{2} \\ \frac{1}{2} & \frac{\sqrt{3}}{2} \end{bmatrix}\begin{bmatrix} 5 \\ 7 \end{bmatrix} = \begin{bmatrix} \frac{5\sqrt{3}}{2} - \frac{7}{2} \\ \frac{5}{2} + \frac{7\sqrt{3}}{2} \end{bmatrix}$

   $= \begin{bmatrix} 0.8301\ldots \\ 8.5621\ldots \end{bmatrix}$

   b. $\cos(\theta + 90°) = \cos\theta \cdot \cos 90°$
   $- \sin\theta \cdot \sin 90°$
   $= \cos\theta \cdot 0 - \sin\theta \cdot 1 = -\sin\theta$;
   $\sin(\theta + 90°) = \sin\theta \cdot \cos 90°$
   $+ \cos\theta \cdot \sin 90°$
   $= \sin\theta \cdot 0 + \cos\theta \cdot 1 = \cos\theta$

   c. Answers will vary.

Chapter 12

Section 12-2

1. a. No xy-term, x^2- and y^2-terms have the same sign but different coefficients $\Rightarrow$ ellipse. $\left(\frac{x-2}{4}\right)^2 + \left(\frac{y-5}{3}\right)^2 = 1$. Center $(2, 5)$, x-radius 4, y-radius 3.

   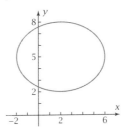

   b. The graph should match part a.

2. a. No xy-term, x^2- and y^2-terms have opposite signs $\Rightarrow$ hyperbola. $\left(\frac{x-2}{5}\right)^2 - \left(\frac{y-4}{3}\right)^2 = 1$. x-term is positive $\Rightarrow$ opens in the x-direction. Center $(2, 4)$, x-radius 5, y-radius 3, asymptotes have $m = \pm\frac{3}{5}$.

   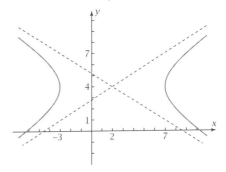

   b. The graph should match part a.

3. a. No xy-term, x^2- and y^2-terms have opposite signs $\Rightarrow$ hyperbola. $-\left(\frac{x+2}{2}\right)^2 + \left(\frac{y-1}{3}\right)^2 = 1$. y-term is positive $\Rightarrow$ opens in the y-direction. Center $(-2, 1)$, x-radius 2, y-radius 3, asymptotes have $m = \pm\frac{3}{2}$.

   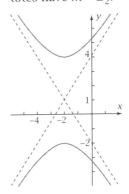

   b. The graph should match part a.

4. a. No xy-term, x^2- and y^2-terms have the same sign but different values $\Rightarrow$ ellipse. $\left(\frac{x-3}{2}\right)^2 + \left(\frac{y+1}{5}\right)^2 = 1$. Center $(3, -1)$, x-radius 2, y-radius 5.

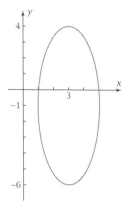

   b. The graph should match part a.

5. a. No xy-term, no y^2-term $\Rightarrow$ parabola opening vertically. $y - 6 = -2(x - 1)^2$. Vertex $(1, 6)$, y-intercept $2(0)^2 - 4(0) + y - 4 = 0 \Rightarrow y = 4$.

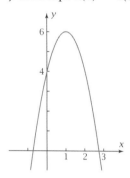

   b. The graph should match part a.

   This graph was *not* made by storing the values of A through F and using the quadratic formula, but rather by solving for y and using the result as $y_1 = -2x^2 + 4x + 4$, because $C = 0$ would make the denominator 0 in the quadratic formula.

6. a. No xy-term, no y^2-term $\Rightarrow$ parabola opening vertically. $y - 2 = \frac{1}{4}(x + 3)^2$. Vertex $(-3, 2)$, y-intercept $(0)^2 + 6(0) - 4y + 17 = 0 \Rightarrow y = \frac{17}{4} = 4.25$.

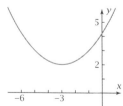

   b. The graph should match part a.
   As in Problem 5, this was graphed using $y_1 = (x^2 + 6x + 17)/4$.

7. a. No xy-term, no x^2-term $\Rightarrow$ parabola opening horizontally. $x + 2 = \frac{2}{9}(y - 4)^2$. Vertex $(-2, 4)$, x-intercept $2(0)^2 - 9x - 16(0) + 14 = 0 \Rightarrow x = \frac{14}{9}$.

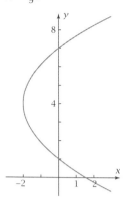

   b. The graph should match part a.

8. a. No xy-term, no x^2-term $\Rightarrow$ parabola opening horizontally. $x - 1 = (y + 3)^2$. Vertex $(1, -3)$, x-intercept $(0)^2 - x + 6(0) + 10 = 0 \Rightarrow x = 10$.

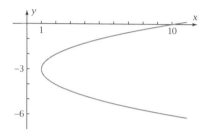

   b. The graph should match part a.

9. a. No xy-term, x^2- and y^2-terms have opposite signs $\Rightarrow$ hyperbola. $\left(\frac{x+3}{3}\right)^2 - \left(\frac{y-0}{1}\right)^2 = 1$. x-term positive $\Rightarrow$ opening horizontally. Center $(-3, 0)$, x-radius 3, y-radius 1, asymptotes have $m = \pm\frac{1}{3}$.

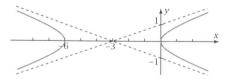

   b. The graph should match part a.

10. a. No xy-term, x^2- and y^2-terms have the same sign but different values $\Rightarrow$ ellipse. $\left(\frac{x-0}{4}\right)^2 + \left(\frac{y+2}{2}\right)^2 = 1$. Center $(0, -2)$, x-radius 4, y-radius 2.

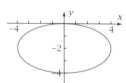

   b. The graph should match part a.

11. a. No xy-term, x^2- and y^2-terms equal $\Rightarrow$ circle. $(x-3)^2 + (y-4)^2 = 5^2$. Center $(3, 4)$, radius 5. This can also be thought of as $\left(\frac{x-3}{5}\right)^2 + \left(\frac{y-4}{5}\right)^2 = 1$, x- and y-radii both 5.

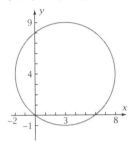

b. The graph should match part a.

12. a. No xy-term, x^2- and y^2-terms equal $\Rightarrow$ circle. $(x-5)^2 + (y-1)^2 = 4^2$. Center $(5, 1)$, radius 4. This can also be thought of as $\left(\frac{x-5}{4}\right)^2 + \left(\frac{y-1}{4}\right)^2 = 1$, x- and y-radii both 4.

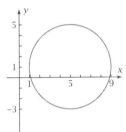

b. The graph should match part a.

13. a.

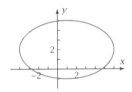

b. $(1, 2)$; 5; 3

c. In each direction, the constant term is the coordinate of the center and the coefficient of the trig function is the radius (or dilation).

d. $x = 1 + 5\cos t \Rightarrow \cos t = \frac{x-1}{5}$;

$y = 2 + 3\sin t \Rightarrow \sin t = \frac{y-2}{3}$;

$\left(\frac{x-1}{5}\right)^2 + \left(\frac{y-2}{3}\right)^2 = \cos^2 t + \sin^2 t = 1$

e. It has the form $\left(\frac{x-h}{a}\right)^2 + \left(\frac{y-k}{b}\right)^2 = 1$, with center $(h, k) = (1, 2)$, x-radius $a = 5$, and y-radius $b = 3$.

14. a.

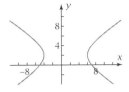

b. $(1, 2)$; 5

c. In each direction, the constant is the coordinate of the center and the coefficient of the trig function is the radius; y-radius $= 3$; asymptotes have $m = \pm\frac{3}{5}$.

d. $y = \frac{3}{5}x + \frac{7}{5}$ and $y = \frac{-3}{5}x + \frac{13}{5}$

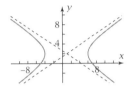

e. $x = 1 + 5\sec t \Rightarrow \sec t = \frac{x-1}{5}$;

$y = 2 - 3\tan t \Rightarrow \tan t = \frac{y-2}{3}$;

$\left(\frac{x-1}{5}\right)^2 - \left(\frac{y-2}{3}\right)^2 = \sec^2 t - \tan^2 t = 1$

f. It has the form $\left(\frac{x-h}{a}\right)^2 - \left(\frac{y-k}{b}\right)^2 = 1$, with center $(h, k) = (1, 2)$, x-radius $a = 5$, and y-radius $b = 3$.

15. a. By matrix multiplication, this is equivalent to $\begin{cases} 5u + 0v = x \\ 0v + 3v = y \end{cases}$, that is, $\begin{cases} x = 5u \\ y = 3v \end{cases}$, in other words, $(u, v) \rightarrow (5u, 3v)$.

b. $\begin{bmatrix} x \\ y \end{bmatrix} = \begin{bmatrix} 5 & 0 \\ 0 & 3 \end{bmatrix}\begin{bmatrix} u \\ v \end{bmatrix} \Rightarrow \begin{bmatrix} u \\ v \end{bmatrix} = \begin{bmatrix} 5 & 0 \\ 0 & 3 \end{bmatrix}^{-1}\begin{bmatrix} x \\ y \end{bmatrix}$

$= \begin{bmatrix} \frac{1}{5} & 0 \\ 0 & \frac{1}{3} \end{bmatrix}\begin{bmatrix} u \\ v \end{bmatrix} = \begin{bmatrix} \frac{x}{5} \\ \frac{y}{3} \end{bmatrix}$, that is, $(u, v) = \left(\frac{x}{5}, \frac{y}{3}\right)$.

16. a. Center $(200, 0)$, x-radius 100.
$\left(\frac{x-200}{100}\right)^2 + \left(\frac{y-0}{b}\right)^2 = 1$. $(x, y) = (130, 20) \Rightarrow$
$\left[\frac{(130)-200}{100}\right]^2 + \left[\frac{(20)-0}{b}\right]^2 = 1 \Rightarrow$
$\left(\frac{70}{100}\right)^2 + \left(\frac{20}{b}\right)^2 = 1 \Rightarrow \left(\frac{20}{b}\right)^2 = 1 - \left(\frac{7}{10}\right)^2$
$= \frac{100-49}{100} = \frac{51}{100} \Rightarrow \frac{20}{b} = \pm\frac{\sqrt{51}}{100} \Rightarrow$
$b = \pm\frac{200}{\sqrt{51}}$

Only the positive value is needed.

$$\left(\frac{x-200}{100}\right)^2 + \left(\frac{y-0}{200/\sqrt{51}}\right)^2 = 1 \text{ or}$$

$$\left(\frac{x-200}{100}\right)^2 + 51\left(\frac{y}{200}\right)^2 = 1$$

b. Vertical clearance = y-radius $= \dfrac{200}{\sqrt{51}} \approx 28.0$ ft

c. $\left(\dfrac{x-200}{100}\right)^2 + 51\left[\dfrac{(25)}{200}\right]^2 = 1 \Rightarrow$

$$\left(\frac{x-200}{100}\right)^2 = 1 - 51\left(\frac{1}{8}\right)^2 = \frac{13}{64} \Rightarrow$$

$$\frac{x-200}{100} = \pm\frac{\sqrt{13}}{8} \Rightarrow x = 200 \pm \frac{100\sqrt{13}}{8}$$

$$= 200 \pm \frac{25\sqrt{13}}{2} \Rightarrow$$

$$\approx 154.9 \text{ ft} \le x \le \approx 245.1 \text{ ft}$$

17. a. Center $(0, 0)$; opens in the x-direction;

x-radius 10; $\dfrac{y - \text{radius}}{10} = \tan\dfrac{70°}{2} \Rightarrow$

y-radius $= 10\tan 35° = (4.7381\ldots)$ units;

$$\left(\frac{x-0}{10}\right)^2 - \left(\frac{y-0}{10\tan 35°}\right)^2 = 1 \text{ or}$$

$$\left(\frac{x}{10}\right)^2 - \left(\frac{y}{4.7381\ldots}\right)^2 = 1$$

b. Solving for y,

$$\left(\frac{y}{10\tan 35°}\right)^2 = \left(\frac{x}{10}\right)^2 - 1 = \frac{x^2-100}{100} \Rightarrow$$

$$\frac{y}{10\tan 35°} = \frac{\sqrt{x^2-100}}{10} \Rightarrow$$

$$y = \sqrt{x^2-100} \cdot \tan 35°$$

x	y
10	0
12	4.6447
14	6.8606
16	8.7456
18	10.48
20	12.128
22	13.721

c. The beam will be $25\tan 35°$ from the horizontal centerline, so the thickness will be

$25\tan 35° - y(25)$

$= 25\tan 35° - \sqrt{25^2 - 100}\,\tan 35°$

$= \left(25 - 5\sqrt{21}\right)\tan 35° = 1.4614\ldots$ in.

d. The bracing on either end of the beam makes the shape of an "I."

Section 12-3

1. a.

By similar triangles, $\dfrac{r}{H-h} = \dfrac{R}{H} \Rightarrow$

$rH = RH - Rh \Rightarrow RH - rH = Rh \Rightarrow$

$H(R-r) = Rh \Rightarrow H = \dfrac{Rh}{R-r}$;

$V_{\text{frustum}} = V_{\text{entire cone}} - V_{\text{cut off}}$

$= \dfrac{1}{3}\pi R^2 H - \dfrac{1}{3}\pi r^2(H-h)$

$= \dfrac{1}{3}\pi(R^2 H - r^2 H + r^2 h)$

$= \dfrac{1}{3}\pi\left(R^2 \cdot \dfrac{Rh}{R-r} - r^2 \cdot \dfrac{Rh}{R-r} + r^2 h\right)$

$= \dfrac{1}{3}\pi h \cdot \dfrac{R^3 - r^2 R + r^2 R - r^3}{R-r}$

$= \dfrac{1}{3}\pi h \cdot \dfrac{R^3 - r^3}{R-r}$

$= \dfrac{1}{3}\pi h \cdot \dfrac{(R-r)(R^2 + Rr + r^2)}{R-r}$

$= \dfrac{1}{3}\pi h(R^2 + Rr + r^2)$

b. $V = \dfrac{1}{3}\pi x(15^2 + 15y + y^2)$

$= \dfrac{1}{3}\pi x\left(225 + 15 \cdot \dfrac{1}{2}\sqrt{900 - x^2} + 900 - x^2\right)$

$= \dfrac{1}{3}\pi x\left(1125 + \dfrac{15}{2}\sqrt{900 - x^2} - x^2\right)$

c.

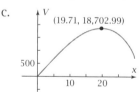

This is $\dfrac{18{,}702.995 - 8{,}162.0971}{8{,}162.0971} \cdot 100\%$

$\approx 129\%$ bigger (229% as big).

2. a. Using p for price per unit and R for revenue (standard terminology in economics) and w for weight and t for time, $w(t) = 600 + 10t$; $p(t) = 0.80 - 0.01t$; $R(t) = w(t) \cdot p(t)$ $= (600 - 10t)(0.80 - 0.01t) = 480 + 2t - 0.1t^2$

    b.
    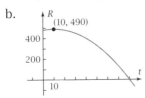

    c. 10 weeks, for $490.00. We can also find this because the function is a quadratic (a parabola), so the maximum is at the vertex, $x = \frac{-b}{2a} = \frac{-2}{2(-0.1)} = 10$ weeks;
    $w(10) = 600 + 10(10) = 700$ lb;
    $p(10) = 0.80 - 0.01(10) = \$0.70/\text{lb}$;
    $R(10) = (700)(0.70) = \$490.00$ or
    $R(10) = 480 + 2(10) - 0.1(10)^2 = \$490.00$.

3. a. By similar triangles, $\frac{y - 30}{100 - x} = \frac{60 - 30}{100} \Rightarrow$
    $y = 60 - \frac{3}{10}x$; and $\frac{z - 20}{x} = \frac{50 - 20}{100} \Rightarrow$
    $z = 20 + \frac{3}{10}x$.

    b. $A = yz = \left(60 - \frac{3}{10}x\right)\left(20 + \frac{3}{10}x\right)$
    $= 1200 + 12x - \frac{9}{100}x^2$; quadratic

    c.
    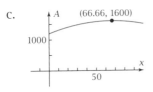

    We can also find the maximum at the vertex,
    $x = \frac{-b}{2a} = \frac{-12}{2\left(-\dfrac{9}{100}\right)} = 66\frac{2}{3}$ in.;

    $A\left(66\frac{2}{3}\right) = 1200 + 12\left(66\frac{2}{3}\right) - \frac{9}{100}\left(66\frac{2}{3}\right)^2$
    $= 1600$ in.^{2}.
    The minimum can be seen on the graph to be at the left endpoint, $x = 0$ in., $y = 60$ in., $z = 20$ in., $A = 60 \cdot 20 = 1200$ in.^{2}.

Section 12-4

1. Sketch showing distances from two points on the curve:

    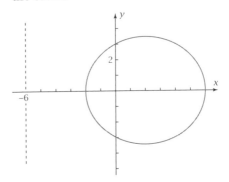

    $0 < e < 1 \Rightarrow$ ellipse.

2. Sketch showing some typical distances:

    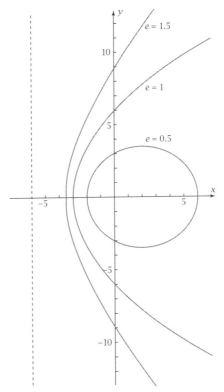

    As the eccentricity increases from 0.5 to 1.5, the curve "widens" vertically from an ellipse to a parabola to a hyperbola.

3. Sketch showing some typical distances:

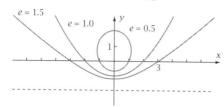

The directrix determines the direction of the principal axis of the conic (namely, perpendicular to the directrix).

As the eccentricity increases from 0.5 to 1.5, the curve widens vertically from an ellipse to a parabola to a hyperbola.

4. $\sqrt{x^2 + y^2} = \frac{5}{2}|x + 3| \Rightarrow$

$21x^2 - 4y^2 + 150x + 225 = 0$ or

$$\frac{\left(x + \frac{25}{7}\right)^2}{\frac{10}{7}} - \left(\frac{y}{\frac{5\sqrt{21}}{7}}\right)^2 = 1.$$

Hyperbola opening horizontally
Center $\left(-\frac{25}{7}, 0\right) = (-3.5714..., 0)$
Semitransverse axis: $y = \frac{10}{7} = 1.4285...$
Semiconjugate axis: $x = \frac{5\sqrt{21}}{7} = 3.2732...$

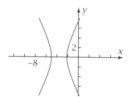

5. $\sqrt{x^2 + y^2} = 0.6|y + 1| \Rightarrow$

$25x^2 + 16y^2 - 18y - 9 = 0$ or

$$\left(\frac{x - 0}{\frac{3}{4}}\right)^2 + \left(\frac{y - \frac{9}{16}}{\frac{15}{16}}\right)^2 = 1.$$

Ellipse
Center $\left(0, \frac{9}{16}\right) = (0, 0.5625)$
Semimajor axis: $x = \frac{15}{16} = 0.9375$
Semiminor axis: $y = \frac{3}{4} = 0.75$

6. $\sqrt{x^2 + (y - 25)^2} = \frac{5}{3}|y - 9| \Rightarrow$

$9x^2 - 16y^2 + 3600 = 0$ or

$$-\left(\frac{x}{20}\right)^2 + \left(\frac{y}{15}\right)^2 = 1$$

Hyperbola opening vertically
Center (0, 0)
Semitransverse axis: $x = 15$
Semiconjugate axis: $y = 20$

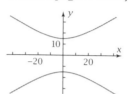

7. $\sqrt{(x - 4)^2 + y^2} = \frac{4}{5}|x - 6.25| \Rightarrow$

$9x^2 + 25y^2 - 225 = 0$ or $\left(\frac{x}{5}\right)^2 + \left(\frac{y}{3}\right)^2 = 1$
Ellipse
Center (0, 0)
Semimajor axis: $y = 5$
Semiminor axis: $x = 3$

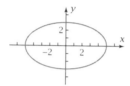

8. $\sqrt{(x - 0.5)^2 + y^2} = 1 \cdot |x + 0.5| \Rightarrow y^2 - 2x = 0$
or $x = \frac{1}{2}y^2$

Parabola opening right
Vertex (0, 0)

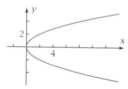

9. $\sqrt{x^2 + \left(y + \frac{1}{4}\right)^2} = 1 \cdot \left|y - \frac{1}{4}\right| \Rightarrow x^2 + y = 0$ or
$y = -x^2$

Parabola opening down
Center (0, 0)

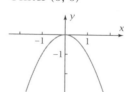

10. Center $\left(6, \frac{10-14}{2}\right) = (6, -2)$;
$b = -2 - (-15) = 13$
$c = 10 - (-2) = -2 - (-14) = 12$
$a = \sqrt{b^2 - c^2} = \sqrt{13^2 - 12^2} = 5$
$\left(\frac{x-6}{5}\right)^2 + \left(\frac{y+2}{13}\right)^2 = 1 \Rightarrow$
$169x^2 + 25y^2 - 2028x + 100y + 6184 = 0$

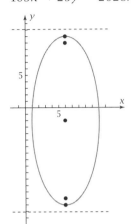

11. Center $\left(-3, \frac{1-5}{2}\right) = (-3, -2)$
$c = \frac{1-(-5)}{2} = 3;\ \frac{a}{b} = m = \frac{3}{2} \Rightarrow a = \frac{3}{2}b;$
$c^2 = a^2 + b^2$
$= \left(\frac{3}{2}b\right)^2 + b^2 = \frac{13}{4}b^2 \Rightarrow b^2 = \frac{4}{13}c^2 = \frac{4}{13} \cdot 3^2$
$= \frac{36}{13} \Rightarrow b = \frac{6}{\sqrt{13}} = 1.6641\ldots$
$a = \frac{3}{2}b = \frac{9}{\sqrt{13}} = 2.4961\ldots$
$-\left(\frac{x+3}{6/\sqrt{13}}\right)^2 + \left(\frac{y+2}{9/\sqrt{13}}\right)^2 = 1 \Rightarrow$
$117x^2 - 52y^2 + 702x - 208y + 1169 = 0$

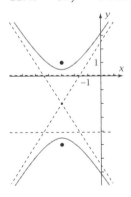

12. Ellipse
$a = -2 - (-7) = 5$
$\frac{c}{a} = e = \frac{3}{5} \Rightarrow c = \frac{3}{5}a = 3$
$b = \sqrt{a^2 - c^2} = 4$
$\left(\frac{x+3}{4}\right)^2 + \left(\frac{y+2}{5}\right)^2 = 1 \Rightarrow$
$25x^2 + 16y^2 + 150x + 64y - 111 = 0$

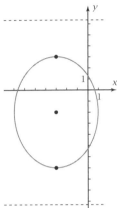

13. Hyperbola opening vertically;
Center $\left(-3, \frac{8-4}{2}\right) = (-3, 2)$
$c = 8 - 2 = 2 - (-4) = 6;$
$\frac{c}{a} = e = 1.2 \Rightarrow a = \frac{c}{1.2} = 5$
$b = \sqrt{c^2 - a^2} = \sqrt{11}$
$-\left(\frac{x+3}{\sqrt{11}}\right)^2 + \left(\frac{y-2}{5}\right)^2 = 1 \Rightarrow$
$25x^2 - 11y^2 + 150x + 44y + 456 = 0$

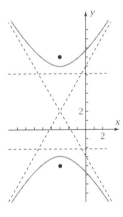

14. Ellipse with major axis horizontal

$c = 3 - 1 = 2$

$d = 7 - 1 = 6$

$a = \sqrt{cd} = \sqrt{12} = 3.4641...$

$b = \sqrt{a^2 - c^2} = \sqrt{8} = 2.8284...$

$\left(\dfrac{x-1}{\sqrt{12}}\right)^2 + \left(\dfrac{y-2}{\sqrt{8}}\right)^2 = 1 \Rightarrow$

$2x^2 + 3y^2 - 4x - 12y - 10 = 0$

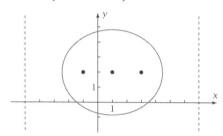

15. Center $\left(3, \dfrac{10-8}{2}\right) = (3, 1)$

$a = 10 - 1 = 1 - (-8) = 9$

$\dfrac{2b^2}{a} = LR = 6 \Rightarrow b = \sqrt{\dfrac{a \cdot LR}{2}} = 3\sqrt{3} = 5.1961...$

$\left(\dfrac{x-3}{3\sqrt{3}}\right)^2 + \left(\dfrac{y-1}{9}\right)^2 = 1 \Rightarrow$

$3x^2 + y^2 - 18x - 2y - 53 = 0$

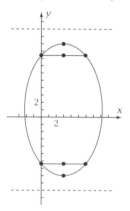

16. a. $a = \dfrac{147.1 + 152.1}{2} = 149.6$ million km

b. $c = 149.6 - 147.1 = 2.5$, so $b = \sqrt{a^2 - c^2}$
   $= 149.5791...$ million km.

c. $e = \dfrac{c}{a} = \dfrac{2.5}{149.6} = 0.0167...$ million km

d. Putting the center at the origin and the foci on the x-axis, $\left(\dfrac{x}{149.6}\right)^2 + \left(\dfrac{y}{149.5791...}\right)^2 = 1$.

e. $d = \dfrac{a^2}{c} = \dfrac{149.6^2}{2.5} \approx 8952$ million km

f. $\sqrt{b^2 - c^2} = a = 149.6$ million km

17. a. In each case, the difference of the distances from two points is a constant, so the locus is a hyperbola with the two points as foci. The airplane satisfies both criteria, so it is at an intersection of the two loci.

b. The first hyperbola has foci on the vertical axis (y-axis), so it opens vertically.

Center $\left(0, \dfrac{4+0}{2}\right) = (0, 2)$

$c = 4 - 2 = 2 - 0 = 2$

$a = \dfrac{d_1 - d_2}{2} = 1$

$b = \sqrt{c^2 - a^2} = \sqrt{3}$

$-\left(\dfrac{x-0}{\sqrt{3}}\right)^2 + \left(\dfrac{y-2}{1}\right)^2 = 1 \Rightarrow$

$x^2 - 3y^2 + 12y - 9 = 0$

The second hyperbola has foci on the horizontal axis (x-axis), so it opens horizontally.

Center $\left(\dfrac{0+6}{2}, 0\right) = (3, 0)$

$c = 6 - 3 = 3 - 0 = 3$

$b = \dfrac{d_2 - d_3}{2} = 2$

$a = \sqrt{c^2 - b^2} = \sqrt{5}$

$\left(\dfrac{x-3}{2}\right)^2 - \left(\dfrac{y-0}{\sqrt{5}}\right)^2 = 1 \Rightarrow$

$5x^2 - 4y^2 + 30x + 25 = 0$

c., d. Four intersections:

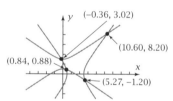

Because $d_1 - d_2 > 0$, $d_1 > d_2$, so the plane is on the lower lobe of the vertically opening hyperbola. Because $d_2 - d_3 > 0$, $d_2 > d_3$, so the plane is on the right lobe of the horizontally opening hyperbola. Therefore, the plane is at the lower-right intersection, $\approx (527$ mi, -120 mi$)$.

Section 12-7

1. a. Hyperbola: $d_2 > d_1$ parabola: $d_2 = d_1$
   Ellipse: $d_2 < d_1$; $e = \dfrac{d_2}{d_1}$

   b. i. Parabola opening left; $d_2 = ed_1 \Rightarrow$
      $\sqrt{x^2 + y^2} = 1 \cdot |6 - x| \Rightarrow y^2 + 12x - 36 = 0$

      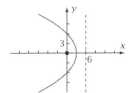

      ii. Hyperbola opening horizontally;
      $d_2 = ed_1 \Rightarrow \sqrt{x^2 + y^2} = \frac{3}{2}|x - 6| \Rightarrow$
      $5x^2 - 4y^2 - 108x + 324 = 0$

      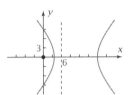

      iii. Ellipse with major axis horizontal;
      $d_2 = ed_1 \Rightarrow \sqrt{x^2 + y^2} = \frac{2}{3}|x - 6| \Rightarrow$
      $5x^2 + 9y^2 + 48x - 144 = 0$

      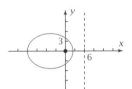

2. a. i. Their sum is constant.
      ii. Their difference is constant.
      iii. They are equal, and the two foci coincide.

   b. Major axis vertical; $d_1 + d_2 = 10 \Rightarrow$
      $\sqrt{x^2 + (y - 4)^2} + \sqrt{x^2 + (y + 4)^2} = 10 \Rightarrow$
      $\sqrt{x^2 + (y - 4)^2} = 10 - \sqrt{x^2 + (y + 4)^2} \Rightarrow$
      $x^2 + y^2 - 8y + 16$
      $= 100 - 20\sqrt{x^2 + (y + 4)^2} + x^2 + y^2 + 8y + 16 \Rightarrow$
      $20\sqrt{x^2 + (y + 4)^2} = 100 + 16y \Rightarrow$
      $5\sqrt{x^2 + (y + 4)^2} = 25 + 4y \Rightarrow$
      $25(x^2 + y^2 + 8y + 16) = 625 + 200y + 16y^2 \Rightarrow$
      $25x^2 + 9y^2 - 225 = 0$

      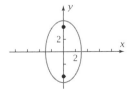

   c. Opening horizontally; $|d_2 - d_1| = 15 \Rightarrow$
      $\sqrt{(x - 17)^2 + y^2} - \sqrt{(x + 17)^2 + y^2} = \pm 15 \Rightarrow$
      $\sqrt{(x - 17)^2 + y^2} = \sqrt{(x + 17)^2 + y^2} \pm 15 \Rightarrow$
      $x^2 - 34x + 289 + y^2$
      $= x^2 + 34x + 289 + y^2$
      $\pm 30\sqrt{(x + 17)^2 + y^2} + 225 \Rightarrow$
      $\pm 30\sqrt{(x + 17)^2 + y^2} = 68x + 225 \Rightarrow$
      $900(x^2 + 34x + 289 + y^2)$
      $= 50{,}625 + 30{,}600x + 4{,}624x^2 \Rightarrow$
      $3{,}724x^2 - 900y^2 - 209{,}475 = 0$

      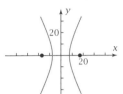

3. Parabola opening up
   Vertex $= (0, 0)$, $a = 0.04$, $p = \frac{1}{4a} = 6.25$
   Focus $= (0, 6.25)$, $e = 1$

   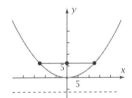

4. Hyperbola; $3x^2 - 7y^2 = 210 \Rightarrow$
   $-\left(\dfrac{x}{\sqrt{30}}\right)^2 + \left(\dfrac{y}{\sqrt{70}}\right)^2 = 1$
   Center $(0, 0)$, $a = \sqrt{70} = 8.3666...$,
   $b = \sqrt{30} = 5.4772...$, $c = \sqrt{a^2 + b^2} = 10$,
   $e = \frac{c}{a} = \frac{\sqrt{70}}{7} = 1.1952...$, slope of asymptotes
   $= \frac{a}{b} = \frac{\sqrt{21}}{3} = 1.5275....$

   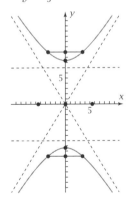

5. Ellipse, major axis horizontal

Center $(2, -4)$, $a = 6$, $b = 3$, $c = \sqrt{a^2 - b^2}$
$= 3\sqrt{3} = 5.1961...$, $e = \frac{c}{a} = \frac{\sqrt{3}}{2} = 0.8660...$,
$LR = \frac{2b^2}{a} = 3$.

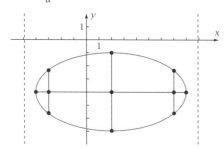

6. $\sqrt{(x+3)^2 + y^2} - \sqrt{(x-3)^2 + y^2} = \pm 4 \Rightarrow$
$5x^2 - 4y^2 - 20 = 0 \Rightarrow \left(\frac{x}{2}\right)^2 - \left(\frac{y}{\sqrt{5}}\right)^2 = 1$

Center $(0, 0)$, $a = 2$, $b = \sqrt{5}$
Asymptotes have $m = \pm\frac{a}{b} = \pm\frac{\sqrt{5}}{2}$.
$c = 3 - 0 = 0 - (-3) = 3$
$d = \frac{a^2}{c} = \frac{4}{3} \Rightarrow$ directrices $x = \pm\frac{4}{3}$
$LR = \frac{2b^2}{a} = 5$

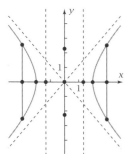

7. $a = 19 - (-6) = 25$
$c = ea = (0.96)(25) = 24$
$b = \sqrt{a^2 - c^2} = 7$
$d = \frac{a^2}{c} = \frac{625}{24} = 26.041\overline{6}$
$LR = \frac{2b^2}{a} = \frac{98}{25} = 3.92$
$\left(\frac{x+6}{25}\right)^2 + \left(\frac{y-8}{7}\right)^2 = 1$ or
$49x^2 + 625y^2 + 588x - 10{,}000y + 11{,}139 = 0$

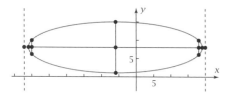

8. Focus $= \left(\frac{0+0}{2}, \frac{-1 + (-9)}{2}\right) = (0, -5)$
$LR = -1 - (-9) = 8$; $a = \frac{1}{LR} = \frac{1}{8}$ (actually $-\frac{1}{8}$
because opening to the left)
$p = \frac{1}{4a} = 2$ (actually -2 because opening to the
left)
Vertex $= (0 - p, -5) = (2, -5)$
Directrix $= x = 2 - p \Rightarrow x = 4$
$x - 2 = -\frac{1}{8}(y + 5)^2$ or $y^2 + 8x + 10y + 9 = 0$

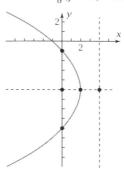

9. Hyperbola, opening vertically
Center $\left(2, \frac{7-5}{2}\right) = (2, 1)$
$c = 7 - 1 = 1 - (-5) = 6$
$a = \frac{c}{e} = 4$
$b = \sqrt{c^2 - a^2} = 2\sqrt{5}$
Asymptotes have $m = \pm\frac{a}{b} = \pm\frac{2\sqrt{5}}{5}$.
$d = \frac{a^2}{c} = \frac{8}{3} \Rightarrow$ directrices $y = 1 \pm \frac{8}{3} \Rightarrow y = \frac{11}{3}$
or $y = -\frac{7}{3}$
$LR = \frac{2b^2}{a} = 10$
$-\left(\frac{x-2}{2\sqrt{5}}\right)^2 + \left(\frac{y-1}{4}\right)^2 = 1 \Rightarrow$
$4x^2 - 5y^2 - 16x + 10y + 12 = 0$

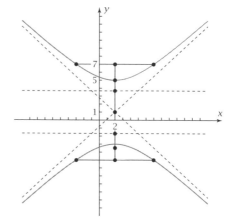

Precalculus with Trigonometry: Instructor's Guide
© 2007 Key Curriculum Press

10. The (absolute value of the) difference between the distances from a point on the hyperbola to the two foci is a constant.

11.

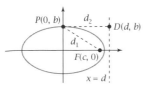

$d_1 = \sqrt{b^2 + c^2} = a;\ d_2 = d - 0 = d;$

$d_1 = ed_2 \Rightarrow a = ed \Rightarrow e = \dfrac{a}{d}$

12. a. x^2- and y^2-terms have the same sign but different coefficients $\Rightarrow$ ellipse

   b., c.

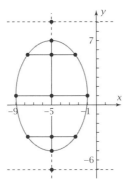

$9x^2 + 4y^2 + 90x - 8y + 85 = 0 \Rightarrow$

$9(x^2 + 10x + 25) + 4(y^2 - 2y + 1)$

$= -85 + 9(25) + 4(1) = 144 \Rightarrow$

$\left(\dfrac{x+5}{4}\right)^2 + \left(\dfrac{y-1}{6}\right)^2 = 1$

Center $(-5, 1)$

$a = 6$

$b = 4$

$c = \sqrt{a^2 - b^2} = 2\sqrt{5}$

$d = \dfrac{a^2}{c} = \dfrac{18\sqrt{5}}{5} \Rightarrow$ directrices $y = -5 \pm \dfrac{18\sqrt{5}}{5}$

$e = \dfrac{c}{a} = \dfrac{a}{d} = \dfrac{\sqrt{5}}{3}$

$LR = \dfrac{2b^2}{a} = \dfrac{16}{3}$

Chapter 13

Section 13-2

1. a. $r = \dfrac{ep}{1 - e \cos \theta}$

   $r - er \cos \theta = ep$

   $r = ep + er \cos \theta = ep + ex$

   $x^2 + y^2 = r^2 = e^2 p^2 + 2e^2 px + e^2 x^2$

   $(e^2 - 1)x^2 - y^2 + 2e^2 px + e^2 p^2 = 0$

   This is the equation of a conic section. Complete the square to find the center, a, and b:

   $(e^2 - 1)\left[x^2 + \dfrac{2e^2 p}{e^2 - 1} + \dfrac{e^4 p^2}{(e^2 - 1)}\right] - y^2$

   $= -e^2 p^2 + (e^2 - 1) \cdot \dfrac{e^4 p^2}{(e^2 - 1)^2}$

   $(e^2 - 1)\left(x^2 + \dfrac{e^2 p}{e^2 - 1}\right)^2 - y^2 = \dfrac{e^2 p^2}{e^2 - 1}$

   $\left(\dfrac{x + \dfrac{e^2 p}{e^2 - 1}}{\dfrac{ep}{(e^2 - 1)}}\right)^2 - \left(\dfrac{y}{\dfrac{ep}{\pm\sqrt{e^2 - 1}}}\right)^2 = 1$

   Center $(h, k) = \left(-\dfrac{e^2 p}{e^2 - 1}, 0\right)$

   $a = \dfrac{ep}{e^2 - 1},\ \ b = \dfrac{ep}{\pm\sqrt{e^2 - 1}}$

   b. $c = \sqrt{a^2 + b^2} = \sqrt{\dfrac{e^2 p^2}{(e^2 - 1)^2} + \dfrac{e^2 p^2}{e^2 - 1}}$

   $= \sqrt{\dfrac{e^4 p^2}{(e^2 - 1)^2}} = \dfrac{e^2 p}{e^2 - 1}$

   Because the center is at $\left(-\dfrac{e^2 p}{e^2 - 1}, 0\right)$, one

   focus is at $x = -\dfrac{e^2 p}{e^2 - 1} + \dfrac{e^2 p}{e^2 - 1} = 0$.

   c. $e = \dfrac{\text{focal radius}}{\text{semimajor axis}} = \dfrac{\dfrac{e^2 p}{e^2 - 1}}{\dfrac{ep}{e^2 - 1}} = e$

   d. $d = \dfrac{\text{semimajor axis}}{\text{eccentricity}} = \dfrac{\dfrac{ep}{e^2 - 1}}{e} = \dfrac{p}{e^2 - 1}$

   Distance from pole to directrix =

   $h - d = \dfrac{e^2 p}{e^2 - 1} - \dfrac{p}{e^2 - 1} = p.$

2. a. The coefficient 7 dilates the original graph by a factor of 7. The 60° rotates the original graph by 60°.

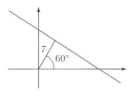

   b. $r = 25 \sec\left(\theta - \cos^{-1}\dfrac{-24}{25}\right)$

   c. The line is 25 units from the pole, rotated by an angle of $\cos^{-1}\dfrac{-24}{25}$.

   $a = 25$ and $\alpha = \cos^{-1}\dfrac{-24}{25}$.

Section 13-4

1. $(\cos\theta + i\sin\theta)^4$
   $= \cos^4\theta + 4i\cos^3\theta\sin\theta + 6i^2\cos^2\theta\sin^2\theta$
   $\quad + 4i^3\cos\theta\sin^3\theta + i^4\sin^4\theta$
   $= \cos^4\theta + 4i\cos^3\theta\sin\theta - 6\cos^2\theta\sin^2\theta$
   $\quad - 4i\cos\theta\sin^3\theta + \sin^4\theta$
   $= \cos^4\theta - 6\cos^2\theta\sin^2\theta + \sin^4\theta$
   $\quad + i(4\cos^3\theta\sin\theta - 4\cos\theta\sin^3\theta)$
   So $\cos 4\theta = \cos^4\theta - 6\cos^2\theta\sin^2\theta + \sin^4\theta$
   and $\sin 4\theta = 4\cos^3\theta\sin\theta - 4\cos\theta\sin^3\theta$).

2. a. $-8 = 8$ cis $180°$
   $\sqrt[3]{-8} = 2$ cis $60°$, 2 cis $180°$, 2 cis $300°$

   b. 2 cis $180° = -2$

   c. $64 = 64$ cis $0°$
   $64^{1/6} = 2$ cis $0°$, 2 cis $60°$, 2 cis $120°$,
   2 cis $180°$, 2 cis $240°$, 2 cis $300°$

   d. 2 cis $0° = 2$, 2 cis $180° = -2$

   e. $(-8)^{1/3} = 2$ cis $60°$, 2 cis $180°$, and 2 cis $300°$ are all $64^{1/6}$, but 2 cis $0°$, 2 cis $120°$, and 2 cis $240°$ are not $(-8)^{1/3}$.

   f. Answers may vary with the calculator used. On a TI-83, $(-8)^{1/3} = -2$ and $(-8)^{2/6} = -2$. Algebraically, $[(-8)^2]^{1/6} = 64^{1/6} = 2$ and $[(-8)^{1/6}]^2 = (\sqrt{-2})^2 = -2$, so it appears that the calculator does the operation $[(-8)^{1/b}]^a$. However, in order even to enter the expressions into the calculator, the fractional exponent must be enclosed in parentheses because exponentiation takes precedence over multiplication or division. Therefore, the calculator does the operations in neither of the suggested orders, but rather it does $y = \frac{a}{b}$ first and then $z = x^y$. It turns out that this order of operations is equivalent to $(x^{1/b})^a$.

3. a. If $k > 0$, then $(-k)^x$ has the form $(k$ cis $180°)^x = k^x$ cis $(180x° + 360xn°)$. But if x is irrational, then $x(180° + 360n°)$ can never be a multiple of $180°$, so none of the values of $(-k)^x$ can be real.

   b. Answers may vary with the calculator used. Some calculators may give a domain error. The function $x^{\sqrt 3}$ is undefined for $x < 0$, so -8 falls outside the domain of the function. The TI-83 gives $36.6604\ldots$ cis $(-48.2308\ldots°)$, equivalent to $8^{\sqrt 3}$ cis $\left(180\sqrt 3°\right)$ because $180\sqrt 3° - 360° = -48.2308\ldots°$.

Chapter 14

Chapter 14 has no Supplementary Problems.

Chapter 15

Section 15-5

1. a. $d(4) = 78$ mi

   b. $d(4.1) = 81.251$ mi
   The rocket traveled $d(4.1) - d(4) = 3.251$ mi with average velocity $\frac{3.251 \text{ mi}}{0.1 \text{ s}} = 32.51$ mi/s.

   c. $[4, 4.01]$:
   $\dfrac{d(4.01) - d(4)}{0.01 \text{ s}} = \dfrac{0.320501 \text{ mi}}{0.01 \text{ s}}$
   $\qquad = 32.0501$ mi/s

   $[4, 4.01]$:
   $\dfrac{d(4.001) - d(4)}{0.001 \text{ s}} = \dfrac{0.032005001 \text{ mi}}{0.001 \text{ s}}$
   $\qquad = 32.005001$ mi/s

   The average velocities seem to approach 32 mi/s.

   d. $\displaystyle\lim_{x\to 4}\frac{d(x) - d(4)}{x - 4}$
   $= \displaystyle\lim_{x\to 4}\frac{(x^3 - 7x^2 + 40x - 34) - (78)}{x - 4}$
   $= \displaystyle\lim_{x\to 4}\frac{x^3 - 7x^2 + 40x - 112}{x - 4}$
   $= \displaystyle\lim_{x\to 4}\frac{(x - 4)(x^2 - 3x + 28)}{x - 4}$
   $= \displaystyle\lim_{x\to 4}(x^2 - 3x + 28) = 32$

Precalculus with Trigonometry: Instructor's Guide